PURE AND APPLIED PHYSICS

A SERIES OF MONOGRAPHS AND TEXTBOOKS

Volume 1. F. H. FIELD and J. L. FRANKLIN, Electron Impact Phenomena and the Properties of Gaseous Ions. 1957

Volume 2. H. KOPFERMANN, Nuclear Moments, English Version Prepared from the Second German Edition by E. E. SCHNEIDER. 1958

Volume 3. WALTER E. THIRRING, Principles of Quantum Electrodynamics. Translated from the German by J. BERNSTEIN. With Corrections and Additions by WALTER E. THIRRING. 1958

Volume 4. U. FANO and G. RACAH, Irreducible Tensorial Sets. 1959

Volume 5. E. P. WIGNER, Group Theory and Its Application to the Quantum Mechanics of Atomic Spectra. Expanded and Improved Edition. Translated from the German by J. J. GRIFFIN. 1959

Volume 6. J. IRVING and N. MULLINEUX, Mathematics in Physics and Engineering. 1959

Volume 7. KARL F. HERZFELD and THEODORE A. LITOVITZ, Absorption and Dispersion of Ultrasonic Waves. 1959

Volume 8. LEON BRILLOUIN, Wave Propagation and Group Velocity. 1960

Volume 9. FAY AJZENBERG-SELOVE (ed.), Nuclear Spectroscopy. Parts A and B. 1960

Volume 10. D. R. BATES (ed.), Quantum Theory. In three volumes. 1961

Volume 11. D. J. THOULESS, The Quantum Mechanics of Many-Body Systems. 1961

Volume 12. W. S. C. WILLIAMS, An Introduction to Elementary Particles. 1961

Volume 13. D. R. BATES (ed.), Atomic and Molecular Processes. 1962

Volume 14. AMOS DE-SHALIT and IGAL TALMI, Nuclear Shell Theory. 1963

Volume 15. WALTER H. BARKAS. Nuclear Research Emulsions. Part I. 1963
Nuclear Research Emulsions. Part II. *In preparation*

Volume 16. JOSEPH CALLAWAY, Energy Band Theory. 1964

Volume 17. JOHN M. BLATT, Theory of Superconductivity. 1964

Volume 18. F. A. KAEMPFFER, Concepts in Quantum Mechanics. 1965

Volume 19. R. E. BURGESS (ed.), Fluctuation Phenomena in Solids, 1965

Volume 20. J. M. DANIELS, Oriented Nuclei: Polarized Targets and Beams. 1965

In preparation

R. H. HUDDLESTONE and S. L. LEONARD (eds.), Plasma Diagnostic Techniques

P. A. EGELSTAFF (ed.), Thermal Neutron Scattering: The Study of Matter through Energy Transfer Experiments

AMNON KATZ, Classical Mechanics, Quantum Mechanics, Field Theory

ABSORPTION AND DISPER

OF ULTRASONIC WAVES

ABSORPTION AND DISPERSION OF ULTRASONIC WAVES

KARL F. HERZFELD and THEODORE A. LITOVITZ
Department of Physics
The Catholic University of America
Washington, D. C.

1959

ACADEMIC PRESS New York and London

ACADEMIC PRESS INC.
111 FIFTH AVENUE
NEW YORK, NEW YORK 10003

United Kingdom Edition
Published by
ACADEMIC PRESS INC. (LONDON) LTD.
BERKELEY SQUARE HOUSE, LONDON W. 1

Library of Congress Catalog Card Number: 59-7683

First Printing, 1959
Second Printing, 1965

PRINTED IN THE UNITED STATES OF AMERICA

PREFACE

The field of ultrasonics has grown enormously in the last forty years; it has not only provided us with much insight into problems of basic physics but also has found a large number of industrial and biological-medical applications. One of the most important basic studies by ultrasonic waves is that of the structure of matter, in which respect ultrasonic spectroscopy has taken a place along with optical and X-ray spectroscopy.

There are several excellent books on ultrasonics but none is devoted exclusively to the molecular basis of ultrasonic absorption and dispersion, nor is their treatment of this subject very detailed. We are principally interested in the information which ultrasonics can give on certain molecular processes in liquids and gases, namely, on relaxation mechanisms associated with the rate of energy exchange and the rate of structural changes in the fluid. The connection between ultrasonic data, the theory of chemical reaction rates, and the theory of the gas, liquid, and glassy states is considered. This book is intended as a treatise on this particular aspect of ultrasonics. In style and content it is halfway between a textbook and a handbook. The theories are extensively developed and we have tried to give the experimental results as completely as possible, but only in so far as they give quantitative information on relaxation processes. Since we hope that the book will be useful to experimental and theoretical physicists and to physical chemists the presentation of the mathematical development is extensive.

In Section A we have given a connected story of the field, with almost no formulae, so that the reader may see which parts of the detailed treatment he may omit if his interest is restricted to part of the subject only.

Unpublished material is included in several sections. Moreover a number of investigations recently published were occasioned by the writing of this book.

There are some important sections which we had to omit, to avoid making the book even longer than it is: the properties of aqueous salt solutions, including sea water, the field of polymers, and ultrasonic propagation in solids. W. P. Mason has just published a book on the latter subject.

We wish to use this occasion to pay homage to two of our late colleagues who were masters in ultrasonics and whose names appear often in the book, namely, the Very Reverend Francis E. Fox, O.S.F.S., and J. C. Hubbard.

We wish also to thank the Princeton University Press and Dr. F. Rossini, editor, for the permission to reprint several pages from K. F. Herzfeld's article in the volume, *Thermodynamics and Physics of Matter*, to the Editors of the *Journal of the Acoustical Society of America* and the *Journal of Chemical Physics* for permission to reproduce several figures, and to the Staff of the Academic Press for their long-suffering patience and help.

Catholic University of America
Washington, D. C.

March 5, 1959

KARL F. HERZFELD
THEODORE A. LITOVITZ

CONTENTS

III. Special Topics

B. GASES

IV. Application of the General Formulas to Gases

V. Experimental Methods to Determine Velocity and Absorption of Ultrasonic Waves in Gases

VI. Experimental Results in Molecules Without Electronic Excitation

VII. Theory of Vibrational and Rotational Energy Exchange

C. LIQUIDS

VIII. General Review of Ultrasonic Absorption and Dispersion in Liquids

IX. Experimental Methods to Determine Dispersion and Absorption of Ultrasonic Waves in Liquids

X. Review of Theories of Liquids

XI. Kneser Liquids

XII. Associated Liquids and Liquids with High Viscosity

NOTATION

a	Amplitude of de Broglie wave (Chapter VII)
	A constant
	Constant in van der Waals equation (Secs. 35, 40)
a_0	Lattice distance (Secs. 89)
a_{js}	Coefficient in the transformation to normal coordinates (Sect. 65, 68)
A	Affinity (Secs. 31, 103)
	Frequency factor (Secs. 55, 70)
	A constant in the equation of state (Sec. 33)
	Abbreviation for $\Delta C'/C_v(C_p - C')$ (Sec. 17)
	Abbreviation for $(\mathfrak{B}^2_\infty - \mathfrak{B}_0{}^2)/\mathfrak{B}^2_\infty$ (Secs. 18, 25)
	A constant defined by $\alpha'/f^2 = A[\tau/(1 + \omega^2\tau^2)] + B$ (Secs. 97, 98, 118)
A, A_j	Quantities related to the virial (Sec. 88)
A_{js}	Certain collision integrals (Sec. 36)
b	A constant
	A coefficient (Sec. 61)
	Constant in van der Waals equation (Secs. 35, 40)
b_2, b_3	Molecular constants (Burnett) (Sec. 47)
b_{sj}	A coefficient in the transformation to normal coordinates (Secs. 65, 68)
B	A constant in the equation of state (Sec. 33)
	A constant in the absorption equation $\alpha'/f^2 = A[\tau/(1 + \omega^2\tau^2)] + B$ (Secs. 97, 98, 118)
	Second virial coefficient (Sec. 35)
B'	$= B/RT$ (Sec. 35)
c	Velocity of light in a vacuum (Sec. 75)
	A constant (Sec. 61)
c_{js}	A coefficient in the transformation to normal coordinates (Secs. 65, 68)
c	Specific heat per gram
C	Specific heat per mole, measured quasi-statically
C'	Specific heat of internal degrees of freedom, relaxing specific heat
$\tilde{C}$ or C_∞	$= C - C'$, specific heat of external degrees of freedom, specific heat at infinite frequency, frozen specific heat

C	Sutherland constant (Secs. 36, 39)
d	Diameter of Pitot tube (Sec. 45)
	Diameter of hard molecule (Secs. 82, 84)
D	Diffusion constant (Secs. 31, 34, 41, 87)
	Symbol indicating material differentiation (Secs. 1, 2, 3, 6)
D_T	Coefficient of thermal diffusion (Sec. 41)
e	Electric charge (Sec. 9)
E	Energy (usually per mole)
	Young's modulus (Sec. 112)
E_j	Energy of state j (per mole)
E'	Relaxing energy
	Internal energy
	$= E_2 - E_1$, energy difference in a two-state system
	Activation energy
E^*	Energy of activated state
[Eu]	Eucken number
f	Frequency
f	Frequency factor (Sec. 92)
f	A function (Secs. 31, 60, 61)
f_0	Maxwell distribution function of velocities (Sec. 36)
F	A function (Secs. 60, 61)
F	A force (Sec. 9)
F	Free energy
F_j	Free energy of state j
F^*	Free energy of activated state
F'	$= F_2 - F_1$, free energy difference in two-state systems
F	Distribution function of molecular velocities (Sec. 36)
g	A constant (Secs. 42, 45)
	A constant used to idealize sound velocities (Sec. 33)
	Degeneracy or weight of a quantum state
	$= 4\pi^2 pl/h$ (Secs. 58, 61, 65)
$g(\tau)$	Normalized distribution function of shear relaxation times (Secs. 105, 108)
$g^{(2)}, g^{(3)}$	Molecular distribution functions in space (Sec. 87)
G	A function (Sec. 24)
$\mathbf{G}$	Collision operator (Sec. 36)
G	$= G' + iG''$, complex shear modulus (Chapter XII)
G_∞	Shear modulus at infinite frequency
h	Planck's constant
	Thickness of a layer (Sec. 83)

	A constant characterizing the forces in triatomic molecules (Secs. 64, 66)	
H	$= E + pV$, enthalpy or heat content	
H_j	Enthalpy of state j	
H'	$= H_2 - H_1$, difference of enthalpy in two-state system	
H^*	Enthalpy of activated state	
H	Hamiltonian	
H'	Perturbating Hamiltonian, Perturbation function	
	Interaction energy	
$\mathcal{I}$	Sound intensity (Sec. 32)	
I	Sound intensity	
	Moment of inertia (Sec. 64)	
j	An index	
	Angular momentum quantum number of relative motion	
J	Angular momentum quantum number of molecular rotation (Secs. 64, 69)	
k	Boltzmann's constant	
k', k''	Constants used in Sec. 42	
$k(\tau)$	Normalized distribution function of compressional relaxation times (Secs. 105, 109)	
k_{js}	Rate constant for transition from state j to state s	
$\bar{k}$	Forward reaction rate constant	
$\tilde{k}$	Backward reaction rate constant	
k''	A rate constant in the thermodynamic theory (Secs. 31, 103)	
K or K_{equil}	Equilibrium constant	
K	$= K' + iK''$ Complex compressional modulus, defined in Equs. 104–4,6	Chapter XII
K_0	Compressional modulus at low frequencies (quasi-static)	
K_∞ or $\tilde{K}$	Instantaneous or frozen compressional modulus	
K_2	$= K_\infty - K_0$ Relaxational part of compressional modulus	
K	Hooke's law force constant (Sec. 9)	
l	Range of repulsive forces (Chapter VII)	
l'	Range of repulsive forces (Secs. 56, 57, 58)	
L	Distance of nuclei in diatomic molecule (Secs. 64, 66)	
	Thickness of transition layer in shockwaves (Sec. 45)	
	Characteristic length for change of shape of high intensity wave (Sec. 33)	
L_1, L_2, L_3	Molecular distances (Sec. 90)	
m	Molecular mass	
$\tilde{m}$	$= m_1 m_1/(m_1 + m_2)$, effective mass	

M	Molecular weight
$\tilde{M}$	Effective molecular weight
M	$= M' + iM''$ Complex longitudinal modulus (defined in Eq. 104–16) (Chapter XII)
M_0	Low frequency (quasi-static) longitudinal modulus (Chapter XII)
M_∞	$= K_\infty + \frac{4}{3} G_\infty$ Instantaneous (frozen) longitudinal modulus (Chapter XII)
n	Refractive index (Sec. 9)
	Number of particles (Sec. 19)
	Total number of moles (Sec. 27)
	Number of particles per unit volume
N	Number of particles
	Number of particles per unit volume (Secs. 9, 36, 40, Chapter X)
$\tilde{N}$	Number of molecules in first neighboring shell (Sec. 86)
N_A	Avogadro number
N_j	Normalization factor (Sec. 64)
p	$= -\frac{1}{3}(P_{11} + P_{22} + P_{33})$, hydrostatic pressure
p	$= mw$ Linear momentum (in Chapter VII only)
$P - P_0$	Excess pressure in high intensity soundwave (Sec. 33)
P	Probability (Sec. 32)
P_{ij}	Stress component
P_{jj}'	$= P_{jj} + p$, deviatory normal stress
P_{ij}'	$= P_{ij}, \quad i \neq j$
P_{jj}''	Normal stress due to volume viscosity
[Pr]	Prandtl number (defined in Eq. 7–20)
q_s	Normal coordinates (Sec. 65)
q	$= 4\pi pl/h$ (Sec. 61)
Q	A molecular quantity (Sec. 36)
	Partition function (Secs. 92, 100)
	Scattering cross section (Secs. 61, 62, 69)
r	Number of rotational degrees of freedom (Secs. 34, 38)
	Distance
	Radius of a tube (Sec. 42)
	Reflection coefficient of amplitude of shear wave (Sec. 108)
r_0	Constant in Lennard-Jones formula
R	Universal gas constant
	Distance of molecule from center of cell (Sec. 86)
	Real part of propagation impedance for longitudinal waves, defined in Eqs. (104–32, 33)
R_s	Real part of propagation impedance for shear wave, defined in Eqs. 108–12, 14

[Re]	$= \rho\mathfrak{V}_0^2/\eta\omega$ Reynolds number (Secs. 7, 47)
s_{ij}	Strain component
s	$= (\rho - \rho_0)/\rho_0 = -\frac{1}{3}(s_{11} + s_{22} + s_{33})$, condensation, defined in Eq. (3–1)
s_{jj}'	$= s_{jj} + s$, deviatory strain component, defined in Eq. (104–3)
s_{ij}'	$= s_{ij}$, $i \neq j$, deviatory strain component, defined in Eq. (104–3)
s	As subscript, solvent (Sec. 29)
	As subscript, shear
	As subscript, running index
S	Entropy
S_j	Entropy of state j
S'	$= S_2 - S_1$ Entropy difference between two states
S^*	Entropy of activated state
S	As subscript means adiabatic or at constant entropy
$\boldsymbol{S}$	An expression used to "reduce" measurements on shear waves (Secs. 108, 109)
t	Time
T	Temperature (Kelvin)
T_{tr}	Temperature of external (translational) degrees of freedom
T'	Temperature of internal (or relaxing) degrees of freedom
T_{rev}	Temperature at the end of a reversible process (Sec. 30)
$T_{ijij}^{(4)}$	A stress tensor (Sec. 88)
u	Velocity of jet (Sec. 45)
u_1, u_2, u_3	Components of flow velocity
U	Relaxing variable (Sec. 9)
	Real part of C_{eff} (Sec. 21)
U_s	Components of unit vectors occurring in Sec. 24
v	Arbitrary volume
v_f	Free volume (Sec. 85)
v_j	Volume element j, of size v' (Sec. 88)
V	Mole volume
V_a	Available volume (Sec. 84)
V_j	Mole volume of state j
V'	$= V_2 - V_1$, volume difference between states (2) and (1)
	Volume of one mole of holes (Sec. 91)
$\mathfrak{V}$	Sound velocity
w	Macroscopic flow velocity
	Molecular velocity (Chapter VII) (W is used in Sec. 62)
	Work (Sec. 32)
w_1, w_2, w_3	Components of macroscopic flow velocity

W_1, W_2, W_3	Components of molecular velocity
iW	Imaginary part of C_{eff} (Sec. 21)
x_1, x_2, x_3	Cartesian coordinates
x, y, z	Cartesian coordinates
x	A variable (Secs. 12, 15)
	Abbreviation for $i\omega$ (Sec. 21) or $-i\omega$ (Sec. 24)
x_j	$= n_j/\Sigma n_s$, mole fraction of component j
x	$= n_2/(n_2 + n_1)$, mole fraction of component (2) in a system of two components only
$\bar{x}$	Mole fraction, calculated in moles of the monomer
X_j	Component of displacement in the direction x_j (Secs. 104, 108)
X_s	Components of unit vectors occurring in Sec. 24
X	An expression defined in Sec. 21
	A mole fraction (Sec. 40)
	Amplitude of vibration (Chapter VII)
	Reactance appearing in the propagation of longitudinal waves, defined in Eq. (104–32, 34)
X_s	Reactance appearing in the propagation of shear waves, defined in Eqs. (108–12, 13)
y	Cartesian coordinate
	A variable (Secs. 12, 15, 21)
Y_s	Components of unit vectors occurring in Sec. 21
$Y(2,2)$	A function (Sec. 62)
z	Cartesian coordinate
Z	$= \tau/\tau_c$, (nearly equal to) average number of collisions necessary for energy transfer
Z	$= R + iX$ Complex longitudinal impedance, defined in Eq. (104–31)
Z_s	$= R_s + iX_s$ Complex shear impedance, defined in Eq. (108–12)
α	Absorption coefficient of amplitude, in Centimeters^{-1}
α_{class}	Classical absorption, defined in Eq. (7–17)
α'	$= \alpha - \alpha_{\text{class}}$, molecular absorption
β or β_0	Quasi-static coefficient of thermal expansion
$\tilde{\beta}$ or β_∞	Instantaneous or frozen coefficient of thermal expansion
β'	$= \beta - \tilde{\beta}$, relaxing part of thermal expansion coefficient
γ	$= C_p/C_v$
γ_∞ or $\tilde{\gamma}$	Instantaneous (frozen) value of γ
Γ	Angle between the molecular axis and the line of approach of a hitting atom (Secs. 64, 69)

δ	A small number
	A small angle
	A symbol for variation
Δ	$= C_p - C_v$, difference of specific heats
Δf	Shift in frequency (Sec. 52)
ΔF	Change of free energy in a reaction (Sec. 27, 28)
	Free energy of activation (Sec. 105)
ΔH	Heat of evaporation
Δr	Amplitude of vibration (Sec. 65)
ΔT	Fluctuation of temperature (Sec. 88)
$\Delta x, \Delta y, \Delta z$	Components of atomic vibration (Sec. 65)
$\Delta \rho$	Fluctuation of density (Sec. 88)
ε	Depth of the potential well in the Lennard Jones formula, defined in Eq. (59–2)
ε_j	Energy of quantum state j
ε'	An energy occurring in the expression for energy transfer, defined in Eq. (56–6′)
ε	$= \varepsilon' - i\varepsilon''$, complex dielectric constant (Sec. 114)
ζ	Brownian motion constant (Sec. 87)
η, η'	Phase factors (Sec. 61)
η	Shear viscosity
η'	Volume, bulk or second viscosity
ϑ	Polar angle
ϑ	$= h\nu/k$, characteristic temperature of molecular vibration, defined in Eq. (58–9)
ϑ'	$= 0.815\, \tilde{M}\vartheta^2 l^2$, a temperature characteristic of the transfer of energy from vibration to translation, defined in Eq. (58–9′)
ϑ_r	A temperature characterizing a rotational energy change, defined by Eq. (69–5)
κ or κ_0	Quasi-static or low frequency compressibility
κ_T or $(\kappa_T)_0$	Isothermal quasi-static compressibility
κ_S or $(\kappa_S)_0$	Adiabatic quasi-static compressibility
$\tilde{\kappa}$ or κ_∞	Instantaneous or frozen compressibility
$\tilde{\kappa}_T, \tilde{\kappa}_S$	Isothermal and adiabatic instantaneous compressibility
κ'	$= \kappa - \tilde{\kappa}$, relaxing part of compressibility
λ	Coefficient of heat conduction (Secs. 7, 34)
	Wave length of sound
λ_0	Wave length of light (Sec. 75)
Λ	Mean free path (Secs. 36, 83)
	A constant used in Sec. 69, defined in Eq. (69–3)

μ	$= \partial A/\partial n$, chemical potential (Sec. 31)
	Cosine of polar angle (Sec. 60)
ν	Frequency of molecular vibration
$\tilde{\nu}$	$= \nu/c = 1/\lambda_0$, wave number of molecular vibration
ξ	Degree of advancement of a reaction defined in Eq. (27–5), generalized in Eq. (31–2)
Π	Indicates a product
ρ	Density
ρ_0	Undisturbed density
$\rho^{(1)}, \rho^{(2)}, \rho^{(3)}$	Probability functions (Sec. 87)
σ	Reciprocal of partition function for angular motion and rotation (Secs. 62, 64)
τ	Relaxation time
τ_c	Time between collisions, defined by Eqs. (36–2, 36–3)
τ_L	$= 4/3\,\eta/\rho\mathfrak{V}_0^2$, Lucas time, defined in Eq. (7–9)
τ_L'	$= (4/3\,\eta + \eta')/\rho\mathfrak{V}_0^2$, modified Lucas time, defined in Eq. (7–9′)
τ_p	Relaxation time at constant pressure
τ_{Sp}	Relaxation time at constant pressure and entropy
τ_v	Relaxation time at constant volume
τ_s	Relaxation time for s'th process
τ_s	Relaxation time for shear
τ', τ'', τ'''	Times proportional to τ occurring in different expressions; see Sec. 18
τ^*	An apparent relaxation time defined in Chapter XII by the equation $\alpha'/f^2 = A\tau^*(1 + \omega^2\tau^{*2}) + B$
φ	Angle
φ, φ'	Phase angle (Secs. 11, 16)
φ	A function (Sec. 39)
	A function of composition in chemical reaction (Secs. 27, 28, 29, 31)
Φ	A function describing deviation from Maxwell's distribution law (Sec. 36)
χ	An angle
$\psi^{(0)}, \psi^{(2)}$	Perturbations in the distribution function g (Sec. 87)
ψ^A	Translational wave function (Chapter VII)
ψ^{BC}	Vibrational wave function (Chapter VII)
ψ_j	Rotational wave function (Chapter VII)
Ψ	Total wave function (Chapter VII)
ω	$= 2\pi f$, circular frequency
$d\Omega$	Element of steric angle

INTRODUCTION

All fluids absorb ultrasonic waves by a "classical" mechanism, namely, loss through shear viscosity and (with very few exceptions) heat conduction, and show a corresponding dispersion. In addition, however, fluids (with the exception of monatomic gases and perhaps monatomic liquids) have an additional, "molecular," absorption and dispersion. Tisza has shown that this can always be formally introduced into the hydrodynamic equations by a "bulk viscosity." The opinion has been expressed that with the introduction of a bulk viscosity the problem is reduced to the integration of the modified hydrodynamic equations of Stokes and Navier.

We take a different standpoint. The problem can be illustrated by an electrical analogy. One could say that the problem of dielectric polarization was solved by the introduction of a dielectric constant by Faraday and Maxwell, and the only task remaining is that of formally integrating Maxwell's equations containing the dielectric constant. Thousands of papers on dielectric properties testify that this is not so. Three important problems are attacked:

1. What is the mechanism of dielectric polarization?

2. How does the dielectric "constant" depend on frequency?

3. How is the numerical value of the dielectric constant determined by the structure of a particular substance, and how does it depend on temperature and pressure?

Exactly the same problems for ultrasonic waves form the substance of this book:

1. What is the molecular mechanism explaining the existence of bulk viscosity?

2. How does bulk viscosity depend on frequency?

3. How is the numerical value of the bulk viscosity determined by the structure of a particular substance, and how does it depend on temperature and pressure?

In amplification of point 2, it is shown in Sec. 108 and Chapter XII that even the shear viscosity (and with it the classical absorption) is not constant at very high frequency.

Of course everybody is free to consider the three problems formulated above as trivial, but to us the attempt to solve them, and through them to get a deeper insight into the processes occurring in fluids, has been the motivating power for our investigations in the field of ultrasonics.

Part A contains that part of the theory which is common to gases and liquids. Newton's equation for the motion of a mass element of the fluid says that mass times acceleration is equal to force. The force in a fluid is due to a state of stress. However, a uniform stress does not produce a force; only the difference of the stress at the two ends of the element does this. The stress is, in the simplest case, the hydrostatic pressure. In next approximation there is added stress due to shear viscosity and bulk viscosity, the former being connected with shear flow, the latter with compressional flow, so that this stress is proportional to the time rate of change in density (Secs. 1 and 2).

The equations of motion are not linear. Usually (except for Sec. 33) the deviations from equilibrium are small, and only first powers of the velocity and of deviations in density, pressure, and temperature are kept (Sec. 3). In Sec. 4, the thermodynamic relations between adiabatic and isothermal processes are discussed, using the energy equation. From here on, the calculations are restricted to motions describable as plane, simple harmonic waves. For a nonviscous, nonheat-conducting liquid the velocity of propagation and the connections among particle velocity, density change, pressure change, and temperature change are deduced in Sec. 5. A more detailed discussion of viscous stresses, for both shear viscosity and bulk viscosity, follows. In particular it is shown why shear viscosity affects a longitudinal sound wave (Sec. 6). In Sec. 7 the effects of viscosity and heat conduction on the propagation of a sound wave are calculated, the liquid being treated as a continuum. The phenomena mentioned above produce both dispersion and absorption. If the absorption (i.e., the absorption per wave length) is small, one gets the classical Stokes-Kirchhoff expressions. If the absorption is not small, more detailed discussion is necessary (Lucas-Truesdell-Greenspan). In case the viscosity (plus possibly a constant bulk viscosity) alone is important, Lucas introduces a characteristic time proportional to the coefficient of viscosity. If the period of the sound wave is equal to the Lucas time, the absorption per wave length has a maximum and the velocity is larger than at low frequency and continues to rise with the frequency. Truesdell has attempted to explain all the dispersion and absorption phenomena with constant viscosity and bulk viscosity coefficients, but at least in monatomic gases an effect of the atomistic structure sets in, while in polyatomic fluids many other factors play a role (Secs. 7 and 8).

We now turn to a discussion of the molecular background of bulk viscosity and its frequency dependence. The notion of relaxation is introduced, discussed for step changes and periodic changes, and contrasted to resonance (Sec. 9). Next, it is shown that slow exchange of energy between different degrees of freedom (in particular between internal and external degrees of freedom) is a relaxation phenomenon. In a sound wave, the temperature changes first affect the translational degrees of freedom; any temperature change in these degrees is followed by a slower process of equalization with the internal degrees of freedom.

Since in the propagation equation the driving force contains as factor the adiabatic change of pressure with density, and since this has as factor C_p/C_v, the propagation equation is affected by the fact that, because of the relaxational energy exchange just mentioned, the specific heat may not have its static value. Instead, there is an effective specific heat, a complex quantity depending on the product of frequency and the relaxation time τ, which is a time characterizing the rate of energy exchange (Sec. 10).

The effective specific heat is

$$(C)_{\text{eff}} = C - C' \frac{i\omega\tau}{1 + i\omega\tau} \tag{11—9}$$

where C is the static specific heat, C' that part of it which is slowly adjusted, and τ the relaxation time. Sections 11 to 18 are devoted to a discussion of the consequences which expression (11—9) has for sound propagation. If the absorption is not too high, the square of the sound velocity $\mathfrak{B}$ is proportional to the real part of $(C_p/C_v)_{\text{eff}}$, while $2\alpha'\mathfrak{B}^3/\mathfrak{B}_0{}^2\omega$ is proportional to its imaginary part (α' nonclassical absorption, $\mathfrak{B}_0$ low-frequency sound velocity, $\omega = 2\pi f$). Purely algebraic transformations show that it is possible to write alternate forms

$$\left(\frac{\mathfrak{B}}{\mathfrak{B}_0}\right)^2 = 1 + A'' \frac{(\omega\tau'')^2}{1 + (\omega\tau'')^2} \tag{13—5}$$

$$\left(\frac{\mathfrak{B}_0}{\mathfrak{B}}\right)^2 = 1 - A' \frac{(\omega\tau')^2}{1 + (\omega\tau')^2} \tag{12—2}$$

$$\frac{\alpha'\mathfrak{B}_0{}^2}{\mathfrak{B}^2} = \frac{1}{2\mathfrak{B}} A' \frac{\omega^2\tau'}{1 + (\omega\tau')^2} \tag{12—3}$$

$$\alpha'\lambda = A''' \frac{\omega\tau'''}{1 + (\omega\tau''')^2}\,. \tag{16—5}$$

The curve for $\alpha'\lambda$, which shows a maximum, and the S-shaped curves for the velocity dispersion, for α' and α'/ω^2, are discussed in detail. The region of dispersion and the region of the peak for $\alpha'\lambda$ extend over several octaves. At low frequency the ratio α' (and of the total absorption α) to the classically calculated value (i.e., from shear viscosity and heat conductivity) is frequency independent, i.e., the total absorption is the classical absorption times a constant factor larger than unity. Ways are discussed in which the constants can be determined if only part of the dispersion curve and/or only low frequency absorption is measured. Methods are also indicated by which one can determine whether a given dispersion or absorption curve can be represented by a single relaxation frequency. In Sec. 17, the exact equations — in which it is not assumed that $\alpha\lambda/2\pi$ is small compared to unity — are discussed.

Section 19 investigates two cases in which the relaxation processes can be characterized by a single relaxation time. The first case is one in which only transitions between two states are involved. Here, the reciprocal relaxation time is the sum of the forward and backward reaction rate constant. These latter are, of course, connected by the thermodynamically determined equilibrium constant. The second case is that of the simple harmonic oscillator. This has two important properties. All the energy differences between neighboring levels are the same, and the transition probability is proportional to the number of the higher of the two levels. Landau and Teller have shown that, as a consequence of these properties, the whole assembly of oscillators in different levels act so that there is a single relaxation time for the vibrational energy. The reciprocal of this time is the difference between the rate constant for transition from the first excited level to ground level and the rate constant for the inverse process.

Sections 20 to 26 deal with those cases in which more than one relaxation time is present. This occurs in polyatomic molecules which have several modes of vibration, in the collision of different molecules which have different vibrational frequencies, and finally even in a single degree of freedom in which the energy jumps do not all have the same value, e.g., in rotation, since then the different jumps have different jump rates, in contradistinction to the case of a simple harmonic oscillator.

In principle, one can distinguish three modes of excitation of several degrees of freedom:

(a) Excitation in parallel. Each internal degree of freedom, independently of the others, exchanges energy with the external degrees of freedom. The objection has been made that many dispersion and absorption curves seem to cover all or nearly all of the vibrational energy, while vibrations with widely different frequencies should have widely different relaxation times, and therefore not give a single dispersion-absorption region.

(b) Excitation in series. Here one particular degree of freedom alone exchanges energy with translation, while all the others are fed from this exceptional one. These two types of excitation have been proposed by Schäfer. However, type (b) is, in general impossible, according to quantum theory, except for near resonance (Sec. 67) or for strongly anharmonic oscillators, since different vibrational modes have quanta of different size. Therefore, a modification due to Schwartz must be introduced, as follows.

(c) Excitation by complex collision (Sec. 65). In this process there is, as in (b), feeding of one vibrational mode from another, but this process also can only occur in a collision, since the difference in the size of the quanta is made up by exchange with translational energy. Therefore, a vibration may still be excited, even if the one from which it is normally "feeding" no longer exchanges energy directly with translation. While in scheme (b) the internal energy is preserved in the exchange between vibrations, in (c) the total number of quanta is preserved. Of course, in general, both types (a) and (c) will be present and it is only a question of which is the more effective.

It was first thought that (a) and (b) could be distinguished experimentally by a different dependence on frequency, but this is not the case. The main part of Secs. 21, 23, and 24, is devoted to these calculations. For case (a) one immediately gets

$$C_{\mathrm{eff}} = C - \sum C_s' \frac{i\omega\tau_s}{1 + i\omega\tau_s}$$

as a generalization of Eq. (11—9), where C_s' is the specific heat and τ_s the relaxation time of the sth vibration. It is then shown that, as generalizations of Eqs. (12–2) and (16–5)

$$\left(\frac{\mathfrak{V}_0}{\mathfrak{V}}\right)^2 = 1 - \sum A_s' \frac{1}{1 + (\omega\tau_s')^2}$$

and

$$\alpha'\lambda = \frac{1}{2} \sum A_s''' \frac{\omega\tau_s'''}{1 + (\omega\tau_s''')^2}$$

follow. The connections between C_s' and τ_s, and A_s', A_s''', and τ_s' are given, and arguments from irreversible thermodynamics prove that all the constants are positive. Only if the relaxation times τ_s lie quite far apart can one conclude from a dispersion curve which rises in several steps directly to the individual values of the C_s'. The same kind of argument is made for cases (b) and (c), although in these cases even the relaxation equations are already complicated. For (c) in particular the calculation is carried through completely if there are only two kinds of vibration.

The behavior of mixtures is introduced in Sec. 26. It has already been stated that this behavior might involve exchange of vibrational quanta between the molecules, but in Sec. 26 only the formal side of the problem is treated. It is assumed that only interaction between pairs of molecules is important (see Secs. 37 and 95). If there is some B mixed with A, the deactivation of a vibrational state of A can go by two different, parallel, ways; namely, by interaction with a molecule of the same kind, A, or by interaction with a foreign molecule, B. Since these are parallel ways, the total rate of deactivation of A is the sum of the two parallel rates. The formulas for the process are developed. If deactivation by the foreign molecule B is much more effective than by a molecule A, a small amount of B may greatly influence the overall relaxation time. If the relaxation time of pure A is already quite short, small amounts of B will not have much effect.

Sections 27, 28, and 29 introduce the possibility that the relaxation phenomenon causing dispersion and excess absorption is a chemical reaction of finite rate, an idea first considered by Einstein in 1920. In a sense this is more general than the relaxation by exchange of internal and external energy discussed in the foregoing. This latter can be considered a special case, since a distinction between "physical" and "chemical" transitions has no sense from the standpoint of thermodynamics and, therefore, transitions between different internal energy levels can be considered as chemical reactions. The thermal relaxation of vibrational energy is only more general in one direction, insofar as a large (infinite) set of levels or states is concerned, but is much more special in two other directions, namely, that one assumes a first order reaction, and that one assumes that the different internal energy states have the same volume, so that the distribution is not affected by a change in density, but only by a change in temperature. These assumptions are not made in the general case treated here, but ideal mixtures are assumed. (Even this restriction is dropped in Sec. 31.) The possibility is included that a solvent is present which does not participate in the reaction.

It is found that one again has equations of types (12–2) and (16–5). The dependence of A and τ on the order of the reaction and the concentration of the reactants is developed. The effect of both volume differences and of energy differences between the reactants and the products of the reaction is then considered. If there is no difference in enthalpy *or* if the coefficient of thermal expansion is zero, the effect of a sound wave is due only to the density variation. If, on the other hand, the enthalpies on the two sides of the chemical equation are not equal and a temperature variation accompanies the sound wave, or if there is an enthalpy difference and a volume difference on the two sides of the equation, one can calculate an internal specific heat associated with the reaction which plays exactly the same role as the internal specific heat C' of a vibration, mentioned earlier, except that as a function of the temperature it has a maximum.

Section 30, following the extended discussion of the different relaxation mechanisms and their effects on sound propagation, effects which can formally be described by a bulk viscosity, raises the question of whether there are actually stresses present which can be associated with this bulk viscosity. The answer, somewhat subtly, is yes. If the system is described by its actual volume and translational temperature (for thermal relaxation) or by its frozen internal distribution (for structural relaxation) the pressure would be statically associated with these conditions. However, because of the rapid change, the translational temperature (in the first case) is not the equilibrium overall temperature, and the stress associated with bulk viscosity is the difference between the pressure associated with equilibrium temperature and that associated with the actual translational temperature.

The next section reports on the formal treatment of relaxation phenomena based on the procedures of nonequilibrium thermodynamics.

After a short review of the formal equations of visco-elasticity, it is assumed that internal states are present and that the distribution of the system over these states, measured by a quantity ξ, influences the overall equation of state. This is similar in general to the chemical reactions described previously, but makes less detailed assumptions. It is then argued that in nonequilibrium the rate equation for changes of ξ is proportional to a quantity "affinity" which acts as driving force. This leads to a generalized equation of visco-elasticity, which contains different relaxation times, one for processes at constant volume and one for processes at constant pressure.

The resulting equation for sound propagation is identical with that from the previous theory. Generalization to several sets of internal states permits proof from the second law that all the constants C''' and τ''' discussed previously for Secs. 20 to 25 are positive.

Sections 32 and 33 deal with subjects somewhat outside the main line of our argument. The question had been raised as to whether the excess absorption could be explained, not as a true loss, but as a scattering of the waves by the small regions of different density or compressibility which occur in every fluid as statistical fluctuation. This can be calculated, and it is shown that the fluctuations are far too small to give appreciable effects except near a critical point (of condensation or of mixing) where the fluctuations are exceptionally large.

It has long been known that at high sound intensities absorption is larger than normal. This had previously been ascribed to cavitation. Section 33 reports an investigation of Fox and Wallace in which it is shown that the effect is due to the nonlinear terms in the hydrodynamic equations which, as previously pointed out by Fay, distort an originally sinusoidal wave. This distortion is equivalent to an admixture of harmonics which, having higher frequency, have higher absorption. It is shown that, after a short distance, a slowly varying state is reached. In this state the excess absorption is a universal function of the pressure, if the pressure is measured in units of a characteristic pressure proportional to the (low intensity) absorption per wave length and inversely proportional to the change of sound velocity with pressure. Comparison with measurements, both in gases and liquids, gives good agreement.

Part *B* deals with gases. The theory which explains relaxation as being due to slowness of energy exchange between internal and external energy is enunciated, and the general equations for this theory are specialized for ideal gases (Sec. 34). Since many velocity measurements needed to get the dispersion curve are made in slightly nonideal gases, Sec. 35 gives the methods of reduction to the ideal gas state. An important new viewpoint, namely, that the usual shear viscosity is also determined by a relaxation process (that of the molecular distribution law) is developed in the next section, following Maxwell and Kohler. If the distribution function were to adjust itself with infinite velocity to the equilibrium state, there would be no shear flow in the usual sense, but only "potential" flow; i.e., uniform motion with complete slip at the boundaries. While this is surely also true for liquids, it is carried through here only for ideal gases (independent of the law of interaction, in generalization of Maxwell). Kohler proves that

$$\eta = p\tau \tag{36–4}$$

where τ is the relaxation time of the perturbed Maxwell distribution. The fact that bulk viscosity is zero for an ideal monatomic gas is also proved (see Sec. 87 for a general discussion of monatomic fluids). Section 37 discusses the experimental evidence for, and the consequences of, the assumption that only binary molecular collisions are needed for the energy transfer. If this is true, it follows that, as long as the gas is ideal, dispersion and the absorption per wave length depend, at a given temperature, only on the ratio f/p.

If only binary collisions are needed, it is useful to introduce a number Z, which is independent of pressure, as the ratio between relaxation time and time between collisions, or roughly as the number of collisions needed to produce equilibrium between internal and external energy. It is then shown that the ratio of experimental to classical absorption at low frequency is independent of frequency and pressure and depends only on Z and the specific heats involved (Sec. 38).

In Sec. 39, the general formulas for mixtures given in Sec. 26 are applied to gases and used to discuss the degree of purity of a gas needed so that its own relaxation time can be measured. The possible effect of triple collisions is considered next (Sec. 40), particularly in the case of O_2 with H_2O as ad-mixture, since it is found that the effect of H_2O on the relaxation time is proportional to the square of the water concentration. Besides the possibility of triple collisions, Boudart's explanation of a resonance transfer (Sec. 67) of vibrational energy is discussed.

In gas mixtures, an additional effect causes absorption: irreversible unmixing by the sound wave (caused by uneven diffusion in a density — and a temperature — gradient); this effect is also proportional to f^2, and probably only noticeable in mixtures of He or H_2 with heavier gases (Sec. 41).

Sections 42 to 46 give a critical review of the precision methods used to measure sound velocity in gases and of the methods used to measure absorption or even relaxation times directly (the latter are discussed in Secs. 45 and 46).

Chapter VI undertakes a review of the experimental results, limited to those data from which conclusions on molecular processes can be drawn. In particular, Sec. 47, on monatomic gases, covers the experimental aspect of the viscosity viewed as a relaxation phenomenon (Sec. 36) and of the ultimate failure of the Truesdell continuum theory (Sec. 7). The contents of the other sections up to and including Sec. 54 are adequately described by their titles. The tables in Sec. 54 are compilations of those data on molecules of more than four atoms which are sufficient for the calculation of Z.

In the preceding, the formal theory of absorption and dispersion, the frequency dependence of these quantities, and the mechanism producing them were discussed. But the expressions always contain one or more quantities τ, the relaxation times. The formal theory tells us the physical meaning of τ as determined by reaction rates (Sec. 19), but does not give us a clue to its *a priori* calculation from the properties of the system, or any knowledge of its temperature dependence. Chapter VII tries to do so for gases.

After an historical introduction, the fundamental paper of Landau and Teller is discussed (Secs. 55 and 56) which is basic for the subsequent developments. According to these authors, the decisive point in the efficiency of a collision is the degree to which the process is adiabatic; this is measured by the ratio of interaction time to the period of vibration. The larger the ratio, the less efficient the collision, or the larger the number Z of collisions needed for energy transfer. The authors make an enlightened guess at the equation, which contains the relative molecular speed, and then average over the Maxwell distribution function of speeds, arriving for the first time at a satisfactory formula for the temperature dependence of Z. This formula, however, contains a length l, characterizing the range of the forces, which is not precisely defined. The authors conclude that only short range forces are effective.

Three other theories are touched upon: a resonance theory, a theory of formation of an active complex, and a radiation theory.

In Sec. 57, the general quantum theory of scattering processes is sketched. An incoming stream of particles, represented by a plane de Broglie wave, hits the molecule to be excited or de-excited, which acts as scatterer. One then gets scattered spherical waves, some with unchanged wavelengths, representing particles scattered elastically, others with changed wavelengths after energy exchange with the scatterer, representing particles scattered inelastically. The general procedure is outlined. The fraction of particles scattered inelastically is given by a "cross section" made up of products, one determined by the change in the translational motion of the scattered particle, the other by the change in vibrational state of the scatterer. In Sec. 58, the interaction potential is chosen as a repulsive exponential function, and Z is calculated explicitly in the one-dimensional case (in which a beam of particles strikes a vibrating wall). However, the actual interaction potential is more correctly written in the Lennard-Jones form. From the previous calculations it follows that the most effective collisions are due to molecules with speeds far beyond the maximum of the Maxwell distribution curve. These will penetrate to distances at which the forces are strongly repulsive, so that it is possible to replace a part of a Lennard-Jones curve by a shifted exponential curve. Since Hirschfelder's group has calculated the constants of the Lennard-Jones potential for many gases from viscosity and its temperature dependence, it is then possible to get the characteristic range l of the forces; in this case, of the order of 0.2 Å (Sec. 59). The effect of the attractive forces on the result is discussed; they act as if the effective collision velocity were increased. Sections 60–62 then generalize these calculations to the three-dimensional case, which is still simplified to the extent that, for example, a diatomic molecule is treated as a breathing sphere. The fact that it is not is taken into account by the adding of a factor, $\overline{(\cos^2 \vartheta)}^{-1} = 3$, in Z. Otherwise, the main difference from the one-dimensional case is the appearance of the centrifugal force term, due to the curved motion of the scattered particle. Treating this approximately, one again ends up with the same results for Z as in the one-dimensional case (Eq. 62–16). Section 61 in particular is a mathematical investigation of whether the boundary condition of the one-dimensional case is valid in the tridimensional one. Section 63 gives some general numerical data, for the purpose of giving the reader a feeling for the order of magnitude of the different quantities. It also discusses the temperature dependence of Z.

In the long section, Sec. 64, the treatment of the diatomic molecule as a breathing sphere is dropped. This amounts to saying that vibrational transitions will in general be accompanied by simultaneous rotational jumps. The calculations are only approximate.

Starting with diatomic molecules, the unrealistic case in which the distance between the nuclei is short compared with the range of the forces is treated first. The other extreme, in which the range of forces, l, is short compared to the nuclear distance, leads to the view that only collisions which are nearly head-on are effective. For actual molecules, this leads to a factor in Z of 5 to 10, instead of 3, as assumed previously. The calculation is then extended to linear triatomic molecules (CO_2, COS, etc.).

The notion of "complex collisions" is then introduced (Sec. 65). These are collisions in which, in polyatomic molecules or in pairs of unlike molecules, two vibrational quantum jumps occur simultaneously in opposite directions. This process is very important in the energy exchange of the vibrations with higher frequencies. These processes are treated according to the scheme of Secs. 23 and 24, and the methods for calculating the exchange relaxation times are discussed. They are then used in Sec. 68 to calculate the relaxation time for the five molecules CH_4, CH_3Cl... CCl_4. Although the latest equations are not used, the agreement with experiment varies from good to fair, the maximum ratio of τ from theory to τ from experiment being 9 (except for one case, in which it is 19).

Next, numerical values are calculated for all simple molecules where enough data are available (Sec. 66). First the choice is made between two ways of choosing the equivalent exponential interaction. One then has data for O_2, N_2, Cl_2, CO_2, N_2O, COS, CS_2, and the pairs O_2-H_2, Cl_2-He, and Cl_2-N_2, some over wide temperature ranges. In five cases the disagreement is by a factor of 20 to 10; the other 19 measurements deviate by factors up to 5 in either direction.

In Sec. 67, the strong effect of water vapor on CO_2 relaxation is explained, with Bauer and Widom, as due to the strong interaction energy. The effect of H_2O on O_2 as a resonance effect according to Boudart is also considered. Section 69 treats the relaxation time for the exchange of rotational and translational energy. Except for H_2, D_2, etc., where the energy jumps are appreciable because of the small moment of inertia, the relaxation time is very short, making perturbation methods doubtful, so that the state of the theory is unsatisfactory.

Section 70 discusses the relation of the preceding theory to the problem of energy transfer in chemical reactions. The experimental facts are reviewed. The conclusion is drawn that the fastest method by which a molecule can attain a state of high vibrational energy is by transfer of vibrational quanta from other vibrationally excited molecules. However, even this process seems slower than is indicated by experiment.

In Part C, Secs. 72–74 give a general review of absorption in liquids. Biquard found in 1936 that this is higher than calculated from classical theory (viscosity and heat conductivity). The values vary widely (from nearly equal to classical absorption to 100 times as much), but the absorption seemed — with a few exceptions — proportional to the square of the frequency. On interpreting the excess absorption as due to a relaxation process, one finds that the relaxation time is, in most cases, too short to be measured with the frequencies now available.

It was first believed that the relaxation mechanism in liquids was the same as that in gases, namely, thermal relaxation of internal degrees of freedom. However, this would have meant that, for water at 4° C, the absorption should have been classical, since at a density maximum no temperature change occurs during compression. Rock and Fox showed in 1946, however, that the ratio of measured to classical absorption is nearly constant, equal to about 3, from 2° to 40° C, and suggested, therefore, that a different mechanism must be effective in water. They suggested, following Debye, a slow structural relaxation. In 1948, Pinkerton proposed a very useful classification of liquids as: (1) Classical liquids, with no or little excess absorption. (2) Liquids in which excess absorption is due to slow energy exchange between external and internal degrees of freedom. These he supposed characterized by a positive temperature coefficient of absorption. They will be called here Kneser liquids. (3) "Associated liquids," in which excess absorption is due to slow structural relaxation. He proposed that these are characterized by a negative temperature coefficient and by a temperature independent ratio, not higher than 3, of the measured to the classical absorption.

In the meantime, it has been possible to find deviations from the constancy of α/f^2 which follow the relaxation theory, and determine relaxation times for a number of liquids. These include carbon disulfide, as a Kneser liquid, and a few others which show this only in minor contributions to α/f^2; acetic and propionic acids, where the effect is due to a chemical association; and very viscous liquids, where the relaxation time has been brought into a measurable range by lowering the temperature (Litovitz).

In Sec. 75, the velocity of so-called hypersonic waves in liquids, i.e., longitudinal waves with a wavelength of a few thousand angstroms, is discussed. Sections 76–80 form a review of those methods which are useful in measuring dispersion and absorption in liquids, different methods being useful in different frequency ranges.

Since in the following we wish to give molecular interpretations of the relaxation phenomena in liquids, we have first to present selected sketches of the relevant parts of different theories of liquids. These are aimed at giving, first, theories of shear viscosity and attempts at getting from them a quantity analogous to the collision time in gases; secondly, other theories, which approach the liquid from the analogy to a solid, and contain "jump times;" thirdly, direct attempts at calculating bulk viscosity and identifying its characteristic relaxation time.

Jäger considered momentum transport in liquids and assumed that the same features which are responsible for the deviation from ideal gas law in the equation of state are also responsible for these deviations in viscosity. This enabled him to calculate the viscosity in liquids from experimental data on the equation of the state. The calculated values agree well with those measured for a series of liquids, including water, but disagree strongly for very viscous liquids (Sec. 82). One can get the number of collisions by considering the frictional heat as a result of randomization of translational energy in collisions (Sec. 83). Section 84 gives a very simple model in which the molecules are arranged in the center of cubic cells and move parallel to the cell edge to head-on collisions with their neighbors.

Assuming that the motion of the molecule in a liquid follows classical mechanics, one can define thermodynamically a "free volume" in the liquid with the help of the entropy difference between liquid and vapor; this free volume is the properly weighted volume swept out by the motions of the molecule (Sec. 85). If one considers it as a sphere, one can calculate, as collision time, the diameter of the sphere divided by the mean thermal velocity. In a modification of this scheme (Sec. 86), which resembles the original cell model of Lennard-Jones more closely, one has the molecule execute simple harmonic vibrations in the center of a sphere, the wall of which is formed by the neighboring molecules, smeared out. The restoring force is calculated from the known Lennard-Jones interaction between a pair of molecules, and the collision time taken as half period of vibration.

A more sophisticated view of the liquid state by Kirkwood and by Born and Green is based on the radial distribution function (Sec. 87). In flow, the equilibrium distribution function is disturbed, and both shear viscosity and bulk viscosity can be calculated easily if this perturbed distribution function is known. Green (Sec. 88) approaches the problem with the methods of irreversible thermodynamics. One calls the (temporal) correlation function the value of a quantity at time t', multiplied with the value of the same quantity at time $t' + t$, averaged over t'. Green uses the correlation function for a quantity, which is essentially the space averaged value of a normal stress component, and integrates it over t. He assumes that this is essentially equal to the mean square fluctuation of this quantity, multiplied with the time it takes to "lose the memory of a previous value," which he identifies with the relaxation time. He then expresses various stress components by these quantities. It is shown in Sec. 88 that Green's formulas lead to the following results: The bulk viscosity of a monatomic fluid depends quadratically on the second derivative of the volume in respect to pressure and also on a correlation length (average size) of the density fluctuation. The bulk viscosity of a fluid with internal degrees of freedom or with two possible structural states has the value calculated from the previous, direct theory. With some additional assumptions, the shear viscosity can be calculated.

The next theories consider the fluid as a disordered crystal. Brillouin's theory (Sec. 89) assumes "crystal" planes moving past each other and, in so doing, setting up acoustic waves responsible for loss. However, the value of η comes out much too small. Eyring (Sec. 90) originally assumed as viscous process the jump of a molecule into a neighboring hole; this introduces into the theory a characteristic jump time as relaxation time, which has an activation energy associated with it. In an improved picture, two molecules roll over each other in shear flow, requiring extra space. Gierer and Wirtz (Sec. 91) have taken over Eyring's first picture to explain bulk viscosity. The essential process is the delayed filling of holes when the pressure is increased.

Section 92 applies the general theory of absolute reaction rates, as developed by Eyring, to the rates of those relaxation processes in which an energy of activation is involved. In particular, equations for the temperature and pressure dependence of such relaxation times are developed.

Chapter XI deals with Kneser liquids. The aims of this chapter are to prove that the relaxation process in these liquids is really the slow exchange between external and internal degrees of freedom, to investigate which internal degrees of freedom are involved, and to understand the numerical value of the relaxation time. In this latter respect, the main question is whether the important process is the cooperative interaction of a particular molecule with all the molecules which form the cell wall, or whether it is a collision with a single other molecule, as in gases. It will be shown that the latter view is correct.

Section 93 reviews the thermal behavior of many organic liquids. It is found that the difference between specific heat at constant pressure and at constant volume is often about $5R$ per mole, with the former often about $10R$ higher than the specific heat of the internal vibrations.

Next, a theory is developed from the idea that the energy exchange is based on the continuous, weak interactions with all the other molecules forming the cell wall. This is a refinement of the calculations of Sec. 86. The force, deduced from the Lennard-Jones interaction potential, is calculated to higher powers of the molecular distance from the cell center. While the first power gives the Hooke's law restoring force, the higher powers produce a coupling between the motion of the molecule as a whole and the internal vibrations. The result is a relaxation time 100 times too long, i.e., an absorption 100 times too high. The conclusion is drawn that these continuous interactions are too weak, and that the energy exchange must proceed by a few, comparatively rare, but violent (i.e., high energy) collisions, as in gases.

To test this conclusion, the following procedure is adopted in Sec. 95. As the main relaxation time in most Kneser liquids has not been measured directly, one calculates a relaxation time which is necessary to give the measured low frequency absorption. This is only true if the extra absorption is due to slow energy exchange between vibrational and external degrees of freedom, and if the whole vibrational energy (know from spectroscopic or thermal data) has one dominant relaxation time. It is done for Kneser liquids for which the relaxation time in the gaseous state has been measured directly. The calculated relaxation time in the liquid state is then found to be 100 to 600 times shorter than in the gas under standard conditions, and this ratio is approximately equal to that of the corresponding densities. If one assumes that the probability of energy transfer per collision (Z^{-1}) is the same in the liquid and in the gas, these data can be used to calculate the time between collisions in the liquid and can be compared with those given by various theories of the liquid state, as discussed in Secs. 83–86.

If the assumption just presented is right, it seems curious that the absorption coefficient increases with the temperature, since Z decreases.

To investigate this, one must have a considerable number of precise thermodynamic data about the liquid. These are available for benzene. The positive temperature coefficient is a complicated result of several partly compensating influences (Sec. 96).

Carbon disulfide (Sec. 97) is the only Kneser liquid in which the main relaxation time has been measured (Lamb and Andreae). One can interpret the data if it is assumed that all of the vibrations have the same relaxation time. It is possible to account both for the temperature and the pressure dependence of the relaxation time (Litovitz) by the simple cubic cell theory of Sec. 84.

In Sec. 98 relaxation due to rotational isomerism is discussed. Liquids which can exist in two or more isomeric forms will exhibit a relaxational loss if these forms have a difference in energy.

Mixtures of Kneser liquids (Sec. 99) behave very much like mixtures of gases, according to Bauer and Sette. A small amount of liquid B added to a highly absorbing liquid A may decrease the absorption coefficient greatly. This behavior also points to an interaction between *pairs* of molecules as the mechanism of energy exchange. Some liquid mixtures show absorption maxima as a function of composition.

Among the "associated" and very viscous liquids, to which Chapter XII is devoted, water has an exceptional position, due to its density maximum and, as a consequence, small thermal expansion coefficient even at temperatures different from 4° C. Two theories of the structure of water are considered, that of Bernal and Fowler (Sec. 100) and that of Eucken (Sec. 101). Bernal and Fowler consider water as a mixture of an ice-like (tridymite-like), a quartz-like, and a close-packed structure. Hall has based a quantitative theory of sound absorption in water on the assumption that it is a mixture of an ice-like and a close-packed structure. Using Eyring's theory of viscosity, he makes a possible, but not necessary assumption about the ratio of the structural relaxation time to the shear relaxation time. From this assumption it is found that the close-packed structure accounts for 25 to 27% of the water, and is nearly constant between 2° and 60° C. (If the two relaxation times had been taken as being equal, there would be 6% close-packed structure.) Eucken, on the other hand, assumes a much more "chemical" equilibrium. He takes liquid water to be a mixture of H_2O, $(H_2O)_2$, $(H_2O)_4$, and $(H_2O)_8$. Only the last complex is considered to have a somewhat different volume per H_2O, although this volume difference is much smaller than that deduced by Hall. It is then possible to calculate from sound absorption a relaxation time which is much longer than Hall's, but still not measurable at present.

The absolute value and the temperature dependence of ultrasonic absorption in water tell us that under the assumptions of the two-state theory, the two states are present in the ratio of about 1:3, and that this ratio is nearly temperature independent, but they do not tell us whether the state present in the lower amount is the one with the larger or smaller specific volume. The fact that absorption decreases with increasing pressure proves that the state present in smaller amount (22—29%) is the one with the larger volume; the quantitative agreement is good. Liebermann has given, under these assumptions, a satisfactory equation of state for water (Sec. 102).

The next section discusses the general behavior of associated liquids other than water. After reviewing the characteristics of their ultrasonic absorption, the concepts of long range and short range order are introduced and their dependence on temperature discussed. A temperature or pressure change brings about a change in order. This change of order contributes to the specific heat, the compressibility, and thermal expansion. However, such a change of order takes time — the relaxation time — and if the external change is too rapid, the required structure change cannot follow it. The relaxation time increases rapidly with decreasing temperature. At temperatures with about 30 min relaxation time, the order cannot adjust itself to equilibrium during the usual time an experiment takes. The momentary state of order is "frozen" in and, according to Simon, the material is in the glassy state which exists below this "glassy transition temperature;" the constants of the glass state are more like those of a solid than those of a liquid. The glass has shear rigidity, because the usual time of stress application is short compared to the shear relaxation time. Recent experiments at Oxford have confirmed this general view of the nature of a glass.

Ultrasonic behavior is connected with this idea insofar as ultrasonic waves produce stress or temperature changes, not of the duration of minutes, but as short as 10^{-7} sec. Therefore, in their behavior in propagating ultrasonic waves, liquids may become "glassy" at much higher temperatures (shorter relaxation times) than for ordinary experiments. They then behave like solids, giving little absorption and showing, for transversal waves, shear rigidity (Sec. 103).

Section 104 does not bring anything physically new, but presents a formal description different from that previously used. In electrical circuit theory, one may either express the voltage by the current, in which case the impedance appears as factor, or the current by voltage, in which case the factor is called admittance. While both descriptions are equivalent, one or the other is more convenient in different cases. For series circuits, the impedances are additive and therefore more convenient; for parallel circuits, the admittances are more convenient. Similarly, in the elastic theory of crystals, one can either express the strains by the stresses or the stresses by the strains, using different (although related) coefficients.

This is the problem treated in Sec. **104**. Previously we have expressed the strains (e.g., compression) by stresses (pressures) using as constants the compressibilities. Now the stresses are expressed by the strains, and the corresponding constants are called "moduli." The concept of impedance of the medium is introduced in this connection. If not all the molecules have the same relaxation time, one can introduce distribution functions — one for compressional, one for shear relaxation times — and generalize the equations for the moduli accordingly (Sec. **105**).

A new problem arises, that of separation of shear and compressional effects, both of which are present in longitudinal sound waves. This has not been difficult up to now, since the relaxation times of the relaxation effects discussed so far — transfer of vibrational energy — are much longer than the relaxation time for shear viscosity. Therefore, in the frequency region important for relaxation of internal energy transfer, the coefficient of viscosity could be treated as constant and the "classical absorption" subtracted (a possible exception is the transfer of rotational energy in gases). However, in the viscous, associated liquids to be discussed, the relaxation times of the structural process and of the viscous flow process lie rather close together. Therefore, attempts have to be made to determine them separately. The subject is still in its infancy. For relatively few liquids are all the data available and, in the historical development, at the beginning not all necessary measurements were made. As a consequence, it is necessary to describe in detail the individual, relatively scarce, measurements and then try to draw conclusions by generalization.

Sections **106** and **107** give the experimental results for the propagation of longitudinal waves in glycerine and *n*-propyl alcohol as a function of temperature and frequency, and the interpretation of these data along the lines just discussed. If the absorption per wavelength is plotted as a function of the temperature (or rather of the viscosity, which is a function of the temperature), one finds in both liquids a maximum, in agreement with the arguments at the end of Sec. **103**. This maximum lies at different temperatures for different frequencies and can only be explained by the occurrence of relaxation, $\omega\tau$ being unity at the maximum. In glycerine, the absorption at $-20°$ C and 30 Mc is less than one-seventh of the classical value, calculated from shear viscosity alone, so that even the shear process must have undergone relaxation. The dispersion has also been measured.

The velocity is frequency independent at low frequency. At intermediate frequencies — the range depending on temperature — it increases with frequency, again becoming independent of frequency if the latter is sufficiently high. This is in agreement with relaxation theory, but contradicts the exact Stokes-Navier theory with constant viscosity coefficient.

In both cases, the absorption and dispersion curves are not as steep as required by the single relaxation theory. The assumption of a distribution of relaxation times is necessary. For the second liquid, sufficient data are available to calculate a possible distribution. This extends, for the compressional viscosity, over a factor of 150, while the shear relaxation time is 8 times larger than the longest compressional one.

In Sec. 108 it is first pointed out that, contrary to what is often said, pure shear waves, i.e., transversal waves, can exist in viscous liquids, although classically their absorption is very high and their velocity increases with frequency. If shear viscosity shows relaxation effects, then the absorption per wavelength goes through a maximum and disappears at very high frequency, while shear rigidity appears, as one should expect in a glass. A method to measure the shear "resistivity" is described. Unfortunately, no conclusions can be drawn from this method relative to either the real or imaginary part of the shear modulus. A proper distribution function of relaxation times has to be found first. For glycerol, such a function, Gaussian with the logarithm of the relaxation time as argument, fits the measurements well and allows calculation of both parts of the shear modulus. It can be shown that it accounts, within the limits of accuracy, for the quasi-static viscosity.

Knowing the shear modulus and the results from dispersion and absorption of longitudinal waves makes it possible to isolate the compressional modulus for glycerol as a function of frequency and temperature (Sec. 109). To represent the results, a distribution function different from that used for shear is necessary. Properly defined mean relaxation times for shear and compression appear equal within the limits of present accuracy.

Next, attempts are made in Secs. 110, 111, and 112 to arrive at some numerical regularities. One can calculate, from the midpoint of the dispersion curve, a certain average over the distribution of the relaxation times. At a viscosity of about 500 poise, this time is of the order of 10^{-8} sec (in seven liquids). The "Lucas relaxation time," which can be calculated from the low-frequency absorption and sound velocity, is between one-half and six times the relaxation time calculated from dispersion. The temperature coefficient of the high-frequency sound velocity is two to three times larger than that of the low-frequency velocity.

The absolute values of the high frequency (glass-like) shear and compressional modulus are then compared with those in a polymer, in quartz, in glass, and in a metal. Both the shear modulus and the relaxational part of the compressional modulus decrease with increasing temperature, contrary to the Eyring-Wirtz expression. For glycerol, at least, the two have the same temperature coefficient. Tentatively, it is assumed that this also holds for the other liquids of this type. If this and the assumption that the relaxation times for shear and bulk viscosity have a temperature independent ratio are true, the experimental fact that the ratio of the bulk and shear viscosity does not vary with temperature can be understood. It is then found empirically that the ratios of the different moduli are nearly the same in the seven organic liquids considered. One finds that the ratio of that part of the compressibility which is subject to relaxation to the low-frequency compressibility varies between 0.19 and 0.52, with an average of 1/3; i.e., the ratio of "glass-like" to "liquid-like" compressibility is 2:3. The direct measurement of that ratio for polymers, selenium, and glucose agrees with this moderately well. If this result is applied to the two-state theory, limits are found for the volume difference between the two states. Finally, an attempt at a molecular explanation for the temperature coefficient of the modulus is made.

The detailed mechanism responsible for structural relaxation is then discussed (Sec. **113**) from the viewpoint of Secs. 27—29. The extreme cases are the existence of a structural specific heat, which does not show up in an isothermal process; and of a slow structural change in volume, which is the same for isothermal and adiabatic processes, as in water. The former affects only γ and the static specific heat of liquid glycerol and of glassy glycerol just below the transition temperature are known. Therefore, the largest possible contribution to the structural, adiabatic compressibility of glycerol which can be explained by a structural specific heat can be calculated. It is only a small fraction of the measured structural compressibility. Forced by the lack of more data to make a bold extrapolation, one assumes that in all associated liquids, just as in water and glycerol, the structural volume viscosity is due mainly to a slow structural change affecting the volume, and occurring in both isothermal and adiabatic processes. In the language of the two-state theory, the ratio of the volume difference between the two states to the overall volume can then be shown to lie between 6 and 50 %, as a consequence of the fact that the structural compressibility is about one-third of the static compressibility.

In dipole molecules, part of the dielectric constant is due to an orientation of the molecules or polar groups in the field (Sec. **114**). In a varying field, the average orientation does not follow the field immediately, since the turning of the dipole is opposed by viscous forces. In an alternating electric field, the effective dielectric constant is of the same form as the moduli discussed in Sec. **104**. If one compares the dielectric relaxation time with the ultrasonically determined time, one finds that the ratio increases with the ratio of CH groups to OH groups, the former ratio being unity for glycerol and propylene glycol.

At very high frequency, it is found (Sec. **115**) that the absorption per wavelength is constant. This unexplained phenomenon, called hysteresis by Mason, is widely spread, occurring also in polymers, protein solutions, solid glasses, and crystalline solids.

In the next two sections, relaxation due to dimer formation and complex formation is discussed. Acetic acid was the first liquid in which a variation of the ratio α/f^2 with frequency was discovered (Bazulin), and the first liquid in which dispersion was found (Pinkerton). The behavior of this acid and of propionic acid can be completely explained by the slow establishment of equilibrium between single and double molecules. Equilibrium and rate constants are calculated. Finally, different mixtures involving polar molecules are discussed.

There are cases in which the solute acts simply as a foreign molecule, facilitating energy transfer. In other cases, dimer formation can be assumed, as it is with pure acetic acid (solutions of phenol or benzoic acid). In still other cases, one can assume complexes between solute or solvent, or partialy unmixing in fluctuations.

Section **118** deals with the effect of pressure on relaxation time and shows how the various mechanisms differ in this respect. For Kneser liquids (illustrated by CS_2) the relaxation time decreases with increasing pressure, because the number of energy transfering collisions increase. For liquids with internal structural isomerism τ is independent of the pressure, being determined by an internal reaction rate (example: triphenylamine). Acetic acid also behaves that way. Finally, in external structural relaxation, as in glycerine, τ increases with increasing pressure, due to the increased hindrances of molecular motion.

To sum up the main content of this book: We are concerned with the mechanism of relaxation and the prediction of relaxation times. In diatomic and polyatomic gases, the mechanism is the slow energy transfer between internal and external degrees of freedom. For the transfer of vibrational energy, at least, the relaxation times can be fairly well calculated in simple molecules, using only molecular constants known from nonacoustic experiments.

In liquids, four mechanisms are known. For many organic liquids ("Kneser liquids") the mechanism is the same as in gases. The relaxation times are several hundred times shorter than for the vapor under standard conditions. The temperature coefficient of absorption is positive, but this is the result of several processes which nearly compensate each other.

In some other nonassociated liquids one deals with an isomeric molecular change.

In "associated" or polar liquids, the relaxation mechanism is a slow change in structure or order. This is principally induced by a density change, and only in a minor way by a temperature change. The relaxation time is roughly proportional to the shear viscosity and is of the order of 10^{-8} sec. when the shear viscosity is 500 poise. The strong increase of the relaxation time with decreasing temperature is related to the possibility of producing a glass state. In fact, these liquids act as glasses toward high frequency sound waves at temperatures considerably above the usual glass transition temperature.

Finally, in some polar liquids the relaxation mechanism is the slow formation and dissociation of chemical complexes, either dimers — as in organic acids — or complexes with the solvent.

A. GENERAL THEORY OF RELAXATION IN FLUIDS

I. The Stokes-Navier Equations of Hydrodynamics

1. The State of the Fluid[1]

(a) *Variation in Space and Time*

The condition and motion of a fluid — which name shall include both gases and liquids — filling a certain volume of space may be characterized by a number of scalars and vectors, and by one tensor.

Among the first are the density ρ and the temperature T; among the second is the flow velocity $\boldsymbol{w}$, with the components u_1, u_2, u_3.

In general these quantities will, at a given moment of time, be different at different places in space. This variation in space is characterized by the differentiation according to space coordinates, $\partial/\partial x$, $\partial/\partial y$, $\partial/\partial z$. If we are interested in a scalar, e.g., the temperature T, the three partial differential quotients with respect to the Cartesian coordinates form three components of a vector, **grad** T (in general **grad** ...).

The quantity concerned may also vary with time. The variation with time at a given place is written $(\partial/\partial t)_{x,y,z}$ or $\partial/\partial t$ for short, and is called the local differentiation with respect to time; e.g., $\partial T/\partial t$ is the variation with time of the temperature at a given spot.

However, we are often interested in the fate of a given small material part of the fluid. The variation with time of a quantity describing the conditions is in general different if we follow the fluid than if we stay in a given place.

Let F be a function of x, y, z, and t. Then after the lapse of time dt, F, as attached to the fluid, has changed, not only because F has changed at a given point, but also because the particle has moved to a different spot. The difference between the two F values is therefore

$$F' - F = \frac{\partial F}{\partial t}\, dt + \frac{\partial F}{\partial x}\, dx + \frac{\partial F}{\partial y}\, dy + \frac{\partial F}{\partial z}\, dz$$

where dx, dy, dz are the components of the displacement of the fluid particle.

---

[1] For further reading on the material discussed in Secs. 1—4, see H. Lamb, "Hydrodynamics," 6th ed. Dover, New York, 1945.

Dividing by dt, one then has

$$F' - F = dt\left\{\frac{\partial F}{\partial t} + u_1\frac{\partial F}{\partial x} + u_2\frac{\partial F}{\partial y} + u_3\frac{\partial F}{\partial z}\right\}.$$

One defines an operator as

$$\frac{D}{Dt} = \frac{\partial}{\partial t} + u_1\frac{\partial}{\partial x} + u_2\frac{\partial}{\partial y} + u_3\frac{\partial}{\partial z} \tag{1–1}$$

or, in vector notation

$$\frac{D}{Dt} = \frac{\partial}{\partial t} + (\boldsymbol{w}\ \mathbf{grad}) \tag{1–1'}$$

and calls the operation the material differentiation with respect to the time. The operation ($\boldsymbol{w}$ **grad**) gives a scalar, e.g., the x component of the acceleration of a small part of the fluid is given by Du_1/Dt.

(b) Forces Acting on the Liquid

In an idealized, nonviscous fluid, only hydrostatic pressure exists. A uniform hydrostatic pressure would not give a resultant *force* on any part of the liquid. Thus, a force results only from differences of pressure; e.g., if the pressure varies in the x direction only, the resultant force on a thin, liquid sheet of area $dydz$ and thickness dx is determined by the difference of pressure on the two sides of the sheet, and the resultant force in the x-direction is

$$\{p(x) - p(x + dx)\}\, dydz = -\frac{\partial p}{\partial x}\, dxdydz.$$

In general, the resultant force on a volume element dv is

$$-\,\mathbf{grad}\, p \cdot dv. \tag{1-2}$$

For a less idealized fluid, however, it is necessary to describe the stresses in the liquid by a more complicated quantity than the scalar hydrostatic pressure, namely, by a symmetrical stress tensor P_{ij}, just as in the theory of elasticity.

Such a symmetrical tensor has three normal components P_{11}, P_{22}, P_{33} (normal to the surfaces considered) and three shear components $P_{12} = P_{21}$, $P_{23} = P_{32}$, $P_{13} = P_{31}$. In the case of the idealized fluid considered earlier,

$$P_{11} = P_{22} = P_{33} = -p$$

and

$$P_{12} = P_{23} = P_{31} = 0$$

(the minus sign comes from the fact that in P a tension or negative pressure is customarily counted as positive).

Again, uniform normal or shearing stresses will not give a resultant force; such a force will be determined by differences of such stress components on different surfaces. One finds as the resultant force on a volume element dv

$$\text{Div}\,\boldsymbol{P}\,dv \tag{1—3}$$

where $\text{Div}\,\boldsymbol{P}$ is the abbreviation for a vector with the components

$$\begin{aligned}
(\text{Div}\,\boldsymbol{P})_1 &= \frac{\partial}{\partial x} P_{11} + \frac{\partial}{\partial y} P_{12} + \frac{\partial}{\partial z} P_{13} \\
(\text{Div}\,\boldsymbol{P})_2 &= \frac{\partial}{\partial x} P_{21} + \frac{\partial}{\partial y} P_{22} + \frac{\partial}{\partial z} P_{23} \\
(\text{Div}\,\boldsymbol{P})_3 &= \frac{\partial}{\partial x} P_{31} + \frac{\partial}{\partial y} P_{32} + \frac{\partial}{\partial z} P_{33}.
\end{aligned} \tag{1—3'}$$

In the ideal liquid, only the diagonal terms exist. It is often useful to take the hydrostatic pressure out of the stress tensor P. The remainder shall be called P'. That means

$$\begin{gathered}
P_{ii} = -p + P'_{ii} \\
P_{12} = P'_{12} \qquad P_{23} = P'_{23} \qquad P_{31} = P'_{31}
\end{gathered} \tag{1—4}$$

The force per unit volume is then

$$\text{Div}\,\boldsymbol{P} = -\,\mathbf{grad}\,p + \text{Div}\,\boldsymbol{P}'. \tag{1—5}$$

2. The Equations of Motion

(*a*) *The Continuity Equation*

This expresses the assumption that any matter newly appearing within a volume element must have gotten there by flow through the boundaries of the element. The vector describing mass flow is $\rho\boldsymbol{w}$, which means that the amount of matter flowing during dt through an area dA normal to the direction of flow is $\rho|\boldsymbol{w}|dAdt$. Since the excess of outward flow over inward flow is given by dv div $(\rho\boldsymbol{w})$, the equation of continuity is

$$\frac{\partial\rho}{\partial t} + \operatorname{div}(\rho\boldsymbol{w}) = 0 \qquad (2-1)$$

which can also be written

$$\frac{\partial\rho}{\partial t} + (\boldsymbol{w}\,\mathbf{grad})\,\rho + \rho\operatorname{div}\boldsymbol{w} = 0.$$

Using Eq. (1—1′) one gets as an alternative form

$$\frac{1}{\rho}\frac{D\rho}{Dt} + \operatorname{div}\boldsymbol{w} = 0. \qquad (2-2)$$

(*b*) *Newton's Equation*

If one next writes Newton's second law of motion for the matter ρdv contained at a given moment in the volume dv, one has, according to Eq. (1—1′), for the product of mass times acceleration $\rho dv(D\boldsymbol{w}/Dt)$ and for the resultant force, Eq. (1-3), dv Div $\boldsymbol{P}$.

Therefore

$$\rho\frac{D\boldsymbol{w}}{Dt} = \operatorname{Div}\boldsymbol{P}. \qquad (2-3)$$

One now needs additional relations which connect the stress tensor P with the quantities describing the momentary condition of the fluid, e.g., ρ, T, and the flow velocity.

In a certain sense the remainder of this book can be considered as being devoted to the discussion of this dependence of P on other variables under the particular conditions of ultrasonic waves.

3. The Linearized Hydrodynamic Equations

From the mathematical standpoint, Eq. (2—1) and Eq. (2—3) have the great disadvantage of being nonlinear.

For instance, Eq. (2—1) contains the product of ρ and $\boldsymbol{w}$; Eq. (2—3), due to the form of D/Dt, even contains triple products like $\rho u_i(\partial u_j/\partial x_i.)$ This nonlinearity, which makes the principle of superposition inapplicable, is mainly responsible for the complexity of aerodynamics.

However, in the case of moderately weak ultrasonic waves, one can "linearize" the equations by introducing the "condensation," s, defined by

$$\rho = \rho_0(1 + s) \tag{3—1}$$

where ρ_0 is the density of the fluid in the absence of the sound wave.

It is then assumed that all quantities characteristic of the sound wave, i.e., s, $\boldsymbol{w}$, are small and all products or powers above the first are neglected. This means that in Eq. (2—2)

$$\frac{D\rho}{Dt} = \rho_0 \frac{\partial s}{\partial t} + \rho_0 u_1 \frac{\partial s}{\partial x} + \rho_0 u_2 \frac{\partial s}{\partial y} + \rho_0 u_3 \frac{\partial s}{\partial z}$$

only the first term is kept, and, analogously, the same is true in Eq. (2—3). There, even in

$$\rho \frac{\partial \boldsymbol{w}}{\partial t} = \rho_0(1 + s) \frac{\partial \boldsymbol{w}}{\partial t}$$

the s is dropped. Numerical data to justify these approximations will be given in Sec. 5. One gets, then

$$\frac{\partial s}{\partial t} + \operatorname{div} \boldsymbol{w} = 0 \tag{3—2}$$

and

$$\rho_0 \frac{\partial \boldsymbol{w}}{\partial t} = \operatorname{Div} \boldsymbol{P}. \tag{3—3}$$

The right side in Eq. (3—3) has next to be linearized. For this purpose it is best to use the form of Eq. (1—5). One first develops

$$p = p_0 + \frac{\partial p}{\partial \rho} \rho_0 s = p_0 - v_0 \frac{\partial p}{\partial v} s = p_0 + \frac{1}{\kappa_0} s.$$

Here p_0 is the constant external pressure, and will drop out upon formation of the gradient; and κ_0 is the compressibility at zero pressure, defined as

$$\kappa_0 = -\frac{1}{v_0}\left(\frac{\partial v}{\partial p}\right)_0 = -\frac{\partial \ln v}{\partial p} = +\frac{\partial \ln \rho}{\partial p} = \left(\frac{1}{\rho}\frac{\partial \rho}{\partial p}\right)_0.$$

The linearization consists of neglecting the dependence of the compressibility on pressure.

As far as P' is concerned, it will have to be linear in the quantities involved. This will be discussed in Sec. 6.

4. Thermodynamic Discussion of the Compressibility

Since the equation of state of a fluid contains three variables, p, T, and v (or ρ), the relation between only two of them, p and ρ, is not uniquely determined and, as a consequence, κ depends on the type of process.

Writing the general volume change, which follows from any equation of state, one has

$$dv = \left(\frac{\partial v}{\partial p}\right)_T dp + \left(\frac{\partial v}{\partial T}\right)_p dT = v(-\kappa_T dp + \beta dT) \qquad (4-1)$$

where β is the coefficient of thermal expansion.

$$\beta = \frac{1}{v}\left(\frac{\partial v}{\partial T}\right)_p .$$

Dividing by $-v$, one has

$$ds = \kappa_T\left(1 - \frac{\beta}{\kappa_T}\frac{dT}{dp}\right)dp. \qquad (4-2)$$

The problem is to find dT/dp, a ratio depending upon the particular process involved, for the conditions occurring in the sound wave.

In a sound wave there is, in first approximation, no external heat put into or taken out of a volume element, and to that extent the process is adiabatic.

The energy equation is then used, expressing the fact that any work done on the element goes toward increasing the internal energy

$$dE = -pdV = -d(pV) + Vdp$$

or

$$d(E + pV) = Vdp.$$

$E + pV$ is the enthalpy or heat content, H. Writing total differentials

$$\left(\frac{\partial H}{\partial T}\right)_p dT + \left(\frac{\partial H}{\partial p}\right)_T dp = Vdp. \qquad (4-3)$$

Now

$$\left(\frac{\partial H}{\partial T}\right)_p = C_p \qquad (4-4)$$

and

$$\left(\frac{\partial H}{\partial p}\right)_T = -T\left(\frac{\partial V}{\partial T}\right)_p + V. \qquad (4-5)$$

Therefore, Eq. (4—3) can be rewritten as the general equation of the isentropic variation (S constant)

$$C_p dT - T\left(\frac{\partial V}{\partial T}\right)_p dp = 0. \qquad (4\text{—}6)$$

Equation (4—3) only presupposed adiabatic conditions ($dQ = 0$). Equation (4—5), however, presupposes reversibility. Equation (4—6) can be rewritten as

$$\left(\frac{\partial T}{\partial p}\right)_S = TV\frac{\beta}{C_p}. \qquad (4\text{—}7)$$

This is the equation connecting temperature and pressure change in an adiabatic reversible compression for any fluid. Inserting Eq. (4—7) in Eq. (4—2), one gets

$$-\frac{1}{v}\left(\frac{\partial v}{\partial p}\right)_{ad} = \left(\frac{\partial s}{\partial p}\right)_{ad} = \kappa_{ad} = \kappa_T\left(1 - TV\frac{\beta^2}{C_p\kappa_T}\right). \qquad (4\text{—}8)$$

However

$$TV\frac{\beta^2}{\kappa_T} = C_p - C_v = \Delta. \qquad (4\text{—}9)$$

Therefore, Eq. (4—8) leads to

$$\kappa_{ad} = \frac{C_v}{C_p}\kappa_T = \frac{1}{\gamma}\kappa_T. \qquad (4\text{—}10)$$

Equations (4—7) and (4—10) are applicable to the isentropic compression of *any* fluid.

The physical reason for the adiabatic compressibility being smaller than the isothermic one is simple. In an adiabatic compression not only does the density increase, but the temperature does also; both processes increase the pressure.

One also finds from a combination of Eqs. (4—7), (4—8), (4—9), and (4—10) that

$$\left(\frac{\partial T}{\partial s}\right)_S = \frac{1}{\beta}(\gamma - 1). \qquad (4\text{—}11)$$

5. The Linearized Wave Equation for a Nonviscous Fluid

The linearized equations for a fluid without dissipative processes are, therefore

$$\frac{\partial s}{\partial t} + \operatorname{div} \boldsymbol{w} = 0 \tag{3—2}$$

and from Eq. (3—3)

$$\frac{\partial \boldsymbol{w}}{\partial t} = -\frac{1}{\rho_0} \,\mathbf{grad}\, p = -\frac{\gamma}{\rho_0 \kappa_{0T}} \,\mathbf{grad}\, s.$$

Since we are not concerned here with theoretical wave problems like diffraction, we can concentrate on a plane wave propagated in the x-direction, which simplifies the equations to (writing u for the x-component of the velocity)

$$\frac{\partial s}{\partial t} = -\frac{\partial u}{\partial x} \tag{5—1}$$

and

$$\frac{\partial u}{\partial t} = -\frac{\gamma}{\rho_0 \kappa_{0T}} \frac{\partial s}{\partial x}. \tag{5—1'}$$

Assuming now that s and u are proportional to $\exp\{i\omega(t - x/\mathfrak{B})\}$, one has

$$s = \frac{u}{\mathfrak{B}} \tag{5—2}$$

and

$$u = \frac{\gamma}{\rho_0 \kappa_{0T}} \frac{s}{\mathfrak{B}}. \tag{5—2'}$$

Inserting Eq. (5—2) into Eq. (5—2'), one gets the well known result

$$\mathfrak{B}^2 = \frac{\gamma}{\rho_0 \kappa_{0T}} = \left(1 + \frac{C_p - C_v}{C_v}\right) \frac{1}{\rho_0 \kappa_{0T}}. \tag{5—3}$$

Combining Eqs. (3—4), (4—10), and (5—2) one obtains the following relation between the different quantities in the wave

$$p - p_0 = \frac{\gamma}{\kappa_{0T}} s = \rho_0 \mathfrak{B}^2 s. \tag{5—4}$$

It follows from Eqs. (5—2) and (5—4) that in a purely progressive non-dissipative wave, s, u, and $p - p_0$ are in phase, as far as space and time are concerned. If, on the other hand, one has a pure standing wave

$$s = s_0 \cos \omega t \cos \frac{\omega}{\mathfrak{B}} x, \tag{5—5}$$

Eq. (5—4) stands but, from Eq. (5—2)

$$\frac{u}{\mathfrak{B}} = s_0 \sin \omega t \sin \frac{\omega}{\mathfrak{B}} x. \tag{5—6}$$

In the progressive wave, the energy contained in 1 cc (if all dimensions are large compared to the wave length) is

$$\frac{1}{2} \rho_0 u^2 + \frac{1}{2} \left(\frac{\gamma}{\kappa_T} \right) s^2 = \frac{1}{2} \rho_0 \{u^2 + \mathfrak{B}^2 s^2\}. \tag{5—7}$$

The two terms are equal at any time and place, but vary with time and place. One has as the average

$$\text{energy density} = \frac{1}{2} \rho_0 u^2_{\max} = \frac{1}{2} \rho_0 \mathfrak{B}^2 s^2_{\max} = \frac{1}{2} \frac{1}{\rho_0 \mathfrak{B}^2} (p_{\max} - p_0)^2. \tag{5—8}$$

In a standing wave, the energy density is also given by Eq. (5—7), but the two terms are equal only on the average, and we have

$$\text{energy density} = \frac{1}{4} \rho_0 u^2_{\max} = \frac{1}{4} \rho_0 \mathfrak{B}^2 s^2_{\max} = \frac{1}{4} \frac{1}{\rho_0 \mathfrak{B}^2} (p_{\max} - p_0)^2. \tag{5—8'}$$

The energy propagated in a progressive wave, passing per second through the unit of area normal to the direction of propagation, is defined as the intensity I, and is equal to the average energy density multiplied by the velocity of propagation. (Actually, this should be the group velocity.) There follows, from Eq. (5—8)

$$I = \frac{1}{2} \rho_0 \mathfrak{B} u^2_{\max} = \frac{1}{2} \rho_0 \mathfrak{B}^3 s^2_{\max} = \frac{1}{2} \frac{1}{\rho_0 \mathfrak{B}} (p_{\max} - p_0)^2. \tag{5—9}$$

One can now estimate the error made in linearizing the equations of motion (Sec. 3).

The replacement of ρ by ρ_0, when multiplied by a factor containing the speed, neglects s_{max} compared to one.

The replacement of D/Dt by $\partial/\partial t$ neglects $\omega(u/\mathfrak{V})$ compared to ω or $u/\mathfrak{V}$ compared to one.

The linearization of p behaves as follows. For an ideal gas, the adiabatic compressibility is $1/\gamma p$ and the relative error made by replacing it $1/\gamma p_0$ is $p/p_0 - 1$. This may therefore be appreciable at intensities of 1 watt/cm² but is smaller than 2×10^{-4} at 10^{-4} watts/cm². For isopentane at 30° C, $(1/v_0\ \partial v/\partial p)_T$ and $(1/v\ \partial v/\partial p)_T$ change by about 1 in 300 per atmosphere.

6. Viscosity

In the equation of motion of a fluid (Eqs. 1—4, 2—3, and 3—3), the general stress tensor P is made up of two parts, the negative hydrostatic pressure $-p$ and a viscosity term P'.

One assumes next that the viscosity stress shall be linear in the first differential quotients of the velocity components. This is based on the following arguments: (a) required linearity (see Sec. 3); (b) no viscosity of fluid at rest (with resultant dependence on velocity components); and (c) no viscosity of fluid in spatially uniform (i.e., rigid) motion, with resultant dependence on spatial differential quotients of velocity components. P' can be further divided into two parts

$$P' = P'' + P''' \tag{6—1}$$

where

$$P''_{ii} = 2\eta\left(\frac{\partial u_i}{\partial x_i} - \frac{1}{3}\,\mathrm{div}\,\boldsymbol{w}\right) \tag{6—2}$$

$$P''_{ij} = \eta\left(\frac{\partial u_i}{\partial x_j} + \frac{\partial u_j}{\partial x_i}\right) \qquad i \neq j \tag{6—2'}$$

$$P'''_{ii} = \eta'\,\mathrm{div}\,\boldsymbol{w} \tag{6—3}$$

$$P'''_{ij} = 0 \qquad i \neq j.$$

P'' is the only expression which is built linearly from first order spatial differential quotients of the velocity components, and which forms a proper symmetrical tensor of the second rank. That is, its components P'_{ij} transform, upon rotation of the coordinate system, like the product $x_i x_j$, whether j is equal to i or not (see Fig. 6—1).

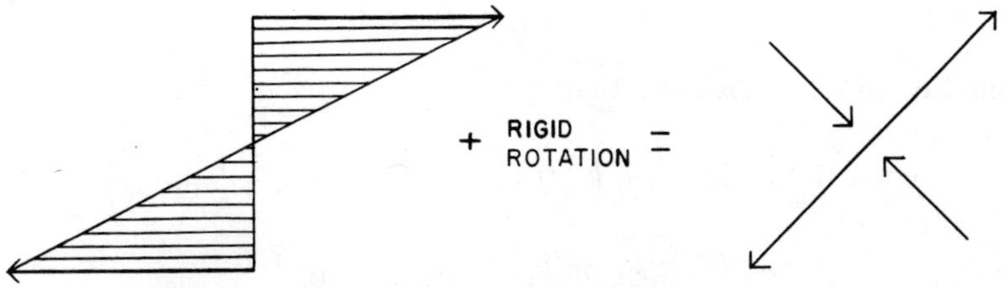

Fig. 6–1. Pure shear flow.

If one wishes to understand the structure of Eq. (6—2), one first considers Eq. (6—2′). In the simple case of flow in the x-direction, with a velocity gradient in the z-direction, one has in the normal manner

$$P''_{13} = \eta \frac{\partial u_1}{\partial z}$$

Since the shear stress is symmetrical in the two indices, it follows immediately that in more general flow patterns, this must be generalized to

$$P''_{13} = \eta \left(\frac{\partial u_1}{\partial z} + \frac{\partial u_3}{\partial x} \right)$$

which is the 1,3 component of Eq. (6—2′).

If the two indices are equal, one gets part of Eq. (6—2)

$$(P''_{11}) = 2\eta \frac{\partial u_1}{\partial x} .$$

If one adds the three components, one finds

$$(P''_{11}) + (P''_{22}) + (P''_{33}) = 2\eta \left(\frac{\partial u_1}{\partial x} + \frac{\partial u_2}{\partial y} + \frac{\partial u_3}{\partial z} \right)$$

$$= 2\eta \operatorname{div} \boldsymbol{w} = -\, 2\eta \frac{1}{\rho} \frac{D\rho}{Dt}$$

[see Eq. (6—6)]. If one does not want P'' to give a contribution to an isotropic pressure for a motion which is purely compressive, i.e., if one wants to exclude the bulk viscosity from P'', one must subtract from all the diagonal terms P''_{jj} the same scalar quantity chosen so that[1]

$$P''_{11} + P''_{22} + P''_{33} = 0.$$

From Eq. (6—2) it follows that

$$P''_{11} + P''_{22} + P''_{33} = 2\eta\left(\frac{\partial u_1}{\partial x} + \frac{\partial u_2}{\partial y} + \frac{\partial u_3}{\partial z} - 3\,\frac{1}{3}\,\mathrm{div}\,\boldsymbol{w}\right)$$

$$= 2\eta\,(\mathrm{div}\,\boldsymbol{w} - \mathrm{div}\,\boldsymbol{w}) = 0.$$

P''' is a scalar, the only scalar which can be built linearly from spatial differential quotients of the velocity components. The most general tensor of the second rank is the sum of a proper tensor of the second rank and of a scalar. The η and η' are independent of the velocity components; η is the usual shear viscosity; η' is called the volume viscosity.

The η is usually measured in cases where the velocity varies in a direction normal to that of the flow, in which case shear stresses [Eq. (6—2′)] arise. The shear viscosity, however, also contributes to the normal stresses even in apparently compressional waves, e.g., in a one-dimensional compressional flow, as in a plane sound wave propagated in the x-direction, where $u_2 = u_3 = 0$, and $\partial/\partial y = \partial/\partial z = 0$, there are contributions to the normal stresses[2]

---

[1] This sum is called the trace of the tensor and is independent of the direction of the coordinate system.

[2] The unidimensional compressional flow described by $\partial u_1/\partial x$ can be considered as the superposition of *two* flows. One, isotropic and purely compressional, is equal to

$$a\left(\frac{\partial u_1}{\partial x} + \frac{\partial u_2}{\partial y} + \frac{\partial u_3}{\partial z}\right)$$

with the three terms equal. This does not contribute to shear loss. The second flow is pure shear, noncompressional, and has the components (see Fig. 6—2)

$$b\,\frac{\partial u_1}{\partial x}, \qquad -\frac{b}{2}\frac{\partial u_1}{\partial x}, \qquad -\frac{b}{2}\frac{\partial u_1}{\partial x}.$$

In order to make the superposition equivalent to a flow in the x-direction alone, equal to $\partial u_1/\partial x$ one has to choose $a + b = 1$; $a - b/2 = 0$; or $a = 1/3$, $b = 2/3$. The flow of the second kind is equivalent to a pure shear flow along axes rotated by 45°, giving stresses as shown in Eqs. (6—4), (6—4′), and (6—4″) see Fig. 6—1.

$$P_{11}'' = 2\eta\left(\frac{\partial u_1}{\partial x} - \frac{1}{3}\frac{\partial u_1}{\partial x}\right) = \frac{4}{3}\eta\frac{\partial u_1}{\partial x} \tag{6—4}$$

$$P_{22}'' = P_{33}'' = -\frac{2}{3}\eta\frac{\partial u_1}{\partial x} \tag{6—4'}$$

and

$$P_{ij}'' = 0 \qquad i \neq j. \tag{6—4''}$$

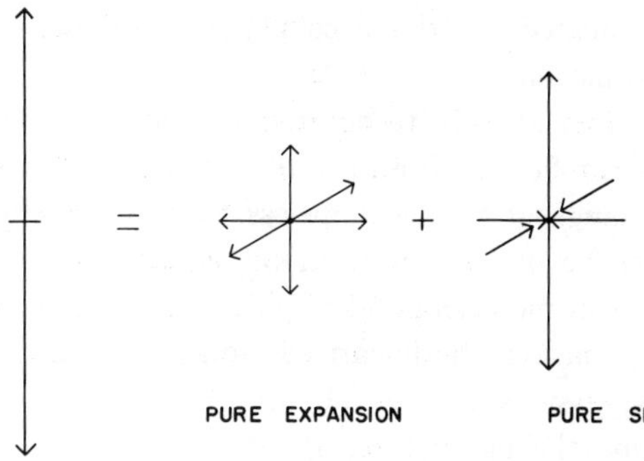

Fig. 6–2. Longitudinal wave, considered as superposition of pure extension and pure shear.

Here, as in general

$$P_{11}'' + P_{22}'' + P_{33}'' = = 2\eta\left\{\frac{\partial u_1}{\partial x} + \frac{\partial u_2}{\partial y} + \frac{\partial u_3}{\partial z} - 3x\frac{1}{3}\operatorname{div}\boldsymbol{w}\right\} = 0. \tag{6—5}$$

P''', the second term in P' [see Eq. (6—3)], does not contribute to the shear stresses at all, but only contributes to the normal stresses. It is a scalar, i.e., it behaves geometrically as a hydrostatic pressure.

By eliminating div $\boldsymbol{w}$ from Eq. (6—3) with the help of the continuity equation in the form of Eq. (2—2), one can write[3, 4]

$$P_{ii}''' = -\eta'\frac{1}{\rho}\frac{D\rho}{Dt}. \tag{6—6}$$

---

[3] L. Tisza, *Phys. Rev.* **61**, 531 (1942).

[4] K. F. Herzfeld, *J. Acoust. Soc. Am.* **13**, 33 (1941).

In the case in which the motion is so small that squares of small quantities may be neglected (low intensity waves), i.e., in the linearized equation, Eq. (6—6) can be written

$$P_{ii}''' = -\eta' \frac{1}{\rho_0} \frac{\partial \rho}{\partial t}. \tag{6—7}$$

P''' is a scalar like the hydrostatic pressure, but differs from it insofar as the latter depends only on the momentary value of density and temperature, while the former depends on the time variation of the density. The distinction is complicated by the necessity of defining temperature in time dependent situations.

Stokes[5,6] had already recognized the possibility of a volume viscosity but since, as can be seen from Eq. (6—6), its effect depends on the time rate of density change, it seemed hopeless to measure effects connected with it and therefore he omitted it from his equations. It will be shown later (Sec. 36) that in monatomic ideal gases the volume viscosity η' is zero.

In one dimension, the linearized equation of motion [Eq. (3—3)], using the stress-expressions in Eqs. (1—4), (6—1), (6—2), and (6—3), has the form (omitting the index 1 on u)

$$\rho_0 \frac{\partial u}{\partial t} = -\frac{\partial p}{\partial x} + \frac{4}{3}\eta \frac{\partial^2 u}{\partial x^2} - \eta' \frac{\partial^2 u}{\partial x^2}. \tag{6—8}$$

7. The Stokes-Navier Equation. "Classical" Sound Absorption

Stokes[1] sets the volume viscosity $\eta' = 0$, so that Eq. (6—8) may be rewritten

$$\rho_0 \frac{\partial u}{\partial t} = -\frac{\partial p}{\partial x} + \frac{4}{3}\eta \frac{\partial^2 u}{\partial x^2}. \tag{7—1}$$

If we wish to calculate the effect of the last, dissipative term on sound propagation, we must also make a correction to our assumption of local adiabatic compression, and include heat conduction, as Kirchhoff[2] has shown.

---

[5] G. Stokes, *Trans. Cambridge Phil. Soc.* **8**, 287 (1845).

[6] M. Brillouin, "Leçons sur la viscosité." Gauthier-Villars, Paris, 1907.

[1] G. Stokes, *Trans. Cambridge Phil. Soc.* **8**, 287 (1845).

[2] G. Kirchhoff, *Poggendorf's Ann. Phys.* **134**, 177 (1868).

Considering the picture of a sound wave at a given time, the density crests will have temperatures above the average; the density troughs, temperatures below average. Heat conduction will tend to equalize the temperature. Accordingly, the compressed regions will, upon re-expanding, return less work than was expended on compressing them. A similar statement applies to the recompression of rarefaction regions. The result is loss, i.e., sound absorption.

Equation (4—3), taken for unit volume, has to be supplemented, on the right side, by the heat conducted in a second, which is ($\lambda =$ heat conductivity)

$$\lambda \frac{\partial^2 T}{\partial x^2}. \tag{7—2}$$

It should be remembered that Eq. (4—3) applies to 1 mole. Therefore, Eq. (4—4) is now to be written (with c_p referring to unit mass)

$$c_p \rho_0 \frac{\partial T}{\partial t} - T\beta \frac{\partial p}{\partial t} = \lambda \frac{\partial^2 T}{\partial x^2}. \tag{7—3}$$

In the absence of dissipative effects (Sec. 5) it is possible to satisfy the equations with an undamped wave. In the equations, only first order derivatives appear, and in the expression of an undamped wave, written in the complex form, a differentiation of any quantity with respect to the time simply multiplies that quantity with the factor $i\omega$, while a differentiation with respect to x gives a factor $-i\omega/\mathfrak{V}$, so that i cancels out. Now, however, Eqs. (7—1) and (7—3) contain, besides the first derivatives, second derivatives.

If the expression of a plane, undamped wave were used again in Eq. (7—1), the differentiation on the left would give a factor $i\omega$, and the first term on the right a factor $- i\omega/\mathfrak{V}$, as before, but the second term on the right would give a factor $- \omega^2/\mathfrak{V}^2$, without i, and therefore i would not cancel out. The situation is similar for Eq. (7—3).

Accordingly, we now assume all the quantities involved, s, u, $p - p_0$, and $T - T_0$, to be proportional to

$$\exp\left\{- \alpha x + i\omega\left(t - \frac{x}{\mathfrak{V}}\right)\right\} = \exp + i\omega\left\{t - \frac{x}{\mathfrak{V}}\left(1 - \frac{i\alpha\mathfrak{V}}{\omega}\right)\right\} \tag{7—4}$$

where α is called the absorption coefficient for the amplitude, and has the dimension cm^{-1}. The amplitude of the quantities involved (s, u, etc.) decreases for each cm of travel by $e^{-\alpha}$, or decreases by the factor e^{-1} for the distance α^{-1}. The absorption coefficient for the intensity is 2α.

Occasionally it is useful to define an absorption coefficient per wave length

$$\alpha_\lambda = \alpha\lambda = 2\pi \frac{\mathfrak{B}}{\omega} \alpha.$$

Then Eq. (7—4) can be rewritten

$$\exp + i\omega \left\{t - \frac{x}{\mathfrak{B}}\left(1 - \frac{i\alpha_\lambda}{2\pi}\right)\right\} = \exp\left\{- \frac{\omega}{2\pi\mathfrak{B}} \alpha_\lambda x + i\omega\left(t - \frac{x}{\mathfrak{B}}\right)\right\}. \tag{7—4'}$$

If Eq. (7—4) is now inserted into the continuity equation (5—1) and Eqs. (7—1), (7—3), and (4—1), one finds

$$i\omega s = \frac{i\omega}{\mathfrak{B}}\left(1 - i\alpha \frac{\mathfrak{B}}{\omega}\right) u \tag{7—5}$$

$$\rho_0 i\omega u = \frac{i\omega}{\mathfrak{B}}\left(1 - i\alpha \frac{\mathfrak{B}}{\omega}\right)(p - p_0) - \frac{4}{3}\eta \frac{\omega^2}{\mathfrak{B}^2}\left(1 - i\alpha \frac{\mathfrak{B}}{\omega}\right)^2 u \tag{7—5'}$$

$$s = \kappa_T(p - p_0) - \beta(T - T_0) \tag{7—5''}$$

[Eq. (7—5″) being equivalent to Eq. (4—2)]

$$i\omega\rho_0 c_p(T - T_0) - i\omega T_0 \beta(p - p_0) = - \frac{\omega^2}{\mathfrak{B}^2}\lambda\left(1 - \frac{i\alpha\mathfrak{B}}{\omega}\right)^2 (T - T_0) \tag{7—5'''}$$

or

$$(T - T_0)\left[c_p - \frac{i\omega}{\rho_0\mathfrak{B}^2}\lambda\left(1 - \frac{i\alpha\mathfrak{B}}{\omega}\right)^2\right] = T_0 \frac{\beta}{\rho_0}(p - p_0). \tag{7—5''''}$$

The effect of heat conductivity is to replace c_p by an effective specific heat

$$(c_p)_{\text{eff}} = c_p - \frac{i\omega}{\rho_0\mathfrak{B}^2}\lambda\left(1 - \frac{i\alpha\mathfrak{B}}{\omega}\right)^2.$$

From Eq. (7—5) one finds, replacing (5—2)

$$s = \frac{u}{\mathfrak{B}}\left(1 - \frac{i\alpha\mathfrak{B}}{\omega}\right) \tag{7—6}$$

so that s and u are not in phase any more.

Eliminating u in Eq. (7—5′) by substitution from Eq. (7—6), one finds the dispersion equation

$$\frac{s}{p-p_0}=\frac{1}{\rho_0\mathfrak{B}^2}\left(1-\frac{i\alpha\mathfrak{B}}{\omega}\right)^2\left[1-\frac{4}{3}\frac{i\eta\omega}{\rho_0\mathfrak{B}^2}\left(1-\frac{i\alpha\mathfrak{B}}{\omega}\right)^2\right]^{-1}. \qquad (7\text{—}7)$$

We will first neglect the effect of heat conductivity, i.e., we will put the right side of Eq. (7—5‴) equal to zero. One then has, from Eqs. (7—5″) and (7—5‴), the classical expression, Eq. (4—10)

$$\frac{s}{p-p_0}=\frac{1}{\gamma}\kappa_T=\frac{1}{\rho_0\mathfrak{B}_0{}^2}$$

where $\mathfrak{B}_0$ is the velocity at low frequency.

Equation (7—7) can then be written

$$1=\left(\frac{\mathfrak{B}_0}{\mathfrak{B}}-\frac{i\alpha\mathfrak{B}_0}{\omega}\right)^2\left[1-\frac{4}{3}i\frac{\eta\omega}{\rho_0\mathfrak{B}_0{}^2}\left(\frac{\mathfrak{B}_0}{\mathfrak{B}}-\frac{i\alpha\mathfrak{B}_0}{\omega}\right)^2\right]^{-1}. \qquad (7\text{—}7')$$

In first approximation, if $(\alpha\mathfrak{B})/\omega \ll 1$, one can then write (setting $\mathfrak{B}=\mathfrak{B}_0$ and neglecting α in the square bracket and α^2)

$$\left(\frac{\mathfrak{B}_0}{\mathfrak{B}}\right)^2-\frac{2i\alpha\mathfrak{B}_0{}^2}{\omega\mathfrak{B}}=1-\frac{4}{3}i\frac{\eta\omega}{\rho_0\mathfrak{B}_0{}^2}$$

or

$$\mathfrak{B}=\mathfrak{B}_0 \qquad \alpha=\frac{2}{3}\eta\frac{1}{\rho_0\mathfrak{B}_0{}^3}\omega^2. \qquad (7\text{—}8)$$

For very high frequencies, a more exact evaluation has to be made. Define with Lucas[3a] a time[3b]

$$\tau_L=\frac{4}{3}\frac{\eta}{\rho_0\mathfrak{B}_0{}^2}=\frac{4}{3}\frac{\eta}{\gamma_0}\kappa_T. \qquad (7\text{—}9)$$

If one also has a constant bulk viscosity η', one can define

$$\tau_L'=\frac{1}{\rho_0\mathfrak{B}_0{}^2}\left(\frac{4}{3}\eta+\eta'\right). \qquad (7\text{—}9')$$

[3a] R. Lucas, *Compt. rend.* **206**, 658 (1938).

[3b] From Eq. (36—4), $\eta = 1.27\,p\tau_c$ for an ideal gas, where τ_c is the time between collisions. $\rho_0\mathfrak{B}_0{}^2=\gamma p$, therefore $\tau_L = 1.7/\gamma\,\tau_c$.

Equation (7—7′) then has the form

$$\left(\frac{\mathfrak{B}_0}{\mathfrak{B}} - i\,\frac{\alpha\mathfrak{B}_0}{\omega}\right)^2 = 1 - i\omega\tau_L\left(\frac{\mathfrak{B}_0}{\mathfrak{B}} - \frac{i\alpha\mathfrak{B}_0}{\omega}\right)^2 \tag{7—10}$$

or

$$\left(\frac{\mathfrak{B}_0}{\mathfrak{B}} - \frac{i\alpha\mathfrak{B}_0}{\omega}\right)^2 = \frac{1}{1 + i\omega\tau_L}. \tag{7—10′}$$

Equation (7—10′) is the usual sound dispersion equation, except that the numerator is unity.

Squaring out Eq. (7—10) and separating real and imaginary parts

$$\left(\frac{\mathfrak{B}_0}{\mathfrak{B}}\right)^2 - \left(\frac{\alpha\mathfrak{B}_0}{\omega}\right)^2 = 1 - 2\omega\tau_L\,\frac{\mathfrak{B}_0}{\mathfrak{B}}\,\frac{\alpha\mathfrak{B}_0}{\omega}$$

$$-\,2\,\frac{\alpha\mathfrak{B}_0}{\omega}\,\frac{\mathfrak{B}_0}{\mathfrak{B}} = -\,\omega\tau_L\left[\left(\frac{\mathfrak{B}_0}{\mathfrak{B}}\right)^2 - \left(\frac{\alpha\mathfrak{B}_0}{\omega}\right)^2\right].$$

These are two quadratic equations, with the unknowns $\mathfrak{B}_0/\mathfrak{B}$ and $\alpha\mathfrak{B}_0/\omega$. They may be easily solved, with the result

$$\left(\frac{\mathfrak{B}_0}{\mathfrak{B}}\right)^2 = \frac{1}{2}\left[\frac{1}{\sqrt{1 + \omega^2\tau_L{}^2}} + \frac{1}{1 + \omega^2\tau_L{}^2}\right] \tag{7—11}$$

$$\left(\frac{\alpha\mathfrak{B}_0}{\omega}\right)^2 = \frac{1}{2}\left[\frac{1}{\sqrt{1 + \omega^2\tau_L{}^2}} - \frac{1}{1 + \omega^2\tau_L{}^2}\right]. \tag{7—11′}$$

One has further, by multiplying Eqs. (7—11) and (7—11′)

$$\frac{\alpha\mathfrak{B}_0}{\omega}\,\frac{\mathfrak{B}_0}{\mathfrak{B}} = \frac{1}{2}\,\frac{\omega\tau_L}{1 + \omega^2\tau_L{}^2} \tag{7—12}$$

which is the usual form of a relaxation absorption.

For small values of $\omega\tau_L$, one has, as in Eq. (7—8)

$$\frac{\alpha\mathfrak{B}_0}{\omega} = \frac{1}{2}\,\omega\,\tau_L,$$

and

$$\frac{\mathfrak{B}_0}{\mathfrak{B}} = 1 - \frac{3}{8}\,\omega^2\tau_L{}^2.$$

A maximum of absorption occurs for $\alpha\mathfrak{V}_0/\omega$ at

$$\omega^2\tau_L{}^2 = 3 \tag{7—13}$$

which is

$$\left(\frac{\alpha\mathfrak{V}_0}{\omega}\right)_{\max} = \frac{1}{2\sqrt{2}}.$$

At even higher frequencies

$$\frac{\alpha\mathfrak{V}_0}{\omega} = \sqrt{\frac{1}{2\omega\tau_L}},$$

i.e., on a plot of $\alpha\lambda$ against $\log\omega$ the high frequency part is only half as steep as the low frequency branch. According to the first of the equations, Eq. (7—11), $\mathfrak{V}$ increases with ω. At the frequency which gives the maximum of $\alpha\lambda$

$$\mathfrak{V} = \mathfrak{V}_0\sqrt{\frac{8}{3}} = 1.633\,\mathfrak{V}_0.$$

At high frequencies

$$\frac{\mathfrak{V}}{\mathfrak{V}_0} = \sqrt{2\omega\tau_L}$$

rising without limit. In this region

$$\frac{\alpha\mathfrak{V}_0}{\omega}\frac{\mathfrak{V}}{\mathfrak{V}_0} = \frac{\alpha\lambda}{2\pi} = 1.$$

The behavior is similar to the skin effect in metals for electromagnetic waves. This similarity is due to the fact that for the sound wave at high frequencies the shear forces predominate over the compressional forces while propagation of the electromagnetic waves is governed by ohmic resistance, formally analogous to a viscous force.

In liquids, no experimental case has yet been found in which the viscosity does not drop off because of relaxation before the condition shown in Eq. (7—13) is reached.

If heat conductivity is not neglected, instead of the adiabatic equation Eq. (4—7), one gets as the connection between s and p for the process

$$s = \kappa_T\left\{1 - \frac{T_0\mathfrak{V}\beta^2}{\kappa_T c_p}\left[1 - \frac{i\omega}{\mathfrak{V}^2}\left(1 - \frac{i\alpha\mathfrak{V}}{\omega}\right)^2\frac{\lambda}{c_p\rho_0}\right]^{-1}\right\}(p - p_0). \tag{7—14}$$

An approximation is next made by assuming that the absorption is not too large, specifically, that

$$\alpha \frac{\mathfrak{V}}{\omega} = \frac{1}{2\pi} \alpha_\lambda < 1. \tag{7—15}$$

If we neglect terms which are of the third or higher order in the small quantities, but include both viscosity and heat conduction, we find[4]

$$\frac{\mathfrak{V}_0{}^2}{\mathfrak{V}^2} - 2i\alpha \frac{\mathfrak{V}_0}{\omega} \frac{\mathfrak{V}_0}{\mathfrak{V}} - \alpha^2 \frac{\mathfrak{V}_0{}^2}{\omega^2} = 1 - \left[\frac{4}{3}\frac{\eta}{\rho_0} + (\gamma - 1)\frac{\lambda}{c\rho_0}\right]\frac{i\omega}{\mathfrak{V}^2}$$

$$- \left[\frac{4}{3}\frac{\eta}{\rho_0} + (\gamma - 1)\frac{\lambda}{c_p\rho_0}\right]\frac{\alpha}{\mathfrak{V}} + \left[\frac{4}{3}\frac{\eta}{\rho_0} + \frac{\lambda}{c_p\rho_0}\right](\gamma - 1)\frac{\lambda}{c_p\,\rho_0}\frac{\omega^2}{\mathfrak{V}^4}. \tag{7—16}$$

One sees that the imaginary parts of Eq. (7—16) contain only the first powers of small quantities; the real parts, zero and second order terms of the small quantities. Accordingly, in writing the equation for α which comes from the imaginary terms, one can replace $\mathfrak{V}$ with $\mathfrak{V}_0$, since the difference is of the second order and, multiplied with the small α, would give third order terms. The absorption coefficient so calculated shall be called the "classical" absorption coefficient, α_{class}.

$$\alpha_{\text{class}} = \frac{2}{3}\frac{\omega^2}{\mathfrak{V}^3\rho_0}\left[\eta + \frac{3}{4}(\gamma - 1)\frac{\lambda}{c_p}\right] \tag{7—17}$$

$$\frac{\mathfrak{V}_0{}^2}{\mathfrak{V}^2} = 1 - \left\{\left(\frac{2}{3}\eta - \frac{\gamma - 1}{2}\frac{\lambda}{c_p}\right)^2 - (\gamma - 1)\left(\frac{\lambda}{c_p}\right)^2\right\}\frac{\omega^2}{\rho_0{}^2\mathfrak{V}^4}. \tag{7—18}$$

Equation (7—17) gives an increase of $\mathfrak{V}$ with ω since, in general, the viscosity term is larger than the heat conductivity term. However, this effect is, in general, small. If η were zero, one would have

$$\left(\frac{\mathfrak{V}_0}{\mathfrak{V}^2}\right)^2 = 1 + (\gamma - 1)(5 - \gamma)\left(\frac{\lambda}{c_p}\right)^2 \frac{\omega^2}{(2\rho_0\mathfrak{V}^2)^2}. \tag{7—19}$$

---

[4] Equations (7—1) and (7—3) have a second solution which represents a strongly damped "temperature" wave. See K. F. Herzfeld, *Phys. Rev.* **53**, 899 (1938).

$\mathfrak{V}$ would decrease with increasing frequency, since the process becomes more isothermal.[5a, 5b]

The effect of viscosity on sound absorption was first calculated by Stokes, that of heat conductivity by Kirchhoff and Langevin.

The exact solution of the combination of Eqs. (7—7) and (7—14), by which the effects of both viscosity and heat conductivity are taken into account, has been put into slightly different form by Greenspan.[6] He introduces, from the field of gas dynamics, the Reynolds number [Re] as a dimensionless variable

$$[\mathrm{Re}] = \frac{\rho_0 \mathfrak{V}_0{}^2}{\eta\omega} = \frac{3}{4}\frac{1}{\omega\tau_L}. \tag{7—20}$$

One other dimensionless quantity is of importance here. The Prandtl number [Pr]

$$[\mathrm{Pr}] = \frac{\eta C_p}{\lambda M} \tag{7—20'}$$

[5a] It follows from Eqs. (7—16, 7—18) as Herzfeld and Rice have pointed out,[5b] that — contrary to opinions expressed in the past — a sound wave behaves more and more adiabatically and isentropically, the lower its frequency is. The reason is that the irreversible heat transfer by conduction is proportional to

$$\frac{\partial^2 T}{\partial x^2} = 4\pi^2 \frac{1}{\lambda^2}(T - T_0),$$

(λ wavelength), i.e., is quadratic with the frequency. While it is true that for a lower frequency there is more time in which the heat conduction can take place, that does not compensate the λ^{-2} above. One would get for the heat lost per period a quantity proportional to $1/f\ 1/\lambda^2 (T - T_0) = f/\mathfrak{V}^2 (T - T_0)$. With this argument, one might ask how it is possible to compress a gas at all slowly and isothermally, if slower and slower changes make the process in the gas more and more adiabatic. One can see that here the finite size of the vessel comes in. If L is a characteristic length of the vessel, then, once the wave length of the sound becomes comparable to and even larger than L, the heat conduction is determined not by the gradient set by the wave length but by a gradient set by the walls of the vessel, i.e., the heat transfer by conduction is proportional to $1/L^2(T - T_0)$, and the heat lost per period is now proportional to $(1/fL^2)(T - T_0)$, i.e., increases with decreasing frequency.

[5b] K. F. Herzfeld and F. O. Rice, *Phys. Rev.* **31**, 691 (1928).

[6] M. Greenspan, *J. Acoust. Soc. Am.* **22**, 568 (1950).

is used by aerodynamicists, but is awkward to use in physics. Instead, we define a related number here and call it the Eucken number [Eu]

$$[\mathrm{Eu}] = \frac{\lambda M}{\eta C_v} = \gamma\ [\mathrm{Pr}]^{-1}. \qquad (7-20'')$$

Then

$$\left(\frac{\mathfrak{V}_0}{\mathfrak{V}} - \frac{i\alpha\mathfrak{V}_0}{\omega}\right)^4 [\mathrm{Eu}] \left(\frac{4}{3} - \frac{i}{\gamma}\right)$$

$$+ \left(\frac{\mathfrak{V}_0}{\mathfrak{V}} - \frac{i\alpha\mathfrak{V}_0}{\omega}\right)^2 [\mathrm{Re}] \left\{[\mathrm{Re}] + i\left(\frac{4}{3} + [\mathrm{Eu}]\right)\right\} = [\mathrm{Re}]^2. \qquad (7-21)$$

Truesdell[7] has discussed in detail and calculated numerically the solutions of Eq. (7—21) for different combinations of the numerical constants η/ρ_0 and $\lambda/c_p\rho_0$, assuming them to be constants, i.e., frequency independent, for the purpose of deciding to what extent the Stokes-Navier equations are sufficient, without the introduction of relaxation. The shape of the resultant curves for $\mathfrak{V}/\mathfrak{V}_0$ and α as functions of ω differ, depending on the numerical constants assumed, but in no case does $\mathfrak{V}/\mathfrak{V}_0$ approach a limiting value for high frequency.

Actually, there are not too many cases in which the dispersion curve has been measured to sufficiently high frequencies to become horizontal: CO_2 (Richards and Reid,[8] Gutowski[9]); $CHCl_3$ (Busala *et al.*[10]); and glycerine (Litovitz *et al.*[11]). One might expect Truesdell's analysis to be valid for gases at frequencies high enough for relaxation to have disappeared. However, it follows from footnote 3b that the characteristic effects will only occur in the neighborhood of frequencies comparable with the number of collisions per second. The question arises as to whether the continuum theory of the Navier-Stokes equations is applicable there. The

---

[7] C. Truesdell, *J. Rational Mech. Anal.* **2**, 643 (1953).

Truesdell distinguishes good conductors of heat (molten metals, liquid helium II), moderate conductors (gases), and poor conductors (most liquids) by the magnitude of the Eucken number.

[8] W. T. Richards and J. A. Reid, *J. Chem. Phys.* **2**, 193 (1934).

[9] F. Gutowski, Ph. D. Dissertation, Catholic Univ., Washington, D.C., 1956; *J. Acoust. Soc. Am.* **28**, 478 (1956).

[10] A. Busala, D. Sette, and J. C. Hubbard, *J. Chem. Phys.* **23**, 787 (1955).

[11] T. A. Litovitz, T. Lyon, and L. Peselnick, *J. Acoust. Soc. Am.* **26**, 566 (1954).

experiments on helium and argon (see Sec. 47) seem to indicate that it is applicable though not completely so.

As to liquids, the theory might be applicable to monatomic liquids (liquid noble gases) and some molten metals (mercury), but there are not sufficient data to judge.[12]

8. Formal Introduction of Volume Viscosity

Except in monatomic gases and possibly monatomic liquids, the experimentally found absorption is always larger than the classical absorption α_{class}, as shown by Eq. (7—17).

As Tisza[1] has first pointed out, this excess absorption can be formally accounted for by a volume viscosity; see Eqs. (6—1) and (6—3). The equation of motion, Eq. (7—1), is then replaced by [see Eq. (6—8)]

$$\rho_0 \frac{\partial u}{\partial t} = -\frac{\partial p}{\partial x} - \frac{\partial}{\partial x}\left\{2\eta \frac{\partial u}{\partial x} - \frac{2}{3}\eta \frac{\partial u}{\partial x} + \eta' \frac{\partial u}{\partial x}\right\}$$

$$= -\frac{\partial p}{\partial x} - \left(\frac{4}{3}\eta + \eta'\right)\frac{\partial^2 u}{\partial x^2} = -\frac{\partial p}{\partial x} - \frac{4}{3}\left((\eta + \frac{3}{4}\eta'\right)\frac{\partial^2 u}{\partial x^2}. \qquad (8\text{—}1)$$

The rest of the calculation proceeds as before, and an expression like that in Eq. (7—8) is again found for the absorption, except that η is replaced by $\eta + 3/4\,\eta'$. In other words

$$\alpha - \alpha_{\text{class}} = \frac{\omega^2}{2\mathfrak{V}^3\rho}\eta', \qquad (8\text{—}2)$$

or

$$\frac{(\alpha - \alpha_{\text{class}})}{\alpha_{\text{class}}} = \frac{3}{4}\frac{\eta'}{\eta}\left\{1 + \frac{3}{4}\frac{\gamma - 1}{c_p}\frac{\lambda}{\eta}\right\}^{-1}. \qquad (8\text{—}3)$$

As will be shown later, the expression $\{1 + 3/4\,(\gamma - 1)/c_p\,\lambda/\eta\}$ can, in liquids, be replaced by unity.

In all cases observed up to now the condition in Eq. (7—15) is fulfilled.[2,3]

---

[12] Truesdell's standpoint [*Proc. Roy. Soc.* **A 226**, 59 (1954)] is similar.

[1] L. Tisza, *Phys. Rev.* **61**, 531 (1942).

[2] L. Mandelstam and M. Leontovic, *Compt. rend. acad. sci. U.R.S.S.* **3**, 111 (1936); *Zhur. Eksperth. i Teoret. Fiz.* **7**, 438 (1938).

[3] For example, in glycerine at $-20°$ C and 30 Mc, α is about 4 cm^{-1}, $\lambda = 1/200$ cm, and $\alpha(\mathfrak{V}/\omega) \sim 1/300$ cm.

The processes responsible for the excess absorption are "relaxation" processes. A general discussion of such processes is given in the next section. In pure substances two types of relaxation phenomena are known to produce excess sound absorption.

(a) A delay in the exchange of external and internal degrees of freedom. This is important if and only insofar as periodic temperature fluctuations (see Sec. 4) occur in the sound wave. A subdivision of this type is given by chemical reactions in the fluid.

(b) Slow structural changes not connected with temperature fluctuations. These only occur in liquids.

Sections 10 to 16 deal with type (a) of the relaxation phenomena. At first one might ask whether in this case the stresses, Eqs. (6—3) and (6—6), connected with the volume viscosity η' as defined in Eq. (8—2), are not fictitious. This question will be discussed in Sec. 30 when we are more familiar with this phenomenon.

Truesdell[4] has questioned the consistency of introducing a "constant" into the hydrodynamical equations — which are supposed to hold for any time dependence — and then making this "constant" frequency dependent, which assumes simple harmonic motion. From the standpoint of consistency, he is quite right, and the only consistent procedure is the one applied in the following sections. However, the other procedure has long been followed in other fields of physics, the most conspicuous example being the dielectric "constant" introduced in Maxwell's equations, which also has to be taken as frequency dependent. For a consistent treatment, see Herzfeld.[5] If η' is considered as a constant, the solutions in the second part of Sec. 7 remain unchanged, except that $\eta + 3/4\,\eta'$ is used instead of η.

[4] C. Truesdell, *J. Rational Mech. Anal.* 2, 643 (1953).

[5] K. F. Herzfeld, *Ann. Physik* [6] 3, 69 (1948).

II. General Considerations on Relaxation

9. General Discussion of Resonance and Relaxation Phenomena

(a) *Resonance*

In classical physics resonance phenomena have been more familiar than relaxation phenomena, e.g., the usual optical dispersion is due to a resonance phenomenon.

This phenomenon is normally governed by a second order linear differential equation in which the second, the first, and the zeroth-differential quotient are present. That is, for the motion of a particle subjected to a Hooke's law restoring force and friction, the governing differential equation for the free motion is

$$m\ddot{x} + b\dot{x} + Kx = 0 \tag{9–1}$$

where the first term describes the inertial force, the second the frictional, and the last the restoring force. If such a particle, originally at rest, is suddenly subjected to a force F_1, which is constant after $t = 0$, the new equilibrium position would be

$$x_1 = \frac{F_1}{K}. \tag{9–2}$$

This new equilibrium position is not assumed immediately. Instead, the particle undergoes damped oscillations about the position ("transient"). These oscillations are such that at $t = 0$ the particle is at its original position $x = 0$. The particle then moves toward the new position x_1, but it does not stop there. Instead, it overshoots it, due to inertia.

If the damping is small, the particle goes (nearly) as far to the other side as the original deviation was, i.e., it goes almost to $2x_1$. Gradually this vibration is then damped out and the particle comes to rest at x_1. If the damping is small, the frequency of this free oscillation is given by

$$2\pi\nu_0 = \omega_0 = \sqrt{\frac{K}{m}}. \tag{9–3}$$

On applying to the particle a periodic force $F_0 e^{i\omega t}$, instead of the steady force, the motion will be periodic with the frequency ω of the impressed force once the transients have died out.

The solution is

$$x = \frac{F_0\, e^{i\omega t}}{m(\omega_0{}^2 - \omega^2 + i\omega\omega')} \tag{9–4}$$

with the abbreviation $\omega' = b/m$.

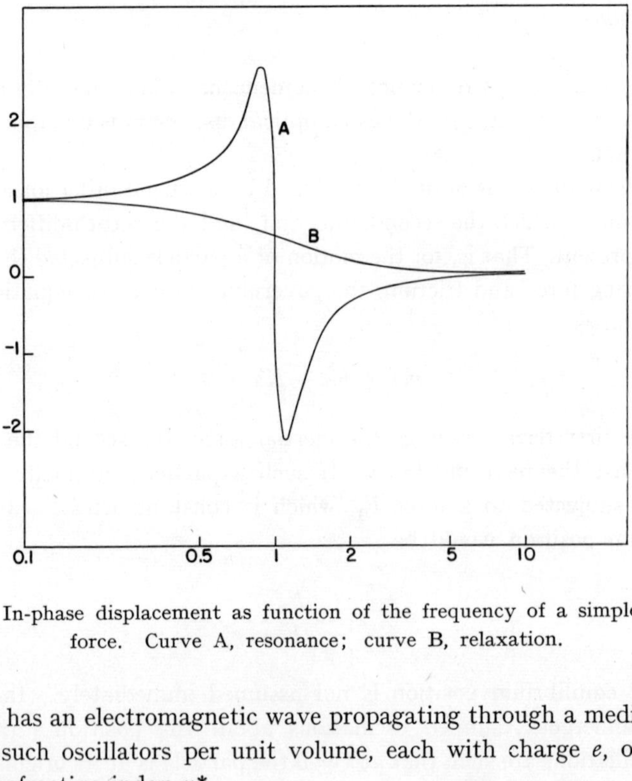

FIG. 9–1. In-phase displacement as function of the frequency of a simple harmonic force. Curve A, resonance; curve B, relaxation.

If one has an electromagnetic wave propagating through a medium made up of N such oscillators per unit volume, each with charge e, one gets a complex refractive index n^*

$$(n^*)^2 - 1 = \frac{4\pi N}{m} \frac{e^2}{\omega_0{}^2 - \omega^2 + i\omega\omega'} \tag{9–5}$$

which can be split, if the absorption is not too strong, into the real refractive index and the absorption

$$n^2 - 1 = \left(\frac{c}{\mathfrak{B}}\right)^2 - 1 = \frac{4\pi N e^2}{m} \frac{\omega_0{}^2 - \omega^2}{(\omega_0{}^2 - \omega^2)^2 + \omega^2(\omega')^2} \tag{9–6}$$

and

$$2n\alpha = 2\frac{c}{\mathfrak{B}}\alpha = \frac{4\pi Ne^2}{m}\frac{\omega\omega'}{({\omega_0}^2 - \omega^2)^2 + \omega^2(\omega')^2}. \tag{9-7}$$

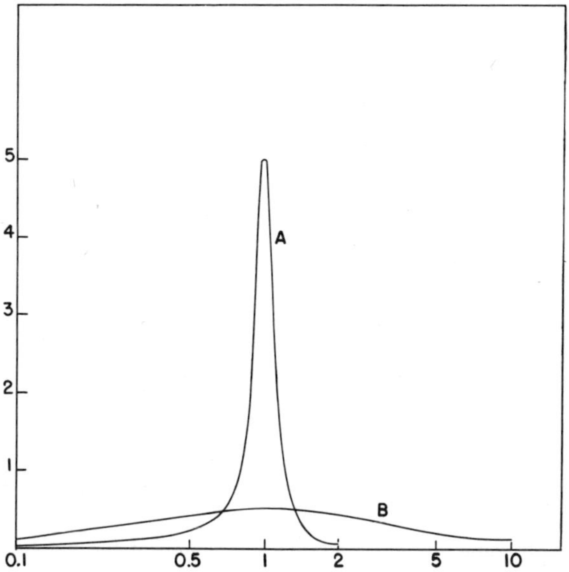

FIG. 9–2. Out-of-phase displacement as function of the frequency of a simple harmonic force. Curve A, resonance; curve B, relaxation.

Figure 9–1, curve A, shows $n^2 - 1$, which is proportional to the real (in-phase) component of the displacement for this case. Figure 9–2, curve A, shows $2n\alpha$, which is proportional to the imaginary (out-of-phase) component of the displacement. Figure 9–3, curve A, shows the absolute value of the displacement. It should be noted that the width of the two curves, 9–3 A and 9–2 A, is proportional to ω' or b/m and may be very narrow; for some spectral lines in gases ω'/ω_0 is about 10^{-6} Furthermore, near resonance, the absolute values of the amplitude may be much higher than the static value, the ratio being ω_0/ω' at resonance.

To get a physical understanding of the behavior, neglect at first the friction term. The inertial term is proportional to the amplitude and to the square of the frequency; the restoring force term is proportional to the amplitude and independent of frequency. In the free motion, inertial and restoring force must cancel. This cannot be brought about by changing the amplitude, since this changes the two terms by the same factor. It must be brought about by choosing the proper frequency.

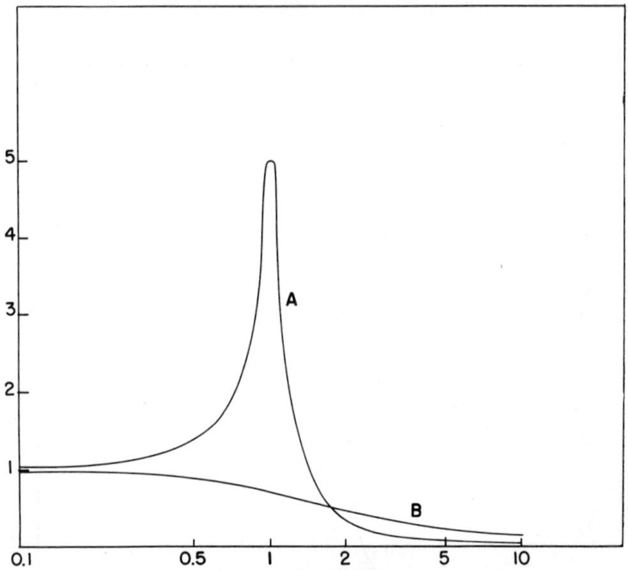

FIG. 9–3. Absolute value of the amplitude as function of the frequency of a simple harmonic force. Curve A, resonance; curve B, relaxation.

If one has an external periodic force, the frequency is given. The *difference* between restoring force and inertial force has to be balanced by the external force. At low frequency, the inertial force is negligible and the motion is quasi-static, the external force balancing the restoring force. At higher frequencies the inertial force increases and cancels part of the restoring force. Only a fraction of the restoring force has to be balanced by the external force, so that the amplitude increases to make the fraction of the restoring force equal to the external force. At resonance, inertial and restoring force cancel exactly, nothing remaining to balance the external force, so that the amplitude would become infinite. This is, of course, not so because of the friction hitherto neglected. Since it contains the *first* differential quotient (as compared to the second and zeroth for inertial and restoring force) it gives a contribution 90° out of phase with the other two. Therefore, no cancellation is possible. This friction contributes a component of displacement 90° out of phase with the force (watt component, friction loss) and, at resonance, this is the only component remaining. Beyond resonance the inertial force is larger than the restoring force, and at high frequencies it is practically alone in balancing the external force.

(b) Relaxation Phenomena

Relaxation phenomena are described normally by linear differential equations, in which only the first and zeroth differential quotients are present. As an example, consider the free fall of a sphere in a viscous liquid. Here the dependent variable is the velocity, which from an initial value changes monotonically to the terminal velocity. Another case is that of an LR circuit (for the current) or of a CR circuit (for the charge). Most of the equations we will encounter can be reduced to reaction rate equations (which contain no inertial term) of the form

$$-\frac{dn}{dt} = k(n - n_0)$$

where n_0 is an equilibrium value. Provisionally calling the dependent variable U (without specifying its nature), the typical relaxation equation is

$$-\frac{dU}{dt} = \frac{1}{\tau}(U - U_0). \tag{9–8}$$

It is clear that once U reaches the value U_0 the process is over and no overshooting occurs; τ is the relaxation time.

We next generalize Eq. (9–8) by permitting U_0 to depend on an external parameter (force, temperature) which is a given function of time. We will then write $\boldsymbol{U}(t)$ for U_0, so that

$$\tau \frac{dU}{dt} = -(U - \boldsymbol{U}). \tag{9–9}$$

To compare results with the resonance case, let $\boldsymbol{U}(t)$ again vary as a step function, being changed from the value U_0 at $t = 0$ to U_1, the latter being kept constant afterward. The solution of Eq. (9–9) is then

$$U = U_1 + (U_0 - U_1)\, e^{-t/\tau}$$

i.e., the "memory" of the previous state U_0 dies out exponentially.

If $\boldsymbol{U}$ varies as a simple harmonic function of time

$$\boldsymbol{U} = \boldsymbol{U}_0\, e^{i\omega t}$$

U can be set proportional to the same exponential and Eq. (9–9) can be written

$$i\omega\tau U = -U + \boldsymbol{U} \tag{9-10}$$

or

$$U = \frac{\boldsymbol{U}}{1 + i\omega\tau} = \boldsymbol{U}_0 \frac{e^{i\omega t}}{1 + i\omega\tau}. \tag{9-11}$$

To this must be added a transient

$$U' e^{-t/\tau}$$

which takes care of the initial conditions and dies out slowly. Equation (9–11) gives an absolute value of the amplitude

$$|U| = \frac{\boldsymbol{U}_0}{(1 + \omega^2\tau^2)^{1/2}}.$$

This starts with the static value $\boldsymbol{U}_0$ at low frequency, and then decreases uniformly to zero, without a maximum. At $\omega\tau \gg 1$, the motion cannot follow $\boldsymbol{U}$ at all.

Equation (9–11) can be rewritten

$$U = \boldsymbol{U}\left(\frac{1}{1 + \omega^2\tau^2} - \frac{i\omega\tau}{1 + \omega^2\tau^2}\right). \tag{9-12}$$

The in-phase component is shown in Fig. 9–1, curve B; the out-of-phase component in Fig. 9–2, curve B; and the absolute value in Fig. 9–3, curve B. The in-phase component starts with the static value and then decreases slowly to zero, without a maximum. This is absent because the differential equation does not contain two differential quotients, differing by two in order, which would give cancelable terms of opposite phase.

The curves are quite broad; the width of the curves is completely fixed if the value of τ (τ also determining the location of the maximum of Fig. 9–2, curve B, through the relation $\omega\tau = 1$) is given. It is to be noted that the frequency always appears in the combination $\omega\tau$.

If $\boldsymbol{U}$ is an arbitrary function of t, the general solution of Eq. (9–9) is

$$U = e^{-t/\tau} \int_{-\infty}^{t} \boldsymbol{U}(t')\, e^{t'/\tau} \frac{dt'}{\tau} = \int_{-\infty}^{0} \boldsymbol{U}(t'' + t)\, e^{t''/\tau} \frac{dt''}{\tau}.$$

It is of interest to state the difference between resonance and relaxation once more. In resonance phenomena you can, by choice of the proper frequency, make the system do something it would not otherwise do. (Think of two cars, with the bumpers hooked, where you can achieve sufficient amplitude for disengaging by resonant loading.) On the other hand, in relaxation phenomena you can, by choosing sufficiently high frequencies, prevent some process from occurring.

In a sense, in ultrasonic waves relaxation phenomena do not produce something which would not occur statically, but may prevent something from happening which would have happened statically. For example, in the case of a relaxation process concerned with energy transfer, in the quasi-static process energy supplied to the external degrees of freedom is distributed between these and the internal degrees of freedom. At sufficiently high frequencies, this does *not* occur. The energy stays in the external degrees of freedom, producing a higher temperature there.

In liquids with structural relaxation, a static pressure produces shortening of distances plus a rearrangement. If the times of pressure application are sufficiently short, no rearrangement occurs.

10. Energy Exchange between Internal and External Degrees of Freedom as Relaxation Phenomenon

The changes in density which occur in a sound wave are usually accompanied by temperature changes. For a reversible process these temperature changes are given by Eq. (4–7) and are inversely proportional to the specific heat.

The primary process which produces the temperature increase upon density increase affects the translational energy of the molecules as a whole.

Consider first an ideal gas, compressed slowly by a piston moving inward with the speed w. A molecule moving toward the piston with an (absolute) velocity component normal to the piston equal to W_3 is reflected from a moving mirror and, therefore, has, after the collision, an (absolute) normal component of $-(W_3 + 2w)$, so that the kinetic energy is increased by

$$\frac{m}{2}(4W_3w + 4w^2) = 2mw\,(W_3 + w) \sim 2mwW_3.$$

This increase of one velocity component is quickly distributed over the other components and shared with other molecules by collision, resulting in an increased translational energy and, therefore, increased "translational temperature."

If the molecules have internal degrees of freedom, these had an average energy E' which was in equilibrium with the former value of the translational energy.

The value of E' in equilibrium with the new, increased translational energy is higher, and therefore energy must flow from the translational to the internal degrees of freedom. This can only occur in collisions and may take time. The time needed to decrease the maladjustment by a factor e^{-1} is called the relaxation time τ.

Since some degrees of freedom (e.g., those of rotation) may be adjusted very rapidly, they may be lumped with the translational degrees of freedom as "external" and distinguished from the "internal" degrees of freedom, which take a longer time for adjustment.

Consider next the mechanism of reversible heating on compressing a crystal. The thermal motion of the molecules (or radicals) in the crystal as a whole can be analyzed into Debye waves of the acoustical branch. If the crystal is slowly compressed, the frequency of each acoustical Debye wave is (adiabatically) increased[1] and, accordingly, the energy of each

---

[1] For a simple ideal crystal (i.e., one without defects) the entropy S depends on the volume only because the vibrational frequency ν depends on the volume. Furthermore, the entropy contains the frequency and the temperature only in the combination $h\nu/kT$. In a compression in which the entropy remains constant, T rises therefore proportionally with ν.

If the crystal is not simple, it contains other branches than the acoustic branch. These other branches correspond to the internal vibrations. Call the acoustic branch 1 and, for simplicity, assume there is one other branch 2. Then

$$S = S_1\left(\frac{h\nu_1}{kT}\right) + S_2\left(\frac{h\nu_2}{kT}\right).$$

Call S' the derivative of S in respect to the argument $h\nu/kT$. Then

$$dS = \frac{\partial S}{\partial T}dT + \frac{\partial S}{\partial V}dV \qquad \frac{\partial S}{\partial T} = -\frac{h\nu}{kT^2}S' \qquad \frac{\partial S}{\partial V} = \frac{h}{kT}\frac{\partial \nu}{\partial V}S' = \frac{h\nu}{kT}S'\frac{\partial \ln \nu}{\partial V}.$$

Therefore

$$0 = -\left(S_1'\frac{h\nu_1}{kT} + S_2'\frac{h\nu_2}{kT}\right)\frac{dT}{T} + \left(S_1'\frac{h\nu_1}{kT}\frac{\partial \ln \nu_1}{\partial V} + S_2'\frac{h\nu_2}{kT}\frac{\partial \ln \nu_2}{\partial V}\right)dV.$$

This would be the equilibrium equation. Since, however, $\partial \ln \nu/\partial V$ is much larger for the acoustic branch than for the internal branches, the quanta and therefore the energy and temperature in the former are at first increased much more than in the latter, so that for a quick process one has

$$-S_1'\frac{h\nu_1}{kT_1}\frac{dT_1}{T_1} + S_1'\frac{h\nu_1}{kT_1}d\ln \nu_1 = 0$$

or $h\nu_1/kT_1$ is constant.

quantum of the Debye waves (phonon) is increased, without changing their number or distribution. This means a corresponding increase in temperature. The increase in temperature is then communicated to the other branches (which correspond to the internal degrees of freedom) by slow processes involving at least two phonons of the other branches and one of the acoustical branch. It is to be remembered that, if the restoring force were to obey Hooke's law strictly, there would be neither temperature increase according to thermodynamics, because the coefficient of thermal expansion vanishes, nor dependence of frequency on volume.

For a liquid we cannot make as detailed a theory, but the situation will be in between those described above for gas and for crystal.

We can see from the previous argument that a new situation will arise if the density change is too rapid. If the relative change in density is small during the relaxation time τ, the processes which are responsible for the energy exchange between external and internal degrees of freedom will keep the two types of degree of freedom nearly in equilibrium. Therefore, the total energy changed into heat motion will be divided between the two, and the temperature rise will be governed by the static specific heat C_v. This, however, can be divided into two parts; one $\tilde{C}_v$, belonging to the external degrees of freedom, the other, C', to the internal degrees. If the rate of density change is increased (e.g., the frequency in a sound wave) the internal energy can follow the changes of external energy less and less and, accordingly, the "effective" specific heat decreases. If the density changes are rapid compared to the adjustment process, only the energy of the external degrees of freedom varies, and the effective specific heat is $\tilde{C}_v$.

This process of slow energy exchange between different degrees of freedom is the relaxation phenomenon responsible for excess absorption of ultrasonic waves in gases (except at very high frequencies) and in many liquids.

Call E' the momentary value of the internal energy and $E'(T_{tr})$ the value it would have in equilibrium with external degrees of freedom which are at T_{tr}. One then assumes the relaxation equation[2]

$$-\frac{dE'}{dt} = \frac{1}{\tau}\,[E' - E'(T_{tr})] \tag{10–1}$$

which contains as individual constant only the relaxation time τ. A justification for this equation will be given in Sec. 19.

[2] K. F. Herzfeld and F. O. Rice, *Phys. Rev.* **31**, 691 (1928). Their τ would be, in our notation, $C'\tau/\tilde{C}_v$.

If the specific heat C' is independent of the temperature, or if the temperature never deviates far from a value T_0, one can write

$$E' - E_0' = C'(T' - T_0)$$

and replace Eq. (10–1) by

$$-\frac{dT'}{dt} = \frac{1}{\tau}(T' - T_{\text{tr}}). \tag{10–2}$$

For further discussion, assume that the translational temperature is raised suddenly at $t = 0$ from T_0 to a value T_1. Two cases may now be distinguished: The external temperature is kept constant at T_1 after $t = 0$, the energy leaking into the internal degrees of freedom being replaced from the outside. The solution of Eq. (10–2) is then

$$T' = T_1 + (T_0 - T_1)\, e^{-t/\tau}.$$

On the other hand, if the external energy is not constant but is deprived of the amount flowing into the internal degrees of freedom, we have

$$0 = \check{C}(T_{\text{tr}} - T_1) + C'(T' - T_0)$$

or

$$\begin{aligned} 0 &= \check{C}(T_{\text{tr}} - T') + \check{C}(T' - T_1) + C'(T' - T_0) = \\ &= \check{C}(T_{\text{tr}} - T') + C(T' - T_2) \end{aligned} \tag{10–3}$$

where

$$T_2 = \frac{\check{C}}{C}\, T_1 + \frac{C'}{C}\, T_0 \tag{10–3'}$$

is the final equilibrium temperature. Eliminating $T_{\text{tr}} - T'$ from Eq. (10–2) with the help of Eq. (10–3), one has

$$-\frac{dT'}{dt} = \frac{C}{\check{C}}\,\frac{1}{\tau}\,(T' - T_2)$$

with the solution

$$T' = T_2 + (T_0 - T_2)\, e^{-t/\tau'}. \tag{10–4}$$

The apparent relaxation time is now

$$\tau' = \frac{\check{C}}{C}\,\tau = \frac{C - C'}{C}\,\tau. \tag{10–4'}$$

It is seen that the measured relaxation time depends on the circumstances.

Eq. (10–2) can be written

$$-\tau \frac{dT'}{dt} = T' - T_0 - (T_{\text{tr}} - T_0) \tag{10–5}$$

or

$$T' - T_0 + \tau \frac{d}{dt}(T' - T_0) = T_{\text{tr}} - T_0. \tag{10–5'}$$

If $T_{\text{tr}} - T_0$ varies periodically with time, i. e., is proportional to $e^{i\omega t}$, $T' - T_0$ will also be proportional to $e^{i\omega t}$. After the transient has died out, this takes the form

$$(T' - T_0)(1 + i\omega\tau) = T_{\text{tr}} - T_0$$

or

$$T' - T_0 = \frac{T_{\text{tr}} - T_0}{1 + i\omega\tau} \tag{10–6}$$

which is to be compared with Eq. (9–11); Eq. (10–6) can also be rewritten

$$\frac{dT'}{dT_{\text{tr}}} = \frac{1}{1 + i\omega\tau}. \tag{10–6'}$$

The effective specific heat, defined in Eq. (10–7''), can then be calculated from

$$dE = (C_v)_{\text{eff}}\, dT_{\text{tr}} = \tilde{C}_v\, dT_{\text{tr}} + C'\, dT' = \left(\tilde{C}_v + C' \frac{dT'}{dT_{\text{tr}}}\right) dT_{\text{tr}} \tag{10–7'}$$

and

$$(C_v)_{\text{eff}} = \tilde{C}_v + \frac{C'}{1 + i\omega\tau} = C_v - \frac{C' i\omega\tau}{1 + i\omega\tau}. \tag{10–7''}$$

11. The Effect of Slow Energy Exchange on Sound Propagation

When a plane simple harmonic sound wave is propagated through a medium with relaxation, it is necessary to introduce absorption, as in Eq. (7–4). The approximation is usually made that the effects of relaxation phenomena on the one side and of classical viscosity and heat conduction on the other side are additive. This is not strictly true. If one makes that assumption, one uses the Stokes-Navier equation without friction or heat conduction to consider the present problem and has, from Eq. (5–1) and the equation of motion

$$\frac{\partial u}{\partial t} = -\frac{1}{\rho_0}\frac{\partial p}{\partial x} = -\frac{1}{\rho_0}\frac{\partial p}{\partial s}\frac{\partial s}{\partial x}$$

$$1 = \frac{1}{\rho_0}\frac{dp}{ds}\left(\frac{1}{\mathfrak{B}} - \frac{i\alpha}{\omega}\right)^2. \tag{11–1}$$

The physical assumption is now made that the equation of state depends on the *translational* temperature T_{tr} only. For an ideal gas, this is self-evident. For a liquid it means, for example, that the internal vibrations do not produce a pressure directly. Then Eqs. (4–1) and (4–2) remain unchanged, with dT_{tr} in the former and dT_{tr}/dp in the latter. The enthalpy equations, Eqs. (4–3) to (4–6), however, are changed. We write

$$H = H_{\text{tr}} + E'. \tag{11–2}$$

We call

$$\left(\frac{\partial H_{\text{tr}}}{\partial T_{\text{tr}}}\right)_p = \tilde{C}_p \qquad \frac{dE'}{dT'} = C'. \tag{11–3}$$

$$\tilde{C}_p + C' = C_p\,(\text{static}).$$

Since we assume that E' does not depend upon pressure at constant T, Eq. (4–6) is replaced by the new enthalpy equation

$$\tilde{C}_p\, dT_{\text{tr}} + C'dT' = T_{\text{tr}}\left(\frac{\partial V}{\partial T}\right)_p dp \tag{11–4}$$

or

$$\tilde{C}_p dT_{\text{tr}} + C'dT' = (C_p)_{\text{eff}}\, dT_{\text{tr}} = T_{\text{tr}}\, V\beta dp. \tag{11–4'}$$

Therefore, Eq. (4–8) is replaced by

$$\frac{ds}{dp} = \kappa_T\left(1 - \frac{\beta}{\kappa_T}\frac{dT_{\text{tr}}}{dp}\right) = \kappa_T\left(1 - \frac{\beta^2 V T_{\text{tr}}}{\kappa_T}\frac{1}{(C_p)_{\text{eff}}}\right) = \kappa_T\left(1 - \frac{\Delta}{(C_p)_{\text{eff}}}\right). \tag{11–5}$$

Here it is assumed that $\Delta = C_p - C_v$ is the same at temperature T_{tr} as it would be statically for the same temperature, since it depends on the equation of state only.

The specific effective heat is defined as

$$(C_p)_{\text{eff}} = \tilde{C}_p + C' \frac{dT'}{dT_{\text{tr}}} = C_p + C'\left(\frac{dT'}{dT_{\text{tr}}} - 1\right). \tag{11–6}$$

Similarly

$$(C_v)_{\text{eff}} = \tilde{C}_v + C' \frac{dT'}{dT_{\text{tr}}} = C_v + C'\left(\frac{dT'}{dT_{\text{tr}}} - 1\right) \tag{11–6′}$$

$$(C_p)_{\text{eff}} = (C_v)_{\text{eff}} + \Delta \tag{11–6″}$$

and

$$\gamma_{\text{eff}} = 1 + \frac{\Delta}{(C_v)_{\text{eff}}} \qquad \frac{1}{\gamma_{\text{eff}}} = 1 - \frac{\Delta}{(C_p)_{\text{eff}}}. \tag{11–6‴}$$

Therefore, Eqs. (11–1) and (11–5) give

$$\left(\frac{1}{\mathfrak{V}} - \frac{i\alpha}{\omega}\right)^2 = \frac{\rho_0 \kappa_T}{\gamma_{\text{eff}}}. \tag{11–7}$$

Designating the quasi-static values by the index zero and multiplying Eq. (11–7) by $\mathfrak{V}_0{}^2$, one gets

$$\left(\frac{\mathfrak{V}_0}{\mathfrak{V}} - \frac{i\alpha\mathfrak{V}_0}{\omega}\right)^2 = \frac{\gamma_0}{\gamma_{\text{eff}}}. \tag{11–8}$$

The only task to be done now is the evaluation of γ_{eff}^{-1}, which involves, from Eq. (11–6), the calculation of dT'/dT_{tr}. This is where relaxation comes in.

Using the relaxation equation in the form of Eq. (11–6), one finds

$$(C_p)_{\text{eff}} = \tilde{C}_p + \frac{C'}{1 + i\omega\tau} = C_p - C' \frac{i\omega\tau}{1 + i\omega\tau}. \tag{11–9}$$

Equation (11–8) then takes the form

$$\begin{aligned}\left(\frac{\mathfrak{V}_0}{\mathfrak{V}} - \frac{i\alpha\mathfrak{V}_0}{\omega}\right)^2 &= \frac{C_p}{C_v}\left(\tilde{C}_v + \frac{C'}{1 + i\omega\tau}\right)\left(\tilde{C}_p + \frac{C'}{1 + i\omega\tau}\right)^{-1} \\ &= \frac{C_p}{C_v}(\tilde{C}_v + \tilde{C}_v i\omega\tau + C')(\tilde{C}_p + \tilde{C}_p i\omega\tau + C')^{-1} \\ &= \left(1 + \frac{\tilde{C}_v}{C_v} i\omega\tau\right)\left(1 + \frac{\tilde{C}_p}{C_p} i\omega\tau\right)^{-1}. \end{aligned} \tag{11–10}$$

Consider first a general algebraic transformation

$$\frac{1+ai\omega\tau}{1+bi\omega\tau} = 1 + (a-b)\,\frac{i\omega\tau}{1+i\omega b\tau} = 1 + \frac{a-b}{b}\,\frac{i\omega\tau'}{1+i\omega\tau'}, \qquad (11\text{–}11)$$

with a new relaxation time

$$\tau' = b\tau. \qquad (11\text{–}12)$$

In the case of Eq. (11–10)

$$a = \frac{\tilde{C}_v}{C_v} = \frac{C_v - C'}{C_v} \qquad b = \frac{\tilde{C}_p}{C_p} = \frac{C_p - C'}{C_p} \qquad (11\text{–}13)$$

$$a - b = \frac{\tilde{C}_v}{C_v} - \frac{\tilde{C}_p}{C_p} = \frac{1}{C_v C_p}\,[\tilde{C}_v(C_v + \Delta) - (\tilde{C}_v + \Delta)C_v] = -\frac{\Delta C'}{C_v C_p} \qquad (11\text{–}13')$$

$$\frac{a-b}{b} = -\frac{\Delta C'}{C_v(C_p - C')} \qquad (11\text{–}13'')$$

$$\tau' = \frac{C_p - C'}{C_p}\,\tau. \qquad (11\text{–}14)$$

The relaxation effects—the second term in Eq. (11–11), which is the right side of Eq. (11–10)—are proportional to $C_p - C_v = \Delta$. If $\Delta = 0$, there is no temperature change connected with density change, and the rate of energy exchange does not matter.

If one takes the reciprocal of Eq. (11–11), a and b are interchanged, i.e.

$$\frac{C_v}{C_p}\frac{(C_p)_{\text{eff}}}{(C_v)_{\text{eff}}} = \left(1 + \frac{\tilde{C}_p}{C_p}\,i\omega\tau\right)\left(1 + \frac{\tilde{C}_v}{C_p}\,i\omega\tau\right)^{-1} = 1 + \frac{b-a}{a}\,\frac{i\omega\tau''}{1+i\omega\tau''} \qquad (11\text{–}15)$$

with

$$\tau'' = a\tau = \frac{C_v - C'}{C_v}\,\tau. \qquad (11\text{–}16)$$

The reason for the existence of this absorption can be explained as follows. In the absence of relaxation, the change in density and pressure are in phase. Therefore, the useful work $V dp = M/\rho\, dp$, when integrated over a period, vanishes (wattless current u only).

According to Eqs. (4–1) and (4–7), one has linear relations with real coefficients between ds, dT, and dp, so that s, $T - T_0$, and $p - p_0$ are all in phase. But relaxation makes $(C_p)_{\text{eff}}$ complex, which introduces a phase difference between dT and dp and, therefore, a phase difference between $d\rho$ and dp, and so produces a watt component.

By using Eqs. (11–9) and (11–4′)

$$dp = \frac{1}{T_0 V\beta}\left(\tilde{C}_p + \frac{C'}{1+i\omega\tau}\right) dT_{\text{tr}}$$

$$= \frac{1}{T_0 V\beta}(C_p + \tilde{C}_p\,\omega^2\tau^2 - iC'\omega\tau)\frac{1}{1+\omega^2\tau^2}\,dT_{\text{tr}}. \tag{11–17}$$

The phase angle φ between $(p - p_0)$ and $(T_{\text{tr}} - T_0)$ is therefore given by

$$\text{tg}\,\varphi = \frac{C'\omega\tau}{C_p + \tilde{C}_p\,\omega^2\tau^2} = \frac{C'}{C_p}\frac{\omega\tau}{1+(\tilde{C}/C_p)\,\omega^2\tau^2}$$

$$= \frac{C'}{\sqrt{C_p(C_p - C')}}\,\frac{\omega\sqrt{(\tilde{C}_p/C_p)}\,\tau}{1+(\tilde{C}_p/C_p)\,\omega^2\tau^2}\,. \tag{11–18}$$

This angle is zero for $\omega = 0$ and $\omega = \infty$ and has a maximum at

$$\omega^{-1} = \left(\frac{C_p - C'}{C_p}\right)^{1/2}\tau$$

which maximum is equal to

$$(\text{tg}\,\varphi)_{\max} = \frac{1}{2}\frac{C'}{\sqrt{C_p(C_p - C')}}\,.$$

The phase angle φ' between s and $p - p_0$ follows[1] from Eq. (11–15) as

$$\text{tg}\,\varphi' = \frac{\Delta C'}{\sqrt{C_v C_p (C_v - C')\,(C_p - C')}}\,\frac{\omega\tau'''}{1+\omega^2(\tau''')^2} \tag{11–19}$$

where τ''' is a quantity defined in Eq. (16–4).

12. Discussion of the Dispersion Equation

To discuss Eq. (11–10) one first separates the real and imaginary parts on the two sides of the equation, and sets the real parts on both sides equal to each other, and the imaginary parts on both sides equal to each other. This is done on the left by squaring out, and on the right by multiplying by $(1 - i\omega\tau')$ in the numerator and the denominator. This gives, on the left

$$\frac{\mathfrak{V}_0^{\,2}}{\mathfrak{V}^2} - 2i\alpha'\,\frac{\mathfrak{V}}{\omega}\,\frac{\mathfrak{V}_0^{\,2}}{\mathfrak{V}^2} - \frac{\alpha'^2\mathfrak{V}_0^{\,2}}{\omega^2} \tag{12–1}$$

---

[1] W. T. Richards, *Revs. Modern Phys.* **11**, **36** (1939).

and separating, as described above

$$\frac{\mathfrak{V}_0{}^2}{\mathfrak{V}^2} - \frac{\alpha'^2\mathfrak{V}_0{}^2}{\omega^2} = 1 + \frac{\Delta C'}{C_v(C_p - C')}\left(\frac{1}{1+\omega^2\tau'^2} - 1\right)$$

$$= 1 - \frac{\Delta C'}{C_v(C_p - C')}\frac{\omega^2\tau'^2}{1+\omega^2\tau'^2} \tag{12–2}$$

$$2\alpha'\frac{\mathfrak{V}}{\omega}\frac{\mathfrak{V}_0{}^2}{\mathfrak{V}^2} = \frac{\Delta C'}{C_v(C_p - C')}\frac{\omega\tau'}{1+\omega^2\tau'^2}. \tag{12–3}$$

Equations (12–2) and (12–3) are rather complicated, since both contain α and $\mathfrak{V}_0/\mathfrak{V}$ as unknowns.

In optical dispersion theory, a similar situation occurs. A complex refractive index, $n - i\alpha$, is introduced and then, by a procedure quite analogous to that described above, two equations are found: $n^2 - \alpha^2 =$ the real part of a function $\Phi(\omega)$, and $2in\alpha =$ the imaginary part of Φ, n being the optical name for $\mathfrak{V}_0/\mathfrak{V}$.

However, in most cases Eq. (12–2) may be simplified: $\alpha\mathfrak{V}_0/\omega$ is $1/2\pi$ times the absorption per wave length, the wave length being calculated with $\mathfrak{V}_0$, not $\mathfrak{V}$. Since $\mathfrak{V}_0 \leqslant \mathfrak{V}$, $\alpha'(\mathfrak{V}_0/\omega) \leqslant \alpha'(\mathfrak{V}/\omega)$. If one neglects the second term on the left, the following errors in the formula for $\mathfrak{V}_0/\mathfrak{V}$ are made.

$\alpha'\lambda$	0.01	0.1	0.3
error in $(\mathfrak{V}_0/\mathfrak{V})^2$	2.57×10^{-6}	2.57×10^{-4}	2.3×10^{-3}
error in $\mathfrak{V}_0/\mathfrak{V}$	1.28×10^{-6}	1.28×10^{-4}	1.15×10^{-3}

Since for the lowest absorption listed above the error is much below the experimental error of any method presently available, and since for most methods the accuracy of velocity measurements decreases considerably for high absorption, it is safe in most cases to neglect the second term. Rhodes[1] has made a correction for it in evaluating his data. Section **17** will give the exact solution. Under the simplifying assumption, the equation reads

$$\left(\frac{\mathfrak{V}_0}{\mathfrak{V}}\right)^2 = 1 - \frac{\Delta C'}{C_v(C_p - C')}\frac{\omega^2\tau'^2}{1+\omega^2\tau'^2}. \tag{12–4}$$

[1] J. E. Rhodes, *Phys. Rev.* **70**, **91**, **932** (**1946**).

At zero frequency, the second term on the right side is zero, and $\mathfrak{B} = \mathfrak{B}_0$, as it should. At very high frequencies, the second fraction on the right approaches unity, and

$$\left(\frac{\mathfrak{B}_0}{\mathfrak{B}_\infty}\right)^2 = 1 - \frac{\Delta C'}{C_v(C_p - C')} = 1 - \frac{C_p - C_v}{C_v}\frac{C'}{C_p - C'} = \frac{C_p}{C_v}\frac{C_v - C'}{C_p - C'} \quad (12\text{–}5)$$

so that

$$\mathfrak{B}_\infty{}^2 = \frac{C_p - C'}{C_v - C'}\frac{1}{\rho\kappa_T}$$

as is necessary.

Before proceeding with the discussion of Eq. (12–4) it will be useful to treat parts of it separately, for further use. From Eq. (12–5)

$$\frac{\mathfrak{B}_\infty{}^2 - \mathfrak{B}_0{}^2}{\mathfrak{B}_\infty{}^2} = \frac{\Delta C'}{C_v(C_p - C')}. \quad (12\text{–}6)$$

Multiplying this with the reciprocal of Eq. (12–5)

$$\frac{\mathfrak{B}_\infty{}^2}{\mathfrak{B}_0{}^2} = \frac{C_p - C'}{C_v - C'}\frac{C_v}{C_p} \quad (12\text{–}6')$$

one has

$$\frac{\mathfrak{B}_\infty{}^2 - \mathfrak{B}_0{}^2}{\mathfrak{B}_0{}^2} = \frac{\Delta C'}{C_p(C_v - C')}. \quad (12\text{–}7)$$

Next we discuss the behavior of the expression

$$y = \frac{\omega^2\tau^2}{1 + \omega^2\tau^2}. \quad (12\text{–}8)$$

It is seen that it is a function of $\omega\tau$ only, since doubling ω gives the same result as cutting τ in half. At low frequency, it starts from zero and is approximately $y = \omega^2\tau^2$, rising parabolically.

At high frequency one has

$$y = \frac{1 + \omega^2\tau^2 - 1}{1 + \omega^2\tau^2} = 1 - \frac{1}{1 + \omega^2\tau^2} \sim 1 - \frac{1}{\omega^2\tau^2}.$$

The function approaches one asymptotically from below.

The half value (1/2) is reached for

$$\omega_{1/2}\tau = 1$$

or

$$f_{1/2} = \frac{1}{2\pi\tau}.$$

The whole rise, however, is very gradual. At $f = 1/2\, f_{1/2}$ and $\omega\tau = 1/2$, $y = 1/5$. At $f = 2f_{1/2}$ and $\omega\tau = 2$, $y = 4/5$. Therefore, the rise of y from 0.2 to 0.8 extends over two octaves.

One can rewrite y

$$y = \frac{1}{2}\left(1 - \frac{1 - \omega^2\tau^2}{1 + \omega^2\tau^2}\right) = \frac{1}{2} - \frac{1}{2}\frac{(1/\omega\tau) - \omega\tau}{(1/\omega\tau) + \omega\tau}. \tag{12–8'}$$

If one now plots y against $\ln \omega$ (or on a logarithmic paper), it is convenient to introduce into the discussion immediately following the notation

$$x = \ln \omega\tau = \ln \omega + \ln \tau.$$

Accordingly, the x scale is found from the $\ln \omega$ scale by a shift of the origin by $\ln \tau$. Equation (12–8′) may then be written as

$$y = \frac{1}{2} + \frac{1}{2}\frac{e^x - e^{-x}}{e^x + e^{-x}}. \tag{12–9}$$

Therefore, the curve of y against x (or $\ln \omega$) has the following property. At $x = 0$ $(\omega\tau = 1)$, $y = 1/2$. For larger x (larger $\omega\tau$), the curve increases asymptotically to 1. To the left of $x = 0$ (i.e., for $\omega\tau < 1$), the curve can be gotten by reflecting the right part first on the vertical axis, then on the horizontal line $y = 1/2$. The point $y = 1/2$ $(\omega\tau = 1)$ is an inflection point of the curve.[2]

---

[2] An inflection point is one which has no curvature, i.e., $d^2y/dx^2 = 0$. Make the substitution $e^{2x} = \omega^2\tau^2$ in

$$y = 1 - \frac{1}{1 + \omega^2\tau^2} = 1 - \frac{1}{1 + e^{2x}}.$$

The first differentiation leads to

$$\frac{dy}{dx} = \frac{2\, e^{2x}}{(1 + e^{2x})^2}$$

the second to

$$\frac{d^2y}{dx^2} = \frac{4\, e^{2x}}{(1 + e^{2x})^2}\left(1 - \frac{2\, e^{2x}}{1 + e^{2x}}\right) = \frac{4\, e^{2x}\,(1 - e^{2x})}{(1 + e^{2x})^3}.$$

This disappears for $1 = e^{2x}$, i.e., $x = 0$, $\omega\tau = 1$. The slope at this point is 1/2. If one plots against ω, the point of inflection is at $\omega\tau = 1/\sqrt{3}$.

13. Different Ways of Evaluating the Dispersion Curve

The simplest way—although not the customary one—of plotting the dispersion curve would be the direct use of Eq. (12–4).

$$\frac{\mathfrak{V}_0^{\,2}}{\mathfrak{V}^2} = 1 - \frac{\mathfrak{V}_\infty^{\,2} - \mathfrak{V}_0^{\,2}}{\mathfrak{V}_\infty^{\,2}}\, y. \tag{13–1}$$

Keeping in mind the behavior of y just discussed and the minus sign, one sees that $\mathfrak{V}_0^{\,2}/\mathfrak{V}^2$ starts at one (as already mentioned, for $\omega = 0$, $\mathfrak{V} = \mathfrak{V}_0$) and then has the form of an inverted "S".

At low frequency, Eq. (13–1) may be approximated by[1]

$$\frac{\mathfrak{V}_0}{\mathfrak{V}} = 1 - \frac{\mathfrak{V}_\infty^{\,2} - \mathfrak{V}_0^{\,2}}{\mathfrak{V}_\infty^{\,2}}\frac{\omega^2\tau'^2}{2} = 1 - \frac{1}{2}\frac{\Delta C'}{C_v(C_p - C')}\left[1 - \frac{1}{4}\frac{\Delta C'}{C_v(C_p - C')}\right]\omega^2\tau'^2. \tag{13–2}$$

A change of the velocity by 1% is reached at

$$0.01 = \frac{1}{2}\frac{\Delta C'}{C_v(C_p - C')}\left[\quad\right]\omega^2\tau'^2$$

or a frequency of

$$0.023\sqrt{\frac{C_v(C_p - C')}{\Delta C'}}\left[\quad\right]^{-1/2}\frac{1}{\tau'}, \tag{13–3}$$

The half value between 1 and $(\mathfrak{V}_0/\mathfrak{V}_\infty)^2$ is reached at

$$\omega\tau' = 1$$

or

$$f = 0.1602\,\frac{1}{\tau'}, \tag{13–4}$$

where, using a scale $\log\omega$, Eq. (13–1) also shows an inflection point. At higher frequencies, the curve straightens out, and can be written, by using

$$1 - \frac{1}{1 + \omega^2\tau'^2} = \frac{\omega^2\tau'^2}{1 + \omega^2\tau'^2}$$

in the form

$$\frac{\mathfrak{V}_0^{\,2}}{\mathfrak{V}^2} = \frac{\mathfrak{V}_0^{\,2}}{\mathfrak{V}_\infty^{\,2}} + \frac{\mathfrak{V}_\infty^{\,2} - \mathfrak{V}_0^{\,2}}{\mathfrak{V}_\infty^{\,2}}\frac{1}{1 + \omega^2\tau'^2} \sim \frac{\mathfrak{V}_0^{\,2}}{\mathfrak{V}_\infty^{\,2}} + \frac{\mathfrak{V}_\infty^{\,2} - \mathfrak{V}_0^{\,2}}{\mathfrak{V}_\infty^{\,2}}\frac{1}{\omega^2\tau'^2}.$$

---

[1] Including the second term on the left of Eq. (12—2). See also Eq. (17—4).

It is, however, customary to discuss $(\mathfrak{V}/\mathfrak{V}_0)^2$ instead of Eq. (13–1). In Eq. (11–15), one writes, with the same approximations as earlier, for the real part

$$\frac{\mathfrak{V}^2}{\mathfrak{V}_0{}^2} = 1 + \frac{\Delta C'}{C_p(C_v - C')} \frac{\omega^2 \tau''^2}{1 + \omega^2 \tau''^2}. \tag{13–5}$$

Equation (13–5) can also be written as

$$\mathfrak{V}^2 = \mathfrak{V}_0{}^2 + (\mathfrak{V}_\infty{}^2 - \mathfrak{V}_0{}^2) \frac{\omega^2 \tau''^2}{1 + \omega^2 \tau''^2} = \mathfrak{V}_\infty{}^2 - (\mathfrak{V}_\infty{}^2 - \mathfrak{V}_0{}^2) \frac{1}{1 + \omega^2 \tau''^2}. \tag{13–6}$$

The discussion is quite analogous to that made before, except that $(\mathfrak{V}/\mathfrak{V}_0)^2$ *rises* from unity to

$$\left(\frac{\mathfrak{V}_\infty}{\mathfrak{V}_0}\right)^2 = \frac{C_p - C'}{C_v - C'} \frac{C_v}{C_p} = 1 + \frac{\Delta C'}{C_p(C_v - C')}.$$

The half value

$$\left(\frac{\mathfrak{V}}{\mathfrak{V}_0}\right)^2 = 1 + \frac{1}{2} \frac{\Delta C'}{C_p(C_v - C')} \tag{13–7}$$

is reached at $\omega\tau'' = 1$.

An increase of $\mathfrak{V}$ by 1% occurs at a frequency

$$0.023 \sqrt{\frac{C_p(C_v - C')}{\Delta C'}} \left\{1 + \frac{3}{4} \frac{\Delta C'}{C_p(C_v - C')}\right\}^{-1/2} \frac{1}{\tau''}. \tag{13–8}$$

This is identical with Eq. (13–3), in view of the relation in Eq. (11–16) between τ' and τ''.

The increase of velocity from

$$\mathfrak{V}^2 = \mathfrak{V}_0{}^2 + 0.2\,(\mathfrak{V}_\infty{}^2 - \mathfrak{V}_0{}^2) \tag{13–9}$$

to

$$\mathfrak{V}^2 = \mathfrak{V}_0{}^2 + 0.8\,(\mathfrak{V}_\infty{}^2 - \mathfrak{V}_0{}^2) \tag{13–9'}$$

extends over two octaves, one below $\omega\tau'' = 1$, one above $\omega\tau'' = 1$.

The range from

$$\mathfrak{V}^2 = \mathfrak{V}_0{}^2 + 0.1\,(\mathfrak{V}_\infty{}^2 - \mathfrak{V}_0{}^2)$$

to

$$\mathfrak{V}^2 = \mathfrak{V}_0{}^2 + 0.9\,(\mathfrak{V}_\infty{}^2 - \mathfrak{V}_0{}^2)$$

is covered by the frequency range from $\omega\tau'' = 0.33$ to $\omega\tau'' = 3$; i.e., a variation of the frequency by a factor of 9. No corresponding increase over a narrower frequency range is possible according to our formulas, although a wider spread is possible if there is more than a single relaxation frequency.

One can sum up the results of dispersion measurements when only one relaxation time is involved in the following way:

If sufficiently high frequencies (or in gases, sufficiently low pressures) can be applied to get the whole dispersion curve, then one has, from the ratio of high and low frequency velocity, see Eq. (12–6′)

$$\left(\frac{\mathfrak{V}_\infty}{\mathfrak{V}_0}\right)^2 = \frac{\gamma_\infty}{\gamma_0} = \frac{C_p - C'}{C_v - C'}\,\frac{C_v}{C_p} = 1 + \frac{\Delta C'}{C_p(C_v - C')}$$

which can be used to determine C', the specific heat of the internal degrees of freedom with which one is concerned, provided the static values C_p and Δ are known. The midpoint in the $(\mathfrak{V}/\mathfrak{V}_0)^2$ curve gives τ'', according to Eq. (13–7).

If the whole dispersion curve cannot be measured, but more than half of it can, so that, plotting $(\mathfrak{V}/\mathfrak{V}_0)^2$ against $\log \omega$, the inflection point can be safely recognized, then C' can again be found from the velocity of the inflection point according to

$$\left(\frac{\mathfrak{V}}{\mathfrak{V}_0}\right)^2_{\text{infl}} = 1 + \frac{1}{2}\,\frac{\Delta C'}{C_p(C_v - C')}$$

and τ'' can again be found from the frequency of the inflection point according to $\omega\tau'' = 1$.

If, finally, only the beginning of the dispersion curve is known, the measurements will have to be very accurate to define the small deviation of $\mathfrak{V}$ from $\mathfrak{V}_0$ and, from Eq. (13–5), one has

$$\frac{\mathfrak{V}^2}{\mathfrak{V}_0^{\,2}} = 1 + \frac{\Delta C'}{C_p(C_v - C')}\left\{\quad\right\}\omega^2\tau''^2 \qquad (13\text{–}10)$$

or, if the deviation is small

$$\frac{\mathfrak{V} - \mathfrak{V}_0}{\mathfrak{V}_0} = \frac{1}{2}\,\frac{\Delta}{C_p}\,\frac{C'}{C_v - C'}\left\{\quad\right\}\omega^2\tau''^2. \qquad (13\text{–}10')$$

In this case, it is not possible to get C' and τ'' separately.

14. The Absorption Curve

From Eq. (12–3), one has

$$\alpha' \frac{\mathfrak{B}}{\omega} \frac{\mathfrak{B}_0^{\,2}}{\mathfrak{B}^2} = \frac{1}{2} \frac{\Delta C'}{C_v(C_p - C')} \frac{\omega\tau'}{1 + \omega^2\tau'^2}. \tag{14–1}$$

This may also be written

$$\frac{\mathfrak{B}_0^{\,2}}{\mathfrak{B}^2} \alpha'\lambda = \pi \frac{\Delta C'}{C_v(C_p - C')} \frac{\omega\tau'}{1 + \omega^2\tau'^2}, \tag{14–2}$$

One might ask whether Eq. (14–1) for α' or Eq. (14–2) for $\alpha'\lambda$ is preferable for discussion. It can be seen that, on principle, the left sides of both Eqs. (14–1) and (14–2) need a knowledge of $\mathfrak{B}/\mathfrak{B}_0$ besides α', but since the measurements of α are not very exact, the measurements of $\mathfrak{B}/\mathfrak{B}_0$ need not be, either. Of the methods used to find the absorption coefficient, some—the interferometer method, the optical method—automatically give both α' (or $\alpha'\lambda$) and $\mathfrak{B}$; others measure absorption directly.

Only in two cases is a knowledge of dispersion unnecessary:

(a) When the internal specific heat is very small compared to C_v. Then we have with sufficient accuracy

$$\mathfrak{B} = \mathfrak{B}_0 \qquad \tau'' = \tau' = \tau$$

and

$$\alpha' = \frac{1}{2} \frac{1}{\mathfrak{B}_0} \frac{\Delta C'}{C_p\, C_v} \frac{\omega^2\tau}{1 + \omega^2\tau^2}. \tag{14–3}$$

(b) If the frequency is so low that dispersion is still negligible, regardless of the value of C'.

$$\omega\tau' \ll 1.$$

Then

$$\alpha' = \frac{1}{2} \frac{1}{\mathfrak{B}_0} \frac{\Delta C'}{C_v(C_p - C')} \omega^2\tau' \tag{14–4}$$

or

$$\alpha'\lambda = \pi \frac{\Delta C'}{C_v(C_p - C')} \omega\tau'. \tag{14–4'}$$

In the general case one can proceed along several lines.

The simplest one starts from Eq. (14–1), using as dependent function $\alpha'(\mathfrak{B}_0/\mathfrak{B})$

$$\alpha' \frac{\mathfrak{B}_0}{\mathfrak{B}} = \frac{1}{2\,\mathfrak{B}_0} \frac{\Delta C'}{C_v(C_p - C')} \frac{\omega^2\tau'}{1+\omega^2\tau'^2}. \tag{14–5}$$

If α' and $\mathfrak{B}$ are known, one can write an expression for both without making the assumption that $\alpha(\mathfrak{B}/\omega)$ is small (see Sec. 12). From Eqs. (12–2) and (12–3), one finds

$$\frac{\mathfrak{B}_0{}^2}{\mathfrak{B}^2} - 1 = \frac{\alpha'^2\mathfrak{B}_0{}^2}{\omega^2} - 2\alpha' \frac{\mathfrak{B}_0{}^2}{\mathfrak{B}}\tau' \tag{14–6}$$

or

$$\frac{\mathfrak{B}^2 - \mathfrak{B}_0{}^2}{\mathfrak{B}_0{}^2} = 2\alpha'\mathfrak{B}\tau' - \frac{\alpha'^2\mathfrak{B}^2}{\omega^2} = \frac{1}{\pi}(\alpha'\lambda)(\omega\tau') - \frac{1}{4\pi^2}(\alpha'\lambda)^2. \tag{14–6$'$}$$

Equation (14–6′) shows that knowledge of dispersion and absorption at any one frequency allows the calculation of τ' without knowing C', i.e., without knowing with what internal degrees of freedom one is dealing. If $(\alpha'\lambda)$ is sufficiently small so that its square may be neglected (assumption of Sec. 12), then at any frequency

$$\frac{\mathfrak{B}^2 - \mathfrak{B}_0{}^2}{\mathfrak{B}_0{}^2} = 2\alpha'\mathfrak{B}\tau'. \tag{14–6$''$}$$

It may be noted that $\mathfrak{B}\tau'$ is the distance the wave travels during the time τ'.

A slightly different form may be found by using Eqs. (12–6) and (14–1), neglecting $(\alpha'\lambda)^2$

$$\frac{\alpha'}{\omega^2}\frac{\mathfrak{B}_0}{\mathfrak{B}} = \frac{\mathfrak{B}_0{}^2}{\mathfrak{B}_\infty{}^2} \frac{\mathfrak{B}_\infty{}^2 - \mathfrak{B}^2}{\mathfrak{B}^2} \frac{1}{2}\frac{\tau'}{\mathfrak{B}_0} \tag{14–7}$$

or

$$\frac{\alpha'}{\omega^2} = \frac{1}{2} \frac{\mathfrak{B}_\infty{}^2 - \mathfrak{B}^2}{\mathfrak{B}_\infty{}^2} \frac{\tau'}{\mathfrak{B}}. \tag{14–7$'$}$$

Returning to the discussion of Eq. (14–5), it is found useful to consider in detail three different quantities:

$$\alpha'\frac{\mathfrak{B}_0}{\mathfrak{B}}; \qquad \alpha'\frac{\mathfrak{B}_0}{\mathfrak{B}}\frac{\mathfrak{B}_0}{\omega} = \alpha'\frac{\mathfrak{B}}{\omega}\frac{\mathfrak{B}_0{}^2}{\mathfrak{B}^2}; \qquad \frac{\alpha'}{\omega^2}\frac{\mathfrak{B}_0}{\mathfrak{B}}.$$

This will be done in the next section.

It is occasionally convenient, for a more exact calculation of τ' than can be gotten by determining the frequency of a flat maximum, to use a procedure due to Mikhailov.[1] One rewrites Eq. (14–5) as

$$\frac{\omega^2 \mathfrak{B}}{\alpha' \mathfrak{B}_0{}^2} = \frac{2C_v(C_p - C')}{\Delta C'} \left(\omega^2 \tau' + \frac{1}{\tau'} \right). \tag{14–8}$$

If the left side is plotted as a function of ω^2, one should get a straight line. The slope is

$$\frac{2C_v(C_p - C')}{\Delta C'} \tau'$$

the (extrapolated) point at which it cuts the ordinate is

$$\frac{2C_v(C_p - C')}{\Delta C'} \frac{1}{\tau'}$$

and the ratio of slope to ordinate of crossing point is $(\tau')^2$.

15. Continuation of the Discussion of Absorption

(a) *The Quantity* $\alpha'(\mathfrak{B}_0/\mathfrak{B})$

This is given by Eq. (14–5). It starts up from zero and increases parabolically with ω. The equation may be rewritten

$$\frac{\alpha' \mathfrak{B}_0}{\mathfrak{B}} = \frac{1}{2\mathfrak{B}_0 \tau'} \frac{\Delta C'}{C_v (C_p - C')} y \tag{15–1}$$

where y is the function defined in Eq. (12–8),

$$y = \frac{\omega^2 \tau'^2}{1 + \omega^2 \tau'^2}.$$

What had been said there may be applied here: $\alpha' \mathfrak{B}_0/\mathfrak{B}$ plotted against $\log \omega$ (or on logarithmic paper) starts out asymptotically from zero and has an inflection point and its half value at

$$\omega \tau' = 1 \tag{15–2}$$

---

[1] I. G. Mikhailov, *Doklady Akad. Nauk S.S.S.R.* **89**, 991 (1953).

i.e., at the same frequency at which $\mathfrak{V}_0^2/\mathfrak{V}^2$ has its inflection point. Eq. (15—1) then approaches asymptotically ($\omega\tau' \gg 1$) the value

$$\left(\alpha' \frac{\mathfrak{V}_0}{\mathfrak{V}}\right)_\infty = \frac{1}{2\mathfrak{V}_0\tau'} \frac{\Delta C'}{C_v(C_p - C')}. \tag{15-3}$$

Equation (15–3) may be rewritten as

$$\alpha'_\infty = \frac{1}{2\,\mathfrak{V}_0\tau'} \frac{\Delta C'}{\sqrt{C_p C_v (C_p - C')\,(C_v - C')}}. \tag{15-3'}$$

To illustrate this expression numerically for an imaginary gas, take $\Delta = R$, $C_v = 5/2\ R + C'$, $\mathfrak{V}_0 = 3.5 \times 10^4$ cm/sec.

	$C' = 0.05\ R$				$C' = R$				
τ'	10^{-9}	2×10^{-8}	10^{-6}	10^{-3}	10^{-9}	2×10^{-8}	10^{-6}	10^{-3}	sec
α_∞	81.6	4.08	0.082	8×10^{-5}	1460	292	1.65	1.65×10^{-3}	cm^{-1}

(*b*) *The Quantity* $(\alpha'/\omega)\ (\mathfrak{V}_0/\mathfrak{V})$

It is more useful to take

$$\alpha' \frac{2\pi}{\omega} \mathfrak{V} \frac{\mathfrak{V}_0^2}{\mathfrak{V}^2} = \alpha'\lambda \frac{\mathfrak{V}_0^2}{\mathfrak{V}^2} = \pi \frac{\Delta C'}{C_v(C_p - C')} \frac{\omega\tau'}{1 + \omega^2\tau'^2} \tag{15-4}$$

where λ is the wave length calculated with the velocity belonging to the frequency ω. If plotted against ω this starts out from zero in a straight line, given by Eq. (14–4'). There is a maximum at

$$\omega\tau' = 1$$

i.e., again at the same frequency at which both $\mathfrak{V}_0^2/\mathfrak{V}^2 - 1$ and $\alpha'(\mathfrak{V}_0/\mathfrak{V})$ have an inflection point. The height of the maximum is

$$\left(\alpha'\lambda \frac{\mathfrak{V}_0^2}{\mathfrak{V}^2}\right)_{\max} = \frac{\pi}{2} \frac{\Delta C'}{C_v(C_p - C')} \tag{15-5}$$

independent of τ'. For the examples given above, $C' = 0.05\ R$ and $C' = R$, the values of $\left(\alpha'\lambda(\mathfrak{V}_0^2/\mathfrak{V}^2)\right)_{\max}$ are 9×10^{-3} and 0.13.

The half values of the expression in Eq. (15–4)

$$\left(\alpha'\lambda\frac{\mathfrak{B}_0{}^2}{\mathfrak{B}^2}\right) = \frac{1}{2}\left(\alpha'\lambda\frac{\mathfrak{B}_0{}^2}{\mathfrak{B}^2}\right)_{\max}$$

occur at

$$\omega\tau' = 2 \pm \sqrt{3} = 0.268;\ 3.732.$$

The region between the half values extends over a frequency range of 1 to 13.9, independent of C', Δ, or τ'. This is the smallest range that may occur. Even broader maxima are possible if several τ' are present, i.e., if the measured absorption curve is the superposition of several unresolved ones. This large width of the maximum is characteristic of relaxation, as contrasted with resonance (Sec. 9). It seems probable that the frequency ratio 13.9:1, which occurs between half values of the absorption curve, will occur not only in the present mechanism (slow exchange of energy between internal and external degrees of freedom) but in all simple relaxation mechanisms.

If Eq. (15–4) is plotted against $\ln \omega$ instead of ω, it is symmetrical to both sides of Eq. (15–2), i.e., with respect to $\ln \omega + \ln \tau' = 0$. For this method of plotting, the curve approaches the abscissa on both sides exponentially, not linearly.

(c) *The Quantity* $(\alpha'/\omega^2)\,(\mathfrak{B}_0/\mathfrak{B})$

It is customary to express ω^2 by f^2, the square of the frequency. Then

$$\frac{\alpha'}{f^2}\frac{\mathfrak{B}_0}{\mathfrak{B}} = \frac{2\pi^2}{\mathfrak{B}_0}\frac{\Delta C'}{C_v(C_p - C')}\frac{\tau'}{1+\omega^2\tau'^2}. \tag{15–6}$$

This equation can also be written in a different form, transforming Eq. (14–7). The last two factors on the right of Eq. (14–7) may be rewritten as

$$\frac{\mathfrak{B}_0{}^2}{\mathfrak{B}_\infty{}^2}\left(\frac{\mathfrak{B}_\infty{}^2}{\mathfrak{B}^2} - 1\right) = \frac{\mathfrak{B}_0{}^2}{\mathfrak{B}^2} - \frac{\mathfrak{B}_0{}^2}{\mathfrak{B}_\infty{}^2} = \frac{\mathfrak{B}_0{}^2}{\mathfrak{B}^2} - 1 + 1 - \frac{\mathfrak{B}_0{}^2}{\mathfrak{B}_\infty{}^2}$$

and therefore

$$\frac{\alpha'}{f^2}\frac{\mathfrak{B}_0}{\mathfrak{B}} = \frac{2\pi^2\tau'}{\mathfrak{B}_0}\left(\frac{\mathfrak{B}_\infty{}^2 - \mathfrak{B}_0{}^2}{\mathfrak{B}_\infty{}^2} - \frac{\mathfrak{B}^2 - \mathfrak{B}_0{}^2}{\mathfrak{B}^2}\right). \tag{15–7}$$

Since in Eq. (15–6)

$$\frac{1}{1+\omega^2\tau'^2} = 1 - \frac{\omega^2\tau'^2}{1+\omega^2\tau'^2} = 1 - y$$

the behavior of Eq. (15–6) is then determined by that of y (Sec. 12) and is the mirror image of that of Eq. (15–1), $\omega = 1/\tau'$ acting as the mirror.

Accordingly, at low frequencies, $(\alpha'/f^2)(\mathfrak{B}_0/\mathfrak{B})$ is constant; namely

$$\frac{\alpha'}{f^2}\frac{\mathfrak{B}_0}{\mathfrak{B}} = \frac{2\pi^2}{\mathfrak{B}_0}\frac{\Delta C'}{C_v(C_p - C')}\tau' . \tag{15–8}$$

At somewhat higher frequencies, this decreases according to

$$\frac{\alpha'}{f^2}\frac{\mathfrak{B}_0}{\mathfrak{B}} = \frac{2\pi^2}{\mathfrak{B}_0}\frac{\Delta C'}{C_v(C_p - C')}\tau'(1-\omega^2\tau'^2). \tag{15–8′}$$

The conclusions just drawn are also in agreement with Eq. (15–7).

The decrease of $(\alpha/f^2)(\mathfrak{B}_0/\mathfrak{B})$ as expressed in the factor $(1-\omega^2\tau'^2)$ of Eq. (15–8′) is given by the second term of Eq. (15–7). One sees, therefore, that if $(\alpha/f^2)(\mathfrak{B}_0/\mathfrak{B})$ is plotted against ω (or $\log\omega$), the drop below the horizontal straight line, as in Eq. (15–8), appears in the same region in which dispersion, $(\mathfrak{B}^2 - \mathfrak{B}_0{}^2)/\mathfrak{B}_0{}^2$, becomes noticeable. With the help of Eq. (13–2), α'/f^2 itself is seen to vary in this region as

$$\frac{\alpha'}{f^2} = \frac{2\pi^2}{\mathfrak{B}_0}\frac{\Delta C'\tau'}{C_v(C_p - C')}\left[1-\omega^2\tau'^2\left(1-\frac{1}{2}\frac{\Delta C'}{C_v(C_p - C')}\right)\right]. \tag{15–8″}$$

The half-way mark is reached by $(\alpha'/f^2)(\mathfrak{B}_0/\mathfrak{B})$ at $\omega\tau' = 1$. If it is plotted against $\log\omega$, it also has an inflection point at this frequency, which is the same frequency at which $\mathfrak{B}_0{}^2/\mathfrak{B}^2$ and $\alpha(\mathfrak{B}_0/\mathfrak{B})$ have an inflection point and at which $(\alpha\mathfrak{B}/\omega)(\mathfrak{B}_0{}^2/\mathfrak{B}^2)$ has its maximum.

The behavior is that described in Sec. 13 for y, i.e., $(\alpha'/f^2)(\mathfrak{B}_0/\mathfrak{B})$ has 0.8 of the value in Eq. (15–8) at $\omega\tau' = 1/2$, and 0.2 of the value in Eq. (15–8) at $\omega\tau' = 2$. For high frequencies, one has

$$\frac{\alpha'}{f^2}\frac{\mathfrak{B}_0}{\mathfrak{B}_\infty} = \frac{2\pi^2}{\mathfrak{B}_0\tau'}\frac{\Delta C'}{C_v(C_p - C')}\frac{1}{\omega^2}. \tag{15–9}$$

Which of the forms discussed above is most suitable depends on the frequency region (or, rather, the value of $\omega\tau'$). At frequencies such that $\omega\tau'$ is small, the use of Eq. (15–6) is best. When $\omega\tau'$ approaches 0 and α' or $\alpha'\lambda$ is plotted, it is difficult to tell both if the curve close to the abscissa has the theoretical form and when this curve begins to deviate from Eq. (14–4) or (14–4').

On the other hand, $(\alpha'/f^2)(\mathfrak{B}_0/\mathfrak{B})$ should be a straight horizontal line at low frequencies. On approaching $\omega\tau' = 1$, the points begin to drop below this line. If, however the measurements cover the region of the maximum, the quantity $\alpha\lambda(\mathfrak{B}_0{}^2/\mathfrak{B}^2)$ is more useful, since the frequency of the maximum gives $1/2\pi\tau'$ directly, while its height, from Eq. (15–5), gives C'.

16. Continuation of the Discussion of Absorption and Dispersion: Kneser's Expression.[1] Calculation of C_{eff}

In the preceding, the advantage of using $\mathfrak{B}_0{}^2/\mathfrak{B}^2$ and $\alpha'(\mathfrak{B}_0/\mathfrak{B})$ has been repeatedly pointed out. They are governed by the same apparent relaxation time, τ', and have an inflection point at the same frequency, $f' = 1/2\pi\tau'$. However, formulas have also been developed, Eq. (13–6), for $(\mathfrak{B}/\mathfrak{B}_0)^2$, in which a different time, τ'', appears. Here the inflection point is at a different frequency, $f'' = 1/2\pi\tau''$. Kneser, to whom the formula for $(\mathfrak{B}/\mathfrak{B}_0)^2$ is due, also introduces an expression for $\alpha'\lambda$ (instead of $\alpha'\lambda(\mathfrak{B}_0{}^2/\mathfrak{B}^2)$). Using the notation of Eq. (11–11), one has

$$\frac{\mathfrak{B}_0{}^2}{\mathfrak{B}^2} = \frac{1 + ab\omega^2\tau^2}{1 + b^2\omega^2\tau^2} \tag{16–1}$$

and

$$\frac{\mathfrak{B}_0{}^2}{\mathfrak{B}^2}\,2\alpha'\,\frac{\mathfrak{B}}{\omega} = \frac{(b-a)\omega\tau}{1 + b^2\omega^2\tau^2}. \tag{16–2}$$

Dividing the second equation by the first, one gets

$$2\alpha'\,\frac{\mathfrak{B}}{\omega} = \frac{(b-a)\omega\tau}{1 + ab\omega^2\tau^2} = \frac{b-a}{\sqrt{ab}}\,\frac{\sqrt{ab}\,\omega\tau}{1 + ab\omega^2\tau^2}. \tag{16–3}$$

Obviously, it will now be convenient to use a time τ'''

$$\tau''' = \sqrt{ab}\,\tau = \sqrt{\frac{(C_p - C')(C_v - C')}{C_pC_v}}\,\tau = \sqrt{\frac{C_p - C'}{C_v - C'}\frac{C_v}{C_p}}\,\tau''$$

$$= \frac{\mathfrak{B}_\infty}{\mathfrak{B}_0}\tau'' = \frac{\mathfrak{B}_0}{\mathfrak{B}_\infty}\tau'. \tag{16–4}$$

---

[1] H. O. Kneser, *Ann. Physik* [5] **16**, **337** (**1933**); see also P. S. H. Henry, *Proc. Cambridge Phil. Soc.* **28**, 249 (1932).

Since $2\alpha'(\mathfrak{V}/\omega) = (1/\pi)\alpha\lambda$

$$\alpha\lambda = \pi \frac{\Delta C'}{\sqrt{C_p C_v (C_p - C')(C_v - C')}} \frac{\omega\tau'''}{1 + \omega^2\tau'''^2}. \tag{16–5}$$

This can be written equal to $\alpha'\lambda = \pi \tan\varphi'$ where φ' is the phase angle between s and $p - p_0$, see Eq. (11–19).

The maximum of Eq. (16–5) occurs at $\omega\tau''' = 1$; $f''' = 1/2\pi\tau'''$; its height is

$$(\alpha'\lambda)_{\max} = \frac{\pi}{2} \frac{\Delta C'}{\sqrt{C_p C_v (C_p - C')(C_v - C')}}. \tag{16–6}$$

However, since this is the maximum value, the use of $\mathfrak{V}_0{}^2/\mathfrak{V}^2$ from Eq. (16–1) might not be good enough, since $(\alpha'\mathfrak{V}_0/\omega)^2$ should be added on the right of Eq. (16–1). Therefore, Eq. (16–6) is somewhat too large.

A somewhat different method of calculation, which needs a little more manipulation of experimental data, but has τ itself as relaxation time, solves Eq. (11–8) for $(C_p)_{\text{eff}}$. One has

$$\frac{1}{\gamma_0}\left(\frac{\mathfrak{V}_0}{\mathfrak{V}} - \frac{i\alpha\mathfrak{V}_0}{\omega}\right)^2 = 1 - \frac{\Delta}{(C_p)_{\text{eff}}} \tag{16–7}$$

or

$$\left[\gamma_0 - \left(\frac{\mathfrak{V}_0}{\mathfrak{V}} - \frac{i\alpha\mathfrak{V}_0}{\omega}\right)^2\right]^{-1} = \frac{1}{\Delta\gamma_0}(C_p)_{\text{eff}}. \tag{16–8}$$

If

$$\frac{\alpha'\mathfrak{V}_0}{\omega} = \frac{\mathfrak{V}_0}{\mathfrak{V}} \frac{\alpha'\lambda}{2\pi}$$

is small[2] compared to $\gamma_0 - 1$, write

$$\frac{\mathfrak{V}^2}{\gamma_0\mathfrak{V}^2 - \mathfrak{V}_0{}^2} = \frac{1}{\Delta\gamma_0}\left(C_p - C' \frac{\omega^2\tau^2}{1 + \omega^2\tau^2}\right) \tag{16–9}$$

$$\left(\frac{\mathfrak{V}\mathfrak{V}_0}{\gamma_0\mathfrak{V}^2 - \mathfrak{V}_0{}^2}\right)^2 \alpha'\lambda = \frac{\pi}{\Delta\gamma_0} C' \frac{\omega\tau}{1 + \omega^2\tau^2}. \tag{16–10}$$

[2] This is so for all frequencies if $1/2\, C'/(C_p - C') \ll 1$. Otherwise it is true only for small values of $\omega\tau$.

17. Exact Calculation of Absorption and Dispersion

The calculations of Secs. 13–16 were based partly on the assumption, made at the beginning of Sec. 12, that $(\alpha'\mathfrak{V}_0/\omega)^2$ in Eq. (12–1) could be neglected compared to unity.

Just as in the analogous case in optics, it is, however, possible to get the exact solution of Eq. (11–10). Use the following abbreviations:

$$\frac{\mathfrak{V}_0}{\mathfrak{V}} = u \qquad \frac{\alpha'\mathfrak{V}_0}{\omega} = v$$

$$A = \frac{\Delta C'}{C_v(C_p - C')} \tag{17–2}$$

Since from Eq. (12–5)

$$1 - A = \frac{C_p}{C_v}\frac{C_v - C'}{C_p - C'} \tag{17–2'}$$

this is never negative and could be zero only if $C_v = C'$, i.e., if the entire specific heat C_v were subject to relaxation. Therefore

$$0 \leqslant A \leqslant 1$$

where the left equality sign implies that $C' = 0$; the right, that $C' = C_v$. One can then write Eqs. (12–2) and (12–3)

$$u^2 - v^2 = 1 - A\,\frac{\omega^2\tau'^2}{1 + \omega^2\tau'^2} \tag{17–3}$$

and

$$2uv = A\,\frac{\omega\tau'}{1 + \omega^2\tau'^2}\,. \tag{17–3'}$$

This is solved in the usual way; from Eq. (17–3')

$$v = \frac{A}{2}\,\frac{\omega\tau'}{1 + \omega^2\tau'^2}\,\frac{1}{u}\,.$$

Insert in Eq. (17–3) and multiply with u^2. One gets the quadratic equation in u^2

$$u^4 - \left(1 - A\,\frac{\omega^2\tau'^2}{1 + \omega^2\tau'^2}\right)u^2 = \frac{1}{4}\left(A\,\frac{\omega\tau'}{1 + \omega^2\tau'^2}\right)^2$$

which gives

$$u^2 = \left(\frac{\mathfrak{V}_0}{\mathfrak{V}}\right)^2$$

$$= \frac{1}{2}\left\{1 - A\,\frac{\omega^2\tau'^2}{1+\omega^2\tau'^2} + \left[\left(1 - A\,\frac{\omega^2\tau'^2}{1+\omega^2\tau'^2}\right)^2 + \left(A\,\frac{\omega\tau'}{1+\omega^2\tau'^2}\right)^2\right]^{1/2}\right\}$$

$$= \frac{1}{2}\,\frac{1}{1+\omega^2\tau'^2}\{[(1+(1-A)\omega^2\tau'^2)^2 + A^2\omega^2\tau'^2]^{1/2} + 1 + (1-A)\omega^2\tau'^2\}. \tag{17–4}$$

$$v^2 = \left(\frac{\alpha'\mathfrak{V}_0}{\omega}\right)^2 = \frac{1}{2}\left\{\left[\left(1 - A\,\frac{\omega^2\tau'^2}{1+\omega^2\tau'^2}\right)^2 + \left(A\,\frac{\omega\tau'}{1+\omega^2\tau'^2}\right)^2\right]^{1/2} - \left(1 - A\,\frac{\omega^2\tau'^2}{1+\omega^2\tau'^2}\right)\right\}$$

$$= \frac{1}{2}\,\frac{1}{1+\omega^2\tau'^2}\{[(1+(1-A)\omega^2\tau'^2)^2 + A^2\omega^2\tau'^2]^{1/2} - [1 + (1-A)\omega^2\tau'^2]\}. \tag{17–4'}$$

If the quantity

$$\left(A\,\frac{\omega\tau'}{1+\omega^2\tau'^2}\right)^2$$

in the { } is considered small compared to unity [i.e., is neglected in Eq. (17–4)], we return to the equations of Sec. 12. On the other hand, we can now understand the different behavior of $\mathfrak{V}$ for large frequencies in the case of relaxation, as compared to the classical, Lucas-Truesdell, case (Sec. 7). For the latter, it goes to infinity; for the former, it reaches a constant upper value.

Consider Eq. (17–4) for large values of $\omega\tau'$. Under the square root, the first term behaves like $(1 - A)^2(\omega\tau')^4$; the second is $A^2(\omega\tau')^2$, and therefore small compared to the first. Accordingly

$$\lim_{\omega\tau'=\infty} \frac{\mathfrak{V}_0{}^2}{\mathfrak{V}^2} = \lim_{\omega\tau'=\infty} \frac{1}{1+\omega^2\tau'^2}(1-A)\omega^2\tau'^2 = 1 - A \tag{17–5}$$

as it should, according to Eq. (17–2').

On the other hand, if $1 - A = 0$, the largest term in the { } of Eq. (17–4) is $[A^2\omega^2\tau'^2]^{1/2}$, and one has

$$\lim_{\omega\tau'=\infty} \frac{\mathfrak{B}_0{}^2}{\mathfrak{B}^2} = \lim_{\omega\tau'=\infty} \frac{1}{2}\frac{\omega\tau'}{1+\omega^2\tau'^2} = \lim \frac{1}{2\omega\tau'} = 0 \qquad (17\text{–}6)$$

or $\lim \mathfrak{B} = \infty$.

Now Eq. (7–10′) is of the form of Eq. (17–3), with $A = 1$. After all, in Eq. (7–10), the *whole* viscosity is involved, not only a *part* of the specific heat, as here.

18. Dependence on τ. Summary of Characteristic Times

In gases, τ is inversely proportional to the pressure. In all fluids, τ depends on temperature and often on impurities. Therefore it is of interest to consider the dependence of the quantities considered in the preceding sections on τ.

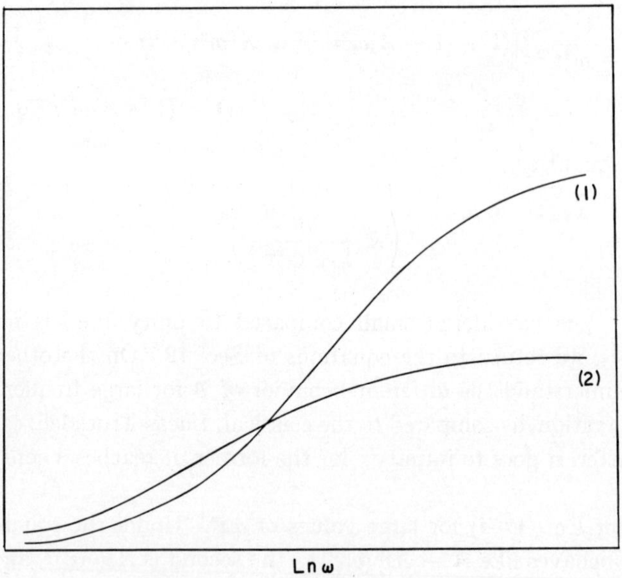

FIG. 18–1. $\alpha'(\mathfrak{B}_0/\mathfrak{B})$ plotted against $\ln\omega$. The factor A is the same for both curves, but the relaxation time is twice as long for curve (2) as for curve (1).

The expression for the velocity depends only on the combination $\omega\tau$. Therefore, any change in τ by a factor a can be compensated for by using the frequency f/a. In plotting $\mathfrak{B}^2$ or $1/\mathfrak{B}^2$ against $\log \omega$, a change in τ only means a rigid horizontal translation of the whole curve by $\log \tau - \log \tau_0$.

The same is true for α'/ω multiplied by any function of $\mathfrak{B}/\mathfrak{B}_0$, for $(\alpha'/\omega)(\mathfrak{B}_0/\mathfrak{B})$, and for $\alpha'\lambda$.

On the other hand, it is not true of $\alpha'(\mathfrak{B}_0/\mathfrak{B})$ or α'. Consider the curve for $\alpha'(\mathfrak{B}_0/\mathfrak{B})$ for two values of τ or τ'; say τ_1' and τ_2' with $\tau_2' = 2\tau_1'$. (See Fig. 18–1.)

At low frequencies both rise parabolically from zero, but

$$\left(\alpha'\frac{\mathfrak{B}_0}{\mathfrak{B}}\right)_1 : \left(\frac{\alpha'\mathfrak{B}_0}{\mathfrak{B}}\right)_2 = \tau_1' : \tau_2'$$

in the assumed case 1 : 2. That means that at low frequency the substance with the longer relaxation time has the higher absorption. However, this curve starts to flatten out earlier, having its inflection point at $f_2' = 1/2\pi\tau_2'$, which is half the frequency of the inflection point f_1'. At still higher frequencies, the curves cross each other, and curve 1, the one with the shorter relaxation time, lies higher. At very high frequencies, both are horizontal and have values proportional to $1/\tau'$, i.e., in our case the absorption of the substance with the smaller relaxation time is twice as large. Mathematically, this comes about because the curve with the smaller relaxation time, while initially slower, continues to rise over a much larger frequency range. It might be useful to give a summary here of the different apparent relaxation times appearing in the formula.

Since later parts of this book will treat cases in which the relaxation mechanism is different from that of slow energy exchange between different degrees of freedom, it will be useful to write the corresponding expressions in the general case. Write

$$\left(\frac{\mathfrak{B}_0}{\mathfrak{B}} - \frac{i\alpha\mathfrak{B}_0}{\omega}\right)^2 = 1 - A\frac{i\omega\tau'}{1 + i\omega\tau'} = 1 - A\frac{(\omega\tau')^2}{1 + (\omega\tau')^2} - Ai\frac{\omega\tau'}{1 + (\omega\tau')^2}. \tag{18–1}$$

It follows that

$$1 - A = \left(\frac{\mathfrak{B}_0}{\mathfrak{B}_\infty}\right)^2 \qquad A = \frac{\mathfrak{B}_\infty{}^2 - \mathfrak{B}_0{}^2}{\mathfrak{B}_\infty{}^2} \tag{18–2}$$

if, as usual

$$\left(\frac{\alpha\mathfrak{B}_0}{\omega}\right)^2 \ll \frac{\mathfrak{B}_\infty{}^2 - \mathfrak{B}_0{}^2}{\mathfrak{B}_\infty{}^2}.$$

Then $\omega\tau' = 1$ defines, as above, the midpoint of the $(\mathfrak{B}_0/\mathfrak{B})^2$ curve and the maximum of $\alpha\mathfrak{B}_0{}^2/\omega\mathfrak{B} = \alpha\lambda/2\pi(\mathfrak{B}_0/\mathfrak{B})^2$. The halfpoint of the curve for $(\mathfrak{B}/\mathfrak{B}_0)^2$ and the maximum of $\alpha\lambda(\mathfrak{B}/\mathfrak{B}_0)^2$ lies at $\omega\tau'' = 1$

$$\tau'' = (1 - A)\tau' = \left(\frac{\mathfrak{B}_0}{\mathfrak{B}_\infty}\right)^2 \tau'. \qquad (18\text{–}3)$$

The position of the maximum of $\alpha\lambda$ is given by

$$\frac{1}{\omega} = \sqrt{1 - A}\,\tau' = \frac{\mathfrak{B}_0}{\mathfrak{B}_\infty}\tau' = \frac{\mathfrak{B}_\infty}{\mathfrak{B}_0}\tau''. \qquad (18\text{–}4)$$

The maximum of $\alpha\lambda_0 = 1/2\pi\,(\alpha\mathfrak{B}_0/\omega)$ occurs at

$$\frac{1}{\omega} = (1 - A)^{1/4}\,\tau' = \sqrt{\frac{\mathfrak{B}_0}{\mathfrak{B}_\infty}}\,\tau' = \left(\frac{\mathfrak{B}_\infty}{\mathfrak{B}_0}\right)^{3/2} \tau''. \qquad (18\text{–}5)$$

Notation	First defined	Kneser's notation	Definition
τ	Eq. (10–1)		true relaxation time
$\tau' = \dfrac{C_p - C'}{C_p}\tau$	Eq. (11–14)		halfpoint of curve $\dfrac{\mathfrak{B}_0{}^2}{\mathfrak{B}^2} - 1$ halfpoint of $\dfrac{\mathfrak{B}_0}{\mathfrak{B}}\dfrac{\alpha'}{f^2}$ maximum of $\dfrac{\mathfrak{B}_0{}^2}{\mathfrak{B}^2}\alpha'\lambda$
$\tau'' = \dfrac{C_v - C'}{C_v}\tau = \dfrac{\mathfrak{B}_0{}^2}{\mathfrak{B}_\infty{}^2}\tau'$	Eq. (11–16)	τ_w	halfpoint of curve $\dfrac{\mathfrak{B}^2}{\mathfrak{B}_0{}^2} - 1$
$\tau''' = \sqrt{\dfrac{(C_p - C')(C_v - C')}{C_pC_v}}\tau = \dfrac{\mathfrak{B}_\infty}{\mathfrak{B}_0}\tau'' = \dfrac{\mathfrak{B}_0}{\mathfrak{B}_\infty}\tau'$	Eq. (16–4)	τ_m	maximum of $\alpha'\lambda$

Finally, according to Lucas (Sec. 7), the maximum of $\alpha\lambda_0$ in the absence of relaxation should occur at

$$\frac{1}{\omega} = \frac{\tau_L}{\sqrt{3}}. \tag{18–6}$$

19. Exchange of Energy and Relaxation Equation

Equation (10–1) is a relaxation equation with a single relaxation time for the whole energy E' of one degree of freedom. In this section the conditions will be discussed under which it is possible to write such an equation. In statistical mechanics, one can treat molecules in different energy states as if they were different kinds of molecules. The primary equations are reaction rate equations for governing the transition of molecules from one energy state to another. In general, there will be such a rate equation for each state, and the question is under what conditions these can be combined to give a single equation for the internal energy as a whole.

Two such cases are known, that in which only two energy states exist, and that of the simple harmonic oscillator.

(a) *Two-State Case*

Two quantum states are assumed, the ground state (index 1), with weight g_1; and the excited state (index 2), with weight g_2 and an energy ε higher than the ground state.

Call the total number of particles n, those at a given moment in the ground state n_1, and those in the upper state n_2. Of course

$$n_1 + n_2 = n. \tag{19–1}$$

The rate at which particles make transitions from the ground state to the excited state is $k_{12}n_1$; the rate in the opposite direction, $k_{21}n_2$.

In cases where the transitions are due to collisions, the values of both k's will be proportional to the total number of molecules per mole. The rate equation is

$$-\frac{dn_2}{dt} = k_{21}n_2 - k_{12}n_1. \tag{19–2}$$

In equilibrium, the left side is zero and therefore

$$k_{21}n_2{}^0 = k_{12}n_1{}^0$$

where the upper index zero indicates the equilibrium number. One can write this

$$\frac{n_2{}^0}{n_1{}^0} = \frac{k_{12}}{k_{21}}. \tag{19-3}$$

The left side, however, is given by the condition of statistical equilibrium

$$\frac{n_2{}^0}{n_1{}^0} = K = \frac{g_2}{g_1} \exp\left(-\frac{\varepsilon}{kT}\right)$$

and therefore

$$k_{12} = Kk_{21} = k_{21} \frac{g_2}{g_1} e^{-\varepsilon/kT}. \tag{19-4}$$

If $\varepsilon > kT_1$, the rate of activation of a given number of molecules is much smaller than the rate of deactivation of the same number of molecules. Essentially this is because in the activating collisions the partner must have an energy higher by ε than in a deactivating collision. Nonetheless, in equilibrium the total number of molecules activated per second is equal to the number deactivated, because the lower rate of activation, k_{12}, is compensated by the higher number n_1 of molecules in the ground state, these being the molecules subject to activation.

Let us first assume that the temperature is constant, but that we start with a distribution different from equilibrium distribution. Eliminate n_1 from Eq. (19–2) with the help of Eq. (19–1)

$$-\frac{dn_2}{dt} = (k_{21} + k_{12})\, n_2 - k_{12} n = (k_{21} + k_{12}) \left[n_2 - \frac{k_{12}}{k_{21} + k_{12}}\, n \right]. \tag{19-5}$$

Equation (19–5) can be rewritten as

$$-\frac{dn_2}{dt} = (k_{21} + k_{12}) \left[n_2 - \frac{K}{K+1}\, n \right] \tag{19-5$'$}$$

but, using Eqs. (19–1) and (19–3), this gives

$$-\frac{dn_2}{dt} = (k_{21} + k_{12})\,(n_2 - n_2{}^0).$$

Define

$$\frac{1}{\tau} = k_{21} + k_{12} = k_{21}(1 + K). \tag{19-6}$$

If $\varepsilon \gg kT$, $1/\tau = k_{21}$. If $\varepsilon < kT$, $1/\tau = k_{21}(g_1 + g_2)/g_1$. If one multiplies Eq. (19–5′) with ε and remembers that $E' = \varepsilon n_2$, one gets

$$-\frac{dE'}{dt} = \frac{1}{\tau}(E' - E_0') \tag{19–7}$$

which is the relaxation equation for the internal energy; see Eq. (10–1).

Next, we have to show that we get Eq. (10–1) for the case in which the temperature of the translational motion is not constant, but varies in a prescribed form. In this case, the rate constants k, which depend on the temperature, vary with time, and so does K.

One sees from Eq. (19–5′) that in this case the exact form of Eq. (19–5′) is

$$-\frac{dn_2}{dt} = \frac{1}{\tau(T_{tr})}[n_2 - n_2(T_{tr})] \tag{19–8}$$

where $n_2(T_{tr})$ is the equilibrium value of n_2 belonging to the momentary temperature T_{tr}. If $E'(T_{tr})$ designates the value of the internal energy E' at T_{tr} in equilibrium, Eq. (19–7) becomes

$$-\frac{dE'}{dt} = \frac{1}{\tau(T_{tr})}[E' - E'(T_{tr})] \tag{19–9}$$

where τ is a function of temperature (because the k's are) and the value belonging to the momentary temperature has to be chosen.

We now make the "acoustical" approximation by assuming that the deviation of T_{tr} from a constant value T_0 is small.

$$|T_{tr} - T_0| \ll T_0.$$

The quantity at the left will be treated as a small quantity of the first order. Then

$$E'(T_{tr}) - E'(T_0) = C'(T_{tr} - T_0).$$

In the relaxation process, since there is no overshooting (Sec. 9), one has

$$|E' - E'(T_0)| \leqq |E'(T_{tr}) - E'(T_0)|_{max}$$

i.e.,

$$|E' - E'(T_{tr})| \leqq C'|T_{tr} - T_0|_{max}.$$

Furthermore, we write

$$\frac{1}{\tau(T_{tr})} = \frac{1}{\tau(T_0)} + (T_{tr} - T_0)\frac{\partial}{\partial T}\frac{1}{\tau}.$$

If we then rewrite Eq. (19–8) as

$$-\frac{dE'}{dt} = \frac{1}{\tau}[E' - E'(T_{\text{tr}})] = \frac{C'}{\tau}(T' - T_{\text{tr}}) \tag{19–10}$$

where τ belongs to the temperature T_0, we have neglected[1] terms quadratic in $T_{\text{tr}} - T_0$. Equation (19–10) is identical with Eq. (10–1).

The above development is a simplification of a treatment by Kneser[2] and Rutgers.[3]

(b) Harmonic Oscillator

The simple harmonic oscillator was first treated by Landau and Teller.[4, 5]

We will not at first specify to the simple harmonic oscillator, but only assume that there are an infinite number of states j, and that transitions are possible only to neighboring states; i.e., $j \to j - 1$ and $j \to j + 1$.

We then write the changes which can occur in the occupation number n_j of the state j. This state can lose particles to the next lower state at the rate

$$k_{j,j-1}n_j$$

gain particles from the next lower state at the rate

$$k_{j-1,j}n_{j-1}$$

lose particles to the next higher state at the rate

$$k_{j,j+1}n_j$$

and gain particles from the next higher state at the rate

$$k_{j+1,j}n_{j+1}$$

or

$$\frac{dn_j}{dt} = k_{j-1,j}n_{j-1} - k_{j,j-1}n_j - [k_{j,j+1}n_j - k_{j+1,j}n_{j+1}]. \tag{19–11}$$

The lowest state, $j = 0$, can only exchange with the next higher state

$$\frac{dn_0}{dt} = k_{10}n_1 - k_{01}n_0.$$

---

1 That is, the temperature variation of K is essential; that of τ may be neglected.

2 H. O. Kneser, *Ann. Physik* [5], **16**, 360 (1933).

3 A. J. Rutgers, *Ann. Physik* [5], **16**, 350 (1933).

4 L. Landau and E. Teller, *Physik. Z. Sowjetunion* **10**, 34 (1936).

5 H. Bethe and E. Teller, *Ballistics Research Lab. Aberdeen Tech. Rept.* **X–117** (1941).

In thermal equilibrium, all the left sides are zero, and therefore

$$0 = k_{j-1,j}\, n_{j-1}^{0} - k_{j,j-1}\, n_j^{0} - [k_{j,j+1}\, n_j^{0} - k_{j+1,j} n_{j+1}^{0}].$$

However, if one starts with the lowest state

$$k_{10} n_1^{0} - k_{01} n_0^{0} = 0$$

and then goes progressively up, one sees that the terms balance pairwise

$$k_{j,j+1}\, n_j^{0} - k_{j+1,j}\, n_{j+1}^{0} = 0$$

(principle of detailed balancing), and one has, as generalization of Eq. (19–4)

$$\frac{k_{j,j+1}}{k_{j+1,j}} = \frac{n_{j+1}^{0}}{n_j^{0}} = K_j = \frac{g_{j+1}}{g_j} \exp\left(-\frac{\varepsilon_{j+1} - \varepsilon_j}{kT}\right). \qquad (19\text{–}12)$$

In general, the rate constants, k, are made up of two factors. One involves the change of kinetic energy of the hitting particle; the second, the internal transition probability of the systems going from state $j + 1$ to j.

The simple harmonic oscillator greatly simplifies calculations for the following reasons:

The energy difference between *any* two neighboring steps is the same; namely $h\nu$, so that the first factor mentioned is the same for all transitions $j + 1 \to j$. The second factor is proportional to the j of the higher state, i.e.,

$$k_{j+1,j} : k_{j,j-1} = (j + 1) : j$$

and thirdly, all weight factors g are unity, so that

$$K_j = K = \exp\left(-\frac{h\nu}{kT}\right) \qquad (19\text{–}13)$$

independent of j. Then, the rate equation reads

$$\frac{dn_j}{dt} = Kjk_{10}n_{j-1} - jk_{10}n_j - [K(j+1)k_{10}n_j - (j+1)k_{10}n_{j+1}]$$

$$= k_{10}[Kjn_{j-1} - jn_j - K(j+1)n_j + (j+1)n_{j+1}] \qquad (19\text{–}14)$$

$$\frac{dn_0}{dt} = k_{10}(n_1 - Kn_0). \qquad (19\text{–}14')$$

We now multiply Eq. (19–14) with $h\nu j$ and add over all j, so that

$$h\nu \frac{d}{dt} \Sigma j n_j = h\nu k_{10} \Sigma \{K j^2 n_{j-1} - j^2 n_j - K(j+1) j n_j + (j+1) j n_{j+1}\}. \quad (19\text{–}15)$$

Renumbering the fourth sum by replacing $j+1$ by j, it now reads

$$\sum_0 j(j-1) n_j.$$

The first occurring j ought then to be 1, but because of the factor j, one may just as well start with zero. The second and fourth terms then give together

$$\sum_0 [-j^2 + j(j-1)] n_j = -\sum_0 j n_j.$$

Combine the first and third terms

$$K\left\{\sum_1 j^2 n_{j-1} - \sum_0 (j+1) j n_j\right\} = K \sum_0 [(j+1)^2 - (j+1) j] n_j$$

$$= K \sum (j+1) n_j = K\left\{\sum j n_j + \sum n_j\right\} = K \sum j n_j + Kn.$$

Remembering that

$$E' = \sum j h\nu n_j \quad (19\text{–}16)$$

we have

$$\frac{dE'}{dt} = k_{10}\{-E' + KE' + h\nu K n\} = -k_{10}(1-K)\left[E' - \frac{K}{1-K} h\nu n\right]. \quad (19\text{–}16')$$

However

$$\frac{K}{1-K} h\nu n = n \frac{h\nu\, e^{-h\nu/kT}}{1 - e^{-h\nu/kT}} = n \frac{h\nu}{e^{h\nu/kT} - 1} = E'(T) \quad (19\text{–}16'')$$

where $E'(T)$ signifies the equilibrium value of E' at T. Therefore, if we define

$$\frac{1}{\tau} = k_{10}(1 - K) = k_{10} - k_{01} \tag{19–17}$$

we get a relaxation equation

$$-\frac{dE'}{dt} = \frac{1}{\tau}[E' - E'(T_{\text{tr}})]. \tag{19–17'}$$

With the same kind of argument as for the two-state system, we can substitute $\tau = \tau(T_0)$ for $\tau = \tau(T_{\text{tr}})$ in the "acoustic" approximation.

It is often said that, for the simple harmonic oscillator, all transitions have the same relaxation time. This is quite wrong.

The relaxation time of the transition $j + 1 \to j$ is by a factor $(j + 1)^{-1}$ smaller than the relaxation time of the transition $1 \to 0$.

The point proved is, on the contrary, that the relaxation times of the different transitions fit together so that they give a single relaxation time for the internal energy as a whole.

Attention should be drawn to the different connection between relaxation time τ and rate constants for the two-state system

$$\frac{1}{\tau} = k_{21} + k_{12} = k_{21}(1 + e^{-\varepsilon/kT}) \tag{19–6}$$

and the harmonic oscillator.

$$\frac{1}{\tau} = k_{10} - k_{01} = k_{10}\,(1 - e^{-h\nu/kT}). \tag{19–17}$$

It is obvious that we cannot say: "In a particular case, the temperature is so low that we neglect in the harmonic oscillator all but the two lowest states, treat the oscillator as a two-state system, and use Eq. (19–6)." If the temperature is so low, then K is very small, and k_{01} is very small compared to k_{10} (or k_{12} is very small compared to k_{21}), and we write, both for the simple harmonic oscillator and the two-state system, $1/\tau = k_{10}$ or k_{21}. However, if we do not go so far, we have no right to substitute Eq. (19–6) for Eq. (19–17).

Rubin and Shuler[6] and Montroll and Shuler[7] have succeeded in integrating the differential Eqs. (19–14) and (19–14′), given the initial conditions, i.e.,

---

[6] R. J. Rubin and K. E. Shuler, *J. Chem. Phys.* **25**, 59, 68 (1956), **26**, 137 (1957).

[7] E. W. Montroll and K. E. Shuler, *J. Chem. Phys.* **26**, 454 (1957).

they have succeeded in showing how an arbitrarily given initial distribution goes over into the equilibrium distribution.

Bourgin[8] has treated the general case of arbitrary energy levels, solving the three-state case approximately. On principle, this is similar to the problem of several vibrational degrees of freedom with different relaxation times, as discussed in Secs. 21–24.

One might ask why in all types of relaxation phenomena the same kind of equation appears. The physical answer is that the phenomena in question either involve an exchange of quanta, which is a kind of chemical reaction; or involve a change of state of molecules (structural relaxation, Chapter XII), which *is* a chemical reaction. For excitation and de-excitation (change in quantum number), the equation may be developed directly from the fundamentals of quantum theory.

20. General Discussion of the Case in Which More Than One Relaxation Time Exists

If there is more than one internal degree of freedom, the question arises as to whether they all show the same relaxation time or not. Rotation and vibration seem to show relaxation times different by a factor of more than 100, wherever both can be estimated. In such a case the two dispersion and absorption regions are entirely separated. That is, when one considers vibrational relaxation, rotation counts as an external degree of freedom; and when one considers rotational relaxation, the vibrational specific heat may be ignored. (These statements do not apply to low-frequency absorption.)

We are concerned here with several vibrational degrees of freedom. If the measurement is not too exact, then usually only one relaxation time seems to be present. The questions are how to explain this, and whether it is true for more exact observation. In this case, Eq. (11–8) is unchanged, and Eq. (11–6) is generalized to

$$(C_p)_{\text{eff}} = \tilde{C}_p + \sum_s C_s' \frac{dT_s'}{dT_{\text{tr}}} = C_p + \sum_s C_s' \left(\frac{dT_s'}{dT_{\text{tr}}} - 1 \right) \tag{20–1}$$

where C_s' and T_s' refer to the degrees of freedom. The remaining problem is to set up relaxation equations to generalize Eq. (10–1).

---

[8] D. G. Bourgin, *Phil. Mag.* [7] **7**, 821 (1929); *Phys. Rev.* **34**, 521 (1929); **42**, 721 (1932); **49**, 411 (1936); **50**, 355 (1936); *J. Acoust. Soc. Am.* **4**, 108 (1932).

Theoretically one can see that two extreme situations may exist which are analogous to different cases in chemical reaction kinetics.

In the first case, each vibrational degree of freedom is "fed" independently from translational (and possibly rotational) kinetic energy. It is assumed that for the external kinetic energy the Maxwell distribution belonging to T_{tr} is preserved, even if the internal degrees of freedom are not in equilibrium with the external ones; in other words, that the effect of the lack of equilibrium on the external degrees of freedom is felt in the momentary value of T_{tr}. This is plausible, since exchange of energy of the external degrees of freedom between different molecules is much faster than between external and internal degrees of freedom. Therefore, the exchange of energy between external kinetic energy and one vibrational degree of freedom does not influence the exchange of energy between external kinetic energy and a second vibrational degree of freedom (for a given value of T_{tr}). These energy exchanges are governed by differential equations like Eq. (10–1), and are analogous to chemical reactions. The case discussed now is therefore analogous to a set of parallel chemical reactions.

Quantum mechanical calculations for gases (Secs. 57–63) show that the relaxation time depends very strongly on the frequency (or characteristic temperature ϑ) of a vibration. In molecules containing only a few atoms the various vibrational degrees of freedom have, in general, very different frequencies, and one should expect that the vibration with lowest ϑ has the shortest relaxation time τ (highest efficiency of energy exchange) and that all other vibrations have *considerably* longer relaxation times.

The other extreme case, according to classical theory, occurs when a particular degree of vibrational freedom (call it "one") is directly fed from the external kinetic energy, and all other vibrations are fed from vibration one. The equations are then

$$-\frac{\partial E_1'}{\partial t} = \frac{1}{\tau_1}\,[E_1' - E_1'(T_{\text{tr}})] - \sum_{s\neq 1} \frac{1}{\tau_{1s}}\,[E_s' - E_s'(T_1')] \qquad (20\text{–}2)$$

or

$$-\frac{\partial T_1'}{\partial t} = \frac{1}{\tau_1}\,(T_1' - T_{\text{tr}}) - \frac{1}{C_1'} \sum \frac{C_s'}{\tau_{1s}}\,(T_s' - T_1')$$

and

$$-\frac{\partial E_s'}{\partial t} = \frac{1}{\tau_{1s}}\,[E_s' - E_s'(T_1')]$$

or

$$-\frac{\partial}{\partial t} T_s' = \frac{1}{\tau_{1s}} (T_s' - T_1') \tag{20-2'}$$

and this case is analogous to a set of chemical reactions in series.

The exchange of energy between different vibrations is determined by their deviation from that of simple harmonic vibrations.

If the restoring force within the molecule obeys Hooke's law for any deflection of any atom from its equilibrium position, the potential energy of the molecule is strictly a second order function of all these deflections. In that case, by forming the proper linear combination of deflection components—which linear combinations are called "normal coordinates"—one can express the potential energy (or rather its increase over the potential energy when everything is in equilibrium) as a sum of squares of the normal coordinates with constant coefficients, mixed products being absent. Each normal coordinate can then execute its proper vibration independently, and no energy can be transferred from one such vibration to another. If the restoring force deviates slightly from Hooke's law, the potential energy will also contain terms of higher than the second order (usually of the third order), with small coefficients. One proceeds by ignoring the higher order terms at first and finding the "unperturbed" normal coordinates, each with its own vibration, and then expressing the whole potential energy, both second and higher order terms, by the normal coordinates.

The potential energy will then consist of two parts: the first, a sum of squares of the normal coordinates, with constant coefficients; the second, a sum of higher order terms in the normal coordinates. If, as will usually be the case, these higher order terms contain mixed products of different normal coordinates, the mixed terms will act as coupling terms which permit internal transfer of energy from one normal coordinate to the other. The bigger these higher order mixed terms, the faster is the energy transfer. However, not much theoretical work has been done on calculations of this kind. Schäfer[1] has considered both cases for gaseous CO_2, which has two longitudinal and one (degenerate) transversal vibrations. The equations for an arbitrary number of vibrations will be developed in the next two sections.

There is still one more point to be considered. The various vibrations, having different frequencies, will have different sized quanta, so that apparently a quantum from one such vibration cannot leak into another one, because it will not fit. It is true that the presence of the higher order terms makes the levels of the individual vibrations less sharp—the larger they are, the truer this is, and the easier it would be to have the energy transfer. (The spread of the vibration frequency ν is of the order $1/\tau_{js}$, τ_{js} being a kind of lifetime of state s.) Whether the process is possible depends on whether the broadened levels of the different vibrations overlap sufficiently. Generally, this is unlikely in simple molecules. In large molecules, with many degrees of freedom, it is much more likely that vibrations lie sufficiently close together to permit energy leaking from one to the other. Such processes are known in photochemistry.

In quantum theory, the second possibility is replaced by a third possibility in which transitions between energy levels of different degrees of freedom which do not have the same energy occur, the energy difference being made up by exchange with external kinetic energy (in gases, by collisions). In this case (for which the quantum theory will be given in Sec. 23), there is the advantage that the translational motion need only supply the difference between energy levels of different degrees of freedom.

21. The Excitation of Different Degrees of Freedom Which Behave like a Group of Parallel Reactions[1]

Assuming each degree of freedom to be vibrational, we have, then, instead of the single vibration in Eq. (10–1), a set of independent equations

$$\frac{\partial E_s'}{\partial t} = -\frac{1}{\tau_s}\{E_s' - E_s'(T_{\text{tr}})\} \tag{21–1}$$

s being an index characterizing a vibration. The sth degree of freedom has a static specific heat C_s'.

In analogy to Eq. (10–6), one gets

$$T_s' - T_0 = \frac{1}{1 + i\omega\tau_s}(T_{\text{tr}} - T_0). \tag{21–2}$$

Equation (11–6′) is replaced by

$$(C_v)_{\text{eff}} = \tilde{C}_v + \sum_s \frac{C_s'}{1 + i\omega\tau_s}. \tag{21–3}$$

Equations (11–8) and (16–7) are unchanged. However, if one wishes to apply the usual calculations, one has to prove that the dispersion and absorption can be represented by a sum of terms of the usual form. This is being done in the following.

---

[1] R. Brout, *J. Chem. Phys.* **22**, 1500 (1954).

The calculation proceeds as in Sec. 11, leading to, see Eq. (11–10)

$$\frac{\mathfrak{B}_0^2}{\mathfrak{B}^2}\left(1 - i\alpha\frac{\mathfrak{B}}{\omega}\right)^2 = \frac{C_p}{C_v}\frac{\tilde{C}_v + \sum \dfrac{C_s'}{1 + i\omega\tau_s}}{\tilde{C}_p + \sum \dfrac{C_s'}{1 + i\omega\tau_s}}. \tag{21–4}$$

Taking the reciprocal and multiplying with $[1 + i\alpha(\mathfrak{B}/\omega)^2]$ one has on the left

$$\left(\frac{\mathfrak{B}}{\mathfrak{B}_0}\right)^2 \frac{\left(1 + i\alpha\dfrac{\mathfrak{B}}{\omega}\right)^2}{\left(1 + \dfrac{\alpha^2\mathfrak{B}^2}{\omega^2}\right)^2}.$$

Under the same assumptions concerning the strength of the absorption, one neglects the square of $\alpha\mathfrak{B}/\omega$ compared to 1, and gets

$$\left(\frac{\mathfrak{B}}{\mathfrak{B}_0}\right)^2\left(1 + 2i\alpha\frac{\mathfrak{B}}{\omega}\right) = \frac{C_v}{C_p}\frac{C_p + \sum\left(\dfrac{C_s'}{1 + i\omega\tau_s} - C_s'\right)}{C_v + \sum\left(\dfrac{C_s'}{1 + i\omega\tau_s} - C_s'\right)}$$

$$= \frac{1 - \dfrac{1}{C_p}\sum\dfrac{C_s' i\omega\tau_s}{1 + i\omega\tau_s}}{1 - \dfrac{1}{C_v}\sum\dfrac{C_s' i\omega\tau_s}{1 + i\omega\tau_s}} = 1 - \left(\frac{1}{C_p} - \frac{1}{C_v}\right)\frac{\sum\dfrac{C_s' i\omega\tau_s}{1 + i\omega\tau_s}}{1 - \dfrac{1}{C_v}\sum\dfrac{C_s' i\omega\tau_s}{1 + i\omega\tau_s}}$$

$$= 1 + \frac{\Delta}{C_p}\frac{\sum\dfrac{C_s' i\omega\tau_s}{1 + i\omega\tau_s}}{C_v - \sum\dfrac{C_s' i\omega\tau_s}{1 + i\omega\tau_s}}. \tag{21–5}$$

One has now to prove that the factor of Δ/C_p on the right side of Eq. (21–5) may be written in the form

$$-\frac{1}{C_v - \Sigma C_s'}\sum\left(\frac{C_s''}{1 + i\omega\tau_s''} - C_s''\right) = \frac{1}{C_v - \Sigma C_s'}\sum_s\frac{C_s'' i\omega\tau_s''}{1 + i\omega\tau_s''}. \tag{21–6}$$

The problem is quite analogous to one found in optics, when molecules, each with more than one absorption frequency, are coupled by the effect of the Lorentz-Lorenz force, and the resulting condensed system has a system of different absorption frequencies.

We first introduce the following notation: $\Pi_j f_j$ shall designate a product over all the functions f_j; Π_s' shall designate the same product, with the function f_s left out, i.e.,

$$\Pi_s' = \frac{\Pi f_j}{f_s}.$$

Let X be the factor of Δ/C_p on the right of Eq. (21–5), and multiply the numerator and denominator of X with the product of all the factors $(1 + i\omega\tau_s)$

$$X = \left\{\sum_j C_s' i\omega\tau_s \Pi_s'(1 + i\omega\tau_j)\right\}\left\{C_v \Pi(1 + i\omega\tau_j) - \sum C_s' i\omega\tau_s \Pi_s'(1 + i\omega\tau_j)\right\}^{-1}. \tag{21–7}$$

If the total number of terms in the sum is n, then one sees that the numerator is a polynomial of degree n in ω, which starts as $i\omega\Sigma C_s'\tau_s$ and ends with $i^n\omega^n(\Sigma C_s')\,(\Pi\tau_j)$, the terms being alternately purely imaginary and real. The denominator is also a polynomial of degree n in ω, starting with C_v and ending with $i^n\omega^n(\Pi\tau_j)\,(C_v - \Sigma C_s')$. If one abbreviates $i\omega$ by x, one then has

$$X = \left\{x \sum C_s'\tau_s'' \ldots A_m x^m \ldots + x^n(\Pi\tau_j) \sum C_s'\right\} \cdot$$

$$\cdot \left\{C_v + \ldots B_m x^m \ldots + x^n(\Pi\tau_j)\,(C_v - \sum C_s')\right\}^{-1}. \tag{21–8}$$

A_m is found as follows. Take the sum of all products of $m - 1$ different τ_j's except τ_s; multiply this sum with $C_s'\tau_s$, and add. B_m is equal to C_v times the sum of all products containing m different τ, minus A_m.

Rewriting X, one has

$$X = \frac{\Sigma C_s'}{C_v - \Sigma C_s'}\{x^n + \ldots D_m x^m + \ldots D_1 x\} \cdot$$

$$\cdot \{x^n + \ldots G_m x^m \ldots + G_0\}^{-1} \tag{21–9}$$

with

$$D_m = \frac{A_m}{\Sigma C_s'} (\Pi \tau_j)^{-1} \qquad D_1 = \frac{\Sigma C_s' \tau_s}{\Sigma C_s'} (\Pi \tau_j)^{-1} \tag{21–9'}$$

$$G_m = \frac{B_m}{C_v - \Sigma C_s'} (\Pi \tau_j)^{-1} \qquad G_0 = \frac{C_v}{C_v - \Sigma C_s'} (\Pi \tau_j)^{-1}. \tag{21–9''}$$

The denominator, set equal to zero, has n real, negative roots, which shall be called $-1/\tau_s''$. This will be proven at the end of this section and methods for solution will be given.

$$x^n + \ldots G_m x^m + \ldots G_0 = \left(x + \frac{1}{\tau_1''}\right)\left(x + \frac{1}{\tau_2''}\right) \ldots \left(x + \frac{1}{\tau_n''}\right). \tag{21–10}$$

By multiplying out, it is clear that

$$\Pi \frac{1}{\tau_j''} = G_0 = \frac{C_v}{C_v - \Sigma C_s'} \Pi \frac{1}{\tau_j} \tag{21–11}$$

or

$$\Pi \tau_j'' = \left(1 - \frac{\Sigma C_s'}{C_v}\right) \Pi \tau_j. \tag{21–11'}$$

Furthermore

$$\sum \frac{1}{\tau''} = G_{n-1} = \left\{ C_v (\Pi \tau_j) \left(\sum \frac{1}{\tau_s} \right) - (\Pi \tau_j) \sum_s C_s' \tau_s \sum_{i \neq s} \frac{1}{\tau_i \tau_s} \right\} \times$$

$$(\Pi \tau_j)^{-1} \frac{1}{C_v - \Sigma C_s'} = \frac{1}{C_v - \Sigma C_s'} \left\{ C_v \left(\sum \frac{1}{\tau_s} \right) - \sum C_s' \left(\sum_i \frac{1}{\tau_i} - \frac{1}{\tau_s} \right) \right\}$$

$$= \frac{1}{C_v - \Sigma C_s'} \left\{ \left(C_v - \sum C_s' \right) \sum \frac{1}{\tau_s} + \sum \frac{C_s'}{\tau_s} \right\}$$

$$= \sum \frac{1}{\tau_s} + \frac{1}{C_v - \Sigma C_s'} \sum \frac{C_s'}{\tau_s}. \tag{21–11''}$$

The denominator of X in the form shown in Eq. (21–9) can be written, from Eqs. (21–10) and (21–11)

$$\Pi \left(x + \frac{1}{\tau_j''} \right) = (\Pi \tau_j'')^{-1} \Pi (i\omega \tau_j'' + 1) = \frac{C_v}{C_v - \Sigma C_s'} (\Pi \tau_j)^{-1} \Pi (1 + i\omega \tau_j'').$$

If one now writes the expression (see Eq. 21—6)

$$X = \left(\sum \frac{C_j''x\tau_j''}{1 + x\tau_j''}\right)\frac{1}{C_v - \Sigma C_s'} \tag{21–12}$$

and brings all terms on the same denominator, one gets

$$X = \frac{1}{C_v - \Sigma C_s'}\left\{\sum C_j''x\tau_j''\Pi_j'(1 + x\tau_s'')\right\}\{\Pi(1 + x\tau_j''\}^{-1}. \tag{21–13}$$

Therefore, one has to identify the two numerators from Eqs. (21–9) and (21–13)

$$\frac{\Sigma C_s'}{C_v - \Sigma C_s'}\{x^n + D_m x^m + D_1 x\}\,(\Pi\tau_j'')$$

$$= \frac{1}{C_v - \Sigma C_s'}\sum C_j''x\tau_j''\Pi_j'(1 + x\tau_s''). \tag{21–14}$$

This equation must be identically fulfilled for all x. That is, it must be fulfilled separately for the coefficients of each power of x on both sides. Therefore, one gets n linear equations for the n unknowns C_j''; e.g., for the coefficient of x^n, one has

$$\frac{\Sigma C_s'}{C_v - \Sigma C_s'} = \frac{\Sigma C_j''}{C_v - \Sigma C_s''} \quad \text{or} \quad \sum C_j'' = \sum C_s'. \tag{21–15}$$

For the coefficient of x

$$\left(\sum C_s'\right)D_1\Pi\tau_j'' = \sum C_j''\tau_j''$$

or, with Eqs. (21–9′) and (21–11′)

$$\sum C_j''\tau_j'' = \sum C_s'\tau_s(\Pi\tau_j'')\,(\Pi\tau_j)^{-1} = \left(1 - \frac{\Sigma C_s'}{C_v}\right)\sum C_s'\tau_s \tag{21–15′}$$

and so on, for the other expressions.

One has, therefore, the dispersion equation in the form

$$\left(\frac{\mathfrak{V}}{\mathfrak{V}_0}\right)^2\left(1 + 2i\alpha'\frac{\mathfrak{V}}{\omega}\right) = 1 + \frac{\Delta}{C_p(C_v - \Sigma C_s')}\sum C_j''\frac{i\omega\tau_j''}{1 + i\omega\tau_j''}. \tag{21–16}$$

The real part is

$$\left(\frac{\mathfrak{V}}{\mathfrak{V}_0}\right)^2 = 1 + \frac{\Delta}{C_p(C_v - \Sigma C_s')} \sum C_s'' \frac{\omega^2 \tau_s''^2}{1 + \omega^2 \tau_s''^2}. \tag{21–17}$$

The imaginary part, divided by i, is

$$2\alpha' \frac{\mathfrak{V}}{\omega}\left(\frac{\mathfrak{V}}{\mathfrak{V}_0}\right)^2 = \frac{\Delta}{C_p(C_v - \Sigma C_s')} \sum \frac{C_s'' \omega \tau_s''}{1 + \omega^2 \tau_s''^2}. \tag{21–18}$$

The low frequency absorption (where one may put $\mathfrak{V} = \mathfrak{V}_0$) is, from Eq. (21–18)

$$2\alpha' \frac{\mathfrak{V}_0}{\omega} = \frac{\Delta}{C_p(C_v - \Sigma C_s'')} \omega \sum C_s'' \tau_s''$$

or

$$\alpha' = \frac{\Delta}{2C_p \mathfrak{V}_0} \omega^2 \frac{1}{C_v - \Sigma C_s''} \sum C_s'' \tau_s''. \tag{21–18′}$$

From Eqs. (21–15) and (21–15′), this can also be written as

$$\alpha' = \frac{\Delta}{2C_p \mathfrak{V}_0} \omega^2 \frac{1}{C_v} \sum C_s' \tau_s \tag{21–18″}$$

so that the low-frequency absorption leads directly to a knowledge of the quantity $\Sigma C_s' \tau_s$. One may define an average relaxation time

$$\bar{\tau} = \frac{\Sigma C_s' \tau_s}{\Sigma C_s'}$$

and write (21–18″) as

$$\alpha' = \frac{\Delta}{2C_p \mathfrak{V}_0} \frac{\Sigma C_s'}{C_v} \omega^2 \bar{\tau}. \tag{21–18‴}$$

One can then prove the following theorem about integrated absorption, which is somewhat analogous to one existing for spectral lines.

If one plots $(\mathfrak{V}^2/\mathfrak{V}_0^2)\alpha'(\mathfrak{V}/\omega)$ against $\ln \omega$ (this time, notice natural logarithms) and integrates with respect to ω from zero to infinity (i.e., with respect to $\ln \omega$ from $-\infty$ to $+\infty$), one takes, in effect, the whole area under the curve, and gets

$$\int_{-\infty}^{\infty} \frac{\mathfrak{B}^2}{\mathfrak{B}_0^2} \alpha' \lambda d(\ln \omega) = \frac{\pi^2}{2} \frac{\Delta}{C_p(C_v - \Sigma C_s')} \sum C_s'' = \frac{\pi^2}{2} \frac{\Delta \Sigma C_s'}{C_p(C_v - \Sigma C_s')} . \quad (21\text{–}19)$$

The total area, therefore, does not depend at all on the relaxation times, but only depends on the specific heats.

If the curve is plotted against decadic logarithms, the area must be multiplied with 2.303 to give the result on the right side.

The proof is a follows. Consider a term in Eq. (21–18)

$$C_s'' \frac{\omega \tau_s''}{1 + \omega^2 \tau_s''^2} .$$

Introduce $x = \ln \omega + \ln \tau_s''$. Then the contribution of the above term to the integral, Eq. (21–19), apart from the factor in front, is

$$C_s'' \int_{-\infty}^{\infty} \frac{e^x \, dx}{1 + e^{2x}} = C_s'' \int_0^{\infty} \frac{dy}{1 + y^2}$$

with $e^x = y$. This integral, by the further substitution $y = \tan \varphi$, gives

$$C_s'' \int_0^{\pi/2} d\varphi = C_s'' \frac{\pi}{2} .$$

These complicated formulas for the velocity are rather simple in the case of two relaxation times. One has, for Eqs. (21–11′) and (21–11″)

$$\tau_1'' \tau_2'' = \left(1 - \frac{C_1' + C_2'}{C_v}\right) \tau_1 \tau_2 \quad (21\text{–}11''')$$

$$\frac{1}{\tau_1''} + \frac{1}{\tau_2''} = (\tau_1'' + \tau_2'') \frac{1}{\tau_1'' \tau_2''} = \frac{1}{\tau_1} + \frac{1}{\tau_2} + \frac{1}{C_v - C_1' - C_2'} \left(\frac{C_1'}{\tau_1} + \frac{C_2'}{\tau_2} \right)$$

$$= \left(\frac{C_v - C_2'}{C_v - C_1' - C_2'} \tau_2 + \frac{C_v - C_1'}{C_v - C_1' - C_2'} \tau_1 \right) \frac{1}{\tau_1 \tau_2}$$

or

$$\tau_1'' + \tau_2'' = \frac{C_v - C_1'}{C_v} \tau_1 + \frac{C_v - C_2'}{C_v} \tau_2 . \quad (21\text{–}11'''')$$

Squaring Eq. (21–11''''), subtracting four times Eq. (21–11'''), and taking the square root gives

$$\tau_1'' - \tau_2'' = \left\{ \left(\frac{C_v - C_1'}{C_v} \tau_1 - \frac{C_v - C_2'}{C_v} \tau_2 \right)^2 + 4 \frac{C_1'C_2'}{C_v^2} \tau_1 \tau_2 \right\}^{1/2}$$

or

$$\tau'' = \frac{1}{2} \left\{ \frac{C_v - C_1'}{C_v} \tau_1 + \frac{C_v - C_2'}{C_v} \tau_2 \right\} \pm \frac{1}{2} \left\{ \left(\frac{C_v - C_1'}{C_v} \tau_1 - \frac{C_v - C_2'}{C_v} \tau_2 \right)^2 + 4 \frac{C_1'C_2'}{C_v^2} \tau_1 \tau_2 . \right\}^{1/2} . \quad (21\text{–}20)$$

If $\tau_1 \gg \tau_2$ or if C_1' and C_2' are sufficiently small compared to C_v, one can develop the root and find

$$\tau_1'' = \frac{C_v - C_1'}{C_v} \tau_1 + \frac{C_1'C_2'}{C_v^2} \tau_1 \tau_2 \left\{ \frac{C_v - C_1'}{C_v} \tau_1 - \frac{C_v - C_2'}{C_v} \tau_2 \right\}^{-1} \quad (21\text{–}21)$$

and

$$\tau_2'' = \frac{C_v - C_2'}{C_v} \tau_2 + \frac{C_1'C_2'}{C_v^2} \tau_1 \tau_2 \left\{ \frac{C_v - C_2'}{C_v} \tau_2 - \frac{C_v - C_1'}{C_v} \tau_1 \right\}^{-1} . \quad (21\text{–}21')$$

As in the case of coupled oscillators, the second term pushes the two τ'' values apart.

Furthermore, from Eqs. (21–15) and (21–15')

$$C_1'' + C_2'' = C_1' + C_2' \quad (21\text{–}22)$$

and

$$C_1''\tau_1'' + C_2''\tau_2'' = \left(1 - \frac{C_1' + C_2'}{C_v} \right) (C_1'\tau_1 + C_2'\tau_2). \quad (21\text{–}22')$$

If Eqs. (21–21) and (21–21') can be used, one can change Eq. (21–22') to the form

$$C_1'' = C_1' - \frac{C_1'C_2'}{C_v} (\tau_1 + \tau_2) \left(\frac{C_v - C_1'}{C_v} \tau_1 - \frac{C_v - C_2'}{C_v} \tau_2 \right)^{-1}$$

$$\left[1 + \frac{\tau_1 \tau_2}{\tau_1 + \tau_2} \left(\frac{C_1' - C_2'}{C_v} - 2 \frac{C_1'C_2'}{C_v^2} \right) \left(\frac{C_v - C_1'}{C_v} \tau_1 - \frac{C_v - C_2'}{C_v} \tau_2 \right)^{-1} \right] . \quad (21\text{–}22'')$$

C_2'' is found by exchanging the indices 1 and 2.

If (21–21) and (21–21′) cannot be applied,

$$C_1''(\tau_1'' - \tau_2'') = \frac{C_v - C_1' - C_2'}{C_v}(C_1'\tau_1' + C_2'\tau_2') - (C_1' + C_2')\tau_2''$$

which can be solved with the help of Eq. (21–20).

If the two τ values are very far apart, i.e., have a ratio of 100:1 or more, one has ($\tau_2 \ll \tau_1$, with, for example, τ_2 referring to rotation, and τ_1, vibration).

$$\tau_1'' = \frac{C_v - C_1'}{C_v}\tau_1 + \frac{C_1'C_2'}{C_v^2}\tau_1\tau_2\frac{C_v}{C_v - C_1'}\frac{1}{\tau_1}$$

$$= \frac{C_v - C_1'}{C_v}\tau_1 + \frac{C_1'C_2'}{C_v(C_v - C_1')}\tau_2 \qquad (21\text{–}21'')$$

and

$$\tau_2'' = \frac{C_v - C_2'}{C_v}\tau_2 - \frac{C_1'C_2'}{C_v(C_v - C_1')}\tau_2 = \frac{C_v - C_1' - C_2'}{C_v - C_1'}\tau_2. \qquad (21\text{–}21''')$$

This means that τ_1'', the apparent long relaxation time of the vibration, is slightly lengthened further, while τ_2'' behaves as if the vibration did not exist (initial specific heat, $C_v - C_1'$; final specific heat, $C_v - C_1' - C_2'$). This calculation proves the statement made at the beginning of Sec. 10.

Usually the problem will be opposite to that solved above. C_1'', C_2'', τ_1'', and τ_2'', will be given experimentally from the dispersion or absorption, while one wants to know C_1', C_2', τ_1, and τ_2.

One then writes for Eq. (21–11‴), in view of Eq. (21–15)

$$\tau_1\tau_2 = \frac{C_v}{C_v - C_1'' - C_2''}\tau_1''\tau_2''. \qquad (21\text{–}23)$$

Equation (21–11⁗) is rewritten, using (21–15′)

$$\tau_1'' + \tau_2'' = \tau_1 + \tau_2 - \frac{1}{C_v}(C_1'\tau_1 + C_2'\tau_2)$$

$$= \tau_1 + \tau_2 - \frac{1}{C_v - C_1'' - C_2''}(C_1''\tau_1'' + C_2''\tau_2'')$$

or

$$\tau_1 + \tau_2 = \frac{C_v - C_2''}{C_v - C_1'' - C_2''}\tau_1'' + \frac{C_v - C_1''}{C_v - C_1'' - C_2''}\tau_2''. \qquad (21\text{–}23')$$

Equation (21–20) is replaced by

$$\tau = \frac{1}{2}\left\{\frac{C_v - C_2''}{C_v - C_1'' - C_2''}\tau_1'' + \frac{C_v - C_1''}{C_v - C_1'' - C_2''}\tau_2''\right\}$$
$$\pm \frac{1}{2}\left\{\left(\frac{C_v - C_2''}{C_v - C_1'' - C_2''}\tau_1'' - \frac{C_v - C_1''}{C_v - C_1'' - C_2''}\tau_2''\right)^2\right.$$
$$\left. + 4\frac{C_1''C_2''}{(C_v - C_1'' - C_2'')^2}\tau_1''\tau_2''\right\}^{1/2}. \tag{21–24}$$

As before, if the two values of τ'' are very different, or C_1'' and C_2'' are small compared with C_v, one finds

$$\tau_1 = \frac{C_v - C_2''}{C_v - C_1'' - C_2''}\tau_1'' + \frac{C_1''C_2''}{(C_v - C_1'' - C_2'')^2}\tau_1''\tau_2''$$
$$\left\{\frac{C_v - C_2''}{C_v - C_1'' - C_2''}\tau_1'' - \frac{C_v - C_1''}{C_v - C_1'' - C_2''}\tau_2''\right\}^{-1} \tag{21–25}$$

and τ_2 follows by exchanging the indices everywhere. C_1' and C_2' follow then from Eqs. (21–23) and (21–23′).

To illustrate these equations, one may use recent results of Cheng[1] on benzene. The dispersion curve could be interpreted as a superposition of two such terms, the first with $C_1'' = 4.44\ R$ and $\tau_1'' = 3.62 \times 10^{-8}$ sec; the second with $C_2'' = 2\ R$ and $\tau_2'' = 1.22 \times 10^{-8}$ sec. Use of Eq. (21–24) gives $\tau_1 = 9.85 \times 10^{-8}$ sec; $\tau_2 = 1.15 \times 10^{-8}$ sec; $C_1' = 5.85\ R$; and $C_2' = 0.59\ R$.

Schäfer[2] has used formulas which are more convenient for numerical calculations, but do not show that the dispersion equation can be written in the form of Eq. (21–17). He defines two quantities which are the real and imaginary parts of $(C_v)_{\text{eff}}$, Eq. (21–3)

$$U = \text{real part of } (C_v)_{\text{eff}} = \tilde{C} + \sum \frac{C_s'}{1 + \omega^2\tau_s^2} \tag{21–26}$$

$$iW = \text{imaginary part of } (C_v)_{\text{eff}} = \sum C_s' \frac{i\omega\tau_s}{1 + \omega^2\tau_s^2} \tag{21–26′}$$

and finds (generalizing his formula from gases to fluids)

$$\frac{\mathfrak{V}^2}{\mathfrak{V}_0^2} = \frac{C_v}{C_p}\left\{1 + \Delta\frac{U}{U^2 + W^2}\right\} \tag{21–26″}$$

[1] L. Cheng, *J. Chem. Phys.* **19**, 693 (1951).
[2] K. Schäfer, *Z. physik. Chem.* **B46**, 212 (1940).

We now return to the proof that the denominator of $(C_p/C_v)_{\text{eff}}$ has only real negative roots. The denominator in Eq. (21–7) can be written

$$\Pi(\tau_j)\left[\tilde{C}_v \Pi\left(\frac{1}{\tau_j}+x\right)+\sum_s \frac{C_s'}{\tau_s}\Pi_s'\left(\frac{1}{\tau_j}+x\right)\right]. \tag{21–27}$$

If the equation is multiplied out, all the coefficients of x^k are positive. According to a theorem of algebra, a polynomial in which all coefficients have the same sign has no positive real roots.

The last square bracket can easily be shown to be equivalent to the determinant *det*

$$det = \begin{vmatrix} \tilde{C}_v & \dfrac{C_1'}{\tau_1} & \cdots & \dfrac{C_s'}{\tau_s} & \cdots & \dfrac{C_n'}{\tau_n} \\ 1 & \dfrac{1}{\tau_1}+x & \cdots & 0 & \cdots & 0 \\ \cdots & \cdots & \cdots & \cdots & \cdots & \cdots \\ 1 & 0 & \cdots & \dfrac{1}{\tau_s}+x & \cdots & 0 \\ \cdots & \cdots & \cdots & \cdots & \cdots & \cdots \\ 1 & 0 & \cdots & 0 & \cdots & \dfrac{1}{\tau_n}+x \end{vmatrix} \tag{21–28}$$

which in turn can be written, multiplying the row number s by $(C_s'/\tau_s)^{-1/2}$ and the column number s by $(C_s'/\tau_s)^{1/2}$

$$det = \begin{vmatrix} \tilde{C}_v & \sqrt{\dfrac{C_1'}{\tau_1}} & \cdots & \sqrt{\dfrac{C_s'}{\tau_s}} & \cdots & \sqrt{\dfrac{C_n'}{\tau_n}} \\ \sqrt{\dfrac{C_1'}{\tau_1}} & \dfrac{1}{\tau_1}+x & \cdots & 0 & \cdots & 0 \\ \cdots & \cdots & \cdots & \cdots & \cdots & \cdots \\ \sqrt{\dfrac{C_s'}{\tau_s}} & 0 & \cdots & \dfrac{1}{\tau_s}+x & \cdots & 0 \\ \cdots & \cdots & \cdots & \cdots & \cdots & \cdots \\ \sqrt{\dfrac{C_n'}{\tau_n}} & 0 & \cdots & 0 & \cdots & \dfrac{1}{\tau_n}+x \end{vmatrix} \tag{21–28'}$$

This is the secular determinant of a set of $n + 1$ linear homogeneous equations, with $n + 1$ unknowns, $Y_0, Y_1 \ldots Y_n$

$$\tilde{C}_v Y_0 + \sqrt{\frac{C_1'}{\tau_1}}\, Y_1 + \ldots \sqrt{\frac{C_s'}{\tau_s}}\, Y_s + \ldots \sqrt{\frac{C_n'}{\tau_n}}\, Y_n = 0$$

$$\sqrt{\frac{C_1'}{\tau_1}}\, Y_0 + \left(\frac{1}{\tau_1} + x\right) Y_1 = 0$$

$$\sqrt{\frac{C_s'}{\tau_s}}\, Y_0 + \left(\frac{1}{\tau_s} + x\right) Y_s = 0. \tag{21–29}$$

Eliminate Y_0 and get n equations. The sth equation is (with s equal to any integer from 1 to n)

$$-\frac{C_s'}{\tilde{C}_v \tau_s} Y_s - \frac{1}{\tilde{C}_v} \sum_{j \neq s} \frac{\sqrt{C_s' C_j'}}{\sqrt{\tau_s \tau_j}} Y_j + \left(\frac{1}{\tau_s} + x\right) Y_s = 0 \tag{21–30}$$

or

$$\left(1 - \frac{C_s'}{\tilde{C}_v}\right) \frac{Y_s}{\tau_s} - \sum_{j \neq s} \frac{\sqrt{C_s' C_j'}}{\tilde{C}_v} \frac{Y_j}{\sqrt{\tau_s \tau_j}} = -\, x Y_s.$$

This is a set of equations giving extreme values of the Y_s for the surface

$$\sum_s \left(1 - \frac{C_s'}{\tilde{C}_v}\right) \frac{Y_s^2}{\tau_s} - 2 \sum_{s \neq j} \sum_j \frac{\sqrt{C_s' C_j'}}{\tilde{C}_v} \frac{Y_s Y_j}{\sqrt{\tau_s \tau_j}} = \text{constant}$$

under the condition of rigid rotation, $\Sigma Y_s^2 = 1$. If a linear equation solver is available, it can be applied to Eq. (21–30). The eigenvalues, $-x$, are equal to the required $1/\tau_s''$. One proves in general that the eigenvalues belonging to a quadratic form with real coefficients are real and, from what has been said near Eq. (21–10), the τ_s'' are positive, as required.

This finishes the proof that the denominator in Eq. (21–7) can be written in the form

$$(C_v - \Sigma C_s')\, \Pi \tau_j''\, \Pi\left(\frac{1}{\tau_j''} + x\right) = (C_v - \Sigma C_j')\, \Pi(1 + i\omega\tau_j'').$$

The value of the first bracket follows if ω is set equal to zero.

22. Excitations of Different Degrees of Freedom Which Behave like Chemical Reactions in Series. Classical Theory

In Sec. 20 two different imaginable modes of excitation were discussed when several different degrees of freedom are present, as in polyatomic molecules or in mixtures: excitation in parallel and excitation in series. It was mentioned that in the latter case, transfer of energy is possible from one degree of freedom to the other without participation of external energy in classical theory only. In spite of this, the calculations for this assumption will be given here, but only for a simple case.

We will assume that there are only two degrees of freedom of vibration, as Schäfer has done, $s = 1, 2$; or that they all only exchange energy with the first, but with equal relaxation times; or that the second degree of freedom exchanges energy with the first vibration with a relaxation time τ_{12}, and all others exchange energy with mode number 2 or among themselves, but that all these relaxation times are much shorter than τ_{12}. In that case, all these degrees of vibrational freedom are practically in equilibrium among themselves, and lack of equilibrium exists between external kinetic energy, vibrational mode one, and the group of other vibrations taken together.

We may then call E_2' the energy, not of the second vibrational mode alone, but of all the vibrational modes except the first, so that

$$E' = E_1' + E_2' \qquad C' = C_1' + C_2'$$

and

$$-\frac{\partial E_1'}{\partial t} = \frac{1}{\tau_1}[E_1' - E_1'(T_{\text{tr}})] - \frac{1}{\tau_{12}}[E_2' - E_2'(T_1')]$$

or

$$-\frac{\partial T_1'}{\partial t} = \frac{1}{\tau_1}(T_1' - T_{\text{tr}}) - \frac{C_2'}{C_1'}\frac{1}{\tau_{12}}(T_2' - T_1') \tag{22–1}$$

$$-\frac{\partial E_2'}{\partial t} = \frac{1}{\tau_{12}}[E_2' - E_2'(T_1')]$$

or

$$-\frac{\partial T_2'}{\partial t} = \frac{1}{\tau_{12}}(T_2' - T_1'). \tag{22–1'}$$

Writing again $T_{tr} - T_0$ proportional to $e^{i\omega t}$, one finds

$$-i\omega\tau_1(T_1' - T_0) = (T_1' - T_0) - (T_{tr} - T_0) - \frac{C_2'}{C_1'}\frac{\tau_1}{\tau_{12}}(T_2' - T_1') \qquad (22\text{–}2)$$

$$-i\omega\tau_{12}(T_2' - T_0) = (T_2' - T_0) - (T_1' - T_0) \qquad (22\text{–}2')$$

or

$$T_2' - T_0 = \frac{1}{1 + i\omega\tau_{12}}(T_1' - T_0) \qquad (22\text{–}3)$$

$$T_2' - T_1' = -\frac{i\omega\tau_{12}}{1 + i\omega\tau_{12}}(T_1' - T_0). \qquad (22\text{–}3')$$

Equation (22–2) gives, after insertion of Eq. (22–3′)

$$(T_1' - T_0)\left[1 + i\omega\tau_1 + \frac{C_2'}{C_1'}\frac{\tau_1}{\tau_{12}}\frac{i\omega\tau_{12}}{1 + i\omega\tau_{12}}\right] = (T_{tr} - T_0). \qquad (22\text{–}3'')$$

The effective specific heat, defined by

$$\tilde{C}(T_{tr} - T_0) + C_1'(T_1' - T_0) + C_2'(T_2' - T_0) = (C_v)_{eff}(T_{tr} - T_0) \qquad (22\text{–}4)$$

is then

$$(C_v)_{eff} = \tilde{C} + \left[C_1' + \frac{C_2'}{1 + i\omega\tau_{12}}\right]\left[1 + i\omega\tau_1 + \frac{C_2'}{C_1'}\frac{i\omega\tau_1}{1 + i\omega\tau_{12}}\right]^{-1} \qquad (22\text{–}5)$$

or, multiplying the numerator and denominator of the second term on the right of Eq. (22–5) by $1 + i\omega\tau_{12}$

$$(C_v)_{eff} = \tilde{C} + [(C_1' + C_2') + C_1' i\omega\tau_{12}]\left[(1 + i\omega\tau_1)(1 + i\omega\tau_{12}) + \frac{C_2'}{C_1'}\, i\omega\tau_1\right]^{-1}. \qquad (22\text{–}6)$$

Proceeding then as in Sec. 12, one gets

$$\frac{\mathfrak{V}^2}{\mathfrak{V}_0^2}\left(1 - i\alpha'\frac{\mathfrak{V}}{\omega}\right)^{-2} = \frac{C_v}{C_p}\frac{(C_v)_{eff} + \Delta}{(C_v)_{eff}} = \frac{C_v}{C_p}\left[1 + \frac{\Delta}{(C_v)_{eff}}\right]$$

$$= \frac{C_v}{C_p} + \frac{C_v\Delta}{C_p(C_v)_{eff}} = 1 - \frac{\Delta}{C_p} + \frac{C_v\Delta}{C_p(C_v)_{eff}} = 1 + \frac{\Delta}{C_p}\left(\frac{C_v}{(C_v)_{eff}} - 1\right)$$

$$= 1 + \frac{\Delta}{C_p}\frac{C_v - (C_v)_{eff}}{(C_v)_{eff}}. \qquad (22\text{–}7)$$

The last fraction turns out to be, after both numerator and denominator have been multiplied by the denominator of Eq. (22–6)

$$\frac{C_v}{(C_v)_{\text{eff}}}-1=\left\{C'(1+i\omega\tau_1)(1+i\omega\tau_{12})+C'\frac{C_2'}{C_1'}i\omega\tau_1-C'-C_1'i\omega\tau_{12}\right\}$$

$$\cdot\left\{(C_v-C')(1+i\omega\tau_1)(1+i\omega\tau_{12})+(C_v-C')\frac{C_2'}{C_1'}i\omega\tau_1+C'+C_1'i\omega\tau_{12}\right\}^{-1}$$

$$=\frac{C'}{C_v-C'}\left\{(i\omega)^2\tau_1\tau_{12}+i\omega\left(\frac{C'}{C_1'}\tau_1+\frac{C_2'}{C'}\tau_{12}\right)\right\}\cdot$$

$$\cdot\left\{(i\omega)^2\tau_1\tau_{12}+i\omega\left(\frac{C'}{C_1'}\tau_1+\frac{C_v-C_2'}{C_v-C'}\tau_{12}\right)+\frac{C_v}{C_v-C'}\right\}^{-1}$$

$$=\frac{C'}{C_v-C'}\left\{(i\omega)^2+i\omega\left(\frac{C'}{C_1'}\frac{1}{\tau_{12}}+\frac{C_2'}{C'}\frac{1}{\tau_1}\right\}\right.\cdot$$

$$\cdot\left\{(i\omega)^2+i\omega\left(\frac{C'}{C_1'}\frac{1}{\tau_{12}}+\frac{C_v-C_2'}{C_v-C'}\frac{1}{\tau_1}\right)+\frac{C_v}{C_v-C'}\frac{1}{\tau_1\tau_{12}}\right\}^{-1}. \tag{22–8}$$

The situation is quite similar to that in Sec. 21. Equation (22–8) may be decomposed, as there, into partial fractions

$$\frac{C_v}{(C_v)_{\text{eff}}}-1=\frac{C'}{C_v-C'}\left\{\frac{C_1''}{C'}\frac{i\omega\tau_1''}{1+i\omega\tau_1''}+\frac{C_2''}{C'}\frac{i\omega\tau_2''}{1+i\omega\tau_2''}\right\} \tag{22–9}$$

so that Eq. (22–7) takes the form

$$\frac{\mathfrak{B}^2}{\mathfrak{B}_0^2}\left(1-i\alpha'\frac{\mathfrak{B}}{\omega}\right)^{-2}=1+\frac{\Delta}{C_p(C_v-C')}\left\{\frac{C_1''i\omega\tau_1''}{1+i\omega\tau_1''}+\frac{C_2''i\omega\tau_2''}{1+i\omega\tau_2''}\right\}. \tag{22–10}$$

If one again separates real and imaginary parts and neglects $(\alpha'\mathfrak{B}/\omega)^2$ compared to unity, as at the beginning of Sec. 12, one finds

$$\frac{\mathfrak{B}^2}{\mathfrak{B}_0^2}=1+\frac{\Delta}{C_p(C_v-C')}\left\{\frac{C_1''\omega^2\tau_1''^2}{1+\omega^2\tau_1''^2}+\frac{C_2''\omega^2\tau_2''^2}{1+\omega^2\tau_2''^2}\right\} \tag{22–11}$$

$$\frac{\mathfrak{B}^2}{\mathfrak{B}_0^2}\alpha'\frac{\mathfrak{B}}{\omega}=\frac{1}{2}\frac{\Delta}{C_p(C_v-C')}\left\{\frac{C_1''\omega\tau_1''}{1+\omega^2\tau_1''^2}+\frac{C_2''\omega\tau_2''}{1+\omega^2\tau_2''^2}\right\}. \tag{22–11'}$$

The form of Eqs. (22–10), (22–11), and (22–11′) is identical with the form of Eqs. (21–16), (21–17), and (21–18). The opinion of Schäfer that the cases in which the transfer of energy to the several modes of vibration behaves either like chemical reactions in parallel or like chemical reactions in series have a different dependence on frequency and can thereby be differentiated experimentally is, therefore, erroneous.

It remains actually to make the decomposition of Eq. (22–8) into partial fractions.

The numerator may be rewritten

$$(i\omega)^2 + i\omega\left(\frac{C'}{C_1'}\frac{1}{\tau_{12}} + \frac{C_v - C_2'}{C_v - C'}\frac{1}{\tau_1}\right) + \frac{C_v}{C_v - C'}\frac{1}{\tau_1\tau_{12}}$$

$$-\frac{1}{\tau_1}\left(\frac{C_v - C_2'}{C_v - C'} - \frac{C_2'}{C'}\right)i\omega - \frac{C_v}{C_v - C'}\frac{1}{\tau_1\tau_{12}}.$$

Therefore, Eq. (22–8), apart from the factor $C'/(C_v - C')$ outside, gives

$$1 - \frac{C_v}{C_v - C'}\frac{1}{\tau_1\tau_{12}}\left\{i\omega\tau_{12}\left(1 - \frac{C_2'}{C'}\right) + 1\right\}$$

$$\cdot\left\{(i\omega)^2 + i\omega\left(\frac{C'}{C_1'}\frac{1}{\tau_{12}} + \frac{C_v - C_2'}{C_v - C'}\frac{1}{\tau_1}\right) + \frac{C_v}{C_v - C'}\frac{1}{\tau_1\tau_{12}}\right\}^{-1}. \quad (22\text{–}12)$$

Write the denominator equal to $(i\omega + 1/\tau_1'')\,(i\omega + 1/\tau_2'')$ with

$$\frac{1}{\tau_1''\tau_2''} = \frac{C_v}{C_v - C'}\frac{1}{\tau_1\tau_{12}}$$

or

$$\tau_1''\tau_2'' = \frac{C_v - C'}{C_v}\,\tau_1\tau_{12}\,. \quad (22\text{–}13)$$

Equation (22–13) is identical with Eq. (21–11‴). Therefore, expression (22–12) may be rewritten

$$1 - \frac{1}{\tau_1''\tau_2''}\left\{i\omega\tau_{12}\frac{C_1'}{C'} + 1\right\}\frac{1}{i\omega + 1/\tau_1''}\frac{1}{i\omega + 1/\tau_2''}$$

$$= 1 - \left\{i\omega\tau_{12}\frac{C_1'}{C'} + 1\right\}\frac{1}{1 + i\omega\tau_1''}\frac{1}{1 + i\omega\tau_2''}. \quad (22\text{–}12')$$

If Eq. (22–12′) is set equal to

$$1 - \frac{C_1''}{C'}\frac{1}{1 + i\omega\tau_1''} - \frac{C_2''}{C'}\frac{1}{1 + i\omega\tau_2''}$$

there follows, see Eqs. (21–15) and (21–22′), respectively

$$\frac{C_1''}{C'} + \frac{C_2''}{C'} = 1 \qquad \text{or} \qquad C_1'' + C_2'' = C' = C_1' + C_2' \tag{22–14}$$

$$\frac{C_1'}{C'}\tau_{12} = \frac{C_1''}{C'}\tau_2'' + \frac{C_2''}{C'}\tau_1'' \qquad \text{or} \qquad C_1'\tau_{12} = C_1''\tau_2'' + C_2''\tau_1''. \tag{22–15}$$

Finally, one has as the second equation for the τ'', from Eqs. (22–12) and (22–13)

$$\frac{C'}{C_1}\frac{1}{\tau_{12}} + \frac{C_v - C_2'}{C_v - C'}\frac{1}{\tau_1} = \frac{1}{\tau_1''} + \frac{1}{\tau_2''}$$

or, multiplying with Eq. (22–13)

$$\begin{aligned}\tau_1'' + \tau_2'' &= \frac{C_v - C'}{C_v}\frac{C'}{C_1'}\tau_1 + \frac{C_v - C_2'}{C_v}\tau_{12} \\ &= \frac{C_v - C'}{C_v}\left(\frac{C'}{C_1'}\tau_1 + \frac{C_v - C_2'}{C_v - C'}\tau_{12}\right).\end{aligned} \tag{22–16}$$

Squaring Eq. (22–16) and subtracting four times Eq. (22–13), one gets

$$\begin{aligned}(\tau_1'' - \tau_2'')^2 &= \left(\frac{C_v - C'}{C_v}\right)^2 \left\{\left(\frac{C'}{C_1'}\tau_1\right)^2 + \left(\frac{C_v - C_2'}{C_v - C'}\tau_{12}\right)^2\right. \\ &\qquad\qquad \left. + 2\left(\frac{C'}{C_1'}\frac{C_v - C_2'}{C_v - C'} - 2\frac{C_v}{C_v - C'}\right)\tau_1\tau_{12}\right\} \\ &= \left(\frac{C_v - C'}{C_v}\right)^2 \left\{\left(\frac{C'}{C_1'}\tau_1 - \frac{C_v - C_2'}{C_v - C'}\tau_{12}\right)^2 + 4\frac{C_2'}{C_1'}\tau_1\tau_{12}\right\}.\end{aligned} \tag{22–17}$$

Therefore, one gets

$$\begin{aligned}\tau'' = \frac{1}{2}\frac{C_v - C'}{C_v}&\left\{\frac{C'}{C_1'}\tau_1 + \frac{C_v - C_2'}{C_v - C'}\tau_{12}\right. \\ &\left.\pm \sqrt{\left(\frac{C'}{C_1'}\tau_1 - \frac{C_v - C_2'}{C_v - C'}\tau_{12}\right)^2 + 4\frac{C_2'}{C_1'}\tau_1\tau_{12}}\right\},\end{aligned} \tag{22–18}$$

From the way Eq. (22–17) was arrived at—or from the fact that both Eqs. (22–13) and (22–16) are positive—it follows that both values of τ'' are positive (and, of course, real), so that Eq. (22–10) is of the form required, provided that the C'' are also positive.

If τ_{12} is very short compared to τ_1, i.e., if the internal exchange is fast compared with the exchange with the external kinetic energy, Eq. (22–18) has the approximate values

$$\tau_1'' = \frac{C_v - C'}{C_v}\frac{C'}{C_1'}\tau_1 + \frac{C_v - C'}{C_v}\frac{C_2'}{C'}\tau_{12} \tag{22–19}$$

and

$$\tau_2'' = \frac{C_1'}{C'}\tau_{12}\left(1 - \frac{C_1' C_2'}{(C')^2}\frac{\tau_{12}}{\tau_1}\right). \tag{22–19'}$$

Schäfer has given his expressions here, as in Sec. 21, in a different form.

$$C_2'' = C_2'\frac{C_v}{C_v - C'}\left(\frac{C_1'}{C'}\right)^2\left(\frac{\tau_{12}}{\tau_1}\right)^2$$

$$C_1'' \sim C_1' + C_2' = C'. \tag{22–19''}$$

In the extreme case of exceptionally fast internal energy exchange, there is only one effective relaxation time τ_1'', and the molecule acts as if this determined the exchange with all the degrees of freedom, see Eq. (22–19''), but because of the definition in Eq. (22–19)

$$\tau_1'' = \frac{C_v - C'}{C_v}\frac{C'}{C_1'}\tau_1. \tag{22–20}$$

For gases in this case, τ_1 is, as usual, $\sim 1/p$, but τ_{12} is independent of the pressure, so that τ_1'', and τ_2'' are *not* $\sim 1/p$.

23. Excitation in Series, with Exchange with Translational Energy (Quantum Theory)

With the exception of a few cases, this is the process occurring in gases and liquids. The treatment here will consist of two parts. First, the relaxation equations will be deduced, in a generalization of Sec. 19, for two different vibrational degrees of freedom (this section). Second, the solution of the generalized relaxation equation will be discussed in Sec. 24.

The deduction of relaxation equations for two degrees of freedom is patterned after papers of Bourgin[1] and Slawsky *et al.*[2] It is again assumed

---

[1] D. G. Bourgin, Phil. Mag. [7] **7**, 821 (1929); *Phys. Rev.* **34**, 521 (1929); **42**, 721 (1932); **49**, 411 (1936); **50**, 355 (1936); *J. Acoust. Soc. Am.* **4**, 108 (1932).

[2] Z. Slawsky, R. N. Schwartz, and K. F. Herzfeld, *J. Chem. Phys.* **20**, 1591 (1952).

that each oscillation can change its quantum number only by unity. Call the oscillations 1 and 2.

Call the vibrational quantum numbers s (oscillator 1) and j (oscillator 2). Then the only two processes of this kind possible are:

$$\text{(a)} \qquad \begin{array}{l} s \to s+1 \\ j \to j-1. \end{array}$$

The energy $h(\nu_2 - \nu_1)$ goes into translational energy if $h\nu_2 > h\nu_1$.

$$\text{(b)} \qquad \begin{array}{l} s \to s-1 \\ j \to j+1. \end{array}$$

The energy $h(\nu_2 - \nu_1)$ is supplied by translational energy if $h\nu_2 > h\nu_1$. Let the following designation be used: The quantum number of the first oscillator will be written as lower index, that of the second as upper index. Plus shall signify that the quantum number increases by one; minus, that it decreases by one.

Also, let n_s signify the fraction of the molecules of type 1 in mixtures of polyatomic molecules, in which the first oscillator has the quantum number s no matter what the quantum number of the second oscillator is. Then the number of processes (a) occurring in unit time is written as

$$k_{s+}^{j-} \, n_s n^{(j)} \tag{23–1}$$

of processes (b)

$$k_{s-}^{j+} \, n_s n^{(j)}. \tag{23–1'}$$

Furthermore, since all the processes of kind (a) involve the same amount of translational energy, independent of s and j, one has, from the transition probabilities of the simple harmonic oscillator

$$k_{s+}^{j-} = (s+1)j k_{0+}^{1-} = (s+1)j\bar{k} \tag{23–2}$$

$$k_{s-}^{j+} = s(j+1) k_{1-}^{0+} = s(j+1)\tilde{k}. \tag{23–2'}$$

This introduces, for easier printing, the notation

$$k_{0+}^{1-} = \bar{k} \qquad k_{1-}^{0+} = \tilde{k}$$

so that $\bar{k}$ refers to the process in which for $h\nu_2 > h\nu_1$ the translational energy gains $h(\nu_2 - \nu_1)$; $\tilde{k}$, to the process in which the kinetic energy loses this.

The total change in the fraction of particles with quantum number s in the first degree of freedom is

$$-\frac{dn_s}{dt} = \sum_j k_{s+}^{j-} n^{(j)} n_s + \sum_j k_{s-}^{j+} n^{(j)} n_s$$

$$-\sum_j k_{(s-1)+}^{j-} n^{(j)} n_{s-1} - \sum k_{(s+1)-}^{j+} n^{(j)} n_{s+1}. \qquad (23\text{–}3)$$

The first term on the right is given by the particles which are lost by going to $s+1$; the second term is given by those lost by going to $s-1$; the third and fourth, by those gained coming from $s-1$ and $s+1$, respectively.

Using Eqs. (23–2) and (23–2′), this can be rewritten

$$-\frac{dn_s}{dt} = n_s\left[(s+1)\bar{k}\sum jn^{(j)} + s\tilde{k}\sum (j+1)n^{(j)}\right]$$

$$-\, n_{s-1}s\bar{k}\sum jn^{(j)} - n_{s+1}(s+1)\tilde{k}\sum (j+1)n^{(j)}. \qquad (23\text{–}3')$$

The vibrational energy of a mole of oscillator 2, apart from zero-point energy, is (N_A, Avogadro number)

$$E_2' = N_A h\nu_2 \sum jn^{(j)} \qquad (23\text{–}4)$$

and

$$\sum n^{(j)} = 1. \qquad (23\text{–}4')$$

Therefore[3]

$$-\frac{dn_s}{dt} = n_s\left[(s+1)\frac{E_2'}{N_A h\nu_2}\bar{k} + s\left(\frac{E_2'}{N_A h\nu_2}+1\right)\tilde{k}\right] -$$

$$sn_{s-1}\frac{E_2'}{N_A h\nu_2}\bar{k} - (s+1)n_{s+1}\left(\frac{E_2'}{N_A h\nu_2}+1\right)\tilde{k}$$

$$= -\left[n_{s+1}\tilde{k}\left(\frac{E_2'}{N_A h\nu_2}+1\right) - n_s\bar{k}\frac{E_2'}{N_A h\nu_2}\right](s+1) +$$

$$\left[n_s\tilde{k}\left(\frac{E_2'}{N_A h\nu_2}+1\right) - n_{s-1}\bar{k}\frac{E_2'}{N_A h\nu_2}\right]s. \qquad (23\text{–}3'')$$

---

[3] In equilibrium, the left side is zero, i.e.,

$$\frac{n_{s+1}}{n_s} = \frac{n_s}{n_{s-1}} = \frac{\bar{k}}{\tilde{k}}\left(1+\frac{N_A h\nu_2}{E_2'}\right)^{-1}.$$

From Eq. (23–9), the right side is $(\bar{k}/\tilde{k})\, e^{-h\nu_2/kT}$. From the symmetry of the two oscillators, the Maxwell distribution law for n_s follows in the text.

One gets, similar to Eq. (23–3″)

$$-\frac{dn^{(j)}}{dt}=n^{(j)}\left[(j+1)\frac{E_1'}{N_A h\nu_1}\tilde{k}+j\left(\frac{E_1'}{N_A h\nu_1}+1\right)\tilde{k}\right]- \qquad (23\text{–}5)$$

$$jn^{(j-1)}\frac{E_1'}{N_A h\nu_1}\tilde{k}-(j+1)\,n^{(j+1)}\left(\frac{E_1'}{N_A h\nu_1}+1\right)\tilde{k}.$$

It should be pointed out that Eq. (23–4) expresses the actual value of E', not the equilibrium value.

Multiply Eq. (23–3″) with s and sum over s from zero to infinity. One then has, on the left, $-(1/N_A h\nu_1)\,dE_1'/dt$. On the right the following sums occur:

(a) as factor of $\tilde{k}$

$$\sum_0^\infty s(s+1)n_s-\sum_1^\infty s^2 n_{s-1}=\sum_0^\infty (s^2+s)n_s-\sum_0^\infty (s+1)^2 n_s$$

$$=\sum_0^\infty (s^2+s-s^2-2s-1)n_s=-\sum_0^\infty (s+1)n_s=-\left(\frac{E_1'}{N_A h\nu_1}+1\right)$$

(b) as factor of $\tilde{k}$

$$\sum_0^\infty s^2 n_s-\sum_0^\infty s(s+1)n_{s+1}=\sum_0^\infty s^2 n_s-\sum_1^\infty (s-1)s\,n_s$$

$$=\sum_0^\infty (s^2-s^2+s)n_s=\sum_0^\infty s\,n_s=\frac{E_1'}{N_A h\nu_1}.$$

In these transformations, the numbering has been changed in the first step of both equations for one summand. In the second step of the second equation, second term, the summation is extended to zero, because the term $s=0$, namely, $(0-1)\,0\,n_0$, automatically disappears. Therefore, one has, exactly

$$-\frac{1}{N_A h\nu_1}\frac{dE_1'}{dt}=\tilde{k}\left(\frac{E_1'}{N_A h\nu_1}+1\right)\frac{E_2'}{N_A h\nu_2}-\tilde{k}\frac{E_1'}{N_A h\nu_1}\left(\frac{E_2'}{N_A h\nu_2}+1\right) \qquad (23\text{–}6)$$

and, analogously

$$-\frac{1}{N_A h\nu_2}\frac{dE_2'}{dt}=\tilde{k}\left(\frac{E_2'}{N_A h\nu_2}+1\right)\frac{E_1'}{N_A h\nu_1}-\tilde{k}\frac{E_2'}{N_A h\nu_2}\left(\frac{E_1'}{N_A h\nu_1}+1\right).$$

(23–6′)

Equations (23–6) and (23–6′) added give

$$\frac{d}{dt}\left\{\frac{E_1{}'}{h\nu_1}+\frac{E_2{}'}{h\nu_2}\right\}=0$$

or conservation of the total number of quanta.

In the process discussed here, the internal energy is not conserved (exchange with translational energy) but the total number of quanta is, one quantum $h\nu_1$ being exchanged against one quantum $h\nu_2$ or vice versa.

Equations (23–6) and (23–6′) are exact. From now on, one makes the approximation that the deviations from equilibrium at T_0 are small. One then writes

$$\frac{E'}{N_A\,h\nu}=(e^{h\nu/kT}-1)^{-1}+\frac{C'}{N_A\,h\nu}(T'-T_0)$$

$$\frac{E'}{N_A\,h\nu}+1=(e^{h\nu/kT}-1)^{-1}+1+\frac{C'}{N_A\,h\nu}(T'-T_0)$$

$$=e^{h\nu/kT}\left(\frac{E'}{N_A\,h\nu}\right)_0+\frac{C'}{N_A\,h\nu}(T'-T_0). \tag{23–7}$$

$$k=(k)_0+\frac{\partial k}{\partial T}(T_{\rm tr}-T_0).$$

Equation (23–6) than takes the following form, in which all the quantities on the right, except $T'-T_0$ and $T_{\rm tr}-T_0$, are assumed to have their equilibrium values at T_0, without the index zero being written out

$$-\frac{1}{N_A\,h\nu_2}\frac{dE_1{}'}{dt}=-\bar{k}\frac{E_1{}'}{N_A\,h\nu_1}e^{h\nu_1/kT}\frac{E_2{}'}{N_A\,h\nu_2}+\tilde{k}\frac{E_1{}'}{N_A\,h\nu_1}\frac{E_2{}'}{N_A\,h\nu_2}e^{h\nu_2/kT}$$
$$-\bar{k}\left[\frac{C_1{}'}{N_A\,h\nu_1}(T_1{}'-T_0)\frac{E_2{}'}{N_A\,h\nu_2}+\frac{E_1{}'}{N_A\,h\nu_2}e^{h\nu_1/kT}\frac{C_2{}'}{N_A\,h\nu_2}(T_2{}'-T_0)\right]$$
$$+\tilde{k}\left[\frac{C_1{}'}{N_A\,h\nu_1}(T_1{}'-T_0)\frac{E_2{}'}{N_A\,h\nu_2}e^{h\nu_2/kT}+\frac{E_1{}'}{N_A\,h\nu_1}\frac{C_2{}'}{N_A\,h\nu_2}(T_2{}'-T_0)\right]$$
$$+\frac{E_1{}'}{N_A\,h\nu_1}\frac{E_2{}'}{N_A\,h\nu_2}\left[-e^{h\nu_1/kT}\frac{\partial\bar{k}}{\partial T}+e^{h\nu_2/kT}\frac{\partial\tilde{k}}{\partial T}\right]. \tag{23–8}$$

In equilibrium ($T'=T_{\rm tr}=T_0$) the first term must be zero, which gives the usual equation, see Eq. (19–4)

$$\tilde{k}=\bar{k}\,e^{-(h/kT)(\nu_2-\nu_1)} \tag{23–9}$$

and, in the last line of Eq. (23–8)

$$e^{h\nu_2/kT} \frac{\partial}{\partial T} \tilde{k} = e^{h\nu_2/kT} \left[\frac{h(\nu_2 - \nu_1)}{kT_0{}^2} \bar{k} + \frac{\partial \bar{k}}{\partial T} \right] e^{-(h/kT)(\nu_2-\nu_1)}$$

$$= e^{h\nu_1/kT} \frac{h}{kT^2} (\nu_2 - \nu_1)\, \bar{k} + e^{h\nu_1/kT} \frac{\partial \bar{k}}{\partial T}.$$

Therefore

$$-\frac{1}{N_A h\nu_1} \frac{dE_1'}{dT} = \frac{C_1'}{N_A h\nu_1} (T_1' - T_0) \frac{E_2'}{N_A h\nu_2} [-\bar{k} + \tilde{k}\, e^{h\nu_2/kT}]$$

$$+ \frac{C_2'}{N_A h\nu_2} (T_2' - T_0) \frac{E_1'}{N_A h\nu_1} [-\bar{k}\, e^{h\nu_1/kT} + \tilde{k}]$$

$$+ \frac{E_1'}{N_A h\nu_1} \frac{E_2'}{N_A h\nu_2} \frac{h\nu_2 - h\nu_1}{kT_0{}^2} e^{h\nu_1/kT} \bar{k} (T_{\text{tr}} - T_0). \tag{23–10}$$

Now

$$C'(1 - e^{-h\nu/kT}) = \frac{h\nu}{kT^2} E' \tag{23–11}$$

so that the last term can be rewritten

$$(T_{\text{tr}} - T_0) \left[\frac{E_1'}{N_A h\nu_1} \frac{C_2'}{N_A h\nu_2} (1 - e^{-h\nu_2/kT})\, \bar{k}\, e^{h\nu_1/kT} \right.$$

$$\left. - \frac{E_2'}{N_A h\nu_2} \frac{C_1'}{N_A h\nu_1} (1 - e^{-h\nu_1/kT})\, \bar{k}\, e^{h\nu_1/kT} \right]$$

$$= (T_{\text{tr}} - T_0) \left[\frac{E_1'}{N_A h\nu_1} \frac{C_2'}{N_A h\nu_2} (\bar{k}\, e^{h\nu_1/kT} - \tilde{k}) - \frac{E_2'}{N_A h\nu_2} \frac{C_1'}{N_A h\nu_1} (\tilde{k}\, e^{h\nu_2/kT} - \bar{k}) \right].$$

Inserting the last result into Eq. (23–10) one gets, by using Eq. (23–7)

$$-\frac{C_1'}{N_A h\nu_1} \frac{dT_1'}{dt} = \frac{C_1'}{N_A h\nu_1} \frac{E_2'}{N_A h\nu_2} [T_1' - T_0 - (T_{\text{tr}} - T_0)]\, [\tilde{k}\, e^{h\nu_2/kT} - \bar{k}]$$

$$+ \frac{C_2'}{N_A h\nu_2} \frac{E_1'}{N_A h\nu_1} [T_2' - T_0 - (T_{\text{tr}} - T_0)]\, [\tilde{k} - \bar{k}\, e^{h\nu_1/kT}]. \tag{23–10′}$$

From Eq. (23–11)

$$\frac{C_2'}{N_A h\nu_2} \frac{E_1'}{N_A h\nu_1} = \frac{\nu_2}{\nu_1} (1 - e^{-h\nu_1/kT})\, (1 - e^{-h\nu_2/kT})^{-1} \frac{C_1'}{N_A h\nu_1} \frac{E_2'}{N_A h\nu_2}.$$

Making use of this expression in the second term of Eq. (23–10′) $C_1'/N_A\, h\nu_1$ can be cancelled out. The value of E_2' is then substituted

$$-\frac{dT_1'}{dt} = \tilde{k}\, e^{h\nu_2/kT}\,(1 - e^{-h\nu_1/kT})\,(e^{h\nu_2/kT} - 1)^{-1}\,(T_1' - T_{\mathrm{tr}})$$

$$+\frac{\nu_2}{\nu_1}\,(1 - e^{-h\nu_1/kT})\,(1 - e^{-h\nu_2/kT})^{-1}\,(e^{h\nu_2/kT} - 1)^{-1}\,\tilde{k}\,(1 - e^{h\nu_2/kT})\,(T_2' - T_{\mathrm{tr}})$$

$$= (1 - e^{-h\nu_1/kT})\,(1 - e^{-h\nu_2/kT})^{-1}\,\tilde{k}\left[(T_1' - T_{\mathrm{tr}}) - \frac{\nu_2}{\nu_1}(T_2' - T_{\mathrm{tr}})\right]. \qquad (23\text{–}10'')$$

To get a symmetrical way of writing Eq. (23–10″) and allow easy generalization to more degrees of freedom, define

$$\frac{1}{\tau_{12}} = \sqrt{\bar{k}\tilde{k}} = \bar{k}\, e^{-h(\nu_2-\nu_1)/2kT} = \tilde{k}\, e^{h(\nu_2-\nu_1)/2kT} \qquad (23\text{–}12)$$

and note that

$$C' = R\left(\frac{h\nu}{kT}\right)^2 \frac{e^{h\nu/kT}}{(e^{h\nu/kT} - 1)^2} = R\left[\frac{h\nu}{kT}\,\frac{e^{h\nu/2kT}}{e^{h\nu/kT} - 1}\right]^2.$$

Introduce the characteristic temperature ϑ of the vibration defined by $\vartheta = h\nu/k$. Therefore

$$\frac{e^{-h\nu/2kT}}{1 - e^{-h\nu/kT}} = \frac{e^{h\nu/2kT}}{e^{h\nu/kT} - 1} = \sqrt{\frac{C'}{R}\,\frac{T}{\vartheta}}. \qquad (23\text{–}12')$$

Then

$$-\frac{dT_1'}{dt} = \frac{1}{\tau_{12}}\sqrt{\frac{C_2'}{C_1'}\,\frac{\vartheta_1}{\vartheta_2}}\left[(T_1' - T_{\mathrm{tr}}) - \frac{\vartheta_2}{\vartheta_1}(T_2' - T_{\mathrm{tr}})\right]. \qquad (23\text{–}10''')$$

Add to Eq. (23–10‴) the effect of the direct exchange of energy between vibration 1 and translation

$$-\frac{dT_1'}{dt} = \frac{1}{\tau_1}(T_1' - T_{\mathrm{tr}}) + \frac{1}{\tau_{12}}\sqrt{\frac{C_2'}{C_1'}\,\frac{\vartheta_1}{\vartheta_2}}\left[(T_1' - T_{\mathrm{tr}}) - \frac{\vartheta_2}{\vartheta_1}(T_2' - T_{\mathrm{tr}})\right] \qquad (23\text{–}13)$$

and, by exchanging the indices 1 and 2

$$-\frac{dT_2'}{dt} = \frac{1}{\tau_{12}}\sqrt{\frac{C_1'}{C_2'}\,\frac{\vartheta_2}{\vartheta_1}}\left[(T_2' - T_{\mathrm{tr}}) - \frac{\vartheta_1}{\vartheta_2}(T_1' - T_{\mathrm{tr}})\right]. \qquad (23\text{–}12'')$$

24. The Solution of the General Equations of Excitation in Series

Assume again that vibration 1 alone exchanges energy directly with the translation, while all other degrees of vibration exchange energy only with each other or with vibration 1. The generalized differential equation, Eq. (23–13), will then have the following form

$$-\frac{dT_1'}{dt} = \frac{1}{\tau_1}(T_1' - T_{\text{tr}}) + \sum_{j\neq 1} \frac{1}{\tau_{1j}} \sqrt{\frac{C_j'}{C_1'}} \left[\frac{\vartheta_1}{\vartheta_j}(T_1' - T_{\text{tr}}) - (T_j' - T_{\text{tr}})\right], \tag{24–1}$$

$$-\frac{dT_s'}{dt} = \sum_{j\neq s} \frac{1}{\tau_{sj}} \sqrt{\frac{C_j'}{C_s'}} \left[\frac{\vartheta_s}{\vartheta_j}(T_s' - T_{\text{tr}}) - (T_j' - T_{\text{tr}})\right] \tag{24–1'}$$

for $s \neq 1$.

Assume that everything is proportional to $e^{i\omega t}$. The operation d/dt then means multiplication with $i\omega$ or

$$-i\omega(T_1' - T_{\text{tr}}) - i\omega(T_{\text{tr}} - T_0) =$$

$$\frac{1}{\tau_1}(T_1' - T_{\text{tr}}) + \sum_{j\neq 1} \frac{1}{\tau_{1j}} \sqrt{\frac{C_j'}{C_1'}} \left[\frac{\vartheta_1}{\vartheta_j}(T_1' - T_{\text{tr}}) - (T_j' - T_{\text{tr}})\right], \tag{24–2}$$

$$-i\omega(T_s' - T_{\text{tr}}) - i\omega(T_{\text{tr}} - T_0) = \sum_{j\neq s} \frac{1}{\tau_{sj}} \sqrt{\frac{C_j'}{C_s'}} \left[\frac{\vartheta_s}{\vartheta_j}(T_s' - T_{\text{tr}}) - (T_j' - T_{\text{tr}})\right]. \tag{24–2'}$$

when s is not unity.

For the solution of these equations, rewrite them as follows. Multiply the equation number s with $\sqrt{C_s'/R}$; collect the terms with $T_s' - T_{\text{tr}}$

$$\left(\frac{1}{\tau_1} + \sum_{j\neq 1} \frac{1}{\tau_{1j}} \sqrt{\frac{C_j'}{C_1'}} \frac{\vartheta_1}{\vartheta_j} + i\omega\right) \sqrt{\frac{C_1'}{R}}(T_1' - T_{\text{tr}}) - \sum_{j\neq 1} \frac{1}{\tau_{1j}} \sqrt{\frac{C_j'}{R}}(T_j' - T_{\text{tr}})$$

$$= -i\omega \sqrt{\frac{C_1'}{R}}(T_{\text{tr}} - T_0) \tag{24–3}$$

$$\left(\sum_{j\neq s} \frac{1}{\tau_{sj}} \sqrt{\frac{C_j'}{C_s'}} \frac{\vartheta_s}{\vartheta_j} + i\omega\right) \sqrt{\frac{C_s'}{R}}(T_s' - T_{\text{tr}}) - \sum_{j\neq s} \frac{1}{\tau_{sj}} \sqrt{\frac{C_j'}{R}}(T_j' - T_{\text{tr}})$$

$$= -i\omega \sqrt{\frac{C_s'}{R}}(T_{\text{tr}} - T_0) \tag{24–3'}$$

for $s \neq 1$. Now define the new relaxation times $\tilde{\tau}$

$$\frac{1}{\tilde{\tau}_1} = \frac{1}{\tau_1} + \sum_{j \neq 1} \frac{1}{\tau_{1j}} \sqrt{\frac{C_j'}{C_1'} \frac{\vartheta_1}{\vartheta_j}}. \tag{24–4}$$

When $s \neq 1$, then

$$\frac{1}{\tilde{\tau}_s} = \sum_{j \neq s} \frac{1}{\tau_{sj}} \sqrt{\frac{C_j'}{C_s'} \frac{\vartheta_s}{\vartheta_j}}. \tag{24–4'}$$

Define a new variable X_s

$$-i\omega X_s = \sqrt{\frac{C_s'}{R}} \frac{T_s' - T_{\text{tr}}}{T_{\text{tr}} - T_0}. \tag{24–5}$$

Then the equations (including $s = 1$) read, after dividing by $T_{\text{tr}} - T_0$ and crossing out $-i\omega$

$$\left(\frac{1}{\tilde{\tau}_s} + i\omega\right) X_s - \sum_{j \neq s} \frac{1}{\tau_{sj}} X_j = \sqrt{\frac{C_s'}{R}}. \tag{24–6}$$

Furthermore, see Eq. (20–1)

$$C_{\text{eff}} = C + \sum_s C_s' \left(\frac{dT_s'}{dT_{\text{tr}}} - 1\right)$$

$$= C + \sum_s C_s' \frac{T_s' - T_{tr}}{T_{\text{tr}} - T_0} = C - i\omega \sum \sqrt{C_s' R}\, X_s. \tag{24–7}$$

Some degrees of freedom might be degenerate. It is also possible that a group of degrees of freedom with similar vibration frequencies either behave similarly, or equalize the energy very rapidly among themselves; then they can be treated as one degenerate vibration.

In these cases, use for C_s' the corresponding sum of specific heats. It is true that only $\sqrt{C_s'}$ appears in Eq. (24–7), so that the effect does not seem additive. But $\sqrt{C_s'}$ also appears on the right side of Eq. (24–6), so that the end result is correct.

We then have to show that $i\omega\Sigma\sqrt{C_s' R} X_s$ can be written in the form

$$i\omega \sum \sqrt{C_s' R}\, X_s = \sum C_s''' \frac{i\omega\tau_s'''}{1 + i\omega\tau_s'''}$$

or

$$\sum \sqrt{C_s' R}\, X_s = \sum \frac{C_s'''\tau_s'''}{1 + i\omega\tau_s'''} = \sum \frac{C_s'''}{(1/\tau_s''') + i\omega} \tag{24–8}$$

with real, positive values of C_s'' and τ_s''.

The set, Eq. (24–6), of linear equations is quite similar in form to the equations which describe the motions of a group of particles of mass unity, attached to certain springs, under the influence of simple harmonic external forces.[1]

The external force acting on the particle s is $\sqrt{C_s'/R}$. The constant of the Hooke's law force of the spring connecting particles s and j is $1/\tau_{sj}$. The particle s is, in addition, tied to a fixed point in space by a force obeying Hooke's law with a spring constant equal to

$$\left(\frac{1}{\tau_1}\right) + \sum_{j\neq s} \frac{1}{\tau_{sj}} \sqrt{\frac{C_j'}{C_s'}\frac{\vartheta_s}{\vartheta_j}} - \sum_{j\neq s} \frac{1}{\tau_{sj}} = \left(\frac{1}{\tau_1}\right) + \sum_{s\neq j} \frac{1}{\tau_{sj}} \left(\sqrt{\frac{C_j'}{C_s'}\frac{\vartheta_s}{\vartheta_j}} - 1\right).$$

The term $1/\tau_1$ is present only for $s = 1$. It is possible that in some cases the analogy leads to a negative restoring force, if the quantity just written is negative.

Furthermore, in the vibration case the quantity $i\omega$ is replaced by $(i\omega)^2 = -\omega^2$. We will call $x = -i\omega$. (In Sec. 21, the sign defining x was the opposite.) The method of solution of Eq. (24–6) is patterned after the vibrational case. One first solves the corresponding homogeneous equations (corresponding to free vibrations). The unknowns shall be called U_j instead of X_j. This work can best be done with a linear equation solver.

The homogeneous equations are

$$\left(\frac{1}{\tilde{\tau}_s} - x\right) U_s - \sum_{j\neq s} \frac{1}{\tau_{sj}} U_j = 0. \tag{24–9}$$

These are only solvable if the "secular" determinant is zero.

$$\begin{vmatrix} \frac{1}{\tilde{\tau}_1} - x & -\frac{1}{\tau_{12}} & \cdots & -\frac{1}{\tau_{1n}} \\ -\frac{1}{\tau_{21}} & \frac{1}{\tilde{\tau}_2} - x & & -\frac{1}{\tau_{2n}} \\ \cdots & \cdots & \cdots & \cdots \\ -\frac{1}{\tau_{n1}} & -\frac{1}{\tau_{n2}} & \cdots & \frac{1}{\tilde{\tau}_n} - x \end{vmatrix} = 0 \tag{24–10}$$

$$\tau_{sj} = \tau_{js}. \tag{24–10′}$$

[1] J. Meixner, *Z. Naturforsch.* **4a**, 594 (1949); **9a**, 654 (1954); *Kolloid-Z.* **134**, 3 (1953).

There are x solutions (eigenvalues) $x_1 \ldots x_n$; possibly not all distinct. Because of Eq. (24–10′)—"symmetric" determinant[2]—all the x are real.

The necessary and sufficient condition for all the x to be positive is for all the following quantities to be positive.

$$\frac{1}{\tilde{\tau}_1} \qquad \begin{vmatrix} \frac{1}{\tilde{\tau}_1} & -\frac{1}{\tau_{12}} \\ -\frac{1}{\tau_{12}} & \frac{1}{\tilde{\tau}_2} \end{vmatrix} \qquad \begin{vmatrix} \frac{1}{\tilde{\tau}_1} & -\frac{1}{\tau_{12}} & -\frac{1}{\tau_{13}} \\ -\frac{1}{\tau_{12}} & \frac{1}{\tilde{\tau}_2} & -\frac{1}{\tau_{23}} \\ -\frac{1}{\tau_{13}} & -\frac{1}{\tau_{23}} & \frac{1}{\tilde{\tau}_3} \end{vmatrix}$$

It is easy to show that the first two expressions are positive. The proof has not been carried through in general, but it will be assumed to be true.

The physical meaning of the x_k is then

$$x_k = \frac{1}{\tau_k'''}. \tag{24–11}$$

For each eigenvalue x_k there is one solution for the U, which is called the "eigenvector" belonging to the eigenvalue x_k, and which we will write $U_1^{(k)}, U_2^{(k)} \ldots U_n^{(k)}$. Actually, only the ratios are determined, but one can add the condition

$$\sum_j (U_j^{(k)})^2 = 1.$$

The eigenvector is then called normalized.

It is proved in the theory of eigenvectors that they have the following property

$$\sum_k U_s^{(k)} U_j^{(k)} = 0 \qquad s \neq j \qquad \sum_k U_s^{(k)} U_s^{(k)} = 1. \tag{24–12}$$

One now has $n + 1$ sets of equations: one inhomogeneous set equal to Eq. (24–6)

$$\left(\frac{1}{\tilde{\tau}_s} - x\right) X_s - \sum_{j \neq s} \frac{1}{\tau_{sj}} X_j = \sqrt{\frac{C_s'}{R}} \tag{24–13}$$

---

[2] See, for example, H. Margenau and G. M. Murphy, "The Mathematics of Physics and Chemistry," sections 10.7 and 10.19, van Nostrand, New York, 1943.

with x arbitrary; and n homogeneous sets, one set for each eigenvalue x_k.

$$\left(\frac{1}{\tilde{\tau}_s} - x_k\right) U_s^{(k)} - \sum_{j \neq s} \frac{1}{\tau_{sj}} U_j^{(k)} = 0. \tag{24–14}$$

Now multiply Eq. (24–13) with $U_s^{(k)}$ and Eq. (24–14) with X_s, then subtract and sum over s

$$\sum_s \left[\left(\frac{1}{\tilde{\tau}_s} - x\right) - \left(\frac{1}{\tilde{\tau}_s} - x_k\right)\right] X_s U_s^{(k)} - \sum_s \sum_{j \neq s} \frac{1}{\tau_{sj}} X_j U_s^{(k)} + \sum_s \sum_{j \neq s} \frac{1}{\tau_{sj}} U_j^{(k)} X_s = \sum_s \sqrt{\frac{C_s'}{R}}\, U_s^{(k)}. \tag{24–15}$$

The double sums on the left can be grouped into pairs, rearranging the second one

$$-\frac{1}{\tau_{sj}} X_j U_s^{(k)} + \frac{1}{\tau_{js}} U_s^{(k)} X_j.$$

Therefore

$$\left(\frac{1}{\tau_k'''} - x\right) \sum_s X_s U_s^{(k)} = \sum_s \sqrt{\frac{C_s'}{R}}\, U_s^{(k)}$$

or

$$\sum_s X_s U_s^{(k)} = \left(\frac{1}{\tau_k'''} - x\right)^{-1} \sum_s \sqrt{\frac{C_s'}{R}}\, U_s^{(k)}. \tag{24–16}$$

Now multiply Eq. (24–16) with $U_j^{(k)}$ and sum over k

$$\sum_k U_j^{(k)} \sum_s X_s U_s^{(k)} = \sum_k U_j^{(k)} \left(\frac{1}{\tau_k'''} - x\right)^{-1} \sum_s \sqrt{\frac{C_s'}{R}}\, U_s^{(k)}. \tag{24–17}$$

Changing the order of summation on the left and exchanging the letters s and j

$$\sum X_j \sum_k U_j^{(k)} U_s^{(k)} = \sum_k U_s^{(k)} \left(\frac{1}{\tau_k'''} - x\right)^{-1} \sum_j \sqrt{\frac{C_j'}{R}}\, U_j^{(k)}. \tag{24–18}$$

From Eq. (24–12), one gets zero on the left in the second sum, except when $j = s$. Therefore, only X_s is left

$$X_s = \sum_k \left[U_s^{(k)} \left(\frac{1}{\tau_k'''} - x \right)^{-1} \sum_j \sqrt{\frac{C_j'}{R}}\, U_j^{(k)} \right] \qquad (24\text{–}19)$$

and, see Eq. (24–8)

$$\sum_s \sqrt{C_s' R}\, X_s = R \sum_k \left[\left(\sum_s \sqrt{\frac{C_s'}{R}}\, U_s^{(k)} \right) \left(\frac{1}{\tau_k'''} - x \right)^{-1} \left(\sum_j \sqrt{\frac{C_j'}{R}}\, U_j^{(k)} \right) \right]$$

$$= \sum_s C_s''' \frac{\tau_s'''}{1 + i\omega\tau_s'''} \qquad (24\text{–}19')$$

$$C_s''' = R \left[\sum_j \sqrt{\frac{C_j'}{R}}\, U_j^{(s)} \right]^2. \qquad (24\text{–}19'')$$

On the right side, the index is written s instead of k. This finishes the required proof—including the fact that all C''' are positive, since they are given by squares. It also gives the simplest method of calculation. By summing over s

$$\sum_s C_s''' = \sum_s \sum_j \sum_k \sqrt{C_j' C_k'}\, U_j^{(s)} U_k^{(s)} = \sum_j \sum_k \sqrt{C_j' C_k'} \sum_s U_j^{(s)} U_k^{(s)}$$

$$= \sum_j C_j' \qquad (24\text{–}19''')$$

considering Eq. (24–12).

Equation (16–10) can be written, in the limit $\omega = 0$

$$\left(\frac{\alpha'}{\omega^2} \right)_0 = \frac{(\gamma_0 - 1)^2}{\gamma_0} \frac{1}{2\mathfrak{V}_0 \Delta} \lim \frac{\operatorname{Im}\,[-(C_p)_{\mathrm{eff}}]}{i\omega}$$

where Im signifies the imaginary part.

From Eq. (24–7) we have, using $\gamma_0 - 1 = \Delta / C_v$

$$\left(\frac{\alpha'}{\omega^2} \right)_0 = \frac{1}{2\mathfrak{V}_0} \frac{\Delta}{C_v C_p} \lim \frac{\operatorname{Im}\,[-(C_p)_{\mathrm{eff}}]}{i\omega} = \frac{1}{2\mathfrak{V}_0} \frac{\Delta}{C_v C_p} \sum_s \sqrt{C_s' R}\, X_s$$

$$= \frac{1}{2\mathfrak{V}_0} \frac{R\Delta}{C_v C_p} \sum_s \tau_s''' \left[\sum_j \sqrt{\frac{C_j'}{R}}\, U_j^{(s)} \right]^2. \qquad (24\text{–}20)$$

To compare the present results with those of Sec. 22, again assume only two vibrations, 1 and 2. Equation (22–2) gives

$$\left(\frac{1}{\tau_1} + i\omega + \frac{1}{\tau_{12}}\frac{C_2'}{C_1'}\right)(T_1' - T_{\text{tr}}) - \frac{1}{\tau_{12}}\frac{C_2'}{C_1'}(T_2' - T_{\text{tr}}) = -\,i\omega(T_{\text{tr}} - T_0) \tag{24–21}$$

$$\left(\frac{1}{\tau_{12}} + i\omega\right)(T_2' - T_{\text{tr}}) - \frac{1}{\tau_{12}}(T_1' - T_{\text{tr}}) = -\,i\omega(T_{\text{tr}} - T_0). \tag{24–21'}$$

One now introduces new relaxation times

$$\frac{1}{\tilde{\tau}_{12}} = \frac{1}{\tau_{12}}\sqrt{\frac{C_2'}{C_1'}} \qquad \frac{1}{\tilde{\tau}_1'} = \frac{1}{\tau_1} + \frac{1}{\tau_{12}}\frac{C_2'}{C_1'} = \frac{1}{\tau_1} + \frac{1}{\tilde{\tau}_{12}}\sqrt{\frac{C_2'}{C_1'}}. \tag{24–22}$$

Then the factor of $(T_1' - T_{\text{tr}})$ in Eq. (24–21) is $1/\tilde{\tau}_1 + i\omega$. The factor of $(T_2' - T_{\text{tr}})$ is $-1/\tilde{\tau}_{12}\sqrt{C_2'/C_1'}$.

Multiply the first equation by $\sqrt{C_1'}$, the second by $\sqrt{C_2'}$, and introduce again the variable, see Eq. (24–5)

$$-\,i\omega X = \sqrt{\frac{C'}{R}}\,\frac{T' - T_{\text{tr}}}{T_{\text{tr}} - T_0}.$$

The equations of Sec. 22 then have the form

$$\left(\frac{1}{\tilde{\tau}_1'} + i\omega\right)X_1 - \frac{1}{\tilde{\tau}_{12}}X_2 = \sqrt{\frac{C_1'}{R}}.$$

$$-\,\frac{1}{\tilde{\tau}_{12}}X_1 + \left(\frac{1}{\tilde{\tau}_2'} + i\omega\right)X_2 = \sqrt{\frac{C_2'}{R}}.$$

These equations have the same form as Eq. (24–13), but have different constants, as shown below.

Section 23, 24	Section 22
$\dfrac{1}{\tilde{\tau}_1} = \dfrac{1}{\tau_1} + \dfrac{1}{\tau_{12}}\sqrt{\dfrac{C_2'}{C_1'}\dfrac{\vartheta_1}{\vartheta_2}}$	$\dfrac{1}{\tilde{\tau}_1'} = \dfrac{1}{\tau_1} + \dfrac{1}{\tau_{12}}\dfrac{C_2'}{C_1'} = \dfrac{1}{\tau_1} + \dfrac{1}{\tilde{\tau}_{12}}\sqrt{\dfrac{C_2'}{C_1'}}$
$\dfrac{1}{\tilde{\tau}_2} = \dfrac{1}{\tau_{12}}\sqrt{\dfrac{C_1'}{C_2'}\dfrac{\vartheta_2}{\vartheta_1}}$	$\dfrac{1}{\tilde{\tau}_2'} = \dfrac{1}{\tau_{12}} = \dfrac{1}{\tilde{\tau}_{12}}\sqrt{\dfrac{C_1'}{C_2'}}$
$\dfrac{1}{\tau_{12}}$	$\dfrac{1}{\tilde{\tau}_{12}} = \dfrac{1}{\tau_{12}}\sqrt{\dfrac{C_2'}{C_1'}}.$

In the case of only two degrees of freedom the secular determinant, Eq. (24–9), when multiplied out, gives a quadratic equation for the relaxation times $\tau'''(= 1/x)$

$$\left(\frac{1}{\tilde{\tau}_1} - x\right)\left(\frac{1}{\tilde{\tau}_2} - x\right) - \frac{1}{{\tau_{12}}^2} = 0 \tag{24–23}$$

or

$$\frac{1}{\tau'''} = \frac{1}{2}\left(\frac{1}{\tilde{\tau}_1} + \frac{1}{\tilde{\tau}_2}\right) \pm \frac{1}{2}\left[\left(\frac{1}{\tilde{\tau}_1} - \frac{1}{\tilde{\tau}_2}\right)^2 + \frac{4}{{\tau_{12}}^2}\right]^{1/2} \tag{24–23'}$$

Inserting the values for $\tilde{\tau}_1$ and $\tilde{\tau}_2$ (see Eqs. (24–4) and (24–4')) this gives

$$\frac{1}{\tau'''} = \frac{1}{2\tau_1} + \frac{1}{2\tau_{12}}\left(\sqrt{\frac{C_2'}{C_1'}}\frac{\vartheta_1}{\vartheta_2} + \sqrt{\frac{C_1'}{C_2'}}\frac{\vartheta_2}{\vartheta_1}\right) \pm \tag{24–23''}$$

$$\frac{1}{2}\left\{\left(\frac{1}{\tau_1} + \frac{1}{\tau_{12}}\left(\sqrt{\frac{C_2'}{C_1'}}\frac{\vartheta_1}{\vartheta_2} - \sqrt{\frac{C_1'}{C_2'}}\frac{\vartheta_2}{\vartheta_1}\right)\right]^2 + \frac{4}{{\tau_{12}}^2}\right\}^{1/2}$$

and, if $\tau_1 > \tau_{12}$

$$\frac{1}{{\tau_2}'''} = \frac{1}{\tau_{12}}\left(\sqrt{\frac{C_2'}{C_1'}}\frac{\vartheta_1}{\vartheta_2} + \sqrt{\frac{C_1'}{C_2'}}\frac{\vartheta_2}{\vartheta_1}\right) + \frac{1}{\tau_1}\frac{C_2'{\vartheta_1}^2}{C_2'{\vartheta_1}^2 + C_1'{\vartheta_2}^2} \tag{24–24}$$

$$\frac{1}{{\tau_1}'''} = \frac{1}{\tau_1}\frac{C_1'{\vartheta_2}^2}{C_1'{\vartheta_2}^2 + C_2'{\vartheta_1}^2} \quad \text{or} \quad {\tau_1}''' = \frac{C_1'{\vartheta_2}^2 + C_2'{\vartheta_1}^2}{C_1'{\vartheta_2}^2}\tau_1. \tag{24–24'}$$

This is to be compared with Eq. (22–19'), which corresponds to

$$\frac{1}{{\tau_1}'''} = \frac{C_1'}{C_1' + C_2'}\frac{1}{\tau_1}.$$

If $\tau_1 < \tau_{12}$

$$\frac{1}{{\tau_2}'''} = \frac{1}{\tau_1} + \frac{1}{\tau_{12}}\sqrt{\frac{C_2'}{C_1'}}\frac{\vartheta_1}{\vartheta_2} \tag{24–24''}$$

$$\frac{1}{{\tau_1}'''} = \frac{1}{\tau_{12}}\sqrt{\frac{C_1'}{C_2'}\frac{\vartheta_2}{\vartheta_1}} \quad \text{or} \quad {\tau_1}''' = \sqrt{\frac{C_2'}{C_1'}\frac{\vartheta_1}{\vartheta_2}}\,\tau_{12}. \tag{24–24'''}$$

In the foregoing, the *longer* relaxation time has been called ${\tau_1}'''$. If the internal adjustment goes fast, the speed of this adjustment does not enter the value of the longest relaxation term, Eq. (24–24'). If the internal adjustment is slow compared to the exchange with transitional energy, it controls the longest relaxation, Eq. (24–24''').

Here, however, is a significant difference from the case treated in Sec. 22, if $\tau_1 \gg \tau_{12}$. In Sec. 22, if the frequency is too high ($\omega\tau_1 \gg 1$) to permit direct energy exchange between the translational energy and vibration 1, which forms the entrance gate, no energy exchange can take place with vibration 2. In the present case this is not so. Even if the sound wave does not disturb the energy distribution of vibration 1 by direct exchange with translation, there still occurs the composite exchange among translation, vibration 2, and vibration 1, governed by τ_{12}. Accordingly, vibration 2 can still participate in the energy exchange since, for example, quanta can still be taken preferentially from vibration 1—even if its own energy distribution would correspond to equilibrium at T_0—and with energy added from the translational energy, assumed at temperature T_{tr} higher than T_0, transferred to vibration 2. Therefore, in the case in which τ_1 is considerably larger than τ_{12}, the hypothesis of Sec. 22 would give a single relaxation time near τ_1, while the present hypothesis would give two relaxation times.

The rest of the calculation is simpler if we do not use the general theory. Since we are only interested in

$$\sqrt{C_1'}\, X_1 + \sqrt{C_2'}\, X_2$$

we proceed as follows. By solving

$$\left(\frac{1}{\tilde{\tau}_1} - x\right) X_1 - \frac{1}{\tau_{12}} X_2 = \sqrt{\frac{C_1'}{R}}$$

$$-\frac{1}{\tau_{12}} X_1 + \left(\frac{1}{\tilde{\tau}_2} - x\right) X_2 = \sqrt{\frac{C_2'}{R}}$$

we find

$$\sqrt{R}\, X_1 = \left[\left(\frac{1}{\tilde{\tau}_2} - x\right)\sqrt{C_1'} + \frac{1}{\tau_{12}}\sqrt{C_2'}\right]\left(\frac{1}{\tau_1'''} - x\right)^{-1}\left(\frac{1}{\tau_2'''} - x\right)^{-1}$$

$$\sqrt{R}\, X_2 = \left[\left(\frac{1}{\tilde{\tau}_1} - x\right)\sqrt{C_2'} + \frac{1}{\tau_{12}}\sqrt{C_1'}\right]\left(\frac{1}{\tau_1'''} - x\right)^{-1}\left(\frac{1}{\tau_2'''} - x\right)^{-1}$$

or

$$\sqrt{R}\,(\sqrt{C_1'}\, X_1 + \sqrt{C_2'}\, X_2) = \left[\left(\frac{1}{\tilde{\tau}_2} C_1' + \frac{1}{\tilde{\tau}_1} C_2' + \frac{2}{\tau_{12}}\sqrt{C_1' C_2'} - x(C_1' + C_2')\right]\left(\frac{1}{\tau_1'''} - x\right)^{-1}\left(\frac{1}{\tau_2'''} - x\right)^{-1}. \qquad (24\text{–}25)$$

Setting this equal to

$$C_1'''\left(\frac{1}{\tau_1'''}-x\right)^{-1}+C_2'''\left(\frac{1}{\tau_2'''}-x\right)^{-1}$$

one gets, besides

$$C_1'''+C_2'''=C_1'+C_2' \tag{24–26}$$

as the term independent of x in the numerator of Eq. (24–25)

$$\frac{1}{\tilde{\tau}_2}C_1'+\frac{1}{\tilde{\tau}_1}C_2'+\frac{2}{\tau_{12}}\sqrt{C_1'C_2}=\frac{C_1'''}{\tau_2'''}+\frac{C_2'''}{\tau_1'''} \tag{24–27}$$

or, introducing the values of $\tilde{\tau}_1$, $\tilde{\tau}_2$

$$\frac{C_1'''}{\tau_2'''}+\frac{C_2'''}{\tau_1'''}=\frac{C_2'}{\tau_1}+\frac{1}{\tau_{12}}\left(C_2'\sqrt{\frac{C_1'}{C_2'}\frac{\vartheta_2}{\vartheta_1}}+C_1'\sqrt{\frac{C_2'}{C_1'}\frac{\vartheta_1}{\vartheta_2}}+2\sqrt{C_1'C_2'}\right)$$

$$=\frac{C_2'}{\tau_1}+\frac{\sqrt{C_1'C_2'}}{\tau_{12}}\left(\sqrt{\frac{\vartheta_1}{\vartheta_2}}+\sqrt{\frac{\vartheta_2}{\vartheta_1}}\right)^2. \tag{24–27'}$$

One can multiply Eq. (24–27) by the reciprocal of the term independent of x in the secular equation

$$\tau_1'''\tau_2'''=\left(\frac{1}{\tilde{\tau}_1\tilde{\tau}_2}-\frac{1}{\tau_{12}^2}\right)^{-1}=\left(\frac{1}{\tau_1\tilde{\tau}_2}+\frac{1}{\tau_{12}^2}-\frac{1}{\tau_{12}^2}\right)^{-1}=\tau_1\tilde{\tau}_2$$

$$=\tau_1\tau_{12}\sqrt{\frac{C_2'}{C_1'}\frac{\vartheta_1}{\vartheta_2}}. \tag{24–28}$$

This leads to

$$C_1'''\tau_1'''+C_2'''\tau_2'''=C_2'\left(1+\frac{\vartheta_1}{\vartheta_2}\right)^2\tau_1+C_2'\sqrt{\frac{C_2'}{C_1'}\frac{\vartheta_1}{\vartheta_2}}\,\tau_{12}$$

$$=C_2'\left\{\left(1+\frac{\vartheta_1}{\vartheta_2}\right)^2\tau_1+\tilde{\tau}_2\right\}. \tag{24–29}$$

The low frequency absorption is therefore given by

$$\left(\frac{\alpha'}{\omega^2}\right)_0=\frac{1}{2\mathfrak{B}_0}\frac{\Delta C'}{C_vC_p}\tau_1\left[\frac{C_2'}{C'}\left(1+\frac{\vartheta_1}{\vartheta_2}\right)^2+\frac{C_2'}{C'}\frac{\tilde{\tau}_2}{\tau_1}\right]. \tag{24–30}$$

Accordingly, an estimate of τ_1, by using

$$\left(\frac{\alpha'}{\omega^2}\right)_0 \left[\frac{1}{2\mathfrak{B}_0}\frac{\Delta C'}{C_v C_p}\right]^{-1}$$

overestimates this time by the factor given inside the square brackets.

One can now write (C may be C_v or C_p)

$$C_{\text{eff}} = \tilde{C} + \frac{C_1'''}{1 + i\omega\tau_1'''} + \frac{C_2'''}{1 + i\omega\tau_2'''}. \tag{24–31}$$

Bringing everything on the same denominator, this is

$$\begin{aligned} C_{\text{eff}} &= \{\tilde{C}\,[1 + i\omega(\tau_1''' + \tau_2''') - \omega^2\tau_1'''\tau_2'''] + \\ &\qquad C_1'''(1 + i\omega\tau_2''') + C_2'''(1 + i\omega\tau_1''')\}\,(1 + i\omega\tau_1''')^{-1}\,(1 + i\omega\tau_2''')^{-1} \\ &= \{C + i\omega\,[\tilde{C}(\tau_1''' + \tau_2''') + C_1'''\tau_2''' + C_2'''\tau_1'''] - \qquad (24\text{–}31') \\ &\qquad \tilde{C}\omega^2\tau_1'''\tau_2'''\}\,(1 + i\omega\tau_1''')^{-1}\,(1 + i\omega\tau_2''')^{-1}. \end{aligned}$$

One now writes

$$C_1'''\tau_2''' + C_2'''\tau_1''' = (C_1''' + C_2''')\,(\tau_1''' + \tau_2''') - C_1'''\tau_1''' - C_2'''\tau_2'''$$

so that the [ ] in Eq. (24–31′) is

$$C(\tau_1''' + \tau_2''') - (C_1'''\tau_1''' + C_2'''\tau_2'''). \tag{24–32}$$

The last term in Eq. (24–32) is given in Eq. (24–29). Furthermore

$$\frac{1}{\tau_1'''} + \frac{1}{\tau_2'''} = \frac{\tau_1''' + \tau_2'''}{\tau_1'''\tau_2'''} = \frac{1}{\tau_1} + \frac{1}{\tau_{12}}\left(\sqrt{\frac{C_2'}{C_1'}\frac{\vartheta_1}{\vartheta_2}} + \sqrt{\frac{C_1'}{C_2'}\frac{\vartheta_2}{\vartheta_1}}\right)$$

from Eq. (24–23″); $\tau_1'''\tau_2'''$ is given by Eq. (24–28). Therefore

$$\frac{\tau_1''' + \tau_2'''}{\tau_1} = 1 + \frac{C_2'}{C_1'}\left(\frac{\vartheta_1}{\vartheta_2}\right)^2 + \frac{\tau_{12}}{\tau_1}\sqrt{\frac{C_2'}{C_1'}\frac{\vartheta_1}{\vartheta_2}} = 1 + \frac{C_2'}{C_1'}\left(\frac{\vartheta_1}{\vartheta_2}\right)^2 + \frac{\tilde{\tau}_2}{\tau_1}.$$

One then gets

$$\begin{aligned} C_{\text{eff}} = C\Bigg\{1 + i\omega\tau_1\Bigg[1 + \frac{C_2'}{C_1'}\left(\frac{\vartheta_1}{\vartheta_2}\right)^2 - \frac{C_2'}{C}\left(1 + \frac{\vartheta_1}{\vartheta_2}\right)^2 + \\ \frac{\tilde{\tau}_2}{\tau_1}\left(1 - \frac{C_2'}{C}\right)\Bigg] - \left(1 - \frac{C'}{C}\right)\frac{\tilde{\tau}_2}{\tau_1}\,\omega^2\tau_1^2\Bigg\}\,(1 + i\omega\tau_1''')^{-1}\,(1 + i\omega\tau_2''')^{-1}. \end{aligned} \tag{24–33}$$

If one now forms

$$\left(\frac{\mathfrak{V}_0}{\mathfrak{V}} - \frac{i\alpha\mathfrak{V}_0}{\omega}\right)^2 = \frac{C_p}{C_v}\left(\frac{C_v}{C_p}\right)_{\text{eff}}$$

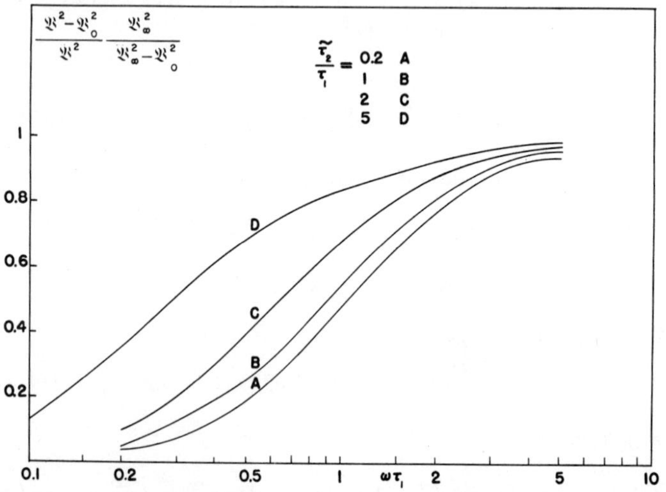

FIG. 24–1. Dispersion curves for two vibrational degrees of freedom. $[(\mathfrak{V}^2 - \mathfrak{V}_0{}^2)/(\mathfrak{V}_\infty{}^2 - \mathfrak{V}_0{}^2)]\ (\mathfrak{V}_\infty{}^2/\mathfrak{V}^2)$ is plotted against $\omega\tau_1$. Curve A is for $\tilde{\tau}_2 = 0.2\tau_1$; curve B, for $\tilde{\tau}_2 = \tau_1$; curve C, for $\tilde{\tau}_2 = 2\tau_1$; and curve D, for $\tilde{\tau}_2 = 5\tau_1$.

both expressions ($)^{-1}$ cancel out, and one finds the ratio of two expressions G of the same form, except that in one, G_v, C is C_v; and in the other G_p, C is C_p, so that

$$1 - \left(\frac{\mathfrak{V}_0}{\mathfrak{V}} - \frac{i\alpha\mathfrak{V}_0}{\omega}\right)^2 = 1 - \frac{G_v}{G_p} = \frac{G_p - G_v}{G_p}$$

$$G_p = 1 + i\omega\tau_1\left[1 + \frac{C_2'}{C_1'}\left(\frac{\vartheta_1}{\vartheta_2}\right)^2 - \frac{C_2'}{C_p}\left(1 + \frac{\vartheta_1}{\vartheta_2}\right)^2 + \frac{\tilde{\tau}_2}{\tau_1}\left(1 - \frac{C_2'}{C_p}\right)\right] - \left(1 - \frac{C'}{C_p}\right)\frac{\tilde{\tau}_2}{\tau_1}\,\omega^2\tau_1{}^2 \qquad (24\text{–}34)$$

$$G_p - G_v = \frac{\Delta}{C_v}\left\{i\omega\tau_1\,\frac{C_2'}{C_p}\left[\left(1 + \frac{\vartheta_1}{\vartheta_2}\right)^2 + \frac{\tilde{\tau}_2}{\tau_1}\right] - \frac{C'}{C_p}\frac{\tilde{\tau}_2}{\tau_1}\,\omega^2\tau_1{}^2\right\}$$

$$= \frac{\Delta C'}{C_vC_p}\,\omega\tau_1\left\{i\,\frac{C_2'}{C'}\left[\left(1 + \frac{\vartheta_1}{\vartheta_2}\right)^2 + \frac{\tilde{\tau}_2}{\tau_1}\right] - \frac{\tilde{\tau}_2}{\tau_1}\,\omega\tau_1\right\}. \qquad (24\text{–}34')$$

As an example, the case of a nonlinear triatomic molecule $C_v - C' = 3\,R$ is considered in which two vibrations have the following values: $\vartheta_1 = 415.9$, $\vartheta_2 = 716.9$; and $C_1'/R = 0.8537$, $C_2'/R = 0.6344$

$$\sqrt{\frac{C_2'}{C_1'}\frac{\vartheta_1}{\vartheta_2}} = \frac{1}{2}.$$

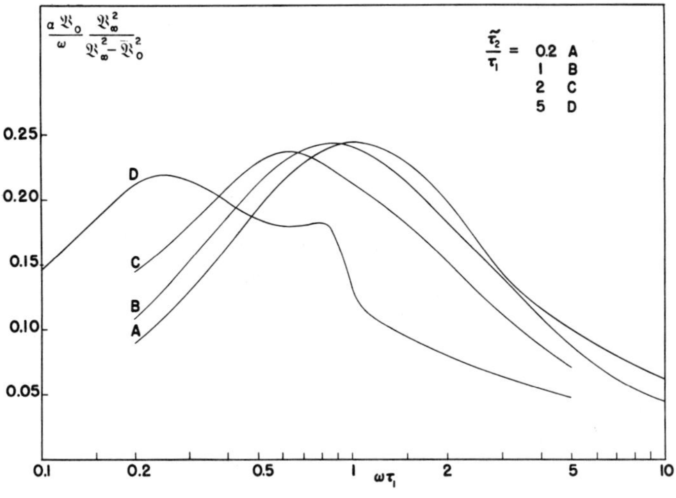

FIG. 24–2. Absorption curves for two vibrational degrees of freedom. $\alpha'\mathfrak{V}_0/\omega\,[(\mathfrak{V}_\infty{}^2)/(\mathfrak{V}_\infty{}^2 - \mathfrak{V}_0{}^2)]$ is plotted against $\omega\tau_1$. Curve A is for $\tilde{\tau}_2 = 0.2\,\tau_1$; curve B, for $\tilde{\tau}_2 = \tau_1$; curve C, for $\tilde{\tau}_2 = 2\tau_1$; and curve D, for $\tilde{\tau}_2 = 5\tau_1$.

Then one has

$$1 - \left(\frac{\mathfrak{V}_0}{\mathfrak{V}} - \frac{i\alpha\mathfrak{V}_0}{\omega}\right)^2 = 0.0603\,\omega\tau_1\left[i\left(1.065 + 0.4265\,\frac{\tilde{\tau}_2}{\tau_1}\right) - \frac{\tilde{\tau}_2}{\tau_1}\,\omega\tau_1\right]\left[1 - 0.729\frac{\tilde{\tau}_2}{\tau_1}\,\omega^2\tau_1{}^2 + i\omega\tau_1\left(0.961 + 0.857\,\frac{\tilde{\tau}_2}{\tau_1}\right)\right]^{-1}.$$

A dispersion curve as function of $\omega\tau_1$ is shown in Fig. 24–1 for various values of $\tilde{\tau}_2/\tau_1$. Similarly, Fig. 24–2 shows $(\alpha'\mathfrak{V}_0)/\omega\,[\mathfrak{V}_\infty^2/(\mathfrak{V}_\infty^2 - \mathfrak{V}_0{}^2)]$ for the same values of the constants. The values for $\tilde{\tau}_2/\tau_1$ are 0.2, 1, 2, and 5.

TABLE 24–1

EFFECTIVE RELAXATION TIMES AND SPECIFIC HEATS

$\tilde{\tau}_2/\tau_1$	τ_1'''/τ_1	τ_2'''/τ_1	C_1'''/C'	C_2'''/C'
0.1	0.971	0.075	0.983	0.017
0.2	0.984	0.149	0.970	0.030
0.5	1.038	0.351	0.942	0.058
1	1.222	0.596	0.882	0.118
2	0.762	1.913	0.247	0.753
5	0.824	4.422	0.206	0.794
10	0.835	8.693	0.132	0.868

The following conclusions can be drawn from the table and the figures. For $\tilde{\tau}_2 < \tau_1$, the system acts nearly as if one had a single degree of freedom, with C_1''' almost equal to C', as long as $\omega\tau_1 < 1$. This is understandable, since under these conditions the energy is rapidly flowing from the first degree of freedom into the second. If $\omega\tau_1 > 1$, however, the first degree of freedom cannot be adjusted any more; and the second degree of freedom exchanges its energy with the translational energy, using energy from the first vibrational degree, the latter being at temperature T_0. One then gets a second, low step in the dispersion curve. On the other hand, if $\tilde{\tau}_2 > \tau_1$, the second degree of vibrational freedom loses its effective energy exchange before the first one; C_2''' is appreciable.

The dispersion curve for $\tilde{\tau}_2 = \tau_1$ does not differ very much from that for a single relaxation time; the curve for $\tilde{\tau}_2 = 2\tau_1$ is somewhat less steep and that for $5\tau_1$ appreciably less steep, than corresponds to single relaxation theory. Of the absorption curves, only the one for $\tilde{\tau}_2 = 5\tau_1$ shows the beginning of a second maximum.

25. Relation of Dispersion and Absorption If More Than One Relaxation Time Is Present. General Shape of the Curves

One may now again profitably take up the connection between the dispersion curve and absorption at low frequencies. We will start with the case of a single relaxation time.

Several formulas given previously—Eqs. (14–6) and (14–6″)—contained the relaxation time explicitly. Now, instead, we will eliminate the relaxation time. Call the relative change in velocity δ

$$\delta = \frac{\mathfrak{V} - \mathfrak{V}_0}{\mathfrak{V}} \sim \frac{1}{2}\left(\frac{\mathfrak{V}_0{}^2}{\mathfrak{V}^2} - 1\right). \tag{25–1}$$

Using Eqs. (13–2) and (14–4) and eliminating τ', one finds as the frequency at which $\mathfrak{V}$ has the relative increase δ

$$f = \pi \sqrt{\frac{2\Delta C'}{C_v(C_p - C')}} \sqrt{\delta} \left(\frac{\alpha'\mathfrak{V}}{f^2}\right)_0^{-1}. \tag{25–2}$$

The dispersion may not start later than shown by Eq. (25–2); i.e., the dispersion curve may not be steeper than given by the theory in Sec. 13. However, dispersion may appear at a lower frequency than calculated from Eq. (25–2); i.e., the dispersion curve may be flatter, if there are several relaxation times.

For the case of Sec. 21 ("parallel reactions") this can be seen from Eqs. (21–17) and (21–18′), since at low frequencies

$$\delta = \frac{\omega^2}{2} \frac{\Delta}{C_p(C_v - \Sigma C_s')} \sum C_s''\tau_s''^2$$

$$\left(\frac{\alpha'\mathfrak{V}}{f^2}\right)_0 = 2\pi^2 \frac{\Delta}{C_p(C_v - \Sigma C_s')} \sum C_s''\tau_s''. \tag{25–3}$$

Using, analogous to Sec. 21, the definitions

$$(\Sigma C_s'')\overline{\tau''} = \Sigma C_s''\tau_s''$$

$$(\Sigma C_s'')\overline{\tau''^2} = \Sigma C_s''\tau_s''^2$$

and

$$C' = \Sigma C_s'' = \Sigma C_s' \tag{25–4}$$

one can write, in analogy to Eqs. (13–2) and (14–4)

$$\delta = \frac{1}{2} \frac{\Delta C'}{C_p(C_v - C')} \omega^2 \overline{\tau''^2} \tag{25–5}$$

$$\left(\frac{\alpha'\mathfrak{V}}{f^2}\right)_0 = 2\pi^2 \frac{\Delta C'}{C_p(C_v - C')} \overline{\tau''}. \tag{25–6}$$

However, one always has[1] $\overline{\tau''^2} \geqslant (\overline{\tau''})^2$.

One finds then for the frequency which gives a (small) relative change δ of the velocity

$$f = \pi \sqrt{\frac{2\Delta C'}{C_p(C_v - C')}} \sqrt{\delta} \frac{\overline{\tau''}}{\sqrt{\overline{\tau''^2}}} \left(\frac{\alpha'\mathfrak{B}}{f^2}\right)_0^{-1}. \tag{25–7}$$

There are experiments which prove this greater extension of the dispersion region for the rotational degrees of freedom (Secs. **48** and **49**).

One should also expect that the maximum of $\alpha'\lambda$ is less than that given by Eq. (16–6), since the absorption curve will be somewhat broader than for a single relaxation time.

Since the dispersion and absorption curves in relaxation phenomena are so broad (see Secs. **12** and **14**), they do not directly show a resolution into distinct parts if more than one relaxation time is present, except where the ratio of the τ is considerable (see Sec. **24**).

Lamb and Huddart[2] have suggested a method to test whether a set of absorption measurements which cover the dispersion region, considered as functions of the frequency, may be represented by a single relaxation time. Their method is extended here to dispersion measurements also.

Consider a formula like Eq. (21–17)

$$\frac{\mathfrak{B}^2 - \mathfrak{B}_0^2}{\mathfrak{B}_0^2} = \frac{\Delta}{C_p(C_v - C')} \left[C_1'' \frac{\omega^2\tau_1''^2}{1 + \omega^2\tau_1''^2} + \sum_{s=2} C_s'' \frac{\omega^2\tau_s''^2}{1 + \omega^2\tau_s''^2} \right]. \tag{25–8}$$

Add to it

$$\frac{\mathfrak{B}^2 - \mathfrak{B}_0^2}{\mathfrak{B}_0^2} \frac{1}{\omega^2\tau_1''^2} = \frac{\Delta}{C_p(C_v - C')} \left[C_1'' \frac{1}{1 + \omega^2\tau_1''^2} + \sum_{s=2} C_s'' \frac{\tau_s''^2}{\tau_1''^2} \frac{1}{1 + \omega^2\tau_2''^2} \right]. \tag{25–8'}$$

---

[1] If there is any set of numbers x_1, x_s, x_n, and coefficients C_s, one can define $\overline{x^n} = \Sigma C_s x_s^n / \Sigma C_s$. The higher the n, the more the large x values are emphasized. For example, take all $C = 1$, and three x values, $x_1 = 1$, $x_2 = 1$, $x_3 = 10$. Then

$$\bar{x} = \frac{1 + 1 + 10}{3} = 4 \qquad \overline{x^3} = \frac{1 + 1 + 1000}{3} = 334$$

while $(\bar{x})^3$ is only 64.

[2] J. Lamb and D. H. A. Huddart, *Trans. Faraday Soc.* **46**, 540 (1950).

The result is

$$\frac{\mathfrak{B}^2 - \mathfrak{B}_0^2}{\mathfrak{B}_0^2} + \frac{\mathfrak{B}^2 - \mathfrak{B}_0^2}{\mathfrak{B}_0^2} \frac{1}{\omega^2 \tau_1''^2}$$

$$= \frac{\Delta}{C_p(C_v - C')} \left[\sum_{s=1} C_s' + \sum_{s=2} C_s'' \frac{\tau_s''^2 - \tau_1''^2}{\tau_1''^2} \frac{1}{1 + \omega^2 \tau_s''^2} \right]$$

$$= \frac{\Delta C'}{C_p(C_v - C')} \left[1 + \sum_{s=2} \frac{C_s''}{C'} \frac{\tau_s''^2 - \tau_1''^2}{\tau_1''^2} \frac{1}{1 + \omega^2 \tau_s''^2} \right]. \tag{25–9}$$

Of course, τ_1'' is not known. But it follows from Eq. (25–9) that, if $(\mathfrak{B}^2 - \mathfrak{B}_0^2)/\mathfrak{B}_0^2\omega^2$ is plotted as a function of $(\mathfrak{B}^2 - \mathfrak{B}_0^2)/\mathfrak{B}_0$, one gets a straight line only if there is a single relaxation time, i.e., if the right side does not contain ω.

Similarly, one has from Eq. (21–18)

$$\frac{\alpha'\mathfrak{B}}{\omega}\left(\frac{\mathfrak{B}}{\mathfrak{B}_0}\right)^2 \omega\tau_1'' + \frac{\alpha'\mathfrak{B}}{\omega}\left(\frac{\mathfrak{B}}{\mathfrak{B}_0}\right)^2 \frac{1}{\omega\tau_1''}$$

$$= \frac{\Delta C'}{C_p(C_v - C')} \left[1 + \sum_{s=2} \frac{C_s''}{C'} \frac{\tau_s''^2 - \tau_1''^2}{\tau_1''\tau_2''} \frac{1}{1 + \omega^2 \tau_s''^2} \right] \tag{25–10}$$

and similar calculations may be made for $\alpha'\mathfrak{B}/\omega$. Of course, one may also use $\alpha'(\mathfrak{B}/\mathfrak{B}_0)$ against $\alpha'(\mathfrak{B}/\mathfrak{B}_0)\ 1/\omega^2\tau'^2$.

Kneser[3] has recommended a presentation which is also used for paramagnetic[4] and dielectric[5] relaxation.

If one writes Eq. (12–2) neglecting $(\alpha'\mathfrak{B}_0/\omega)^2$ and using the abbreviation

$$a = \frac{\Delta C'}{C_v(C_p - C')} = \frac{\mathfrak{B}_\infty^2 - \mathfrak{B}_0^2}{\mathfrak{B}_\infty^2}$$

one has

$$\left(\frac{\mathfrak{B}_0}{\mathfrak{B}}\right)^2 = 1 - a\frac{(\omega\tau')^2}{1 + (\omega\tau')^2} = 1 - a + \frac{a}{1 + (\omega\tau')^2}.$$

---

[3] H. O. Kneser, *Ann. Physik* [5] **43**, 465 (1943); *Ergeb. exakt. Naturw.* **22**, 121 (1949).

[4] H. B. G. Casimir, D. Bijl, and F. K. du Pré, *Physica* **8**, 449 (1941).

[5] K. S. Cole and R. H. Cole, *J. Chem. Phys.* **9**, 341 (1941).

One squares Eq. (12–3)

$$\left(\frac{2\alpha'\lambda}{2\pi}\frac{\mathfrak{B}_0{}^2}{\mathfrak{B}^2}\right)^2 = a^2\frac{(\omega\tau')^2}{[1+(\omega\tau')^2]^2}$$

$$= a^2\left\{\frac{1}{1+(\omega\tau')^2} - \frac{1}{[1+(\omega\tau')^2]^2}\right\} = -\,a^2\left[\frac{1}{1+(\omega\tau')^2} - \frac{1}{2}\right]^2 + \frac{a^2}{4}$$

$$= -\left[\frac{a}{1+(\omega\tau')^2} - \frac{a}{2}\right]^2 + \frac{a^2}{4}$$

or

$$\left(\frac{2\alpha'\lambda}{2\pi}\frac{\mathfrak{B}_0{}^2}{\mathfrak{B}^2}\right)^2 + \left[\frac{\mathfrak{B}_0{}^2}{\mathfrak{B}^2} - 1 + a - \frac{a}{2}\right]^2 = \frac{a^2}{4}$$

or

$$\left(\frac{2\alpha'\lambda}{2\pi}\frac{\mathfrak{B}_0{}^2}{\mathfrak{B}^2}\right)^2 + \left[\frac{\mathfrak{B}_0{}^2}{\mathfrak{B}^2} - \frac{\mathfrak{B}_0{}^2+\mathfrak{B}_\infty{}^2}{2\mathfrak{B}_\infty{}^2}\right]^2 = \left(\frac{\mathfrak{B}_\infty{}^2-\mathfrak{B}_0{}^2}{2\mathfrak{B}_\infty{}^2}\right)^2. \qquad (25\text{–}11)$$

If one therefore plots $(2\alpha'\lambda/2\pi)\,\mathfrak{B}_0{}^2/\mathfrak{B}^2$ against $\mathfrak{B}_0{}^2/\mathfrak{B}^2$, one gets a half circle, with its center at $\mathfrak{B}_0{}^2/\mathfrak{B}^2 = (\mathfrak{B}_0{}^2+\mathfrak{B}_\infty{}^2)/2\mathfrak{B}_\infty{}^2$, and a radius equal to $(\mathfrak{B}_\infty{}^2-\mathfrak{B}_0{}^2)/2\mathfrak{B}_\infty{}^2$. If there are several relaxation times, the half circle is distorted.

By multiplying Eq. (25–11) with $(\mathfrak{B}/\mathfrak{B}_0)^4\,(\mathfrak{B}_\infty/\mathfrak{B}_0)^2$ one gets

$$\left(\frac{2\alpha'\lambda}{2\pi}\frac{\mathfrak{B}_\infty}{\mathfrak{B}_0}\right)^2 + \left[\frac{\mathfrak{B}^2}{\mathfrak{B}_0{}^2} - \frac{1}{2}\frac{\mathfrak{B}_0{}^2+\mathfrak{B}_\infty{}^2}{\mathfrak{B}_0{}^2}\right]^2 = \left(\frac{\mathfrak{B}_\infty{}^2-\mathfrak{B}_0{}^2}{2\mathfrak{B}_0{}^2}\right)^2 \qquad (25\text{–}12)$$

so that, by plotting $(2\alpha'\lambda/2\pi)\,\mathfrak{B}_\infty/\mathfrak{B}_0$ against $\mathfrak{B}/\mathfrak{B}_0$ one gets a half circle of radius $(\mathfrak{B}_\infty{}^2-\mathfrak{B}_0{}^2)/2\mathfrak{B}_0{}^2$ with center at $(\mathfrak{B}_0{}^2+\mathfrak{B}_\infty{}^2)/2\mathfrak{B}_0{}^2$. This expression differs from that of Kneser's first paper, but agrees with that in his second. In the preceding, it has been shown that in the presence of several relaxation processes one can write

$$\left(\frac{\mathfrak{B}_0}{\mathfrak{B}}\right)^2 = 1 - A\sum g_s\frac{\omega^2\tau_s{}^2}{1+\omega^2\tau_s{}^2} = \left(\frac{\mathfrak{B}_0}{\mathfrak{B}_\infty}\right)^2 + A\sum\frac{g_s}{1+\omega^2\tau_s{}^2} \qquad (25\text{–}13)$$

$$\left(\frac{\alpha'\mathfrak{B}_0{}^2}{\mathfrak{B}}\right)_\infty - \frac{\alpha'\mathfrak{B}_0{}^2}{\mathfrak{B}} = \frac{A}{2}\sum\frac{g_s}{\tau_s}\frac{1}{1+\omega^2\tau_s{}^2} \qquad (25\text{–}13')$$

where the g_s are normalized

$$\sum g_s = 1. \qquad (25\text{–}13'')$$

In liquids, there may even be a continuous distribution (Sec. 105)

$$\left(\frac{\mathfrak{B}_0}{\mathfrak{B}}\right)^2 - \left(\frac{\mathfrak{B}_0}{\mathfrak{B}_\infty}\right)^2 = A \int \frac{g(\tau)}{1 + \omega^2\tau^2} d\tau \tag{25–14}$$

$$\left(\frac{\alpha'\mathfrak{B}_0{}^2}{\mathfrak{B}}\right)_\infty - \frac{\alpha'\mathfrak{B}_0{}^2}{\mathfrak{B}} = \frac{A}{2} \int \frac{g(\tau)}{1 + \omega^2\tau^2} \frac{d\tau}{\tau} \tag{25–14'}$$

with

$$\int g(\tau) d\tau = 1. \tag{25–14''}$$

The problem arises as to whether one can generally calculate the dispersion if the absorption is known as a function of the frequency, and vice versa. Ginzberg[6] has proved the validity of the following expressions:

$$\left(\frac{\mathfrak{B}_0}{\mathfrak{B}}\right)^2 - \left(\frac{\mathfrak{B}_0}{\mathfrak{B}_\infty}\right)^2 = \frac{2\,\mathfrak{B}_0}{\pi} \int_0^\infty \left[\frac{\alpha'}{\omega'} - \left(\frac{\alpha'}{\omega'}\right)_\infty\right] \frac{\omega' d\omega'}{(\omega')^2 - \omega^2}. \tag{25–15}$$

$$\frac{\alpha'}{\omega} - \left(\frac{\alpha'}{\omega}\right)_\infty = \frac{2\,\omega}{\pi \mathfrak{B}_0} \int_0^\infty \left[\left(\frac{\mathfrak{B}_0}{\mathfrak{B}}\right)^2 - \left(\frac{\mathfrak{B}_0}{\mathfrak{B}_\infty}\right)^2\right] \frac{d\omega'}{(\omega')^2 - \omega^2}. \tag{25–15'}$$

There are some uncertainties involved in the question of whether in the integration to infinity and in the quantities like $\mathfrak{B}_\infty$ one has to take into account the region in which the molecular structure of the medium starts to play a role. The proof of the above equation uses integration in the complex plane, and is based on the fact that if a step function is applied to the system at a time $t = t_0$, no effects can arise before $t = t_0$. In optics, there are analogous relations known as the Kronig-Kramers relations.[7]

Since

$$\int_0^\infty e^{-t/\tau} \cos \omega t dt = \frac{1}{1 + \omega^2\tau^2} \tag{25–16}$$

one can apply the theory of Fourier transforms to Eq. (25–14), which results in

$$\frac{1}{2\,\pi} \int_0^\infty \left[\left(\frac{\mathfrak{B}_0}{\mathfrak{B}}\right)^2 - \left(\frac{\mathfrak{B}_0}{\mathfrak{B}}\right)^2\right] \cos \omega t \, d\omega = \int_0^\infty g(\tau)\, e^{-t/\tau}\, d\tau. \tag{25–17}$$

---

[6] V. L. Ginzberg, *Soviet Phys. Acoustics*, **1**, 32 (1957).

[7] R. Kronig, *J. Opt. Soc. Am.* **12**, 547 (1926); H. A. Kramers, *Physik. Z.* **30**, 522 (1929).

The right side is closely related to the "Laplace transform" of g. For further details, see Macdonald and Brachman.[8]

26. Mixtures

It was observed early that some substances, admixed even in small quantities, have a very marked effect on the dispersion and absorption of ultrasonic waves in gases. General considerations of such an effect were made by Eucken and Becker.[1] In recent years, investigations of sound absorption in liquid mixtures led to the development of formal theories of more and more refinement by Pinkerton,[2] Bauer,[3] and Sette.[4] The word "formal" in the preceding sentence means that these theories do not tell why a particular molecule is a very efficient agent for the exchange of energy—a question which shall be discussed later—but discuss instead the dependence on concentration. For gases the natural assumption is made that only pairs of molecules interact. (There might be one exception to that; see Secs. 40 and 67.) This same assumption—that transfer of energy occurs only between pairs of molecules—is also made for liquid solutions, where it is the simplest assumption, but where deviations are not out of the question. One qualitative statement can be made if one has a large amount of substance A with a small admixture of B. If the exchange of energy between molecules A is very inefficient, while that between molecules A and B is very efficient, then a very small amount of B may appreciably decrease the effective relaxation time of the mixture, decreasing the low frequency absorption. In the opposite case, however, in which the efficiency of energy exchange between molecules A is high and that between A and B low, a very small amount of B will not appreciably affect the effective relaxation time of the mixture, which will be near that of pure A.

An analogy will make this clear. Consider a vessel filled with water, as a picture of the internal energy; the picture of energy exchange will be given by the flow of water out of this vessel. In the first case, where the energy exchange between molecules of A is very inefficient, the picture of

---

[8] An extensive treatment of related problems is given by J. R. Macdonald and M. K. Brachman, *Revs. Modern Phys.* **28**, 393 (1956).

[1] A. Eucken and R. Becker, *Z. physik. Chem.* **B27**, 219 (1934).

[2] J. M. M. Pinkerton, *Proc. Phys. Soc.* (*London*) **A62**, 129 (1949).

[3] E. Bauer, *Proc. Phys. Soc.* (*London*) **A62**, 141 (1949).

[4] D. Sette, *Nuovo cimento* [9] **7**, Suppl. **2**, 318 (1950).

energy exchange in pure A is given by many very small pinholes. Adding very little B means then adding a few, but much larger, holes, which may make a very considerable difference in the resultant flow. In the second case, the exchange between A, being already efficient, is represented by many holes of appreciable size. Adding B means replacing some A molecules by inefficient B's, i.e., at worst, plugging up a fraction of the holes, which cannot affect the flow in a higher proportion than the (supposedly small) ratio B/A, or a few times that ratio, if a molecule B is much larger than a molecule A, and replaces several of them in space.

Consider first a mixture of two gases A and B. Call the mole fraction of A, $1 - x$; that of B, x. The total pressure is p_0. Each of these gases shall be treated as a gas with a single relaxation time, when by itself.

Call τ_A the relaxation time of gas A at the pressure p_0 (i.e., at a pressure equal to the total pressure of the mixture); and τ_B the relaxation time of a molecule B in pure B at pressure p_0. Furthermore, call τ_{AB} the relaxation time of one molecule A in otherwise pure B of pressure p_0, and τ_{BA} the relaxation time of one molecule B in pure A.

The number of deactivations per second of molecule A in the mixture is

$$\frac{1-x}{\tau_A} + \frac{x}{\tau_{AB}} \tag{26–1}$$

since it makes only $(1 - x)$ times as many collisions with other molecules A than it would have made if only A had been present at pressure p_0, and x times as many with B molecules than if these alone had been present at pressure p_0. Similarly, the number of active collisions per second of a molecule B are

$$\frac{x}{\tau_B} + \frac{1-x}{\tau_{BA}}. \tag{26–1'}$$

The mixture is now treated exactly as one gas with several degrees of internal freedom excited in parallel would be; see Sec. 21. For this purpose one has

$$\frac{1}{\tau_1} = \frac{1-x}{\tau_A} + \frac{x}{\tau_{AB}} \tag{26–2}$$

$$\frac{1}{\tau_2} = \frac{x}{\tau_B} + \frac{1-x}{\tau_{BA}} \tag{26–2'}$$

$$C_v = (1 - x)\,(C_v)_A + x(C_v)_B \tag{26–2''}$$

$$C_1' = (1 - x)C_A' \qquad C_2' = xC_B'. \tag{26–2'''}$$

One finds the low-frequency absorption [see Eq. (21–18′)]

$$\frac{\alpha'}{\omega^2} = \frac{1}{2\mathfrak{V}_0} \frac{R}{R + (1 - x)\,(C_v)_A + x(C_v)_B} \frac{1}{(1 - x)\,(C_v)_A + x\,(C_v)_B}$$

$$\left\{(1 - x)C_A'\left[\frac{1 - x}{\tau_A} + \frac{x}{\tau_{AB}}\right]^{-1} + xC_B'\left[\frac{x}{\tau_B} + \frac{1 - x}{\tau_{BA}}\right]^{-1}\right\}. \qquad (26\text{–}3)$$

If $x \ll 1$, $\tau_{AB} \ll \tau_A$, so that $x\tau_A > (1 - x)\tau_{AB}$, and $\tau_B > \tau_{BA}$, one gets

$$\frac{\alpha'}{\omega^2} = \frac{1}{2\mathfrak{V}_0} \frac{RC_A'}{(C_p)_A\,(C_v)_A} \frac{1 - x}{x} \tau_{AB}\,.$$

This can be generalized to liquids by replacing R by the more general Δ, if one assumes the rule of mixtures for C_v; see Sec. 99.

27. The Effect of Chemical Reactions

The effect of a finite rate of a chemical reaction on sound propagation was the first relaxation phenomenon discussed in this connection. In a paper published in 1920, Einstein[1] suggested the use of sound dispersion measurements to estimate the rate of the reaction $N_2O_4 \rightleftarrows 2NO_2$. This treatment has been amplified by Kneser and Gauler[2] and generalized to liquids by Hall,[3] Bauer,[4] Lamb and Pinkerton,[5] Liebermann,[6] Karpovich,[7] and Barthel.[8] Particularly general and thorough discussions are due to Damköhler,[9] Freedman,[10] and Manes.[11] One assumes a chemical equilibrium, which is shifted in the sound wave.

---

[1] A. Einstein, *Sitzber. der Akad. Wiss. Berlin, Math. naturw. Kl.* p. 380 (1920).

[2] H. O. Kneser and O. Gauler, *Physik. Z.* **37**, 677 (1936).

[3] L. Hall, *Phys. Rev.* **73**, 775 (1948).

[4] E. Bauer, *Proc. Phys. Soc. (London)* **A62**, 129 (1949).

[5] J. Lamb and J. M. M. Pinkerton, *Proc. Roy. Soc.* **A199**, 114 (1949).

[6] L. Liebermann, *Phys. Rev.* **76**, 1520 (1949).

[7] J. Karpovich, *J. Chem. Phys.* **22**, 1767 (1954).

[8] R. Barthel, *J. Acoust. Soc. Am.* **24**, 313 (1952).

[9] G. Damköhler, *Z. Elektrochem.* **48**, 62 (1942).

[10] E. Freedman, *J. Chem. Phys.* **21**, 1784 (1953).

[11] M. Manes, *J. Chem. Phys.* **21**, 1791 (1953).

The effect on sound propagation or, more precisely, on $dp/d\rho$ is twofold:

1. The temperature rise in the compression shifts the equilibrium. According to the Braun—Le Chatelier principle, the shift occurs in such a direction that is *absorbs* heat. Accordingly, the shift provides an additional internal specific heat C'. However, contrary to the case of rotational or vibrational specific heats, there are only two energy levels, that of the reactants and that of the products. Therefore, the calculations leading to Eq. (19–7) apply here.

2. We have assumed that the internal energy does not change if the density is changed at constant temperature (Sec. 11). Here, however, an isothermal density change may shift the equilibrium; this happens if the reaction involves a volume change. Then, according to the Braun-Le Chatelier principle, an isothermal pressure increase shifts the equilibrium toward the side having the smaller volume.

Accordingly, under these circumstances it is possible to have a relaxation process if the specific rate constant for the reaction is small, even in the rare case where $\Delta = 0$ (heat expansion coefficient zero), so that the compression and expansion in the sound wave are isothermal and it does not matter how the specific heats behave.

In the following, it is assumed that we have either an ideal gas, an ideal mixture or solution, or a dilute solution.

Consider the chemical reaction

$$aA + bB + \ldots \rightleftarrows cC + dD + \ldots . \tag{27–1}$$

Here, the A, B, C, D signify chemical formulas, the a, b small integers; e.g.

$$2H_2 + O_2 \rightleftarrows 2H_2O.$$

Let x_A, $x_B \ldots$ be the mole fractions of the chemicals A, $B \ldots$, and n_A, $n_B \ldots$ the total number of moles present. Assume[12] that, if the reaction occurred isothermally and at constant pressure, the amount H' of heat would be absorbed and the volume would increase by V' if, in a very large mass of

[12] In strict thermodynamical language, if H is the total heat content and V the total volume of the mixture

$$H' = \ldots c\frac{\partial H}{\partial n_C} \ldots - a\frac{\partial H}{\partial n_A} - b\frac{\partial H}{\partial n_B}$$

$$V' = \ldots c\frac{\partial V}{\partial n_C} \ldots - a\frac{\partial V}{\partial n_A} - b\frac{\partial V}{\partial n_B}.$$

the mixture, a moles of A, b moles of B... went over into c moles of C.... The chemists usually write ΔH for H', ΔV for V'.

One then has, in equilibrium

$$\frac{(x_C{}^0)^c \ldots}{(x_A{}^0)^a \, (x_B{}^0)^b} = K \tag{27–2}$$

the mass action law. The chemists usually write

$$K = e^{\Delta F/RT}. \tag{27–3}$$

Call n_A, n_B, n_C, the total number of moles of A, B, C present, and n_S the total number of moles of the solvent. Call further

$$n_A + n_B + n_C + n_S = n.$$

Then

$$x_A = \frac{n_A}{n}. \tag{27—1'}$$

Taking the logarithm of Eq. (27–2) one has

$$c \ln x_C - a \ln x_A - b \ln x_B = c \ln n_C - a \ln n_A - b \ln n_B - (c - a - b) \ln n = \ln K. \tag{27–4}$$

If one now varies temperature and pressure

$$c \frac{\delta n_C}{n_C} - a \frac{\delta n_A}{n_A} - b \frac{\delta n_B}{n_B} - (c - a - b) \frac{1}{n} (\delta n_A + \delta n_B + \delta n_C) = \delta \ln K. \tag{27–4'}$$

Since the concentration changes are due to reaction (27–1) one has the relationship

$$\frac{1}{c} \delta n_C = - \frac{1}{a} \delta n_A = - \frac{1}{b} \delta n_B = \delta \xi \tag{27–5}$$

where $\delta \xi$ is the "degree of advancement" which indicates how many times the amount indicated by Eq. (27–1) has reacted. Therefore

$$\left\{ c^2 \frac{1}{n_C} + a^2 \frac{1}{n_A} + b^2 \frac{1}{n_B} - (c - a - b)^2 \frac{1}{n} \right\} \delta \xi = \left\{ \frac{c^2}{x_C} + \frac{a^2}{x_A} + \frac{b^2}{x_B} - (c - a - b)^2 \right\} \frac{1}{n} \delta \xi = \delta \ln K. \tag{27–6}$$

Define

$$\varphi^{-1} = \frac{c^2}{x_C} + \frac{a^2}{x_A} + \frac{b^2}{x_B} - (c - a - b)^2. \tag{27–7}$$

One has from thermodynamics according to van t'Hoff

$$\left(\frac{\partial \ln K}{\partial T}\right)_p = \frac{H'}{RT^2} \tag{27–8}$$

$$\left(\frac{\partial \ln K}{\partial p}\right)_T = -\frac{V'}{RT}. \tag{27–8'}$$

Now assume a reaction rate equation

$$-\frac{1}{n}\frac{1}{c}\frac{dn_C}{dt} = \frac{1}{an}\frac{dn_A}{dt} = \frac{1}{bn}\frac{dn_B}{dt} = -\frac{1}{n}\frac{d\xi}{dt} = \bar{k}(x_C)^c - \tilde{k}(x_A)^a (x_B)^b.$$

(27–9)

The equilibrium condition gives $K = \tilde{k}/\bar{k}$, analogous to Eqs. (19–4) and (23–9).

Now make a calculation similar to the one in Secs. 19 and 23. Let

$$x_A = x_A{}^0 + \delta x_A$$

$$(x_A)^a = (x_A{}^0)^a\left(1 + \frac{\delta x_A}{x_A}\right)^a = (x_A{}^0)^a\left(1 + a\frac{\delta x_A}{x_A}\right)$$

$$= (x_A{}^0)^a\left\{1 - \frac{\delta\xi}{n}\left[\frac{a^2}{x_A} - (c - a - b)a\right]\right\}$$

so that the right side of Eq. (27–9) takes the form, keeping only the first power of $\delta\xi$

$$\bar{k}_0(x_C{}^0)^c - \tilde{k}_0(x_A{}^0)^a(x_B{}^0)^b + \bar{k}_0(x_C{}^0)^c\frac{\delta\xi}{n}\left[\frac{c^2}{x_c} - c(c - a - b)\right] +$$

$$\tilde{k}_0(x_A{}^0)^a(x_B{}^0)^b\frac{\delta\xi}{n}\left[\frac{a^2}{x_A} + \frac{b^2}{x_B} + (a + b)(c - a - b)\right] +$$

$$\delta\bar{k}(x_C{}^0)^c - \delta\tilde{k}(x_A{}^0)^a (x_B{}^0)^b.$$

The last term contains

$$\delta\tilde{k} = \delta(\bar{k}K) = K\delta\bar{k} + \bar{k}\delta K = K\delta\bar{k} + \tilde{k}_0\delta\ln K.$$

Again using the equilibrium equations (27–2) and (27–7), one gets the relaxation equation

$$-\frac{d\delta\xi}{dt} = \bar{k}_0(x_C{}^0)^c\{\varphi^{-1}\,\delta\xi - n\delta\ln K\} \tag{27–10}$$

$$= \bar{k}_0(x_C{}^0)^c\,\varphi^{-1}\left\{\delta\xi - n\varphi\,\frac{H'}{RT^2}\,\delta T + n\varphi\,\frac{V'}{RT}\,\delta p\right\}.$$

Assume now that everything is again proportional to $e^{i\omega t}$. Define the relaxation time

$$\frac{1}{\tau} = \bar{k}_0(x_C{}^0)^c\,\varphi^{-1}. \tag{27–11}$$

Then, after multiplying Eq. (27–10) with τ

$$(1 + i\omega\tau)\,\frac{\delta\xi}{n} = \varphi\,\frac{H'}{RT^2}\,(T_{\mathrm{tr}} - T_0) - \varphi\,\frac{V'}{RT}\,(p - p_0). \tag{27–12}$$

At low frequencies, $\omega\tau = 0$, the heat taken in for a temperature increase δT is

$$H'\,\frac{\delta\xi}{n} = \varphi\left\{\frac{(H')^2}{RT^2} - H'\,\frac{V'}{RT}\,\frac{p - p_0}{T_{\mathrm{tr}} - T_0}\right\}\delta T \tag{27–13}$$

so that the equilibrium shift is equivalent to an internal specific heat per mole of

$$\frac{C'}{R} = \varphi\left\{\left(\frac{H'}{RT}\right)^2 - \frac{H'}{RT}\,\frac{V'}{R}\,\frac{p - p_0}{T_{\mathrm{tr}} - T}\right\}. \tag{27–14}$$

The situation is simplest if $V' = 0$. This is the case for an ideal gas in which an equal number of molecules appears on both sides of Eq. (27–1)

$$a + b + \ldots = c + \ldots +.$$

No general rule can be given for a liquid, but the condition is probably nearly fulfilled if we deal with an isomeric internal change

$$a = c = 1 \qquad b = 0.$$

In general, the order of magnitude of the two terms in Eq. (27–14) will be in the ratio

$$\frac{V'T}{H'}\left(\frac{\partial p}{\partial T}\right)_{ad} = \frac{V'T}{H'}\,\frac{\beta}{\kappa_{ad}}.$$

For an ideal gas at room temperature, the ratio is about

$$(c - a - b)\,\frac{RT}{H'}.$$

For a typical liquid, e.g., toluene, the ratio is about

$$0.1\,\frac{V'}{H'}$$

with V' in cc and H' in kcal.

If $V' = 0$, then

$$\frac{C'}{R} = \varphi\left(\frac{H'}{RT}\right)^2. \tag{27–15}$$

As in Eq. (11–14), the effective relaxation time is

$$\tau' = \frac{C_p - C'}{C_p}\,\tau. \tag{27–16}$$

28. Discussion of Special Cases. Various Orders of the Reaction

If there are only two components, $x_C = x_1$, and $x_A = x_2$, so that the reaction is $C \rightleftarrows A$, one has $\varphi = x_1 x_2/(x_1 + x_2)$.

Define $x_0 = x_1 + x_2$. If all parts of the mixture react, i.e., if only A and C are present

$$x_1 + x_2 = 1 \qquad \varphi = x(1 - x).$$

However, if an inactive solvent is present, it has to be included in the numerical calculation of the x, but not explicitly in φ. Using Eqs. (27–3), (27–2), and the definition of the hyperbolic cosine

$$\cosh y = \frac{1}{2}\,(e^y + e^{-y})$$

one finds

$$\frac{C'}{R} = x_0\left[\frac{1}{2\cosh \Delta F/2RT}\right]^2 \frac{H'}{RT}\left[\frac{H'}{RT} - \frac{V'}{R}\left(\frac{dp}{dT}\right)_{ad}\right]. \tag{28–1}$$

Furthermore [Eq. (27–11)]

$$\tau = \frac{1}{\bar{k}x_C}\,\frac{x_A x_C}{x_A + x_C} = \frac{1}{\bar{k}}\left(1 + \frac{x_C}{x_A}\right)^{-1}$$
$$= \frac{1}{\bar{k}}\,\frac{1}{1 + K} = \frac{1}{\bar{k} + \tilde{k}} \tag{28–2}$$

as in Eq. (19–7).

This case behaves, as a function of dilution, in the same manner as the effect of an internal degree of freedom would. However, C' has a maximum as a function of T (Karpovich).[1]

In the case of dissociation, three cases are important:

(a) $A = B$, with the solvent not involved;

(b) $A \neq B$, $n_A = n_B$, with the solvent not involved; and

(c) B fixed, the solvent acting as buffer.

The last case will not be discussed further.

For (a), one has

$$\varphi^{-1} = \frac{2^2}{x_A} + \frac{1}{x_C} - (1-2)^2 = \frac{4}{x_A} + \frac{1}{x_C} - 1$$

$$= \frac{4}{x_A} + \frac{1}{Kx_A{}^2} - 1$$

$$\varphi = \frac{x_C}{4Kx_A + 1 - x_C} = \frac{Kx_A{}^2}{4Kx_A + 1 - Kx_A{}^2} \tag{28–3}$$

and

$$\tau = \frac{1}{\bar{k}x_C}\varphi = \frac{1}{\bar{k}} \frac{1}{4Kx_A + 1 - x_C}. \tag{28–4}$$

For case (b) one replaces "4" by "2".

If the liquid is pure

$$x_A + x_C = x_A + Kx_A{}^2 = 1 \tag{28–5}$$

$$Kx_A = \frac{1}{2}(\sqrt{4K+1} - 1) \tag{28–5'}$$

$$\varphi = \frac{Kx_A}{4K+1} = \frac{1}{2}\{(4K+1)^{-1/2} - (4K+1)^{-1}\} \tag{28–5''}$$

$$\frac{C'}{R} = \frac{1}{2}\{(4K+1)^{-1/2} - (4K+1)^{-1}\}\frac{H'}{RT}\left\{\frac{H'}{RT} - \frac{V'}{R}\left(\frac{dp}{dT}\right)_{ad}\right\} \tag{28–6}$$

and

$$\tau = \frac{1}{\bar{k}} \frac{2K}{4K+1}\{\sqrt{4K+1} - 1\}^{-1} = \frac{1}{2\bar{k}}\{(4K+1)^{-1/2} + (4K+1)^{-1}\}. \tag{28–7}$$

---

[1] J. Karpovich, *J. Chem. Phys.* **22**, 1767 (1954).

In case (b) expression (28–5) is replaced by

$$2x_A + x_C = 2x_A + Kx_A{}^2 = 1 \tag{28–8}$$

and

$$Kx_A = \sqrt{K+1} - 1. \tag{28–8′}$$

In Eqs. (28–6) and (28–7), $4K$ is replaced by K.

If a solvent is present, only case (a) will be treated. Call x' the mole fraction of the solute which one would calculate if all the solute were dissociated, i.e., present as A

$$x' = (n_A + 2n_C)\,(n_A + 2n_C + n_S)^{-1} = (x_A + 2x_C)\,(1 + x_C)^{-1} \tag{28–9}$$

or

$$x_C = Kx_A{}^2 = \frac{x' - x_A}{2 - x'} \tag{28–9′}$$

$$Kx_A = \frac{1}{2\,(2 - x')}\{\sqrt{4Kx'(2 - x') + 1} - 1\} \tag{28–9″}$$

$$\frac{C'}{R} = \varphi\,\frac{H'}{RT}\left[\frac{H'}{RT} - \frac{V'}{R}\left(\frac{dp}{dT}\right)_{ad}\right] = \frac{H'}{RT}\left[\frac{H'}{RT} - \frac{V'}{R}\left(\frac{dp}{dT}\right)_{ad}\right] \cdot$$

$$\{2Kx'(2 - x') + 1 - \sqrt{4Kx'(2 - x') + 1}\}\,\{[4K(2 - x') + 1]\cdot \sqrt{4Kx'(2 - x') + 1} - [4Kx'(2 - x') + 1]\}^{-1} \tag{28–10}$$

$$\tau = \frac{1}{k}\,2K(2 - x')^2\,\{[4K(2 - x') + 1]\sqrt{4Kx'(2 - x') + 1} - [4Kx'(2 - x') + 1]\}^{-1}. \tag{28–11}$$

This will be discussed in three regions:

1. $K \ll 1$;

$$\frac{C'}{R} = \frac{H'}{RT}\left[\frac{H'}{RT} - \frac{V'}{R}\left(\frac{dp}{dT}\right)_{ad}\right]\frac{K}{4}\,x'^2 \tag{28–12}$$

$$\tau = \frac{1}{k}\,\frac{1}{1 + 4Kx'}. \tag{28–13}$$

2. $K \gg 1$; $Kx' \ll 1$ as under 1.

3. $K \gg 1$, $Kx' \gg 1$;

$$\frac{C'}{R} = \frac{H'}{RT}\left\{\frac{H'}{RT} - \frac{V'}{R}\left(\frac{dp}{dT}\right)_{ad}\right\}\frac{x'}{4}$$

$$\{[Kx'(2-x')]^{-1/2} - [Kx'(2-x')]^{-1}\} \qquad (28\text{–}12')$$

$$\tau = \frac{1}{2\bar{k}} \frac{2-x'}{\sqrt{4Kx'(2-x')+1-x'}}. \qquad (28\text{–}13')$$

If Kx' is very large compared to unity

$$\tau = \frac{1}{2\bar{k}} \frac{1}{\sqrt{2Kx'}} = \frac{1}{2\sqrt{2k\bar{k}x'}} \qquad (28\text{–}13'')$$

and the factor which appears in the expression of α/ω^2 is

$$\frac{\Delta C'\tau}{C_v C_p} = \frac{\Delta R}{C_v C_p}\frac{H'}{RT}\left[\frac{H'}{RT} - \frac{V'}{R}\left(\frac{\partial p}{\partial T}\right)_{ad}\right]\frac{1}{16\bar{k}K}$$

$$= \frac{\Delta R}{C_v C_p}\frac{H'}{RT}\left[\frac{H'}{RT} - \frac{V'}{R}\left(\frac{\partial p}{\partial T}\right)_{ad}\right]\frac{1}{16\bar{k}} \qquad (28\text{–}12'')$$

independent of x', while for a C' due to an internal degree of freedom this quantity would be proportional to x'.

If K is kept constant and x' varied from 0 to 1, C'/R increases monotonously from zero through Eqs. (28–12), (28–12′) to Eq. (28–6) and τ varies from $1/\bar{k}$ through Eqs. (28–13), (28–13′) to Eq. (28–7).

To sum up, one cannot distinguish a relaxation due to slow chemical reaction from one due to slow energy exchange by the *form* of the dispersion or absorption curve. This is natural, since statistical mechanics does not distinguish fundamentally between "chemical" and "physical" changes.

It comes down to a semantic discussion if we have, for example, transitions from vibration to internal rotation.

The distinction can be made only by considering the value for C', which for chemical reactions will be different from that expected for vibrational degrees of freedom; by considering its dependence on temperature, concentration and pressure.

An additional relaxation will usually exist due to the slow exchange of internal and external energy. This will be parallel to the chemical relaxation (see Sec. 21). The two cannot be distinguished by their dependence on ω but only—if at all—by the numerical values of C' or by their dependence on concentration. This makes the results of experiments with the $N_2O_4 \rightleftarrows 2NO_2$ reaction ambiguous.

29. Continuation of Discussion. Different Values of V' and H'

(a) In case V' is zero, the change in pressure has no direct effect on the equilibrium; only the change in temperature has. In this case, the expressions of Sec. 28 are valid if one sets $V' = 0$.

(b) We now discuss first the opposite case, where no temperature change occurs, i.e., where $T_{tr} - T_0 = 0$. This is the treatment by Hall and Frenkel (see Secs. 100 and 103). We assume only two forms

$$A \rightleftarrows C \qquad (x_1; x_2)$$

and a solvent s which is not involved. Accordingly

$$\frac{x_2}{x_1} = \frac{x_2}{x_0 - x_2} = K. \tag{29–1}$$

Then

$$V = V_s(1 - x_1 - x_2) + V_1'x_1 + V_2'x_2 = V_s + (V_1' - V_s)x_1 + (V_2' - V_s)x_2. \tag{29—1'}$$

On static pressure application, one has

$$\frac{\partial V}{\partial p} = -V\kappa_T = \frac{\partial V_s}{\partial p} + \left(\frac{\partial V_1'}{\partial p} - \frac{\partial V_s}{\partial p}\right)x_1 + \left(\frac{\partial V_2'}{\partial p} - \frac{\partial V_s}{\partial p}\right)x_2 + (V_1' - V_s)\frac{\partial x_1}{\partial p} + (V_2' - V_s)\frac{\partial x_2}{\partial p}. \tag{29–2}$$

Since $-\partial x_1/\partial p = \partial x_2/\partial p$, the last two terms are equal to

$$[-(V_1' - V_s) + V_2' - V_s]\frac{\partial x_2}{\partial p} = (V_2' - V_1')\frac{\partial x_2}{\partial p} = V'\frac{\partial x_2}{\partial p}. \tag{29—2'}$$

Define now a quantity κ_∞

$$-V\kappa_\infty = \frac{\partial V_s}{\partial p} + \left(\frac{\partial V_1'}{\partial p} - \frac{\partial V_s}{\partial p}\right)x_1 + \left(\frac{\partial V_2'}{\partial p} - \frac{\partial V_s}{\partial p}\right)x_2 \tag{29–3}$$

so that

$$\kappa_T = \kappa_\infty - \frac{V'}{V}\frac{\partial x_2}{\partial p}. \tag{29–3'}$$

Therefore, κ_∞ is the compressibility one would find with the equilibrium frozen.

To calculate $(\partial x_2/\partial p)_{\text{static}}$, differentiate Eq. (29–1) with respect to p

$$\left[\frac{1}{x_0 - x_2} + \frac{x_2}{(x_0 - x_2)^2}\right]\frac{\partial x_2}{\partial p} = \frac{x_0}{(x_0 - x_2)^2}\frac{\partial x_2}{\partial p} = \frac{x_0}{x_2}\frac{x_2}{x_1}\frac{1}{x_0 - x_2}\frac{\partial x_2}{\partial p}$$

$$= K\frac{x_0}{x_1 x_2}\frac{\partial x_2}{\partial p} = \frac{\partial K}{\partial p}$$

or

$$\left(\frac{\partial x_2}{\partial p}\right)_{\text{static}} = \frac{x_1 x_2}{x_0}\frac{\partial \ln K}{\partial p} = -\frac{x_1 x_2}{x_0}\frac{V'}{RT} \tag{29–4}$$

with $x_1 x_2/x_0$, of course, the function φ of Sec. 27. Therefore

$$\kappa_T = \kappa_\infty + \frac{x_1 x_2}{x_0}\frac{(V')^2}{VRT}. \tag{29–5}$$

Consider now a time-dependent process, and assume that only the chemical adjustment is slow. Then

$$\frac{dV}{dt} = \left[\frac{\partial V_s}{\partial p} + \left(\frac{\partial V_1'}{\partial p} - \frac{\partial V_s}{\partial p}\right)x_1 + \left(\frac{\partial V_2'}{\partial p} - \frac{\partial V_s}{\partial p}\right)x_2\right]\frac{dp}{dt} + V'\frac{d\delta x}{dt} \tag{29–6}$$

or

$$\frac{1}{V}\frac{dV}{dt} = -\kappa_\infty\frac{dp}{dt} + \frac{V'}{V}\frac{d\delta x}{dt} = -\left[\kappa_T - \frac{x_1 x_2}{x_0}\frac{V'^2}{VRT}\right]\frac{dp}{dt} + \frac{V'}{V}\frac{d\delta x}{dt}. \tag{29–6′}$$

Next, one writes the relaxation equation, keeping small terms of the first order only

$$-\frac{dx_2}{dt} = -\frac{d\delta x}{dt} = \bar{k}x_2 - \tilde{k}x_1 = \bar{k}_0 x_2^0 - \tilde{k}_0 x_1^0 + \bar{k}_0(x_2 - x_2^0) -$$

$$\tilde{k}_0(x_1 - x_1^0) + \left[x_2^0\frac{\partial \bar{k}}{\partial p} - x_1^0\frac{\partial \tilde{k}}{\partial p}\right](p - p_0)$$

$$= (\bar{k}_0 + \tilde{k}_0)\delta x + \left(x_2^0\frac{\partial \bar{k}}{\partial p} - x_1^0\frac{\partial \bar{k}K}{\partial p}\right)(p - p_0) \tag{29–7}$$

with

$$\frac{\tilde{k}_0}{\bar{k}_0} = K$$

following from the equilibrium condition. The last bracket before $p - p_0$ is

$$x_2{}^0 \frac{\partial \bar{k}}{\partial p} - K x_1{}^0 \frac{\partial \bar{k}}{\partial p} - \bar{k}_0 x_1{}^0 \frac{\partial K}{\partial p} = - \bar{k}_0 K x_1{}^0 \frac{\partial \ln K}{\partial p} = + \bar{k}_0 x_2{}^0 \cdot \frac{V'}{RT} \qquad (29\text{–}7')$$

so that the relaxation equation takes the form

$$-\frac{d\delta x}{dt} = (\bar{k} + \tilde{k})\delta x + \bar{k}_0 x_2{}^0 \frac{V'}{RT}(p - p_0)$$

or, defining—see Eq. (19–6)

$$\frac{1}{\tau} = \bar{k}_0 + \tilde{k}_0 = \bar{k}_0(1 + K) = \bar{k}_0 x_2{}^0 \frac{x_0}{x_1{}^0 x_2{}^0} = \bar{k} x_2 \varphi^{-1} \qquad (29\text{–}8)$$

as in Eq. (19–5)[1]

$$-\frac{d\delta x}{dt} = \frac{1}{\tau}\left[\delta x + \frac{x_1 x_2}{x_0}\frac{V'}{RT}(p - p_0)\right]. \qquad (29\text{–}9)$$

Assuming everything proportional to $e^{i\omega t}$, one has

$$(1 + i\omega\tau)\delta x + \frac{x_1 x_2}{x_0}\frac{V'}{RT}(p - p_0) = 0 \qquad (29\text{–}9')$$

or

$$\frac{d\delta x}{dt} = -\frac{1}{1 + i\omega\tau}\frac{x_1 x_2}{x_0}\frac{V'}{RT}\frac{dp}{dt}. \qquad (29\text{–}9'')$$

Inserting this in Eq. (29–6′) one gets, after division by dp/dt

$$-\frac{1}{V}\frac{dV}{dt}\Big/\frac{dp}{dt} = \frac{1}{\rho}\frac{d\rho}{dp} = \kappa_\infty + \frac{x_1 x_2}{x_0}\frac{(V')^2}{VRT}\frac{1}{1 + i\omega\tau}$$

$$= \kappa_T - \frac{x_1 x_2}{x_0}\frac{(V')^2}{VRT}\frac{i\omega\tau}{1 + i\omega\tau}$$

and

$$\left(\frac{1}{\mathfrak{B}} - \frac{i\alpha'}{\omega}\right)^2 = \rho\left\{\kappa_T - \frac{x_1 x_2}{x_0}\frac{(V')^2}{VRT}\frac{i\omega\tau}{1 + i\omega\tau}\right\}.$$

Multiplying this expression with

$$\mathfrak{B}_0{}^2 = (\rho\kappa_T)^{-1} \qquad (\gamma = 1!)$$

---

[1] The index zero is omitted on x and k from now on.

finally gives

$$\left(\frac{\mathfrak{V}_0}{\mathfrak{V}} - \frac{i\alpha'\mathfrak{V}_0}{\omega}\right)^2 = 1 - \rho{\mathfrak{V}_0}^2 \frac{x_1 x_2}{x_0} \frac{(V')^2}{VRT} \frac{i\omega\tau}{1 + i\omega\tau}. \tag{29–10}$$

This has exactly the form of Eqs. (12–1) and (12–2) with

$$\frac{\kappa_T - \kappa_\infty}{\kappa_T} = \rho{\mathfrak{V}_0}^2 \frac{x_1 x_2}{x_0} \frac{(V')^2}{VRT}$$

taking the place of $\Delta \cdot C'/[C_v(C_p - C')]$, or

$$\eta' = \rho{\mathfrak{V}_0}^2 \frac{x_1 x_2}{x_0} \frac{(V')^2}{VRT} \frac{\tau}{1 + (\omega\tau)^2}. \tag{29–10'}$$

One can use again, as in Eq. (28–1)

$$\frac{x_1 x_2}{x_0} = \varphi = x_0 \left[2 \cosh \frac{\Delta F}{2RT}\right]^{-2}.$$

For cases of a more complicated reaction than $A \rightleftarrows C$, Eq. (29–9) is replaced by

$$-\frac{1}{n}\frac{d}{dt}\,\delta\xi = \bar{k}x_{C^c}\left[\varphi^{-1}\frac{\delta\xi}{n} + \frac{V'}{RT}\,\delta p\right].$$

One then defines, as a generalization of Eq. (29–8)

$$\frac{1}{\tau} = \bar{k}x_{C^c} \ldots \varphi^{-1} \qquad (29–11) = (27–11)$$

and, with simple harmonic processes

$$(1 + i\omega\tau)\,\frac{\delta\xi}{n} + \varphi\,\frac{V'}{RT}(p - p_0) = 0.$$

Everything else follows the previous argument, φ replacing $x_1 x_2/x_0$ in Eq. (29–10).

(c) Both the temperature and the volume effect are important. To Eq. (29–6′), one has to add $\tilde{\beta}(dT_{\text{tr}}/dt)$, so that

$$\frac{1}{V}\frac{dV}{dt} = -\kappa_\infty \frac{dp}{dt} + \tilde{\beta}\frac{dT_{\text{tr}}}{dt} + \frac{V'}{V}\frac{d\delta x}{dt} \tag{29–13}$$

as equation of state. Here, $\tilde{\beta}$ is the "frozen" coefficient of expansion

$$\tilde{\beta} = \frac{1}{V}\left(\frac{\partial V_s}{\partial T}\right)_p + \frac{1}{V}\left(\frac{\partial V_1'}{\partial T} - \frac{\partial V_s}{\partial T}\right)_p x_1 + \frac{1}{V}\left(\frac{\partial V_2'}{\partial T} - \frac{\partial V_s}{\partial T}\right)_p x_2 = \beta - \frac{V'}{V}\left(\frac{\partial \delta x}{\partial T}\right)_p. \quad (29\text{–}13')$$

Then one has the relaxation equation, Eq. (27–9), treated like Eq. (29–9′)

$$\frac{d\delta x}{dt} = \frac{1}{1 + i\omega\tau}\varphi\left[\frac{H'}{RT^2}\frac{dT_{\text{tr}}}{dt} - \frac{V'}{RT}\frac{dp}{dt}\right] \quad (29\text{–}14)$$

and the equation for the heat content

$$\frac{dH}{dt} = V\frac{dp}{dt}. \quad (29\text{–}15)$$

Since the experimental C_p also includes the effect of the shift in x, call the "frozen" specific heat $\tilde{C}$

$$\tilde{C}_p = C_p - H'\left(\frac{\partial \delta x}{\partial T}\right)_{p,\ \text{static}} = C_p - R\varphi\left(\frac{H'}{RT}\right)^2. \quad (29\text{–}15')$$

Then, see Eq. (4–5)

$$dH = \left(\frac{\partial H}{\partial T}\right)_{p,x} dT_{\text{tr}} + \left(\frac{\partial H}{\partial p}\right)_{T,x} dp + \left(\frac{\partial H}{\partial x}\right)_{p,T} \delta x$$
$$= \tilde{C}_p\, dT_{\text{tr}} + [-TV\tilde{\beta} + V]dp + H'\delta x$$

or, with the use of Eq. (29–15)

$$\tilde{C}_p\frac{dT_{\text{tr}}}{dt} - TV\tilde{\beta}\frac{dp}{dt} + H'\frac{d\delta x}{dt} = 0. \quad (29\text{–}15'')$$

Eliminate $d\delta x/dt$ and then dT_{tr}/dt from the three equations, Eqs. (29–13), (29–14), and (29–15″)

$$\tilde{C}_p\frac{dT_{\text{tr}}}{dt} - TV\tilde{\beta}\frac{dp}{dt} + \frac{H'\varphi}{1 + i\omega\tau}\left[\frac{H'}{RT^2}\frac{dT_{\text{tr}}}{dt} - \frac{V'}{RT}\frac{dp}{dt}\right] = 0 \quad (29\text{–}15''')$$

or

$$\left[\tilde{C}_p + R\frac{\varphi}{1 + i\omega\tau}\left(\frac{H'}{RT}\right)^2\right]\frac{dT_{\text{tr}}}{dt} = TV\left[\tilde{\beta} + \frac{V'}{V}\frac{H'}{RT^2}\frac{\varphi}{1 + i\omega\tau}\right]\frac{dp}{dt}.$$

Comparing with Eq. (11–4′), the effective C_p is obviously

$$(C_p)_{\text{eff}} = \tilde{C}_p + R\varphi\left(\frac{H'}{RT}\right)^2 \frac{1}{1+i\omega\tau} = C_p - R\varphi\left(\frac{H'}{RT}\right)^2 \frac{i\omega\tau}{1+i\omega\tau} \tag{29–16}$$

and

$$\beta_{\text{eff}} = \tilde{\beta} + \varphi\frac{V'}{V}\frac{H'}{RT^2}\frac{1}{1+i\omega\tau} = \beta - \varphi\frac{V'}{V}\frac{H'}{RT^2}\frac{i\omega\tau}{1+i\omega\tau}. \tag{29–16′}$$

Equation (29–13) becomes

$$\begin{aligned}\frac{1}{\rho}\frac{d\rho}{dt} &= \kappa_\infty\frac{dp}{dt} - \tilde{\beta}\frac{dT_{\text{tr}}}{dt} - \frac{V'}{V}\frac{\varphi}{1+i\omega\tau}\left(\frac{H'}{RT^2}\frac{dT_{\text{tr}}}{dt} - \frac{V'}{RT}\frac{dp}{dt}\right)\\ &= \left[\kappa_\infty + \varphi\frac{(V')^2}{VRT}\frac{1}{1+i\omega\tau}\right]\frac{dp}{dt} - \left[\tilde{\beta} + \varphi\frac{V'}{V}\frac{H'}{RT^2}\frac{1}{1+i\omega\tau}\right]\frac{dT_{\text{tr}}}{dt}.\end{aligned} \tag{29–13″}$$

Eliminate dT_{tr}/dt from Eq. (29–13) with the help of Eq. (29–15‴)

$$\begin{aligned}\frac{1}{\rho}\frac{d\rho}{dt} = \Bigg\{&\kappa_\infty + \varphi\frac{(V')^2}{VRT}\frac{1}{1+i\omega\tau} - \left[\tilde{\beta} + \varphi\frac{V'}{V}\frac{H'}{RT^2}\frac{1}{1+i\omega\tau}\right]\cdot\\ &TV\cdot\left[\tilde{\beta} + \varphi\frac{V'}{V}\frac{H'}{RT^2}\frac{\varphi}{1+i\omega\tau}\right]\left[\tilde{C}_p + R\varphi\left(\frac{H'}{RT}\right)^2\frac{1}{1+i\omega\tau}\right]^{-1}\Bigg\}\frac{dp}{dt}.\end{aligned}$$

Therefore, using Eqs. (29–16) and (29–16′) and multiplying out with $1 + i\omega\tau$

$$\begin{aligned}\left(\frac{1}{\mathfrak{V}} - \frac{i\alpha'}{\omega}\right)^2 &= \frac{d\rho}{dp}\\ &= \rho\left\{\kappa_T - \varphi\frac{V'^2}{VRT}\frac{i\omega\tau}{1+i\omega\tau} - TV\,[\beta + \tilde{\beta}i\omega\tau]^2\,[1+i\omega\tau]^{-1}\,[C_p + \tilde{C}_p i\omega\tau]^{-1}\right\}.\end{aligned} \tag{29–17}$$

Compare this with Eq. (11–5).

The last three brackets may be written

$$-TV\frac{\beta^2}{C_p}\left[1 + \frac{\tilde{\beta}}{\beta}i\omega\tau\right]^2 [1+i\omega\tau]^{-1}\left[1 + \frac{\tilde{C}_p}{C_p}i\omega\tau\right]^{-1}.$$

This needs a decomposition into partial fractions. It gives

$$- TV \frac{\beta^2}{C_p}\left[1 - \left(1 - \frac{\tilde{\beta}}{\beta}\right)^2 \frac{C_p}{C_p - \tilde{C}_p} \frac{i\omega\tau}{1 + i\omega\tau} + \left(\frac{\tilde{\beta}}{\beta} - \frac{\tilde{C}_p}{C_p}\right)^2 \frac{C_p}{\tilde{C}_p} \frac{C_p}{C_p - \tilde{C}_p} \frac{i\omega\tau'}{1 + i\omega\tau'}\right] \tag{29–18}$$

with

$$\tau' = \frac{\tilde{C}_p}{C_p}\tau. \tag{29–19) = (27–14}$$

The expression can be further simplified to

$$- TV \frac{\beta^2}{C_p} + TV \frac{(\beta - \tilde{\beta})^2}{C_p - \tilde{C}_p} \frac{i\omega\tau}{1 + i\omega\tau} - \frac{TV}{C_p - \tilde{C}_p}\left(\frac{\tilde{\beta}C_p - \beta\tilde{C}_p}{\sqrt{C_p\tilde{C}_p}}\right)^2 \frac{i\omega\tau'}{1 + i\omega\tau'}.$$

Furthermore, from Eqs. (29–16, 16′)

$$TV \frac{(\beta - \tilde{\beta})^2}{C_p - \tilde{C}_p} = TV\left(\frac{V'}{V}\frac{H'}{RT^2}\varphi\right)^2 \left[R\left(\frac{H'}{RT}\right)^2 \varphi\right]^{-1}$$

$$= \frac{(V')^2}{VRT}\varphi. \tag{29–20}$$

As a consequence, the second term in Eq. (29–20) cancels the second term in Eq. (29–17). Therefore, after multiplying Eq. (29–17) with $\mathfrak{B}_0{}^2$

$$\left(\frac{\mathfrak{B}_0}{\mathfrak{B}} - \frac{i\alpha'\mathfrak{B}_0}{\omega}\right)^2 = \rho\mathfrak{B}_0{}^2\left(\kappa_T - TV\frac{\beta^2}{C_p}\right) - \rho\mathfrak{B}_0{}^2 \frac{TV}{R}\left(\frac{RT}{H'}\right)^2 \varphi^{-1}\left(\frac{\tilde{\beta}C_p - \beta\tilde{C}_p}{\sqrt{C_p\tilde{C}_p}}\right)^2 \frac{i\omega\tau'}{1 + i\omega\tau'}. \tag{29–21}$$

This means that

$$TV\frac{\beta^2}{\kappa_T C_p} = \frac{\gamma_0 - 1}{\gamma_0} \qquad TV\frac{\beta^2}{\kappa_T} = \Delta$$

as usual. Accordingly

$$\left(\frac{\kappa_0 - \kappa_\infty}{\kappa_0}\right)_S = \rho\mathfrak{B}_0{}^2 \frac{TV}{R}\left(\frac{RT}{H'}\right)^2 \varphi^{-1}\left(\frac{\tilde{\beta}C_p - \beta\tilde{C}_p}{\sqrt{C_p\tilde{C}_p}}\right)^2 \tag{29–22}$$

plays the role of $\Delta C'/[C_v(C_p - C')]$ in the usual dispersion and absorption equations.

For ideal gases, $\tilde{\beta} = 1/T$, while for liquids it is better to use an experimental β. Therefore

$$\tilde{\beta}C_p - \beta\tilde{C}_p = \tilde{\beta}\left[\tilde{C}_p + R\left(\frac{H'}{RT}\right)^2 \varphi\right] - \left[\tilde{\beta} + \frac{V'}{V}\frac{H'}{RT^2}\varphi\right]\tilde{C}_p$$

$$= \left[\tilde{\beta}R\frac{H'}{RT} - \frac{V'}{VT}\tilde{C}_p\right]\frac{H'}{RT}\varphi = \left[\frac{H'}{T} - \frac{V'}{V}\tilde{C}_p\right]\frac{H'}{RT^2}\varphi \quad \text{for gases,}$$

$$= \left[\beta - \frac{V'}{V}\frac{H'}{RT^2}\varphi\right]C_p - \beta\left[C_p - R\left(\frac{H'}{RT}\right)^2\varphi\right]$$

$$= \beta R\left(\frac{H'}{RT}\right)^2\varphi - \frac{V'}{V}\frac{H'}{RT^2}\varphi\, C_p = \frac{H'}{RT}\varphi\left[\beta R\frac{H'}{RT} - \frac{V'}{VT}C_p\right]$$

$$= \frac{H'}{RT^2}\varphi\left[\beta H' - \frac{V'}{V}C_p\right] \quad \text{for liquids.}$$

To sum up, one has in general

$$\left(\frac{1}{\mathfrak{V}} - \frac{i\alpha}{\omega}\right)^2 = \frac{1}{\gamma}\left(\frac{\partial\rho}{\partial p}\right)_T = \frac{1}{\mathfrak{V}_0{}^2}\left(1 - A\,\frac{i\omega\tau'}{1 + i\omega\tau'}\right). \qquad (29\text{–}23)$$

For a two-state ideal system, the following cases are important:

1. $V' = 0$, no direct pressure effect, only γ is subject to relaxation

$$A = \frac{\Delta C'}{C_v(C_p - C')} \qquad (29\text{–}24)$$

$$\frac{C'}{R} = \left(\frac{H'}{RT}\right)^2 x(1-x) \qquad (29\text{–}24') = (27\text{–}15)$$

$$\tau' = \frac{C_p - C'}{C_p}\,\frac{1}{\bar{k} + \tilde{k}}. \qquad (29\text{–}24'') = (27\text{–}16)$$

2a. If also $\beta = 0$, then $\Delta = 0$ and no temperature change occurs; $A = 0$.

2b. $H' = 0$; the two states have the same enthalpy.

$$A = \rho\mathfrak{V}_0{}^2\left(\frac{V'}{V}\right)^2\frac{V}{RT}x(1-x) \qquad (29\text{–}25) = (29\text{–}10)$$

$$\tau' = \frac{1}{\bar{k} + \tilde{k}}. \qquad (29\text{–}25') = (29\text{–}8)$$

3. The general case $H' \neq 0$, $V' \neq 0$ is given by Eq. (29–21), which can be rewritten in the form of Eq. (29–23) by noting that

$$\kappa_T - TV\frac{\beta^2}{C_p} = \kappa_T/\gamma_0 = \kappa_S.$$

$$A = \rho\mathfrak{V}_0{}^2 x(1-x)\frac{VRT}{C_p\tilde{C}_p}\left[\beta\frac{H'}{RT} - \frac{V'}{V}\frac{C_p}{RT}\right]^2$$

$$= \rho\mathfrak{V}_0{}^2 x(1-x)VRT\frac{C_p}{\tilde{C}_p}\left[\left(\frac{\beta}{C_p}\frac{H'}{RT}\right)^2 - 2\frac{\beta}{C_p}\frac{H'}{RT}\frac{V'}{VRT} + \left(\frac{V'}{VRT}\right)^2\right] \tag{29–26}$$

$$\tau' = \frac{\tilde{C}_p}{C_p}\frac{1}{\bar{k} + \tilde{k}}. \tag{29–26'}$$

It is seen that A contains three terms; the first, due to the energy difference H', appears only if $\beta \neq 0$; the last is due only to the volume difference V'; the middle term is mixed, a shift in equilibrium due to H' and β producing a volume change, and vice versa.

By using

$$C_p - \tilde{C}_p = R\left(\frac{H'}{RT}\right)^2 \varphi \tag{29–27}$$

see Eq. (29–16)

$$\kappa_T - \tilde{\kappa}_T = \left(\frac{V'}{V}\right)^2 \frac{V}{RT}\varphi \tag{29–27'}$$

see Eq. (29–10)

$$\beta - \tilde{\beta} = \frac{V'}{V}\frac{H'}{RT^2}\varphi \tag{29–27''}$$

see Eq. (29–16′), one gets[2]

$$VT(\beta - \tilde{\beta})^2 = (\kappa_T - \tilde{\kappa}_T)\,(C_p - \tilde{C}_p). \tag{29–28}$$

---

[2] I. Prigogine and R. Defay, "Chemical Thermodynamics." Longmans, Green, New York, 1954. These authors give an extended treatment of $C - \tilde{C}$, $\kappa - \tilde{\kappa}$, $\beta - \tilde{\beta}$ in their Chap. XIX, using the methods of our Sec. **31**.

30. Does the "Volume Viscosity" Provide Actual Stresses, Even if the Relaxation Phenomenon is the Slow Energy Exchange with Internal Degrees of Freedom or a Chemical Reaction?

The question in the title was asked in Sec. 8 and shall be answered here positively. It could not be discussed before the effects of the slow energy exchange had been developed (Secs. 10 and 11).

To avoid unnecessary complications, consider first the case where P'', the shear stress, is zero; this would be the case in a uniform compression. Call the total stress P, as in Sec. 6. Then

$$P = -p + P'''.$$

Since both p and P''' are scalars, a distinction between them—not only in the above case, but in general—cannot be made from geometrical considerations.

The assumption was made in Sec. 11 that the stress depends only on the energy of the translational degrees of freedom. The corollary to this statement is that, for a given temperature, the energy of the internal degrees of freedom does not depend on the density.

$$\left(\frac{\partial E'}{\partial \rho}\right)_T = 0. \tag{30–1}$$

While in Sec. 11 the stress was written as pure hydrostatic pressure $-p$, we will now write it as P.

Then, if the usual equation of state is

$$p = f(\rho, T) \tag{30–2}$$

the stress equation under variable stress is

$$P = -f(\rho, T_{\text{tr}}). \tag{30–3}$$

It is still perfectly legitimate to identify P with the hydrostatic pressure (as we have done in Sec. 11 by our notation), but this depends then on the rate of change. Instead, one can define a temperature T_{rev}, which would be reached if the same process occured reversibly, and call hydrostatic pressure the quantity

$$p = f(\rho, T_{\text{rev}}). \tag{30–4}$$

Then, one has

$$P''' = P + p = -f(\rho, T_{\text{tr}}) + f(\rho, T_{\text{rev}})$$

$$= \left(\frac{\partial f}{\partial T}\right)_\rho (T_{\text{rev}} - T_{\text{tr}}) = \left(\frac{\partial p}{\partial T}\right)_\rho (T_{\text{rev}} - T_{\text{tr}})$$

$$= \frac{\beta}{\kappa_T} (T_{\text{rev}} - T_{\text{tr}}). \tag{30–5}$$

Now one has, from Eq. (4–11)

$$T_{\text{rev}} - T_0 = \frac{1}{\beta} (\gamma - 1)s. \tag{30–6}$$

Equation (11–4), written as

$$(C_p)_{\text{eff}}\, dT_{\text{tr}} = -V_0 T_0 \beta dP \tag{30–7}$$

together with

$$dP = -\left(\frac{\partial f}{\partial \rho}\right)_T \rho_0\, ds - \left(\frac{\partial f}{\partial T}\right)_\rho dT_{\text{tr}} = -\frac{1}{\kappa_T} ds - \frac{\beta}{\kappa_T} dT_{\text{tr}} \tag{30–8}$$

gives

$$(C_p)_{\text{eff}}\, dT_{\text{tr}} = V_0 T_0 \frac{\beta}{\kappa_T} ds + V_0 T_0 \frac{\beta^2}{\kappa_T} dT_{\text{tr}}$$

and, with Eq. (4–9)

$$(C_v)_{\text{eff}}\, dT_{\text{tr}} = V_0 T_0 \frac{\beta}{\kappa_T} ds = \frac{(C_p - C_v)}{\beta} ds.$$

Therefore, one has

$$T_{\text{tr}} - T_0 = \frac{1}{\beta} (\gamma - 1)_{\text{eff}}\, s \tag{30–9}$$

and, from Eq. (30–5)

$$P''' = -\frac{1}{\kappa_T} (\gamma_{\text{eff}} - \gamma_{\text{rev}})s. \tag{30–10}$$

Therefore

$$-P''' = \left(\frac{\Delta}{(C_v)_{\text{eff}}} - \frac{\Delta}{C_v}\right)\frac{1}{\kappa_T} s$$

$$= \frac{\gamma_{\text{rev}}}{\kappa_T}\frac{C_v}{C_p}\Delta\,\frac{C_v - (C_v)_{\text{eff}}}{C_v (C_v)_{\text{eff}}} s$$

$$= \rho_0 \mathfrak{B}_0{}^2 \frac{\Delta}{C_p}\,\frac{C_v - (C_v)_{\text{eff}}}{(C_v)_{\text{eff}}} s. \tag{30–11}$$

From Eqs. (11–6″) and (11–9)

$$(C_v)_{\text{eff}} = C_v - C' + \frac{C'}{1 + i\omega\tau}$$

and

$$\frac{C_v - (C_v)_{\text{eff}}}{(C_v)_{\text{eff}}} = \frac{C' \dfrac{i\omega\tau}{1 + i\omega\tau}}{C_v - C' + \dfrac{C'}{1 + i\omega\tau}} = \frac{C' i\omega\tau}{C_v + (C_v - C')i\omega\tau}.$$

Introducing with Eq. (11–16)

$$\tau'' = \frac{C_v - C'}{C_v}\tau$$

one has

$$\frac{C_v - (C_v)_{\text{eff}}}{(C_v)_{\text{eff}}} = \frac{C'}{C_v - C'}\,\frac{i\omega\tau''}{1 + i\omega\tau''} \tag{30–12}$$

and

$$-P''' = \rho_0 \mathfrak{B}_0{}^2 \frac{\Delta C'}{C_p (C_v - C')}\,\frac{i\omega\tau''}{1 + i\omega\tau''} s. \tag{30–13}$$

However, using Eq. (11–15)

$$i\,\frac{\mathfrak{B}^3}{\mathfrak{B}_0{}^2}\,\frac{\alpha'}{\omega} = \frac{1}{2}\,\frac{\Delta C'}{C_p (C_v - C')}\,\frac{i\omega\tau''}{1 + i\omega\tau''}$$

so that

$$-P''' = \rho \mathfrak{B}^3 2i \frac{\alpha'}{\omega} s = 2\rho \mathfrak{B}^3 \frac{\alpha'}{\omega^2}\,\frac{1}{\rho}\,\frac{\partial \rho}{\partial t}. \tag{30–14}$$

Therefore, the lack of equilibrium with the internal degrees of freedom has the effect that the normal stress has a different value from the one which would exist if the process had been conducted infinitely slowly and, from Eq. (6–6)

$$\eta' = 2\rho_0 \mathfrak{V}^3 \frac{\alpha'}{\omega^2}. \tag{30–15}$$

The results obtained are in agreement with those of Tisza.[1]

31. Thermodynamic Theory of Relaxation

A very general formalism for relaxation phenomena has been developed,[1] most extensively by Meixner,[2] which does not specify the processes in molecular details, but allows all kind of molecular processes. The first to use this method was Clerk Maxwell.[3] He applied it to shear processes in "viscoelastic" liquids, but it can just as well be used for compressional processes if one introduces the bulk viscosity η'.

The connection between excess pressure, $p - p_0$, and condensation s (in general, deformation), is written

$$p - p_0 = \frac{1}{\kappa} s + \eta' \frac{\partial s}{\partial t}. \tag{31–1}$$

This equation defines the coefficients κ and η'. It has the character of the relaxation equation.

If one defines

$$\tau = \kappa \eta' \tag{31–2}$$

then

$$p - p_0 = \frac{1}{\kappa}\left(s + \tau \frac{\partial s}{\partial t}\right). \tag{31–1'}$$

---

[1] L. Tisza, *Phys. Rev.* **61**, 531 (1942).

[1] L. Mandelstam and M. Leontovič, *Compt. rend. acad. sci. U.R.S.S.* **3**, 111 (1936); *Zhur. Eksptl. i Teoret. Fiz.* **7**, 438 (1938).

[2] J. Meixner, *Ann. Physik* [5] **43**, 470 (1943); *Z. Naturforsch.* **4a**, 594 (1949); **9a**, 654 (1954); *Acoustica* **2**, 101 (1952); *Kolloid-Z.* **134**, 3 (1953).

[3] J. Clerk Maxwell, *Phil. Mag.* [4] **35**, 134 (1867); *Phil. Trans. Roy. Soc.* **157**, 49 (1867); see also E. Jenckel, *Kolloid-Z.* **134**, 47 (1953).

A step function, applied to $p - p_0$ at $t = 0$, gives

$$s = \kappa(p - p_0)\,(1 - e^{-t/\tau}).$$

In the simple harmonic case

$$s = \kappa(p - p_0)\,\frac{1}{1 + i\omega\tau}$$

or

$$\frac{d\rho}{dp} = \rho\,\frac{s}{p - p_0} = \frac{\rho\kappa}{1 + i\omega\tau}\,. \tag{31–3}$$

Equation (31–1) has been elaborated for the treatment of plastic substances. The details may be looked up in, for example, Prager and Hodge's[4] or Kolsky's book.[5] The problem will be taken up again in the chapter on liquids. Meixner's treatment is much more general than the usual one presented in Secs. 9 to 29, insofar as no assumption is made about the "ideality" of the substance. A parameter ξ is introduced to measure the internal state of the system. This may be $T' - T_0$, δx, or any other internal variable. Later on, a whole set of such parameters may be considered instead of a single one.

The next problem is that of setting up the relaxation equation. In non-equilibrium generalized thermodynamics one considers changes as due to the "driving forces" opposed by frictionlike forces. For example, in the one-dimensional diffusion in an ideal solution in the z direction, the flow is given by

$$-D\,\frac{\partial x_1}{\partial z} \tag{31–4}$$

x_1 being the mole fraction of solute (1). The question arises as to what should take the place of x_1 if the solution is not ideal.

Now consider a case of equilibrium in which a concentration gradient is opposed by a gravity field in the z direction. The general thermodynamical equilibrium condition is

$$\mu_1 + M'gz = \text{constant} \tag{31–5}$$

---

[4] W. Prager and P. G. Hodge, Jr., "Theory of Perfectly Plastic Solids." Wiley, New York, 1951.

[5] H. Kolsky, "Stress Waves in Solids." Oxford Univ. Press, London and New York, 1953.

where μ_1 is the so-called chemical potential of substance (1) in the solution; $M'gz$, the potential energy of the gravity field; and M', the effective molecular weight (i.e., including buoyancy) of the solute. There μ_1 is defined as

$$\mu_1 = \frac{\partial F}{\partial n_1}$$

i.e., the increase of free energy of a very large amount of solution if one mole of substance (1) is added. The equilibrium can, however, also be considered dynamically, insofar as the flow produced by gravity is exactly canceled by the flow produced by the concentration gradient, or insofar as the force of gravity on one mole of substance (1) is canceled by the "driving force" of the concentration gradient. One gets this by differentiating Eq. (31–5) with respect to z

$$\frac{\partial \mu_1}{\partial z} + M'g = \frac{\partial \mu_1}{\partial x_1}\frac{\partial x_1}{\partial z} + M'g = 0.$$

i.e., $-(\partial\mu_1/\partial z) = -(\partial\mu_1/\partial x_1)\,\partial x_1/\partial z$ is the "driving force" of the concentration gradient.

This concept is then generalized, giving a general relaxation equation

$$\frac{d\xi}{dt} = \overline{\overline{k}}A \tag{31–6}$$

where $\overline{\overline{k}}$ is a rate constant and A the thermodynamical activity, defined by Gibbs' expression

$$dH = TdS + Vdp - Ad\xi. \tag{31–7}$$

For example, if we have a chemical isomeric reaction (1) $\rightleftarrows$ (2) this is

$$d(H_2 - H_1) = Td(S_2 - S_1) + (V_2 - V_1)dp - (\mu_1 - \mu_2)d\xi.$$

In equilibrium we have $A = 0$. Then A can be developed in the neighborhood of equilibrium into a power series

$$A = A_0 + \frac{\partial A}{\partial \xi}(\xi - \xi_0)$$

or

$$\frac{d\xi}{dt} = \overline{\overline{k}}\left(\frac{\partial A}{\partial \xi}\right)(\xi - \xi_0).$$

Defining

$$\frac{1}{\tau} = -\bar{k}\left(\frac{\partial A}{\partial \xi}\right) \qquad (31\text{–}8)$$

this gives

$$\frac{d\xi}{dt} = -\frac{1}{\tau}(\xi - \xi_0). \qquad (31\text{–}9)$$

However, the value of $\partial A/\partial \xi$ depends on the condition of the experiment, or on the question of which variables are kept constant in the differentiation in Eq. (31–8). The value of A itself is independent of the question of whether or not V or p is kept constant, as long as T is, since then

$$-A = \left(\frac{\partial F}{\partial \xi}\right)_T = \sum \mu_j \frac{\partial n_j}{\partial \xi}$$

with $\partial n_j/\partial \xi$ a pure number, depending only on the composition and the definition of ξ.

One has, for example, using Eq. (31–7)[6]

$$\left(\frac{1}{\tau}\right)_{TV} = -\bar{k}\left(\frac{\partial A}{\partial \xi}\right)_{T,V} \qquad \left(\frac{1}{\tau}\right)_{Tp} = -\bar{k}\left(\frac{\partial A}{\partial \xi}\right)_{T,p}. \qquad (31\text{–}10)$$

Meixner proves that in general

$$\tau_{SV} \leqslant \tau_{TV} \leqslant \tau_{Tp} \qquad \tau_{SV} \leqslant \tau_{Sp} \leqslant \tau_{Tp}. \qquad (31\text{–}10')$$

---

[6] According to I. Prigogine and R. Defay, "Chemical Thermodynamics." Longmans, Green, 1954, one has—see their Eqs. (4.70) and (6.59)

$$\left(\frac{\partial A}{\partial \xi}\right)_{T,p} = \left(\frac{\partial A}{\partial \xi}\right)_{T,V} + \frac{V}{\tilde{\kappa}_T}\left(\frac{1}{V}\frac{\partial V}{\partial \xi}\right)^2_{T,p}. \qquad (31\text{–}10'')$$

Similarly

$$\left(\frac{\partial A}{\partial \xi}\right)_S = \left(\frac{\partial A}{\partial \xi}\right)_T + \left(\frac{\partial S}{\partial \xi}\right)_T \left[\left(\frac{\partial \xi}{\partial T}\right)_S\right]^{-1}$$

$$= \left(\frac{\partial A}{\partial \xi}\right)_T - \frac{T}{\tilde{C}}\left[\left(\frac{\partial S}{\partial \xi}\right)_T\right]^2. \qquad (31\text{–}10''')$$

The second index may be either V or p ($\tilde{C}_v$ or $\tilde{C}_p$). In Eq. (31–10″), the index T may be replaced by the index S.

Generalizing the development, one gets

$$\frac{1}{\bar{\bar{k}}}\frac{d\xi}{dt} = \left(\frac{\partial A}{\partial T}\right)_{V,\xi}(T - T_0) + \left(\frac{\partial A}{\partial V}\right)_{T,\xi}(V - V_0) + \left(\frac{\partial A}{\partial \xi}\right)_{T,V}(\xi - \xi_0) \tag{31–11}$$

where ξ_0 is the equilibrium value of ξ for $T = T_0$, $V = V_0$. The equilibrium value ξ^0 of ξ at T, V is given by

$$0 = \left(\frac{\partial A}{\partial T}\right)_{V,\xi}(T - T_0) + \left(\frac{\partial A}{\partial V}\right)_{T,\xi}(V - V_0) + \left(\frac{\partial A}{\partial \xi}\right)_{T,V}(\xi^0 - \xi_0). \tag{31–11′}$$

Subtracting Eq. (31–11′) from (31–11), one gets Eq. (31–9) back in the form

$$\frac{d\xi}{dt} = -\frac{1}{\tau}(\xi - \xi^0) \tag{31–11″}$$

for T, V varying in time.

Next, one writes the equation of state

$$p - p_0 = \left(\frac{\partial p}{\partial T}\right)_{V,\xi}(T - T_0) + \left(\frac{\partial p}{\partial V}\right)_{T,\xi}(V - V_0) + \left(\frac{\partial p}{\partial \xi}\right)_{T,V}(\xi - \xi_0). \tag{31–12}$$

In equilibrium $\xi = \xi^0$, and one gets, by eliminating $\xi^0 - \xi_0$ with the help of Eq. (31–11′)

$$(p - p_0)_{\text{equ}} = \left\{\left(\frac{\partial p}{\partial T}\right)_{V,\xi} - \left(\frac{\partial p}{\partial \xi}\right)_{T,V}\left[\left(\frac{\partial A}{\partial \xi}\right)_{T,V}\right]^{-1}\left(\frac{\partial A}{\partial T}\right)_{V,\xi}\right\}(T - T_0) + \left\{\left(\frac{\partial p}{\partial V}\right)_{T,\xi} - \left(\frac{\partial p}{\partial \xi}\right)_{T,V}\left[\left(\frac{\partial A}{\partial \xi}\right)_{T,V}\right]^{-1}\left(\frac{\partial A}{\partial V}\right)_{T,\xi}\right\}(V - V_0). \tag{31–12′}$$

This means, for example, that

$$\left(\frac{\partial p}{\partial V}\right)_{T\text{equ}} = -\frac{1}{V}\frac{1}{\kappa_T} = \left(\frac{\partial p}{\partial V}\right)_{T,\xi} - \left(\frac{\partial p}{\partial \xi}\right)_{T,V}\left[\left(\frac{\partial A}{\partial \xi}\right)_{T,V}\right]^{-1}\left(\frac{\partial A}{\partial V}\right)_{T,\xi}. \tag{31–13}$$

The first term on the right is connected with the "frozen compressibility" $\tilde{\kappa}$

$$-\left(\frac{\partial p}{\partial V}\right)_{T,\xi} = \frac{1}{V}\frac{1}{\tilde{\kappa}_T}.$$

Similarly

$$\left(\frac{\partial p}{\partial T}\right)_{V\text{equ}} = \frac{\beta}{\kappa_T} = \left(\frac{\partial p}{\partial T}\right)_{V,\xi} - \left(\frac{\partial p}{\partial \xi}\right)_{T,V}\left[\left(\frac{\partial A}{\partial \xi}\right)_{T,V}\right]^{-1}\left(\frac{\partial A}{\partial T}\right)_{V,\xi}$$

$$\left(\frac{\partial p}{\partial T}\right)_{V,\xi} = \frac{\tilde{\beta}}{\tilde{\kappa}_T}. \tag{31–13′}$$

To treat nonequilibrium, one eliminates $\xi - \xi_0$ from Eq. (31–12) with the help of Eq. (31–11). One does this by differentiating Eq. (31–12) with respect to time, substituting on the right the expression for $d\xi/dt$ from Eq. (31–11), and then eliminating $\xi - \xi_0$ by a second use of Eq. (31–12). The result is

$$p - p_0 + \tau_{TV}\frac{dp}{dt} = \left(\frac{\partial p}{\partial T}\right)_{V\text{equ}}(T - T_0) + \left(\frac{\widetilde{\partial p}}{\partial T}\right)_V \tau_{TV}\frac{dT}{dt} +$$
$$\left(\frac{\partial p}{\partial V}\right)_{T\text{equ}}(V - V_0) + \left(\frac{\widetilde{\partial p}}{\partial V}\right)_T \tau_{TV}\frac{dV}{dt} \tag{31–14}$$

where, as usual, the circumflex means the frozen values ($\xi = \xi_0$). Introducing the abbreviations

$$\tau_{Vp} = \left(\frac{\widetilde{\partial p}}{\partial T}\right)_V\left[\left(\frac{\partial p}{\partial T}\right)_{V\text{equ}}\right]^{-1}\tau_{TV} = \frac{\tilde{\beta}}{\tilde{\kappa}_T}\frac{\kappa_T}{\beta}\tau_{TV} \tag{31–15}$$

$$\tau_{Tp} = \left(\frac{\widetilde{\partial p}}{\partial V}\right)_T\left[\left(\frac{\partial p}{\partial V}\right)_{T\text{equ}}\right]^{-1}\tau_{TV} = \frac{\kappa_T}{\tilde{\kappa}_T}\tau_{TV} \tag{31–15′}$$

see footnote 7, one then has

$$p - p_0 + \tau_{TV}\frac{dp}{dt} = \frac{\beta}{\kappa_T}\left[T - T_0 + \tau_{Vp}\frac{dT}{dt}\right] - \frac{1}{V\kappa_T}\left[V - V_0 + \tau_{Tp}\frac{dV}{dt}\right]. \tag{31–14′}$$

---

[7] With the help of Eq. (31–13), one gets

$$\frac{\tau_{TV}}{\tau_{Tp}} = \left(\frac{\partial p}{\partial V}\right)_{T\,\text{equ}}\left[\left(\frac{\widetilde{\partial p}}{\partial V}\right)_T\right]^{-1} = 1 - V\tilde{\kappa}\left(\frac{\partial p}{\partial \xi}\right)_{T,V}\left(\frac{\partial A}{\partial V}\right)_{T,\xi}\left[\left(\frac{\partial A}{\partial \xi}\right)_{T,V}\right]^{-1}$$

According to the Prigogine-Defay Eqs. (4.38) and (4.69), the right side is

$$1 - V\tilde{\kappa}\left(\frac{\partial p}{\partial \xi}\right)^2_{T,V}\left[\left(\frac{\partial A}{\partial \xi}\right)_{T,V}\right]^{-1} = 1 - \frac{1}{V\tilde{\kappa}}\left(\frac{\partial V}{\partial \xi}\right)^2_{T,p}\left[\left(\frac{\partial A}{\partial \xi}\right)_{T,V}\right]^{-1}.$$

This, however, is, following Eq. (4–70), equal to $(\partial A/\partial\xi)_{T,p}[(\partial A/\partial\xi)_{T,V}]^{-1}$, so that the quantity τ_{Tp} defined in Eq. (31–15′) is the same as that defined in Eq. (31–10).

If, for the sake of simplicity, we consider the isothermal case, Eq. (31–14′) is reduced to

$$p - p_0 + \tau_{TV}\frac{dp}{dt} = -\frac{1}{V\kappa_T}\left[(V - V_0) + \tau_{Tp}\frac{dV}{dt}\right]. \tag{31–14″}$$

This is an improved, more general form of Eq. (31–1).

However, for the acoustic case it is more convenient to use as independent variables S, V, ξ instead of T, V, ξ, so that the rate equation is

$$\frac{1}{\overline{\overline{k}}}\frac{d\xi}{dt} = \left(\frac{\partial A}{\partial S}\right)_{V,\xi}(S - S_0) + \left(\frac{\partial A}{\partial V}\right)_{S,\xi}(V - V_0) + \left(\frac{\partial A}{\partial \xi}\right)_{S,V}(\xi - \xi_0) \tag{31–16}$$

and with the definition

$$\frac{1}{\tau_{SV}} = -\overline{\overline{k}}\left(\frac{\partial A}{\partial \xi}\right)_{S,V} \tag{31–17}$$

the rate equation can be rewritten

$$\frac{d\xi}{dt} = -\frac{1}{\tau_{SV}}(\xi - \xi^0). \tag{31–16′}$$

The equation of state is

$$\begin{aligned} p - p_0 &= \left(\frac{\partial p}{\partial S}\right)_{V,\xi}(S - S_0) + \left(\frac{\partial p}{\partial V}\right)_{S,\xi}(V - V_0) + \left(\frac{\partial p}{\partial \xi}\right)_{S,V}(\xi - \xi_0) \\ &= \left(\frac{\partial \tilde{p}}{\partial S}\right)_{V}(S - S_0) - \frac{1}{V\tilde{\kappa}_S}(V - V_0) + \left(\frac{\partial p}{\partial \xi}\right)_{S,V}(\xi - \xi_0). \end{aligned} \tag{31–18}$$

Define now

$$\frac{1}{\kappa_S} = \frac{\gamma}{\kappa_T} = \frac{1}{\tilde{\kappa}_S} + \left(\frac{\partial p}{\partial \xi}\right)_{S,V}\left[\left(\frac{\partial A}{\partial \xi}\right)_{S,V}\right]^{-1}\left(\frac{\partial A}{\partial V}\right)_{S,\xi} = \frac{1}{\tilde{\kappa}_S} + \left[\left(\frac{\partial p}{\partial \xi}\right)_{S,V}\right]^2\left[\left(\frac{\partial A}{\partial \xi}\right)_{S,V}\right]^{-1} \tag{31–18′}$$

$$\left(\frac{\partial p}{\partial S}\right)_{V} = \left(\frac{\partial \tilde{p}}{\partial S}\right)_{V} - \left(\frac{\partial p}{\partial \xi}\right)_{S,V}\left[\left(\frac{\partial A}{\partial \xi}\right)_{S,V}\right]^{-1}\left(\frac{\partial A}{\partial S}\right)_{V,\xi} \tag{31–18″}$$

$$\tau_{pV}{}^{*} = \left(\frac{\partial \tilde{p}}{\partial S}\right)_{V}\left[\left(\frac{\partial p}{\partial S}\right)_{V}\right]^{-1}\tau_{SV} \tag{31–17′}$$

$$\tau_{Sp} = \frac{\kappa_S}{\tilde{\kappa}_S}\tau_{SV} = \frac{\tilde{\gamma}}{\gamma}\frac{\kappa_T}{\tilde{\kappa}_T}\tau_{SV}\,. \tag{31–17″}$$

One then gets as relaxation equation

$$p - p_0 + \tau_{SV} \frac{dp}{dt} = \left(\frac{\partial p}{\partial S}\right)_V \left[S - S_0 + \tau_{pV}{}^* \frac{dS}{dt}\right] - \frac{1}{\kappa_S} \frac{1}{V} \left[V - V_0 + \tau_{Sp} \frac{dV}{dt}\right]. \tag{31–19}$$

For an isentropic process, the first term on the right is zero. A relaxation process is, while adiabatic, not isentropic, because it is irreversible. However, if the sound amplitude is considered a small quantity of the first order, the entropy variation is of the second order, since the entropy in equilibrium is a maximum. Therefore, we can write for small amplitudes (but not in shock waves)

$$p - p_0 + \tau_{SV} \frac{dp}{dt} = \frac{1}{\kappa_S} \left[s + \tau_{Sp} \frac{ds}{dt}\right] \tag{31–19′}$$

where s is again the condensation, $s = (V_0 - V)/V$. We now investigate the behavior of the system if subject to a "stepfunction", i.e., we suddenly change either the pressure from p_0 to p_1, or the condensation from zero to s_1. We integrate Eq. (31–19′) over the very short time of the "sudden" change

$$\int (p - p_0)\, dt + \tau_{SV} \int \frac{dp}{dt} dt = \frac{1}{\kappa_S} \left[\int s\, dt + \tau_{Sp} \int \frac{ds}{dt} dt\right]. \tag{31–19″}$$

During the rapid change, the first terms on both sides of Eq. (31–19″) can be neglected compared to the second terms, so that

$$\tau_{SV} (p' - p_0) = \frac{1}{\kappa_S} \tau_{Sp}\, s' \tag{31–20}$$

where p', s' are the instantaneous values of p and s immediately after the application of the step function. In view of Eq. (31–17″), the relation between the instantaneous changes is given by

$$p' - p_0 = \frac{1}{\tilde{\kappa}_S} s' \tag{31–20′}$$

i.e., by the "frozen" compressibility, as one might have expected. The behavior from then on depends upon whether one keeps the pressure constant $p_1 = p'$ and lets the material "give", or keeps the deformation constant $s' = s_1$ and lets the stress "relax".

In the first case

$$p_1 - p_0 = \frac{1}{\kappa_S}\left(s + \tau_{Sp}\frac{ds}{dt}\right) \tag{31–20''}$$

$$s = s_1 + (s' - s_1)\, e^{-t/\tau_p} = (p_1 - p_0)\,[\tilde{\kappa}_S + (\kappa_S - \tilde{\kappa}_S)\,(1 - e^{-t/\tau_p})].$$

In the case of stress relaxation, the equation is

$$p - p_0 + \tau_V \frac{dp}{dt} = \frac{1}{\kappa_S}\, s_1$$

$$p - p_0 = p_1 - p_0 + (p' - p_1)\, e^{-t/\tau_V} = s_1\left[\frac{1}{\tilde{\kappa}_S} - \left(\frac{1}{\tilde{\kappa}_S} - \frac{1}{\kappa_S}\right)(1 - e^{-t/\tau_V})\right]. \tag{31–20'''}$$

The index S is understood to be the second index on τ_p and τ_V. Equation (31–1) would give no instantaneous strain in the first case, and no stress relaxation in the second, but instead very high momentary stresses.

Next, discuss simple harmonic motion. Then Eq. (31–19') gives

$$(1 + i\omega\tau_{SV})\,(p - p_0) = \frac{1}{\kappa_S}\,(1 + i\omega\tau_{Sp})\, s. \tag{31–21}$$

One gets for a progressive wave

$$\frac{s}{p - p_0} = \frac{1}{\rho}\left(\frac{1}{\mathfrak{B}} - \frac{i\alpha}{\omega}\right)^2 = \kappa_S \frac{1 + i\omega\tau_{SV}}{1 + i\omega\tau_{Sp}} \tag{31–21'}$$

or

$$\left(\frac{\mathfrak{B}_0}{\mathfrak{B}} - \frac{i\alpha\mathfrak{B}_0}{\omega}\right)^2 = \frac{1 + i\omega\tau_{SV}}{1 + i\omega\tau_{Sp}} = 1 - \frac{\tau_{Sp} - \tau_{SV}}{\tau_{Sp}}\,\frac{i\omega\tau_{Sp}}{1 + i\omega\tau_{Sp}}$$

$$= 1 - \frac{\kappa_S - \tilde{\kappa}_S}{\kappa_S}\,\frac{i\omega\tau_{Sp}}{1 + i\omega\tau_{Sp}} \tag{31–22}$$

Because of the Braun-Le Chatelier principle, we always have $\kappa_S \geqslant \tilde{\kappa}_S$. Equation (31–22) is the normal dispersion and absorption equation. If we had taken the reciprocal of Eq. (31–22)—to get, as approximate real part, $\mathfrak{B}^2/\mathfrak{B}_0{}^2$—it would have been

$$1 + \frac{\kappa_S - \tilde{\kappa}_S}{\tilde{\kappa}_S}\,\frac{i\omega\tau_{SV}}{1 + i\omega\tau_{SV}}. \tag{31–22'}$$

The low-frequency volume viscosity at constant entropy—which is the quantity usually meant—follows from Eq. (31–22) as

$$(\eta')_S = \rho\,\mathfrak{V}_0{}^2 \frac{\kappa_S - \tilde{\kappa}_S}{\kappa_S} \tau_{Sp} = \frac{\kappa_S - \tilde{\kappa}_S}{\kappa_S{}^2} \tau_{Sp} = \frac{\kappa_S - \tilde{\kappa}_S}{\kappa_S \tilde{\kappa}_S} \tau_{SV} = \rho \mathfrak{V}_0{}^2 \frac{\kappa_S - \tilde{\kappa}_S}{\tilde{\kappa}_S} \tau_{SV}\,. \tag{31–23}$$

This differs from the expression (31–2) by the factor $(\kappa_S - \tilde{\kappa}_S)/\kappa_S$. Equation (31–1) does not lead to an instantaneous compressibility $\tilde{\kappa}_S$. In general, there seems to be no simple relationship between τ_V and the elementary time $(\bar{\bar{k}})^{-1}$.

Next, this theory is generalized by introducing a set of ξ's. One has

$$\frac{d\xi_j}{dt} = \sum_i \left(\sum_s \bar{\bar{k}}_{js} \frac{\partial A_s}{\partial \xi_i} \right) (\xi_i - \xi_i{}^0) + (V - V_0) \sum_s \bar{\bar{k}}_{js} \left(\frac{\partial A_s}{\partial V} \right)_{T,\xi} + (T - T_0) \sum_s \bar{\bar{k}}_{js} \left(\frac{\partial A_s}{\partial T} \right)_{V,\xi} . \tag{31–24}$$

The so-called Onsager relations give

$$\bar{\bar{k}}_{sj} = \bar{\bar{k}}_{js}$$

This is, of course, the general theory for the problems treated in Secs. 21 to 26.

It follows from Eq. (31–7), by writing

$$dH = dF + TdS + SdT$$

that

$$A_j = \left(\frac{\partial F}{\partial \xi_j} \right)_{p,T} \tag{31–25}$$

and

$$\left(\frac{\partial A_j}{\partial \xi_s} \right)_{p,T} = \left(\frac{\partial^2 F}{\partial \xi_j \partial \xi_s} \right)_{p,T} = \left(\frac{\partial A_s}{\partial \xi_j} \right)_{p,T} . \tag{31–26}$$

To illustrate the preceding case of a two-state system, one has

$$A = \mu_1 - \mu_2$$

$$d\xi = dn_1 = -dn_2 = n dx$$

$$\frac{\partial A}{\partial \xi} = \frac{1}{n} \left(\frac{\partial \mu_1}{\partial x} - \frac{\partial \mu_2}{\partial x} \right).$$

Using the Duhem-Margules equation

$$\frac{x}{1-x}\frac{\partial \mu_1}{\partial x} = -\frac{\partial \mu_2}{\partial x}$$

—which expresses the fact that the chemical potentials are not changed by adding substances (1) and (2) in the ratio $x : 1 - x$—one gets

$$\frac{\partial A}{\partial \xi} = \frac{1}{n}\frac{1}{1-x}\frac{\partial \mu_1}{\partial x}.$$

If the mixture of (1) and (2) is ideal

$$\mu_1 = \mu_1^0(p,T) + RT \ln x$$

and

$$\left(\frac{\partial A}{\partial \xi}\right)_{Tp} = \frac{RT}{n}\frac{1}{x(1-x)} = \frac{RT}{n}\varphi^{-1}$$

$$\frac{\partial V}{\partial \xi} = V_1 - V_2 = -V'.$$

It is seen that $\bar{\bar{k}}$ is not directly the rate of a molecular process, since in the above case

$$\frac{1}{\tau_{Tp}} = \frac{RT}{n}\bar{\bar{k}}\varphi^{-1}.$$

Meixner next shows the equivalence of the relaxation equations to an "after effect" theory. This theory was first developed by Maxwell[3] and Boltzmann[8] to describe elastic and magnetic hysteresis, in which the value of the dependent variable (deformation or magnetization) also depends on *past* values of the independent variable (stress or magnetic field). Of course, we now conversely describe elastic after effects by relaxation. The basic assumption of the theory is the principle of superposition, i.e., the linearity of the equations. It is also assumed that the effect of a force previously applied and then withdrawn dies down in time.

---

[8] L. Boltzmann, *Sitzber. Akad. Wiss. Wien Math. naturw. Kl. Abt. II a* **70**, 275 (1874); J. Hopkinson, *Phil. Trans. Roy. Soc.* **166**, 489 (1876); **167**, 599 (1877–1878); *Phil. Mag.* [5] **2**, 314 (1876).

The general picture[9,10] of the relation between a description by differential equations and by the after effect theory is as follows: The problem is only important if the external forces—here, for example, the stress, $p - p_0$ — vary in a prescribed, complicated manner with time. Then there are two simple methods of solving for the resultant motion.

(a) One solves the equations for a simple harmonic force. One then subjects the given force to a Fourier analysis. The motion induced by each Fourier component has just been calculated. The resultant motion is the sum of all the motions produced by the Fourier components of the force. In the case treated here, this is the simplest method, since we always assume a simple harmonic force, i.e., a single Fourier component.

(b) One investigates the motion at time t which has been produced by an impulsive force applied at a previous time t'. An impulsive force is one which is zero up to time t', then has the value $P(t')$ during the time dt', and goes back to zero afterward. Let the result of such a motion (deformation) at t be

$$s = f(t - t')P(t')dt'.$$

It is assumed that f goes to zero with increasing elapsed time $t - t'$. One then decomposes the force which has acted in the past ($t' \leqq t$) into impulsive forces and superposes the result

$$s = \int_{-\infty}^{t} f(t - t')P(t')dt'. \qquad (31\text{–}27)$$

This is the after effect theory; in the case of relaxation phenomena, the f are sums of exponential functions with real negative exponents $-t/\tau_S$. Meixner also treats the more complicated case in which the number of internal variables is infinite, and deals with its relation to the after effect presentation. In an additional paper, the results are generalized to non-isotropic substances.

[9] E. Hiedemann and R. Spence, *Z. Physik* **133**, 109 (1952).

[10] B. Gross, "Mathematical Structure of the Theories of Viscoelasticity." Hermann, Paris, 1953.

III. Special Topics

32. Scattering

It has been suggested that the excess absorption in fluids is only apparent and, in reality, is due to the scattering of the sound wave on small regions of the fluid which, due to statistical fluctuation, have different densities. That this cannot be so in general can, however, be seen from the fact that the statistical density fluctuations are the same in all ideal gases at a given temperature and pressure, so that all ideal gases would have the same excess absorption if the explanation were true. The calculation given below—which is a modification of one first published by Lucas—shows that the scattering effect is in general much too small to influence the measured absorption. However, near a critical point of unmixing of a liquid solution the fluctuations become so great that the effect is quite noticeable, as Lucas and Biquard[1] have shown experimentally.

The calculation falls into two parts: first, the scattering by a given fluctuation; and second, the statistics of fluctuations.

According to Anderson,[2] the wave scattered by a fluid sphere, of density ρ' and compressibility κ', imbedded in a fluid of density ρ and compressibility κ, has, at a distance r, an amplitude given by

$$\frac{r_0}{r}\left(\frac{\omega r_0}{\mathfrak{B}}\right)^2\left[\frac{1}{3}\left(\frac{\kappa'}{\kappa}-1\right)+\cos\theta\,\frac{1-(\rho'/\rho)}{1+2\,(\rho'/\rho)}\right] \tag{32–1}$$

if the amplitude of the incident wave is set equal to one and the radius of the sphere, r_0, is small compared to the wavelength. If one integrates over the surface of the sphere, the total energy scattered per second is

$$4\pi r_0^{\,2}\left(\frac{\omega r_0}{\mathfrak{B}}\right)^4\left\{\frac{1}{9}\left(\frac{\kappa'}{\kappa}-1\right)^2+\frac{1}{3}\left(\frac{1-(\rho'/\rho)}{1+2\,(\rho'/\rho)}\right)^2\right\}\mathscr{I} \tag{32–2}$$

---

[1] R. Lucas and P. Biquard, *Trans. Faraday Soc.* **33**, 130 (1937).

[2] V. C. Anderson, *J. Acoust. Soc. Am.* **22**, 426 (1950).

where $\mathscr{I}$ is the intensity of the incident sound wave. If there are n spheres per cc, the absorption coefficient for amplitude due to scattering is

$$\alpha_{SC} = 2\pi n r_0^2 \left(\frac{\omega r_0}{\mathfrak{B}}\right)^4 \left\{\frac{1}{9}\left(\frac{\kappa'}{\kappa} - 1\right)^2 + \frac{1}{3}\left(\frac{1-(\rho'/\rho)}{1+2(\rho'/\rho)}\right)^2\right\}. \qquad (32\text{–}3)$$

We now assume that the sphere consists of the same liquid, slightly compressed

$$\rho' = \rho(1+s)$$

that s is treated as small of the first order, and that κ' differs from κ only because the liquid is compressed, i.e.

$$\kappa' = \kappa + \frac{\partial\kappa}{\partial\rho}(\rho'-\rho) = \kappa\left(1 + \frac{1}{\kappa}\frac{\partial\kappa}{\partial\rho}\rho s\right). \qquad (32\text{–}4)$$

Then finally

$$\alpha_{SC} = \frac{2\pi}{27} n r_0^2 \left(\frac{\omega r_0}{\mathfrak{B}}\right)^4 \left[1 + 3\left(\frac{\rho}{\kappa}\frac{\partial\kappa}{\partial\rho}\right)^2\right] s^2 \qquad (32\text{–}5)$$

or, with $v_0 = (4\pi/3)r_0^3$

$$\alpha_{SC} = \frac{1}{24\pi} n v_0^2 \left(\frac{\omega}{\mathfrak{B}}\right)^4 \left[1 + 3\left(\frac{\rho}{\kappa}\frac{\partial\kappa}{\partial\rho}\right)^2\right] s^2. \qquad (32\text{–}6)$$

Next comes the probability calculation,[3] which proceeds according to the presentation given to the ideas of Smoluchowski and Einstein by Fowler.[4]

The work necessary to form the sphere of density ρ' reversibly and isothermally is

$$w = \int_v^{v_0} p\,dV = \int \frac{1}{\kappa_T} s\,dV = \frac{v_0}{\kappa_T}\int s\,ds = \frac{v_0}{\kappa_T}\frac{s^2}{2} \qquad (32\text{–}7)$$

provided κ_T is not zero, i.e., if we are not at the critical point.

---

[3] The notation in this section—P for probability, w for work, and v_0 for a volume—does not occur elsewhere in this book.

[4] R. H. Fowler, "Statistical Mechanics," 2nd ed. Cambridge Univ. Press, London and New York, 1936.

The probability of having a volume v_0 with a compression between s and $s + ds$ is given by

$$dP = Be^{-w/kT}\, ds = B' \exp\left(-\frac{v_0}{\kappa_T kT}\, s^2\right) d(\sqrt{v_0}\, s) \tag{32–8}$$

where B' is a constant such that the sum of all probabilities is one

$$\int dP = B' \int_{-\infty}^{\infty} \exp\left(-\frac{v_0}{\kappa_T kT}\, s^2\right) d(\sqrt{v_0}\, s).$$

Since

$$\int_{-\infty}^{\infty} e^{-x^2}\, dx = \sqrt{\pi}$$

one finds

$$B' = \sqrt{\frac{1}{\pi\kappa kT}}.$$

Accordingly, the average value of $v_0 s^2$ is found as

$$\overline{v_0 s^2} = \int v_0 s^2 dP = B' \int_{-\infty}^{\infty} v_0 s^2 \exp\left(-\frac{v_0 s^2}{\kappa kT}\right) d(\sqrt{v_0}\, s) = \frac{1}{2}\kappa kT. \tag{32–9}$$

From Eq. (32–8) to Eq. (32–9) the index T on κ has been left out.

One now puts[5]

$$n v_0 = 1 \tag{32–10}$$

assuming the fluctuations to fill the vessel.

Then, from Eq. (32–6)

$$\begin{aligned}\overline{\alpha_{SC}} &= \frac{1}{24\pi}\, n v_0\, \overline{v_0\, s^2} \left(\frac{\omega}{\mathfrak{V}}\right)^4 \left[1 + 3\left(\frac{\rho}{\kappa}\frac{\partial\kappa}{\partial\rho}\right)^2\right] \\ &= \frac{1}{48\pi}\, \kappa_T kT \left(\frac{\omega}{\mathfrak{V}}\right)^4 \left[1 + 3\left(\frac{\rho}{\kappa}\frac{\partial\kappa}{\partial\rho}\right)^2\right] \\ &= \frac{1}{48\pi}\, \kappa_T kT \left(\frac{\omega}{\mathfrak{V}}\right)^4 \left[1 + 3\left(\frac{1}{\kappa^2}\frac{\partial\kappa}{\partial p}\right)^2\right]\end{aligned} \tag{32–11}$$

[5] This at least gives an upper limit for α_{SC}.

since

$$\rho \frac{\partial \kappa}{\partial \rho} = \frac{\partial \kappa}{\partial p} \rho \frac{\partial p}{\partial \rho} = \frac{\partial \kappa}{\partial p}\left(-V \frac{\partial p}{\partial V}\right).$$

For an ideal gas, $\kappa = 1/p$, the bracket in Eq. (32–11) is equal to 4, and one has

$$\alpha_{SC} = \frac{1}{12\pi} \frac{kT}{p} \left(\frac{\omega}{\mathfrak{B}}\right)^4$$

or

$$\frac{\alpha_{SC}}{f^2} = \frac{\pi}{3} \frac{kT}{p} \frac{1}{\mathfrak{B}^2} \left(\frac{\omega}{\mathfrak{B}}\right)^2. \tag{32–12}$$

For a gas like nitrogen, at room temperature and 1 atm, this would be equal to $3 \times 10^{-38} \omega^2$. Since under these conditions $\alpha_{class}/f^2 \sim 1.3 \times 10^{-13}$, ω would have to be 2×10^{11} to make α_{SC} equal to 1% of the classical absorption. Equation (32–12) and the classical absorption depend on the pressure in the same manner.

For a liquid like benzene, $\kappa \sim 90 \times 10^{-6}$/atm, $1/\kappa\,(\partial\kappa/\partial p) \sim 1/1100$ per atm, and $1/\kappa^2\,(\partial\kappa/\partial p) \gg 1$. Therefore

$$\frac{\bar{\alpha}_{SC}}{f^2} = \frac{\pi}{4} \frac{1}{\kappa_T} kT \frac{\omega^2}{\mathfrak{B}^4} \left(\frac{1}{\kappa} \frac{\partial \kappa}{\partial p}\right)^2 \tag{32–13}$$

or, for benzene

$$\frac{\bar{\alpha}_{SC}}{f^2} = 10^{-35} \omega^2.$$

To have the scattering contribute 1% to classical absorption (or 0.01% to the actual absorption), ω has to be 5×10^7, so that experimentally the effect of scattering on absorption is negligible.

33. Absorption of High Intensity Sound Waves

Fox and Rock[1] observed that the absorption of a sound wave increases if its intensity transcends 0.04 watts cm^{-2} and ascribed this to cavitation. Fox[2]

---

[1] F. E. Fox and G. D. Rock, *J. Acoust. Soc. Am.* **12**, 505 (1941); *Phys. Rev.* **70**, 68 (1946). See also L. Bergmann, "Ultrasonics", Transl. by H. S. Hatfield, J. Wiley and Sons, New York, 1938. p. 132.

[2] F. E. Fox, *Nuovo Cimento* **7**, *Suppl.* 2, 198 (1950).

undertook for the first time quantitative measurements of the phenomenon and made an attempt to test the theory. He found that the increase in absorption does not seem to be connected with cavitation; at the intensities and frequencies used (5 and 10 Mc) one should not expect cavitation and none was observed. Furthermore, aerated and degassed water behave alike, while their cavitation should be very different.

Fox and Wallace[3] gave an alternate theory of the phenomenon. At the high intensities involved, the linearization of the hydrodynamic equations (Sec. 3) is not justified any more. Accordingly, a wave originally sinusoidal is being distorted, producing higher harmonics. However, if one is in the frequency region in which the absorption is proportional to the square of the frequency, the nth harmonic has an absorption n^2 times that of the fundamental, so that one may expect the production of harmonics to increase the over-all absorption.

To get a physical picture of the distortion of the waves of large amplitude, one can look at it in the following way: Compressibility always decreases with increasing pressure. Therefore, the compressibility is smaller at the crest—where the pressure is higher—than in the medium at rest; and greater in the trough, where there is underpressure. As a consequence, the speed at which a particular disturbance is propagated is higher than $\mathfrak{V}_0$ at the crest and lower than $\mathfrak{V}_0$ at the trough. Accordingly, the crests tend to overtake the troughs, and a wave which starts out sinusoidally becomes steeper in front and less steep in back, until a shock wave is formed. However, for intermediate intensities, a comparatively stable waveform is reached. This happens because the friction loss increases with the steepness of the velocity gradient, until the friction loss exactly compensates the effect which would further steepen the wave. Gradually the amplitude gets less, because of absorption loss, and the wave returns to sinusoidal form. This behavior of the comparatively stable wave form—like a sawtooth at high intensity, more like a sinusoidal wave at low intensity—has been particularly studied by Fay[4] and Mendousse.[5] However, the emphasis on the steepness of the front does not make it clear whether other causes of loss act in the same way as classical viscosity, and does not make it easy to calculate the over-all, apparent absorption along the wave.

---

[3] F. E. Fox and W. A. Wallace, *J. Acoust. Soc. Am.* **26**, 994 (1954).

[4] R. D. Fay, *J. Acoust. Soc. Am.* **3**, 222 (1931).

[5] J. S. Mendousse, *J. Acoust. Soc. Am.* **25**, 51 (1953).

A different approach is used to calculate the appearance of higher harmonics. This was done by Thuras *et al.*[6] for the very beginning of travel, where the amplitude of the higher harmonics is developed into a power series of x, the distance from the transducer.

The solution of Fox and Wallace is better suited for larger distances, and is principally designed to find the resultant absorption.

In the following, only first order deviations from the linearized equation will be considered. Assume an equation of state for adiabatic changes of the form

$$p - p_0 = A\frac{\rho - \rho_0}{\rho_0} + \frac{B}{2}\left(\frac{\rho - \rho_0}{\rho_0}\right)^2 = As + \frac{B}{2}s^2 \tag{33–1}$$

or

$$\mathfrak{V}^2 = \frac{dp}{d\rho} = \frac{A}{\rho_0}\left(1 + \frac{B}{A}s\right) = \mathfrak{V}_0{}^2\left(1 + \frac{B}{A}s\right). \tag{33–2}$$

Taking the square root, one gets

$$\mathfrak{V} = \mathfrak{V}_0\left(1 + \frac{B}{2A}s\right) = \mathfrak{V}_0\left[1 + \frac{1}{2}\frac{B}{A}\frac{1}{\rho_0\mathfrak{V}_0{}^2}(p - p_0)\right] \tag{33–3}$$

by using the zero order approximation

$$s = \frac{1}{\gamma}\kappa_T(p - p_0) = \frac{1}{\rho_0\mathfrak{V}_0{}^2}(p - p_0).$$

Here $\mathfrak{V}$ is the velocity of propagation of the local disturbance (s or $p - p_0$). For an ideal gas

$$\frac{p}{p_0} = \left(\frac{\rho}{\rho_0}\right)^\gamma \quad \text{or} \quad \frac{B}{A} = \gamma + 1. \tag{33–4}$$

One can also write

$$\frac{B}{A} = \frac{\kappa_0 - \kappa}{\kappa_0{}^2}(p - p_0)^{-1} + 1 \tag{33–4$'$}$$

where κ is the adiabatic compressibility at p and κ_0 at p_0.

Consider a wave progressing to the right. At a given moment, let p be the pressure at x'. The pressure $p + dp$ exists at that moment at $x' + dx'$. (At the front side of the wave, dp is negative if dx' is positive.)

---

[6] A. L. Thuras, R. T. Jenkins, and H. T. O'Neil, *J. Acoust. Soc. Am.* **6**, 173 (1935).

After a time t, the disturbance with pressure p has moved to a place x

$$x - x' = \mathfrak{V}t \tag{33–5}$$

while the location of the pressure $p + dp$, which has the propagation velocity

$$\mathfrak{V} + \frac{d\mathfrak{V}}{dp}\,dp \tag{33–5$'$}$$

has moved to $x + dx$.

$$x + dx - (x' + dx') = \left(\mathfrak{V} + \frac{d\mathfrak{V}}{dp}\,dp\right)t$$

$$= \left(\mathfrak{V} + \frac{d\mathfrak{V}}{dp}\,dp\right)\frac{x - x'}{\mathfrak{V}} = (x - x')\left(1 + \frac{1}{\mathfrak{V}}\frac{d\mathfrak{V}}{dp}\,dp\right). \tag{33–5$''$}$$

The left side can be written

$$x - x' + dx - dx'$$

so that

$$dx - dx' = (x - x')\frac{1}{\mathfrak{V}}\frac{d\mathfrak{V}}{dp}\,dp = (x - x')\frac{1}{\mathfrak{V}}\frac{d\mathfrak{V}}{dp}\frac{\partial p}{\partial x'}\,dx'$$

or

$$\frac{dx}{dx'} = 1 + (x - x')\frac{1}{\mathfrak{V}}\frac{d\mathfrak{V}}{dp}\frac{\partial p}{\partial x'}.$$

One then gets for the pressure gradient at x

$$\frac{\partial p}{\partial x} = \frac{\partial p}{\partial x'}\frac{dx'}{dx} = \frac{\partial p}{\partial x'}\left[1 + (x - x')\frac{1}{\mathfrak{V}}\frac{d\mathfrak{V}}{dp}\frac{\partial p}{\partial x'}\right]^{-1}. \tag{33–5$'''$}$$

To make the expression nondimensional, introduce

$$P = (p - p_0)_{\max}$$

the peak pressure in the sound wave. Then multiply Eq. (33–5$'''$) by $\lambda/2\pi P$

$$\frac{\lambda}{2\pi P}\frac{\partial p}{\partial x} = \frac{\lambda}{2\pi P}\frac{\partial p}{\partial x'}\left[1 + (x - x')\frac{1}{\mathfrak{V}}\frac{d\mathfrak{V}}{dp}\frac{2\pi P}{\lambda}\frac{\lambda}{2\pi P}\frac{\partial p}{\partial x'}\right]^{-1}. \tag{33–6}$$

One now introduces a length L

$$\frac{1}{L} = \frac{1}{\mathfrak{B}}\frac{d\mathfrak{B}}{dp}\frac{2\pi P}{\lambda} = \frac{\pi}{\rho_0 \mathfrak{B}_0{}^2}\frac{B}{A}\frac{P}{\lambda}$$

or

$$\frac{L}{\lambda} = \frac{\rho_0 \mathfrak{B}_0{}^2}{\pi}\left(\frac{B}{A}P\right)^{-1}. \tag{33–7}$$

For an ideal gas

$$\frac{L}{\lambda} = \frac{\gamma}{\gamma+1}\frac{1}{\pi}\frac{p_0}{P}. \tag{33–7'}$$

Some examples are given in Table 33–1.

TABLE 33–1

EXAMPLES OF L/λ

	Air	H_2O liquid	CCl_4 liquid
B/A	$1.4 + 1 = 2.4$	~7	~11
P in atm	0.006	10	5
I in watt/cm^2		4	7
L/λ	30	270	90

If one uses $(\lambda/2\pi)\, 1/P\, (\partial p/\partial x)$ as ordinate, one has a quantity which depends only on the shape of the wave, $(p - p_0)/P$ measuring the local pressure relative to the peak pressure P, and $2\pi x/\lambda$ measuring the phase. If one starts with a sinusoidal wave

$$p - p_0 = P \sin\left(\omega t - \frac{2\pi x'}{\lambda}\right)$$

then the quantity is

$$\frac{\lambda}{2\pi}\frac{1}{P}\frac{\partial p}{\partial x'} = -\cos\left(\omega t - \frac{2\pi x'}{\lambda}\right)$$

and has the maximum negative value -1.

Equation (33–6) then gives the progressive distortion

$$\left(\frac{\lambda}{2\pi}\frac{1}{P}\frac{\partial p}{\partial x}\right) = \left(\frac{\lambda}{2\pi}\frac{1}{P}\frac{\partial p}{\partial x'}\right)\left[1 + \frac{x - x'}{L}\left(\frac{\lambda}{2\pi}\frac{1}{P}\frac{\partial p}{\partial x'}\right)\right]^{-1}. \tag{33–8}$$

From this equation one concludes that in a lossless medium, L is the distance at which a wave, originally sinusoidal, becomes a shock wave

$$\frac{\lambda}{2\pi}\frac{1}{P}\frac{\partial p}{\partial x} = -\infty.$$

The distortion is the same in all originally sinusoidal waves, independent of frequency, intensity, and the nature of the medium, provided the distances are measured in units of L. Of course, all these quantities enter into the calculation of L.

Fox and Wallace then construct graphically the wave forms for $0.1\,L$, $0.2\,L \ldots L$ and make a Fourier analysis of each wave form. This is done for a lossless medium. It is then assumed that in each section $0.1\,L$ the nth harmonic suffers an amplitude absorption loss $\exp(-n^2\alpha_1\,0.1\,L)$. The fundamental is given by $n = 1$, and α_1 is its absorption coefficient. The comparatively stable wave form is assumed to be reached when the increase of the second harmonic by feeding from the fundamental is just compensated by the loss by absorption. If $P_1, P_2 \ldots$ signify the local peak pressures of the fundamental, first harmonic, etc., the resultant over-all absorption coefficient α_{eff} is defined by

$$2\alpha_{\text{eff}} = -\,[P_1^{\,2} + P_2^{\,2} + \ldots]^{-1}\frac{\partial}{\partial x}[P_1^{\,2}\,e^{-2\alpha_1 x} + P_2^{\,2}\,e^{-8\alpha_1 x} + \ldots]. \tag{33–9}$$

For the presentation of the result, it is useful to introduce that value of the peak pressure P for which the second harmonic becomes stationary at $x - x' = 0.1\,L$. This turns out to be

$$P_{\text{th}} = 0.138\,\alpha\lambda\rho_0\mathfrak{V}_0^{\,2}\left(\frac{B}{A}\right)^{-1}. \tag{33–10}$$

The corresponding intensity is

$$I_{th} = \frac{1}{2\rho_0\mathfrak{V}_0}P_{\text{th}}^{\,2} = 0.0095\,(\alpha\lambda)^2\rho_0\mathfrak{V}_0^{\,3}\left(\frac{B}{A}\right)^{-2}\ \text{ergs sec}^{-1}\ \text{cm}^{-2}$$

$$= 9.5\times 10^{-10}\,(\alpha\lambda)^2\rho_0\mathfrak{V}_0^{\,3}\left(\frac{B}{A}\right)^{-2}\ \text{watt cm}^{-2}. \tag{33–10′}$$

It is found that the increase in absorption, $\alpha_{\text{eff}}/\alpha_1$, is a function of the ratio $P : P_{\text{th}}$ (or $I : I_{\text{th}}$) only, once the comparatively stable wave form is reached. This function is tabulated in Table 33–2.

TABLE 33–2

EXCESS ABSORPTION AS FUNCTION OF INTENSITY

P/P_{th}	I/I_{th}	$\alpha_{\text{eff}}/\alpha_1$
1.00	1.00	1.00
1.31	1.72	1.01
1.76	3.10	1.05
2.43	5.90	1.09
3.50	12.2	1.18
5.10	26.0	1.31
7.18	51.5	1.50
9.27	86.0	1.72
11.8	146	2.08
19.2	370	2.90

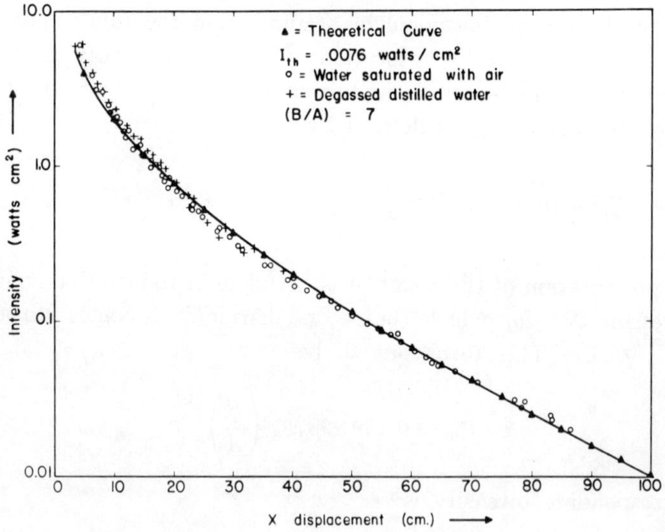

FIG. 33–1. Absorption coefficient as function of intensity according to Fox and Wallace.[3]

The experimental data of Fox on water and CCl_4 fit the theory very well; see Fig. 33–1. For water at 10 Mc, $I_{\text{th}} = 0.007$ watts cm^{-2} calculated, 0.0076 for best fit; the absorption is at 4 watts cm^{-2}, 5 times the low intensity absorption. For CCl_4 at 5 Mc the numbers are: $I_{th} = 0.065$ watts cm^{-2} calculated; 0.05 for best fit; $\alpha_{eff}/\alpha_1 = 2$ at 7 watts cm^{-2}.

For low intensities one can integrate the equation of motion analytically in first approximation. One finds

$$\frac{P_2}{P_1} = -0.054 \frac{P_1}{P_{th}} (1 - e^{-2\alpha_1 x}) \tag{33–11}$$

where P_1 and P_2 are the local pressure amplitudes of fundamental and next harmonic. The last bracket describes the establishment of the comparatively stable wave form, which is reached at distances greater than $1/2\alpha_1$.

If Eq. (33–11) can be applied, one finds, since for $x \gg 1/2\alpha$ the quantity $P_2{}^2$ is proportional to $P_1{}^4$

$$\begin{aligned} 2\alpha_{eff} &= -\frac{1}{P_1{}^2 + P_2{}^2} \frac{d}{dx} [P_1{}^2 + P_2{}^2] \\ &= \frac{1}{P_1{}^2 + P_2{}^2} [2\alpha_1 P_1{}^2 + 4\alpha_1 P_2{}^2] \\ &= 2\alpha_1 \frac{P_1{}^2 + 2P_2{}^2}{P_1{}^2 + P_2{}^2} \end{aligned}$$

$$\frac{\alpha_{eff}}{\alpha_1} = 1 + \frac{P_2{}^2}{P_1{}^2} = 1 + 2.9 \times 10^{-3} \left(\frac{P_1}{P_{th}}\right)^2. \tag{33–12}$$

Towle and Lindsay[7] have measured the increase of absorption with amplitude in several liquids. They found no change in velocity. Narasimhan and Beyer[8] investigated the change in absorption in water and in solutions of $MnSO_4$ and of acetic acid. The measurements reached acoustic peak pressures of 5 atm. While below 2 atm the increase in absorption in water is not very dependent on frequency, it is much smaller at 8.7 Mc than at 3.8 Mc between 3 and 5 atm. This seems contrary to Eq. (33–10) and Table 33–2.

The theory has been further elaborated by Z. Goldberg.[9] Zarembo *et al.*[10] have experimentally confirmed the production of the higher harmonics.

---

[7] D. M. Towle and R. B. Lindsay, *J. Acoust. Soc. Am.* **27**, 530 (1955).

[8] V. Narasimhan and R. T. Beyer, *J. Acoust. Soc. Am.* **28**, 1233 (1956).

[9] Z. Goldberg, *Soviet Phys. Acoustics*, **2**, 346 (1957).

[10] L. K. Zarembo, V. A. Krasilnikov and P. P. Shklovskaia-Kordi, *Soviet Phys. Acoustics* **3**, 27 (1957).

B. GASES

IV. Application of the General Formulas to Gases

34. Application of Previous Equations to Ideal Gases

The equations previously developed are all applicable to ideal gases, which in addition introduce further simplifications.

(*a*) *Sound Velocity at Zero Frequency*

For a mole of an ideal gas

$$pV = RT \qquad \rho = \frac{M}{V}. \tag{34–1}$$

Therefore

$$p = \frac{RT}{M}\rho$$

$$\left(\frac{\partial p}{\partial \rho}\right)_T = \frac{RT}{M} = \frac{p}{\rho}$$

and

$$\mathfrak{V}_0^{\,2} = \gamma_0 \frac{RT}{M} = \gamma_0 \frac{p}{\rho}.$$

In the literature, this equation is usually found in the second form

$$\mathfrak{V}_0^{\,2} = \gamma_0 \frac{p}{\rho}. \tag{34–2}$$

However, the first form

$$\mathfrak{V}_0^{\,2} = \gamma_0 \frac{RT}{M} \tag{34–2$'$}$$

is much easier to handle; it is valid even for gas mixtures, where M is calculated from the rule of mixtures; and it shows that at fixed temperature $\mathfrak{V}_0^{\,2}$ is independent of pressure, and that for variable temperature it changes like $\gamma_0 T$. Both Eqs. (34–2) and (34–2′) hold only for ideal gases. Only if one knows nothing at all about the gas and determines ρ experimentally —or if one uses the sound velocity as an analytical tool—is Eq. (34–2) preferable.

(b) Difference in Specific Heats

$$\Delta = C_p - C_v = -T_0 \left(\frac{\partial V}{\partial T}\right)_p^2 \left(\frac{\partial p}{\partial V}\right)_T = T\left(\frac{R}{p}\right)^2 \frac{RT}{V^2} = R \qquad (34\text{–}3)$$

independent of temperature, pressure, and nature of the gas.

(c) Specific Heat C_v

In the case of a monatomic gas

$$C_v = 3/2\, R. \qquad (34\text{–}4)$$

In the case of a gas made up of linear molecules with n atoms

$C_v = 3/2\, R$ (translation) $+ R$ (rotation) $+ (3n - 5)$ contributions from vibrations. (34–5)

For a gas made up of nonlinear molecules

$C_v = 3/2\, R$ (translation) $+ 3/2\, R$ (rotation) $+ (3n - 6)$ contributions from vibrations. (34–6)

The vibrational contributions can usually be calculated sufficiently well with Einstein formulas.

Equation (34–5) and (34–6) are subject to the restriction that the rotation behaves classically, which is not the case for H_2 up to room temperature and not true for N_2 below 190° K.

Furthermore, in some molecules (like $H_3C\text{-}CH_3$) internal rotations replace one or more vibrations.

(d) Heat Conductivity

According to the kinetic theory of gases, the following relation exists between shear viscosity and heat conductivity for monatomic gases

$$\lambda = 2.5\, \eta \frac{C_v}{M}. \qquad (34\text{–}7)$$

For polyatomic gases, the factor 2.5 may be replaced with good accuracy, as Eucken[1] has shown, by $1/4\,(9\,\gamma - 5)$. Therefore, in general

$$\lambda = \frac{1}{4}(9\gamma - 5)\eta\frac{C_v}{M}. \tag{34–8}$$

However, recent investigations have shown[2–4] that Eq. (34–8) should be replaced by

$$[\mathrm{Eu}] = \frac{\lambda M}{\eta C_v} = \frac{5}{2}\left[\left(\frac{3}{2} - \frac{3}{5}\frac{\rho D}{\eta}\right)\gamma - \frac{3}{2} + \frac{\rho D}{\eta}\right] \tag{34–8′}$$

where D is the diffusion coefficient. Since, however, the contribution of heat conductivity to absorption is small in polyatomic molecules and Eq. (34–8′) does not differ very much from Eq. (34–8), we will continue to use Eq. (34–8).

(e) *Classical Absorption and Dispersion*

The part of classical absorption due to heat conduction contains the factor, see Eq. (7–10)

$$\frac{3}{4}(\gamma - 1)\frac{\lambda}{c_p} = \frac{3}{4}(\gamma - 1)\frac{\lambda M}{C_p}.$$

According to Eq. (34–8), this is

$$\frac{3}{16}\frac{\gamma - 1}{\gamma}(9\,\gamma - 5)\,\eta$$

so that one has, from Eq. (7–17)

$$\alpha_{\text{class}} = \frac{2}{3}\frac{\omega^2}{\mathfrak{B}^3\rho_0}\eta\left[1 + \frac{3}{16}\frac{\gamma - 1}{\gamma}(9\gamma - 5)\right]$$

$$= \frac{2}{3}\frac{\omega^2}{\mathfrak{B}^3\rho_0}\eta\left[1 + \frac{3}{4}\frac{R}{C_v}\left(1 + \frac{5}{4}\frac{R}{C_p}\right)\right]. \tag{34–9}$$

---

[1] A. Eucken, *Physik. Z.* **14**, 324 (1913).

[2] R. G. Vines and L. A. Bennett, *J. Chem. Phys.* **22**, 360 (1954).

[3] S. Chapman and T. G. Cowling, "The Mathematical Theory of Non-Uniform Gases," p. 237. Cambridge Univ. Press, London and New York, 1939.

[4] J. Meixner, *Z. Naturforsch.* **8a**, 69 (1953).

Similarly, from Eq. (7–18)

$$\frac{\mathfrak{B}_0^{\,2}}{\mathfrak{B}^2} = 1 - \frac{4}{9}\,\frac{\omega^2}{\rho_0^{\,2}\mathfrak{B}^4}\,\eta^2 \left\{\left[1 - \frac{3}{16}\,\frac{\gamma-1}{\gamma}\,(9\gamma-5)\right]^2 - \frac{9}{64}\,\frac{\gamma-1}{\gamma^2}\,(9\gamma-5)^2\right\} \tag{34–10}$$

(*f*) *Maximum of* $\alpha'\lambda$

Equation (16–6) takes the following form: If we are dealing with a vibrational absorption

$$(\alpha'\lambda)_{\max} = 2\pi\,\frac{C'}{R}\left\{\left(5 + r + \frac{2C'}{R}\right)\left(3 + r + \frac{2C'}{R}\right)(5+r)\,(3+r)\right\}^{-1/2} \tag{34–11}$$

where r designates the number of rotational degrees of freedom. If we are dealing with rotational dispersion

$$(\alpha'\lambda)_{\max} = 2\pi r\,\{15\,(5+r)\,(3+r)\}^{-1/2}. \tag{34–12}$$

Equation (34–12) probably gives too high a value, since the $(\alpha'\lambda)$ is probably spread over a larger frequency range because the different rotational transitions do not show the same τ_r.

35. Correction for Nonideality of the Gas

For precision measurements of the velocity, and for organic vapors, corrections for the deviation of the gas from the behavior of ideal gases must be considered even in the neighborhood of 1 atm.

A convenient equation of state to use—assuming the deviations are small—is

$$\frac{pV}{RT} = 1 + B'p. \tag{35–1}$$

B' is simply connected with the second virial coefficient in the Kammerlingh-Onnes equation of state

$$\frac{pV}{RT} = 1 + \frac{B}{V}. \tag{35–2}$$

Since the term $B'p$ is a small correction, one can use the ideal gas equation for p in this term, getting

$$B'p = \frac{B'RT}{V} = \frac{B}{V}$$

or

$$B' = \frac{B}{RT}. \tag{35-3}$$

With the van der Waals notation

$$B = b - \frac{a}{RT}$$

$$B' = \frac{b}{RT} - \frac{a}{(RT)^2}. \tag{35-4}$$

In the equation for the low-frequency sound velocity

$$\mathfrak{V}^2 = \frac{C_p}{C_v}\left(\frac{dp}{d\rho}\right)_T$$

$(dp/d\rho)_T$, C_p, and C_v have to be corrected. Rewrite Eq. (35–1)

$$V = RT\left(\frac{1}{p} + B'\right). \tag{35-5}$$

Then

$$\left(\frac{\partial V}{\partial p}\right)_T = -\frac{RT}{p^2}$$

$$-\frac{1}{V^2}\left(\frac{\partial V}{\partial p}\right)_T = \frac{1}{M}\frac{\partial \rho}{\partial p} = \frac{RT}{p^2}\frac{1}{(RT)^2}\frac{p^2}{(1 + B'p)^2}.$$

Therefore

$$\left(\frac{\partial p}{\partial \rho}\right)_T = \frac{RT}{M}(1 + B'p)^2. \tag{35-6}$$

As an addition to the remarks in Sec. **34**(a), one sees that, distinct from Eq. (35–6)

$$\frac{p}{\rho} = \frac{RT}{M}(1 + B'p).$$

Next, one has, after differentiating Eq. (4–5) with respect to T and considering Eq. (4–4)

$$\frac{\partial C_p}{\partial p} = -T\left(\frac{\partial^2 V}{\partial T^2}\right)_p; \tag{35–7}$$

with the form of Eq. (35–5) for V

$$\frac{\partial C_p}{\partial p} = -RT\frac{\partial^2}{\partial T^2}B'T. \tag{35–8}$$

Since we keep in the region where all deviations are linear in p

$$C_p = C_p{}^0 - pRT\frac{\partial^2}{\partial T^2}(B'T). \tag{35–9}$$

Using Eq. (4–9) for $C_p - C_v$

$$C_p - C_v = -TV\frac{1}{V^2}\left(\frac{\partial V}{\partial T}\right)_p^2 V\left(\frac{\partial p}{\partial V}\right)_T = -T\left(\frac{\partial V}{\partial T}\right)_p^2\left(\frac{\partial p}{\partial V}\right)_T. \tag{35–10}$$

From Eq. (35–5)

$$\left(\frac{\partial V}{\partial T}\right)_P = \frac{R}{p} + R\frac{\partial}{\partial T}(TB') = \frac{R}{p}\left[1 + p\frac{\partial}{\partial T}(TB')\right].$$

According to the equation following Eq. (35–5)

$$\left(\frac{\partial p}{\partial V}\right)_T = -\frac{p^2}{RT}.$$

Inserting all this in Eq. (35–9)

$$\begin{aligned} C_p - C_v &= T\frac{R^2}{p^2}\left[1 + p\frac{\partial}{\partial T}(TB')\right]^2\frac{p^2}{RT} \\ &= R\left[1 + p\frac{\partial}{\partial T}(TB')\right]^2. \end{aligned} \tag{35–11}$$

Since we have kept only the first power of p to describe the deviations from the ideal gas law in the equation of state, Eq. (35–1), it would not be justified to keep higher powers in the corrections just calculated. Therefore, Eqs. (35–6) and (35–11) should be replaced by

$$\frac{\partial p}{\partial \rho} = \frac{RT}{M}(1 + 2B'p) \tag{35–6′}$$

$$C_p - C_v = R\left[1 + 2p\frac{\partial(TB')}{\partial T}\right]. \tag{35–11′}$$

From Eqs. (35–11′) and (35–9)

$$C_v = C_p - (C_p - C_v) = C_v^0 - pR\left[2\frac{\partial(TB')}{\partial T} + T\frac{\partial^2(TB')}{\partial T^2}\right]. \tag{35–12}$$

From Eqs. (35–9) and (35–12) one has

$$\gamma = \frac{C_p^0 - pRT\dfrac{\partial^2(TB')}{\partial T^2}}{C_v^0 - pR\left[T\dfrac{\partial^2(TB')}{\partial T^2} + 2\dfrac{\partial(TB')}{\partial T}\right]}$$

$$= \frac{C_p^0}{C_v^0}\left[1 - \frac{pRT}{C_p^0}\frac{\partial^2(TB')}{\partial T^2} + \frac{pR}{C_v^0}\left\{T\frac{\partial^2(TB')}{\partial T^2} + 2\frac{\partial(TB')}{\partial T}\right\}\right] \tag{35–13}$$

$$= \gamma_0\left\{1 + p\frac{R}{C_v^0}\left[\frac{R}{C_p^0}T\frac{\partial^2(TB')}{\partial T^2} + 2\frac{\partial(TB')}{\partial T}\right]\right\}$$

and with Eq. (35–6′)

$$\mathfrak{B}^2 = \mathfrak{B}_0{}^2\left\{1 + 2p\left[B' + \frac{R}{C_v^0}\frac{\partial(TB')}{\partial T} + \frac{1}{2}\frac{R^2}{C_p^0C_v^0}T\frac{\partial^2(TB')}{\partial T^2}\right]\right\}. \tag{35–14}$$

A correction to the ideal gas formulas was first applied by Richards and Reid,[1] using the van der Waals equations in their simplest form. Eucken and Becker[2] applied the Sutherland equation, van Itterbeek and Mariens[3] the second virial coefficient, and Rossing and Legvold[4] the Beattie equation.

---

[1] W. T. Richards and J. A. Reid, *J. Chem. Phys.* **2**, 193 (1934).

[2] A. Eucken and R. Becker, *Z. physik. Chem.* **B20**, 467 (1933); **B27**, 219 (1934).

[3] A. van Itterbeek and P. Mariens, *Physica* **4**, 207, 609 (1937).

[4] T. D. Rossing and S. Legvold, *J. Chem. Phys.* **23**, 1118 (1955).

Beyer[5] made the calculations for the van der Waals equation, keeping the quadratic terms in Eq. (11–5) in a higher approximation. None of these authors discusses possible effects of nonideality on the dependence of τ on p, which will be developed in Sec. 95.

As will be discussed later, the dispersion curve for a given ideal gas is a function of f/p only. If one uses two crystal frequencies f_1 and f_2 and different pressures, the sound velocity should be the same if two different pressures p_1 and p_2 are chosen, so that

$$\frac{f_1}{p_1} = \frac{f_2}{p_2}.$$

However, if the gas is not ideal, then, if f_2 is larger than f_1, the corresponding p_2 is larger than p_1, and if one is in the region of appreciable deviation from ideality, the sound velocity for the larger p, i.e., the larger f, is lower for the same f/p because of the larger deviation from ideality.

In addition, for a fixed f the velocity does not approach a constant (low frequency) value if f/p is decreased by increasing p, again because of an increasing deviation from ideality.

Both effects are shown in Fig. 1 in a paper by Ener *et al.*[6] for methyl alcohol. Neglect of this effect has in the past led to wrong conclusions about relaxation times, as, for example, for dichloroethylene[7] (as pointed out by Boudart[8]) and for acetaldehyde.[9] This is an additional reason to compare velocity as extrapolated to low values of f/p from the measurements with velocity calculated with the static γ and ideal gas law.

A set of empirical equations for B has been given by Buschmann and Schäfer.[10]

$$CO_2: \quad B = 27.5 - 66.40 \times 10^4\, T^{-1.5} - 28.63 \times 10^{11}\, T^{-4.5}$$

$$N_2O: \quad B = -161.7 \text{ cm}^3 \text{ at } 292^\circ \text{ K}, \; dB/dT = 1.103 \text{ cm}^3/\text{degree},$$
$$d^2B/dT^2 = -0.107 \text{ cm}^3/(\text{degree})^2$$

$$NO: \quad B = 32 - 88.80 \times 10^4\, T^{-1.5} - 6.71 \times 10^9\, T^{-3.5}.$$

---

[5] R. T. Beyer, *J. Acoust. Soc. Amer.* **24**, 714 (1952); O. Noma, *Bull. Kobayasi Inst.* **1**, 162 (1953).

[6] C. Ener, A. Busala, and J. C. Hubbard, *J. Chem. Phys.* **23**, 155 (1955).

[7] A. Busala, D. Sette, and J. C. Hubbard, *J. Chem. Phys.* **20**, 1899 (1952).

[8] M. Boudart, *J. Chem. Phys.* **21**, 955 (1953).

[9] J. D. Lambert and J. S. Rowlinson, *Proc. Roy. Soc.* **A204**, 424 (1951); corrected by P. G. T. Fogg, P. A. Hanks, and J. D. Lambert, *Proc. Roy. Soc.* **A219**, 490 (1953).

[10] K. F. Buschmann and K. Schäfer, *Z. physik. Chem.* **B50**, 73 (1941).

Hubbard and his co-workers[11,12] have determined the first order corrections by which to multiply the experimental $\mathfrak{V}_e$ to arrive at the idealized velocity $\mathfrak{V}_i$.

$$\mathfrak{V}_e = \mathfrak{V}_i(1 - gp).$$

(Hubbard used α instead of g). If p is in atmospheres, one has, near 30 °C, the data shown in Table 35–1.

TABLE 35–1

TABULATION OF THE CONSTANT g USED TO IDEALIZE EXPERIMENTAL VELOCITY DATA

Gas	g	Reference
CH_4	0.000424	11
CH_3Cl	0.00927	11
CH_2Cl_2	0.0232	11
$CHCl_3$	0.03086	11
$CHCl_4$	0.04422	11
$ClH_2C\text{-}CH_2Cl$	0.0387	12
$Cl_2HC\text{-}CH_3$	0.0331	12

The empirical data fit well with those calculated from the Berthelot equation of state.

For methyl alcohol, the equation linear in p does not suffice. Ener *et al.*[6] have drawn an empirical curve and compared it with data from different equations of state. Even at a pressure of only 8 cm Hg, the empirical velocity is 1% less than the idealized velocity.

If one wishes to evaluate a dispersion curve or the maximum of $\alpha'\lambda$ in the case of a gas which deviates greatly from an ideal gas, the procedure has to be somewhat different from that in an ideal gas. Of course, if one plots the velocity squared or $\alpha'\lambda$ as function of the frequency at constant pressure or density, no change has to be made. If, however—as is usually the case—one plots these quantities at fixed frequency as function of the pressure (or density), one has to remember that now the factors

$$\frac{\Delta C'}{C_v(C_p - C')} \quad \text{or} \quad \frac{\Delta C'}{C_p(C_v - C')}$$

[11] D. Sette, A. Busala, and J. C. Hubbard, *J. Chem. Phys.* **23**, 787 (1955).

[12] T. S. Rao and J. C. Hubbard, *J. Acoust. Soc. Am.* **27**, 321 (1955).

also depend on pressure and therefore all processes involving differentiation with respect to pressure lead to results different from the case of the ideal gas.

For dispersion measurements, one has to plot both $\mathfrak{V}_0{}^2$ and $\mathfrak{V}_\infty{}^2$ (or their reciprocals) as function of pressure. If one then plots experimental points of $\mathfrak{V}^2$ at a given frequency but different pressure, one has to find the point for which

$$\mathfrak{V}^2 - \mathfrak{V}_0{}^2 = \mathfrak{V}_\infty{}^2 - \mathfrak{V}^2$$

or

$$\mathfrak{V}^2 = \frac{1}{2}(\mathfrak{V}_0{}^2 + \mathfrak{V}_\infty{}^2) \tag{35–15}$$

all taken at the same pressure; i.e., the point at which the experimental curve crosses the vertical in the middle between $\mathfrak{V}_0{}^2$ and $\mathfrak{V}_\infty{}^2$ (or a similar statement for the reciprocals). This is the point at which $\omega\tau'' = 1$ (or $\omega\tau' = 1$), but it is *not* the inflection point on the $\mathfrak{V}^2$ curve.

Similarly, for absorption, one has to plot

$$\alpha'\lambda \frac{R}{\Delta}\left[\frac{C_p}{R}\frac{C_p - C'}{R}\frac{C_v}{R}\frac{C_v - C'}{R}\right]^{1/2} = \frac{C'}{R}\frac{\omega\tau'}{1 + (\omega\tau')^2} \tag{35–16}$$

against p for fixed ω. The maximum of this expression, but not the maximum of $\alpha'\lambda$, occurs at $\omega\tau' = 1$ and has the value $C'/2R$.

36. Viscosity and Relaxation Time for Translational Energy

For an ideal gas with rigid sphere molecules, the exact expression for the viscosity is

$$\eta = 0.499\, mN\bar{W}\Lambda \tag{36–1}$$

where N is the number of molecules per cc, $\bar{W}$ the average thermal velocity, and Λ the mean free path. Multiply and divide Eq. (36–1) by $\bar{W}$; one has

$$mN\bar{W}^2 = \frac{8}{3\pi} mN\,\overline{W^2} = \frac{8}{\pi} p.$$

Setting further

$$\tau_c = \frac{\Lambda}{\bar{W}} \tag{36–2}$$

one can interpret τ_c as the average time between collisions. This is inversely proportional to the density. Equation (36–1) can then be rewritten

$$\eta = 0.499 \frac{8}{\pi} p\tau_c = 1.271\, p\tau_c. \tag{36–3}$$

In the case of nonrigid molecules the mean free path and the notion of collision need a more exact definition; nonetheless, one may use Eq. (36–3) even then.

Kohler,[1] following a lead of Maxwell,[2] interprets viscosity as due to the existence of a relaxation time necessary for the adjustment of translational energy. He writes that

$$\eta = p\tau_{\text{tr}} \tag{36–4}$$

where

$$\tau_{\text{tr}} = 1.271\, \tau_c \tag{36–4'}$$

is the relaxation time necessary for the adjustment of translational energy. The factor 1.27 means that slightly more than one collision is needed to decrease the excess of an exceptional motion to $1/e$ of its value (persistence of velocities, Jeans[2]).

Kohler's argument, slightly modified, is as follows. Call W the thermal velocity, i.e., the molecular velocity relative to the macroscopic flow, or

$$\boldsymbol{W} = \text{molecular velocity} - \boldsymbol{w} \tag{36–5}$$

and select the axes properly (principal axes; in a two-dimensional plane shear flow, x and y at 45° to the flow, z normal to it).

One can then write a distribution function in first approximation

$$F = f_0(1 + \Phi) \tag{36–6}$$

$$f_0 = N\left(\frac{m}{2\pi kT}\right)^{3/2} \exp\left\{-\frac{m}{2kT}(W_1{}^2 + W_2{}^2 + W_3{}^2)\right\} \tag{36–7}$$

$$\Phi = a\,\Lambda\left(\frac{m}{2kT}\right)^{3/2}\left\{\left(W_1{}^2 - \frac{1}{3}W^2\right)\left(\frac{\partial u_1}{\partial x} - \frac{1}{3}\operatorname{div}\boldsymbol{w}\right) + \right. \tag{36–8}$$

$$\left.\left(W_2{}^2 - \frac{1}{3}W^2\right)\left(\frac{\partial u_2}{\partial y} - \frac{1}{3}\operatorname{div}\boldsymbol{w}\right) + \left(W_3{}^2 - \frac{1}{3}W^2\right)\left(\frac{\partial u_3}{\partial z} - \frac{1}{3}\operatorname{div}\boldsymbol{w}\right)\right\}.$$

---

[1] M. Kohler, *Z. Physik* **125**, 715 (1948).

[2] See J. J. Jeans, "Kinetic Theory of Gases," p. 294. Cambridge Univ. Press, London, 1905.

The Φ is the deviation from Maxwell's distribution function caused by the shear flow, a is a dimensionless constant, and Λ is the mean free path.

Define temperatures T_1, T_2, T_3 so that

$$|T_1 - T_0| \ll T_0$$

and consider the function

$$\begin{aligned}
\exp\left\{-\frac{m}{2k}\frac{W_1^2}{T_1}\right\} &= \exp\left\{-\frac{m}{2k}\frac{W_1^2}{T_0 + T_1 - T_0}\right\} \\
&= \exp\left\{-\frac{mW_1^2}{2kT_0}\left(1 - \frac{T_1 - T_0}{T_0}\right)\right\} \\
&= \left(1 + \frac{mW_1^2}{2kT_0}\frac{T_1 - T_0}{T_0}\right)\exp\left\{-\frac{mW_1^2}{2kT_0}\right\} \\
&= \left[1 + \frac{m}{2kT_0}\left(W_1^2 - \frac{1}{3}W^2\right)\frac{T_1 - T_0}{T_0}\right] \times \\
&\qquad \left(1 + \frac{m}{6kT_0}W^2\frac{T_1 - T_0}{T_0}\right)\exp\left\{-\frac{mW_1^2}{2kT_0}\right\}.
\end{aligned} \tag{36–9}$$

Multiplying three such expressions with the indices 1, 2, 3, one sees that one can write

$$F = N\left(\frac{m}{2\pi kT_0}\right)^{3/2}\left(1 - \frac{m}{6kT_0}W^2\frac{T_1 + T_2 + T_3 - 3T_0}{T_0}\right) \exp\left\{-\frac{m}{2k}\left(\frac{W_1^2}{T_1} + \frac{W_2^2}{T_2} + \frac{W_3^2}{T_3}\right)\right\} \tag{36–10}$$

provided one chooses T_1, T_2, T_3 so that

$$\frac{m}{2kT}\left(W_1^2 - \frac{1}{3}W^2\right)\frac{T_1 - T_0}{T_0} = a\Lambda\left(\frac{m}{2kT}\right)^{3/2}\left(W_1^2 - \frac{1}{3}W^2\right)\left(\frac{\partial u_1}{\partial x} - \frac{1}{3}\operatorname{div}\boldsymbol{w}\right)$$

$$\frac{T_1 - T_0}{T_0} = a\Lambda\left(\frac{m}{2kT}\right)^{1/2}\left(\frac{\partial u_1}{\partial x} - \frac{1}{3}\operatorname{div}\boldsymbol{w}\right). \tag{36–11}$$

By adding the three equations (36–11) with indices 1, 2, 3, one gets

$$T_1 - T_0 + T_2 - T_0 + T_3 - T_0 = 0. \tag{36–12}$$

From this one finds

$$\sqrt{T_1 T_2 T_3} = T_0^{3/2} \left\{ \left(1 + \frac{T_1 - T_0}{T_0}\right) \left(1 + \frac{T_2 - T_0}{T_0}\right) \times \right.$$

$$\left. \left(1 + \frac{T_3 - T_0}{T_0}\right) \right\}^{1/2} = T_0^{3/2}.$$

Therefore F, Eq. (36–10), can be rewritten

$$F = N \left(\frac{m}{2\pi k T_1}\right)^{1/2} e^{-mW_1^2/2kT_1} \left(\frac{m}{2\pi k T_2}\right)^{1/2} e^{-mW_2^2/2kT_2} \left(\frac{m}{2\pi k T_3}\right)^{1/2} e^{-mW_3^3/2kT_3}. \tag{36–13}$$

It follows from the form of Eq. (36–13) that

$$\frac{m}{2} \overline{W_1^2} = \frac{1}{2} k T_1 \tag{36–14}$$

etc., and, from Eqs. (36–12) and (36–13), as usual

$$\frac{m}{2} \overline{W^2} = \frac{3}{2} k\, T_0.$$

In the present coordinates, the principal stresses are [Eq. (6–2)]

$$- P_{jj} = NmW_j^2 = NkT_j = NkT_0 + Nk(T_j - T_0)$$

$$= p - 2\eta \left(\frac{\partial u_j}{\partial x_j} - \frac{1}{3} \operatorname{div} \boldsymbol{w}\right) \tag{36–15}$$

or, from Eq. (36–11)

$$- \eta = NkT_0 \Lambda \frac{a}{2} \left(\frac{m}{2kT}\right)^{1/2}$$

$$= Nm\bar{W}\Lambda \frac{a}{8} \sqrt{\pi} \tag{36–16}$$

with the usual expression

$$\bar{W} = 2 \sqrt{\frac{2kT}{\pi m}}.$$

One next uses Boltzmann's fundamental equation of gas theory (see, e.g., Hirschfelder's[3] book) which describes the effect of the collisions on the distribution function. The collisions do not change any distribution function (or part of it) which has the form of Maxwell's distribution function. If one uses expression (36–6) for F, only the part Φ is affected.

Assuming a distribution function of the general form of Eq. (36–6), the change by collision of a quantity Q, which depends on the molecular velocities alone, during unit time is given by

$$-\int Q\boldsymbol{G}\Phi dW_1\, dW_2\, dW_3 \tag{36–18}$$

where $\boldsymbol{G}$ is called by Kohler the "collision operator".

The equation of Boltzmann is then used in two ways:

1. It is assumed that at a $t = 0$ in some way a distribution is established

$$\Phi = \frac{m}{2kT_0}\left\{\left(W_1{}^2 - \frac{1}{3}W^2\right)\frac{T_1 - T_0}{T_0} + \left(W_2{}^2 - \frac{1}{3}\right)W^2\frac{T_2 - T_0}{T_0} + \left(W_3{}^2 - \frac{1}{3}W^2\right)\frac{T_3 - T_0}{T_0}\right\}$$

where T_1, T_2, T_3 are constants obeying Eq. (36–12) but not Eq. (36–11), since no superposed macroscopic flow velocity $\boldsymbol{w}$ is supposed to exist.

We now choose, as quantity Q

$$Q = m\left(W_1{}^2 - \frac{1}{3}W^2\right)$$

and ask how fast equilibrium (i.e., $T_1 = T_2 = T_3 = T_0$) is established by the collisions.

Then one has

$$-\frac{\partial\bar{Q}}{\partial t}$$

$$= \frac{1}{2kT_0{}^2}(T_1 - T_0)\int m\left(W_1{}^2 - \frac{1}{3}W^2\right)\boldsymbol{G}\, m\left(W_1{}^2 - \frac{1}{3}W^2\right)dW_1\, dW_2\, dW_3 +$$

$$\frac{1}{2kT_0{}^2}(T_2 - T_0)\int m\left(W_1{}^2 - \frac{1}{3}W^2\right)\boldsymbol{G}\, m\left(W_2{}^2 - \frac{1}{3}W^2\right)dW_1\, dW_2\, dW_3 + \dots . \tag{36–19}$$

[3] J. O. Hirschfelder, C. F. Curtiss, and R. B. Bird, "Molecular Theory of Gases and Liquids." Wiley, New York, 1954.

Inserting on the left Eq. (36–14), one has

$$-\frac{\partial}{\partial T}(T_1 - T_0) = (T_1 - T_0)\,A_{11} + (T_2 - T_0)\,A_{12} + (T_3 - T_0)\,A_{13} \qquad (36\text{–}19')$$

with

$$A_{js} = \frac{1}{2\,k^2 T_0^{\,2}} \int m\left(W_j^{\,2} - \frac{1}{3}W^2\right) \boldsymbol{G}\, m\left(W_s^{\,2} - \frac{1}{3}W^2\right) dW_1\, dW_2\, dW_3. \qquad (36\text{–}19'')$$

Because of the structure of Eq. (36–19″), there are only two different values of A, A_{jj} and A_{js}, $j \neq s$; furthermore, these are connected by

$$\sum_s A_{js} = 0 \qquad \text{or} \qquad A_{11} + 2A_{12} = 0$$

since the sums contain under the integral the factor

$$W_1^{\,2} - \frac{1}{3}W^2 + W_2^{\,2} - \frac{1}{3}W^2 + W_3^{\,2} - \frac{1}{3}W^2 = 0.$$

It follows from Eq. (36–12)

$$-\frac{\partial}{\partial t}(T_1 - T_0) = (T_1 - T_0)A_{11} + (T_2 - T_0 + T_3 - T_0)A_{12}$$

$$= -\,3A_{12}(T_1 - T_0) = +\frac{1}{\tau}(T_1 - T_0) \qquad (36\text{–}20)$$

$$\frac{1}{\tau} = -\,3A_{12}. \qquad (36\text{–}20')$$

2. One assumes next a steady-state shear flow with a distribution of molecular velocities as given by Eqs. (36–6) to (36–8). The condition following from Boltzmann's equation for a quantity Q in steady flow is then the average value of

$$-\left\{W_1 \frac{\partial}{\partial x}\left(u_1 \frac{\partial Q}{\partial W_1} + u_2 \frac{\partial Q}{\partial W_2} + u_3 \frac{\partial Q}{\partial W_3}\right) + \right.$$

$$\left. W_2 \frac{\partial}{\partial y}\left(u_1 \frac{\partial Q}{\partial W_1} + u_2 \frac{\partial Q}{\partial W_2} + u_3 \frac{\partial Q}{\partial W_3}\right) + W_3 \frac{\partial}{\partial z}\left(u_1 \frac{\partial Q}{\partial W_1} + u_2 \frac{\partial Q}{\partial W_2} + u_3 \frac{\partial Q}{\partial W_3}\right)\right\}$$

$$= -\int Q\boldsymbol{G}\Phi\, dW_1\, dW_2\, dW_3. \qquad (36\text{–}21)$$

Taking

$$Q = m\left(W_1^2 - \frac{1}{3}W^2\right)$$

one has, making use, on the right side of Eqs. (36–8), (36–11), (36–19), and (36–19′)

$$-2m\left\{\frac{2}{3}\overline{W_1{}^2}\frac{\partial u_1}{\partial x} - \frac{1}{3}\overline{W_1W_2}\frac{\partial u_2}{\partial x} - \frac{1}{3}\overline{W_1W_3}\frac{\partial u_3}{\partial x} + \frac{2}{3}\overline{W_2W_1}\frac{\partial u_1}{\partial y} - \frac{1}{3}\overline{W_2{}^2}\frac{\partial u_2}{\partial y} - \frac{1}{3}\overline{W_2W_3}\frac{\partial u_2}{\partial z} + \frac{2}{3}\overline{W_3W_1}\frac{\partial u_1}{\partial z} - \frac{1}{3}\overline{W_3W_2}\frac{\partial u_2}{\partial z} - \frac{1}{3}\overline{W_3{}^2}\frac{\partial u_3}{\partial z}\right\} = kA_{11}(T_1 - T_0) + kA_{12}(T_2 - T_0) + kA_{13}(T_3 - T_0)$$

$$= \frac{k}{\tau}(T_1 - T_0). \tag{36–22}$$

On the left

$$\overline{W_1W_2} = \overline{W_2W_3} = \overline{W_3W_1} = 0$$

because of Eq. (36–13), so that the left side is reduced to

$$-2m\left(\frac{2}{3}\overline{W_1{}^2}\frac{\partial u_1}{\partial x} - \frac{1}{3}\overline{W_2{}^2}\frac{\partial u_2}{\partial y} - \frac{1}{3}\overline{W_3{}^2}\frac{\partial u_3}{\partial z}\right).$$

Since the quantities $\partial u_1/\partial x$, etc. are supposed to be small of the first order, one can replace $\overline{W_1{}^2}$ by its equilibrium value $1/3\,\overline{W^2} = p/\rho$, and Eq. (36–22) can be written

$$2\frac{p}{N}\left(\frac{\partial u_1}{\partial x} - \frac{1}{3}\operatorname{div}\boldsymbol{w}\right) = -\frac{k}{\tau}(T_1 - T_0). \tag{36–23}$$

Then, from Eq. (36–15)

$$2\frac{p}{N}\left(\frac{\partial u_1}{\partial x} - \frac{1}{3}\operatorname{div}\boldsymbol{w}\right) = \frac{1}{\tau}\frac{2\eta}{N}\left(\frac{\partial u_1}{\partial x} - \frac{1}{3}\operatorname{div}\boldsymbol{w}\right)$$

from which Eq. (36–4) follows.

Maxwell[2,4] had proved Eq. (36–4) by direct calculation for so-called "Maxwellian" molecules, i.e., points attracting each other with a potential $\sim r^{-4}$; Kohler's proof shows that the result is independent of the force law.

---

[4] J. C. Maxwell, *Phil. Trans.* **157**, 49 (1867).

Kohler gives the following relaxation times in 10^{-10} sec for translational energy at 0° C and 760 mm Hg: He, 1.91; Ne, 3.02; A, 2.13; H_2, 0.86; D_2, 1.20; N_2, 1.70; O_2, 1.95; CO_2, 1.40; Cl_2, 1.33; and CH_4, 1.05. The τ is inversely proportional to the density (for a given gas) at constant T. Often the viscosity can be represented by Sutherland's formula (C = Sutherland's constant, a constant characteristic of the gas)

$$\eta \sim T^{1/2}\left(1+\frac{C}{T}\right)^{-1} = T^{1/2}\frac{T}{T+C}. \tag{36–24}$$

Here the factor $T^{1/2}$ is due to the temperature variation of the average molecular speed, while the factor $(T+C)/T$ measures the decrease of the effective molecular cross section with increasing molecular speed. If Eq. (36–24) is applicable, then the temperature variation of τ_c at constant pressure is also given by

$$\tau_c \sim T^{1/2}\frac{T}{T+C}. \tag{36–24′}$$

While the last factor again measures the variation of effective cross section, the first factor, $T^{1/2}$, arises in the following manner: At constant density, τ_c would vary according to $T^{-1/2}$, because a greater molecular speed decreases the time between collisions. However, this is overcompensated if the pressure is kept constant, since the density is then proportional to $1/T$ and, therefore, the mean free path (apart from the Sutherland correction) is proportional to T.

According to Eq. (36–24′), τ_c always increases with increasing T. If one writes the classical absorption Eq. (26–9), one now gets

$$\alpha_{\text{class}} = \frac{2}{3}\frac{\omega^2}{\mathfrak{B}^3\rho_0}p \times 1.271\left[1+\frac{3}{16}\frac{\gamma-1}{\gamma}(9\gamma-5)\right]\tau_c \tag{36–25}$$

or, using Eq. (34–2)

$$\alpha_{\text{class}} = \frac{2}{3}\frac{\omega^2}{\mathfrak{B}}\frac{\mathfrak{B}_0{}^2}{\mathfrak{B}^2}\frac{1.271}{\gamma_0}\left[1+\frac{3}{16}\frac{\gamma-1}{\gamma}(9\gamma-5)\right]\tau_c. \tag{36–25′}$$

At low frequencies in particular

$$\alpha_{\text{class}} = \frac{2}{3}\frac{\omega^2}{\mathfrak{B}_0}\frac{1.271}{\gamma_0}\left[1+\frac{3}{16}\frac{\gamma_0-1}{\gamma_0}(9\gamma_0-5)\right]\tau_c. \tag{36–25″}$$

The previous equations also can be used to prove the absence of a volume viscosity in an ideal monatomic gas.

Because the gas is ideal, the whole stress comes from momentum carried kinetically, i.e.,

$$P_{11} + P_{22} + P_{33} = Nm\,(\overline{W_1^{\,2}} + \overline{W_2^{\,2}} + \overline{W_3^{\,2}}) = Nm\overline{W^2} \qquad (36\text{–}26)$$

which is twice the total momentary energy per unit volume, and independent of any time variation. The identification of $(Nm/2)\,W^2$ with the total energy limits this to monatomic gases.

37. Assumption That Only Binary Collisions Are Effective (See also Sec. 26)

In ideal gases the molecules move, in the absence of external forces, most of the time in straight lines with constant speed, without influencing each other. Only during relatively short intervals, "collisions," are they able to exchange energy. Since the time during which they move along straight lines is, at constant temperature, inversely proportional to the pressure, the time between collisions, τ_c, is also inversely proportional to the pressure. Since energy can only be exchanged during collisions, and since—if no internal processes in the molecule occur, as in Sec. 22—the effect of one collision is unaffected by the question of when the last collision occured, all times τ (except τ_{12} in Sec. 22) are, at a given temperature, inversely proportional to the pressure. So are all τ', τ'', since the specific heats for an ideal gas are independent of the pressure.

In the more detailed calculation of Sec. 19, this means that all the reaction constants k_{ij} are proportional to the density, so that Eq. (19–2) represents bimolecular reactions, as Kneser and Rutgers have assumed.

One can, then, replace $\omega\tau$ everywhere by

$$\omega(\tau_0)\,\frac{p_0}{p} = \frac{\omega}{p}\,(\tau_0)\,p_0$$

where p_0 is a conveniently chosen standard pressure and (τ_0) the time constant for this standard pressure. (If one also wants to vary the temperature, the situation is somewhat more complicated.)

Since $\mathfrak{V}/\mathfrak{V}_0$ and $\alpha'\lambda$ contain the frequency only in the combination $\omega\tau$, one sees that these quantities are only functions of ω/p or f/p. This is of importance experimentally, since it is easier to vary the pressure continuously than the frequency. The above fact was first noted by Richards and Reid,[1] and is now often used in experimental investigations.

As stated in Sec. 35, the success of plotting on the same dispersion curve velocities found for the same value of ω/p, although the individual values of ω and p are different, is a proof of the correctness of the assumption. A number of examples can be found in the paper by Richards and Reid[1] and in the papers by Hubbard and his collaborators, cited in Sec. 35.

Buschmann and Schäfer[2] believed that they had found a deviation from the law that $\tau p =$ constant, but it seems more probable that the ideality correction was not made correctly (Sec. 35).

At high pressures, where the gas is not ideal—when the densities approach nearly liquid densities—Henderson and Peselnick[3] found that $\tau\rho$ is nearly constant, not τp (see Sec. 95).

38. Low Frequency Absorption. Ratio of Relaxation Absorption to Classical Absorption at Maximum

(a) *Ratio of Relaxation and Classical Absorption at Low Frequencies*

We will now define a number Z_s as the number of collisions necessary for the adjustment of the energy of the internal degree of freedom s. More precisely, it is the number of collisions necessary to reduce an excess of that internal energy over its equilibrium value to $1/e$ of the previous excess

$$\tau_s = Z_s \tau_c. \tag{38–1}$$

We will write the formulas here only for the case in which all τ values are so far apart that they do not disturb each other. In particular, we will deal only with one rotational and one vibrational τ.

The rotational degrees of freedom have a specific heat—if the temperature is high enough that they are classical—of

$$C_r' = \frac{r}{2} R \tag{38–2}$$

---

[1] W. T. Richards and J. A. Reid, *J. Chem. Phys.* **2**, 193, 206 (1934).

[2] K. F. Buschmann and K. Schäfer, *Z. Physik. Chem.* **B50**, 73 (1941).

[3] M. C. Henderson and L. Peselnick, *J. Acoust. Soc. Am.* **29**, 1074 (1957).

where $r = 2$ for a linear and 3 for a nonlinear molecule. (See Sec. **34**.) According to Eq. (21–18″), at low pressures

$$\alpha' = \frac{1}{2}\frac{R}{C_p C_v}\frac{\omega^2}{\mathfrak{B}_0}\left(\frac{r}{2}R\tau_r + C'\tau_v\right)$$

$$= \frac{1}{2}\frac{1}{\gamma_0}\frac{R^2}{C_v{}^2}\frac{\omega^2}{\mathfrak{B}_0}\left(\frac{r}{2}\tau_r + \frac{C'}{R}\tau_v\right)$$

$$= \frac{R^2}{2\gamma_0\left(\frac{3}{2}R + (r/2)R + C'\right)^2}\frac{\omega^2}{\mathfrak{B}_0}\frac{\tau_c}{2}\left(rZ_r + 2\frac{C'}{R}Z_v\right)$$

$$= \frac{1}{\gamma_0}\frac{\omega^2}{\mathfrak{B}_0}\tau_c\frac{1}{(3 + r + 2(C'/R))^2}\left(rZ_r + 2\frac{C'}{R}Z_v\right) \tag{38–3}$$

where Z_r is the effective collision number for rotation, Z_v the effective collision number for vibration, and C' will be written in this section for the vibrational specific heat. If one now uses Eq. (36–25″), one gets

$$\frac{\alpha'}{\alpha_{\text{class}}} = \frac{3}{2}\frac{\gamma_0}{1.271}\frac{1}{\gamma_0}\frac{1}{(3 + r + 2(C'/R))^2}\left(rZ_r + 2\frac{C'}{R}Z_v\right). \tag{38–4}$$

$$\left[1 + \frac{3}{16}\frac{\gamma - 1}{\gamma}(9\gamma - 5)\right]^{-1}$$

$$= \frac{1.1802}{(3 + r + 2(C'/R))^2}\left[1 + \frac{3}{16}\frac{\gamma - 1}{\gamma}(9\gamma - 5)\right]^{-1}\left(rZ_r + \frac{2C'}{R}Z_v\right)$$

and for the total absorption coefficient, $\alpha = \alpha_{\text{class}} + \alpha'$

$$\frac{\alpha}{\alpha_{\text{class}}} = 1 + \frac{1.1802}{(3 + r + 2(C'/R))^2}\left[1 + \frac{3}{16}\frac{\gamma - 1}{\gamma}(9\gamma - 5)\right]^{-1}\left(rZ_r + \frac{2C'}{R}Z_v\right). \tag{38–5}$$

If C', the specific heat of the vibrations, can be neglected[1] next to R, then for $r = 2$, $\gamma_0 = 1.4$; and for $r = 3$, $\gamma_0 = 4/3$. Accordingly, for $r = 2$, $(3/16)(\gamma - 1)(9\gamma - 5)/\gamma = 0.407$

$$\frac{\alpha}{\alpha_{\text{class}}} = 1 + 0.0671\left(Z_r + \frac{C'}{R}Z_v\right) \tag{38–6}$$

---

[1] $C' = 0.15\,R$ would decrease the coefficients in front of the brackets in Eqs. (38–6) and (38–6′) by roughly 10%.

and for $r = 3$, $(3/16)(\gamma - 1)(9\gamma - 5)/\gamma = 0.328$

$$\frac{\alpha}{\alpha_{\text{class}}} = 1 + 0.074\left(Z_r + \frac{2}{3}\frac{C'}{R} Z_v.\right) \tag{38–6'}$$

Kohler[2] has written as rotational contribution to the volume viscosity in the absence of vibration

$$\eta' = \frac{RC_r'}{C_v^2} p\bar{\tau}_r = \frac{2r}{(3+r)^2} p\bar{\tau}_r. \tag{38–7}$$

(His time $\bar{\tau}_r$ is related to ours by $\bar{\tau}_r = \dfrac{C_v - C_r'}{C_v}\tau_r = \dfrac{3}{3+r}\tau_r$, and therefore corresponds to our τ''.) He develops Eq. (38–7) by an argument similar to that leading to Eq. (36–4). Using Eq. (8–2), this leads to the same results as Eq. (38–3) with $C' = 0$.

Next, Kohler argues the case in which both rotational and vibrational specific heat exists, under the following restrictive conditions: First, the vibrational specific heat is small, so that only the first excited state matters. From the investigations of Bethe and Teller (Sec. 19), we know that this restriction is unnecessary. Second, the rotational and vibrational relaxation times are far apart. (Otherwise the calculations of Sec. 21 become significant.) Third the rotational and vibrational energies are practically exchanged only with translational energy, and the direct exchange between them is insignificant, an assumption also made in Sec. 21. He gets

$$\eta_{\text{vibr}}' = \frac{RC'}{C_v^2} p\bar{\tau}_v \tag{38–8}$$

a formula equivalent to Eq. (38–4).

Equations (38–6) and (38–6') were developed by Herzfeld, and were first published in two Catholic University dissertations, that for rotation by Zmuda,[3] and that for vibration by Cheng.[4]

---

[2] M. Kohler, *Z. Physik* **125**, 715 (1948).

[3] A. Zmuda, *J. Acoust. Soc. Am.* **23**, 472 (1951).

[4] L. Cheng, *J. Chem. Phys.* **19**, 693 (1951).

(*b*) *Ratio of Relaxation and Classical Absorption at Maximum*

According to Eq. (36–25″)

$$(\alpha\lambda)_{\text{class}} = \frac{4\pi}{3} \times \frac{1.271}{\gamma} [\ \ ]\, \tau_c \omega$$

where [ ] includes the effect of heat conductivity. At the frequency $\omega''' = 1/\tau'''$, Eq. (16–5), where the relaxation absorption has its maximum, this is

$$(\alpha\lambda)_{\text{class}} = \frac{4\pi}{3} \times \frac{1.271}{\gamma} [\ \ ] \frac{\tau_c}{\tau'''} = \frac{4\pi}{3} \times \frac{1.271}{\gamma} [\ \ ] \frac{\tau_c}{\tau} \frac{\tau}{\tau'''}$$

$$= \frac{4\pi}{3} \times \frac{1.271}{\gamma} [\ \ ] \frac{1}{Z} \frac{\tau}{\tau'''} = \frac{5.084\pi}{3\gamma} [\ \ ] \frac{1}{Z} \sqrt{\frac{C_p C_v}{(C_p - C')(C_v - C')}}.$$

Using, then, Eq. (16–6), one has, with $\Delta = R$

$$\frac{(\alpha'\lambda)_{\max}}{(\alpha\lambda)_{\text{class}}} = \left(\frac{\alpha'}{\alpha_{\text{class}}}\right)_{\max} = \frac{3\gamma}{10.17\,[\ \ ]} \frac{RC'}{C_p C_v} Z. \qquad (38\text{–}9)$$

39. Gas Mixtures

(*a*) *The Relaxation Times* (See Sec. 26.)

For pure gases, e.g., the gas A, we expressed, in Sec. 38, the relaxation time through a product of a collision time (τ_c) and a required number of collisions Z_A.

Similarly, we can write

$$\tau_{AB} = (\tau_c)_{AB} Z_{AB} \qquad (39\text{–}1)$$

The $(\tau_c)_A$ had been connected with the viscosity by (36–3). Let us find $(\tau_c)_{AB}$, the number of collisions a molecule B makes in gas A. We note that, according to Hirschfelder and his collaborators, η_A is proportional to $1/r_A^2 \sqrt{M_A}$ times a function of the temperature, which, in case the Sutherland equation, Eq. (36–24), is valid, may be replaced by $T/(T + C_A)$; C_A being the corresponding Sutherland constant, and r_A a characteristic radius for the molecule. From Hirschfelder's investigations, one can write the characteristic radius $1/2\,(r_A + r_B)$ for the collisions between two different molecules and the Sutherland constant

$$C_{AB} = \sqrt{C_A C_B}. \tag{39–2}$$

The time between collisions of B in the gas A is

$$(\tau_c)_{AB} \sim \frac{\Lambda_{AB}}{\overline{W}_{AB}} = \frac{\Lambda_{AB}}{\overline{W}_A}\sqrt{\frac{2M_B}{M_A + M_B}} \tag{39–3}$$

where Λ_{AB} is the mean free path of B in A and W_{AB} is the mean relative velocity of B in A.

Therefore, one has

$$(\tau_c)_{AB} : (\tau_c)_A = \left(\frac{2r_A}{r_A + r_B}\right)^2 \frac{T + C_A}{T + C_{AB}} \sqrt{\frac{2M_B}{M_A + M_B}}. \tag{39–4}$$

Since

$$\eta_B : \eta_A = \left(\frac{r_A}{r_B}\right)^2 \frac{T + C_A}{T + C_{AB}} \sqrt{\frac{M_B}{M_A}} \tag{39–5}$$

$$\left(\frac{r_B}{r_A}\right)^2 = \frac{\eta_A}{\eta_B} \frac{T + C_A}{T + C_B} \sqrt{\frac{M_B}{M_A}}. \tag{39–5'}$$

Finally one has, after inserting Eq. (39–5′) in Eq. (39–4)

$$(\tau_c)_{AB} : (\tau_c)_A = 4\left[1 + \left(\frac{M_B}{M_A}\right)^{1/4} \left(\frac{\eta_A}{\eta_B} \frac{T + C_A}{T + C_B}\right)^{1/2}\right]^{-2} \frac{T + C_A}{T + \sqrt{C_A C_B}} \sqrt{\frac{2M_B}{M_A + M_B}}$$

$$= \frac{4\eta_B}{\eta_A}\left[\left(\frac{\eta_B}{\eta_A} \frac{T + \sqrt{C_A C_B}}{T + C_A}\right)^{1/2} \left(\frac{M_A + M_B}{2M_B}\right)^{1/4} + \right. \tag{39–6}$$

$$\left. \left(\frac{T + \sqrt{C_A C_B}}{T + C_B}\right)^{1/2} \left(\frac{M_A + M_B}{2M_A}\right)^{1/4}\right]^{-2}$$

or

$$(\tau_c)_{AB} = \frac{1}{1.271\,p}\,\varphi_{AB} \tag{39–6'}$$

where

$$\varphi_{AB} = \left[\left(\frac{1}{4\eta_A} \frac{T + \sqrt{C_A C_B}}{T + C_A}\right)^{1/2} \left(\frac{M_A + M_B}{2M_B}\right)^{1/4} + \right. \tag{39–6''}$$

$$\left. \left(\frac{1}{4\eta_B} \frac{T + \sqrt{C_A C_B}}{T + C_B}\right)^{1/2} \left(\frac{M_A + M_B}{2M_A}\right)^{1/4}\right]^{-2}.$$

Equation (39–6″) is symmetrical in A and B, i.e., $\varphi_{AB} = \varphi_{BA}$, and, from Eq. (39–6′)

$$(\tau_c)_{AB} = (\tau_c)_{BA}. \tag{39–6‴}$$

For numerical calculation, Eq. (39–6′) is more convenient. Equation (26–1) now takes the form

$$\frac{1}{\tau_1} = \left[\frac{(1-x)}{Z_A} + \frac{x}{Z_{AB}}\frac{(\tau_c)_A}{(\tau_c)_{AB}}\right]\frac{1}{(\tau_c)_A}$$
$$= \frac{1}{\tau_A}\left[1 + x\left(\frac{Z_A}{Z_{AB}}\frac{(\tau_c)_A}{(\tau_c)_{AB}} - 1\right)\right]. \tag{39–7}$$

(*b*) *Purity of the Gas*

In some gases with large Z_A, some admixtures, principally of H_2O, affect τ_1 enormously (see also Sec. 40). In this case we have the situation dealt with in the last part of Sec. 26.

The practical question might then arise in the laboratory as to what extent the impurity B must be removed for an unknown small amount of it not to affect the measured relaxation time τ_1, which will then be identified with τ_A. Equation (39–7) shows that this depends essentially on the ratio of Z_A/Z_{AB}. If one wishes to be sure that τ is not affected by more than 10%, this means, from Eq. (39–7)

$$0.1 \geqslant x\left[\frac{Z_A}{Z_{AB}}\frac{(\tau_c)_A}{(\tau_c)_{AB}} - 1\right]. \tag{39–8}$$

As an example, assume one has a sample with an impurity B; its exact amount x is not known, but x is not larger than 1%. One makes a measurement of the τ_1 of the mixture, and calculates an effective Z_{eff}, $\tau_1 = Z_{\text{eff}}(\tau_c)_A$. Then, putting, for simplicity, $(\tau_c)_{AB} = (\tau_c)_A$

$$\frac{1}{Z_{\text{eff}}} = \frac{1}{Z_A} + x\left(\frac{1}{Z_{AB}} - \frac{1}{Z_A}\right). \tag{39–9}$$

Now Z_{AB} can, at the lowest, be 1, and will probably be somewhat larger, so that the last term cannot contribute more than 0.01, and probably less. If Z_{eff} has been found to be 40, then the left side is 0.025, and $1/Z_A$ lies between 0.025 and 0.015, i.e., Z_A is between 40 and 70, more likely between 40 and 50. If this information is sufficient, one need not take further care to eliminate B. On the other hand, if Z_{eff} turns out to be 1000, i.e., the left side of Eq. (39–9) is 0.001, one cannot draw further conclusions concerning Z_A. If one knew that x actually was as high as 0.01, one could conclude that Z_{AB} would have to be at least 10, or the second term by itself would be too large.

If one adds a known amount x' of B to the gas and measures again, finding as effective Z, Z_{eff}', one has (if $x' \gg x$)

$$\frac{1}{Z_{\text{eff}}'} - \frac{1}{Z_{\text{eff}}} = x' \left[\frac{(\tau_c)_A}{(\tau_c)_{AB}} \frac{1}{Z_{AB}} - \frac{1}{Z_A} \right]$$

and since one can usually neglect the last term

$$Z_{AB} = x' \frac{(\tau_c)_A}{(\tau_c)_{AB}} \frac{Z_{\text{eff}} Z_{\text{eff}}'}{Z_{\text{eff}} - Z_{\text{eff}}'} . \tag{39–10}$$

In the case in which triple collisions are important (Sec. 40), a measurement with a single amount, x', added would not be sufficient. If one now knows Z_{AB}, one may be able to narrow the limits laid down by Eq. (39–9) considerably more than by using the lowest imaginable value of Z_{AB}, namely, unity.

40. Triple Collisions in Pure Gases and in Mixtures

In the preceding, it has been assumed that only pairs of molecules interact in the process of energy exchange. One might ask whether this is always true, at least in nearly ideal gases.

A triple collision cannot be defined exactly, and therefore the number of such collisions can only be calculated as to order of magnitude.

For such an estimate, one may fix one's attention on a particular molecule A and follow its motion. During this motion, it will make collisions with other molecules B if its center comes closer to the center of B than a certain distance $r_1 + r_2$. If there is no other molecule near enough to B while A collides with it, we have a pair collision; if there is a third molecule C close enough to B while A collides with B, we have a triple collision between A, B, and C. The uncertainty arises from the definition of "close enough." We will arbitrarily say that "close enough" means that the center of C lies within a spherical shell—with center in B—of radius $r_1 + r_2$ and thickness r_3, where r_3 is given by the fact that we are interested in a cooperation of all three molecules in the transfer of internal energy.

If x_3 is the mole fraction of molecules of the kind C in the mixture, and p is the total pressure, then there are $x_3\,(p/kT)$ molecules of kind C per unit volume.

If they are distributed at random, the number of molecules C in a particular volume is $x_3\,(p/kT)$ times that volume. Now the total volume of the spherical shells mentioned above, which are centered on molecules B, is in unit volume

$$x_2 \frac{p}{kT}\, 4\pi(r_1 + r_2)^2\, r_3 \tag{40–1}$$

where the second factor is the volume of one shell and the first factor the number of shells (i.e., molecules B) in unit volume.

The number of molecules C lying in shells around B is then given by

$$\left[x_2 \frac{p}{kT}\, 4\pi(r_1 + r_2)^2\, r_3 \right] x_3 \frac{p}{kT} \tag{40–2}$$

where the expression in square brackets is the fraction of space occupied by the shells. The fraction of the shells around molecules B which contain a molecule C is the above number divided by the total number of shells, or is

$$4\pi(r_1 + r_2)^2\, r_3 x_3 \frac{p}{kT}\,. \tag{40–3}$$

This is also the fraction of all collisions between A and B which will be triple collisions. If, in rough approximation, we write $r_1 = r_2 = r_3$, we can abbreviate

$$4\pi(r_1 + r_2)^2 r_3 = 16\pi r_1{}^3 = 3\,\frac{b}{N_A} \tag{40–4}$$

where b is the van der Waals quantity usually so designated (four times the true volume occupied by the molecules).

Therefore, the fraction of collisions which are triple collisions is

$$x_3 \frac{p}{kT}\, 3\, \frac{b}{N_A} = 3x_3 \frac{p}{RT}\, b \sim x_3 \frac{b}{8000}\, \frac{300}{T}\, p$$

where b is measured in cubic centimeters, and p in atmospheres. Because of a possible clustering effect due to attractive forces, Eq. (40–4) should be multipled by $\exp\,(\varepsilon_{23}/kT)$, where ε_{23} is the interaction between a molecule B and a molecule C.

The total rate of deactivating collisions of a molecule A at 1 atm is then

$$k_{10}{}^A = k_{AA}(1 - x) + k_{AB}x + \{k_{AAA}(1 - x)^2 + k_{AAB}(1 - x)x + k_{ABB}x^2\}\, p\, \frac{b}{8000}\, \frac{300}{T}\,. \tag{40–5}$$

Here, molecules A and B are assumed to be of the same kind, C (now called B) is an impurity, present in mole fraction x; k_{AA} is the deactivation rate of a molecule A if it moves in pure A of 1 atm standard pressure (p is then measured in atmospheres). The k_{AAA} is the probability of deactivation of a particular A in triple collision with a pair AA, multiplied with the number of collisions between A and A (so that $k_{AAA} : k_{AA}$ is the ratio of probabilities of deactivation in *one* triple collision and *one* double collision). Similarly, k_{ABB} is the probability of deactivation of an A in a triple collision with two B's multiplied by the number of double collisions one A makes per second wandering through pure B of one atm.

If one also takes the activation processes into account (Sec. 19) one finds

$$\frac{1}{\tau_A} = \frac{1}{\tau_{AA}}(1-x)p + \frac{1}{\tau_{AB}}xp + \left\{\frac{1}{\tau_{AA}}\frac{\tau_{AA}}{\tau_{AAA}}(1-x)^2 + \frac{1}{\tau_{AB}}\left[\frac{\tau_{AB}}{\tau_{AAB}}(1-x)x + \frac{\tau_{AB}}{\tau_{ABB}}x^2\right]\right\}p^2\frac{b}{8000}\frac{300}{T}. \quad (40\text{–}6)$$

Here, the relaxation times τ_{AA}, τ_{AB} refer to one atm. pure A or pure B, and the ratios $\tau_{AA} : \tau_{AAA}$ are independent of pressure.

These equations are only approximate, except insofar as dependence on x and p is concerned.

For a pure gas, this would be

$$\frac{1}{\tau_A} = \frac{1}{\tau_{AA}}p\left\{1 + \frac{\tau_{AA}}{\tau_{AAA}}p\frac{b}{8000}\frac{300}{T}\right\}. \quad (40\text{–}7)$$

A direct test has been undertaken by Walker *et al.*,[1] who investigated the relaxation time of N_2O when pure and when mixed with 10 to 50% He, A, and N_2. They found, for example, that for pure N_2O, the product τp is constant; its value, for $p = 0.25$, 0.5, 1 and 2 atm, is 0.94, 0.93, and 0.93×10^{-6} sec atm^{-1}.

For H_2O as molecule B in CO_2, Knötzel and Knötzel[2] found a term proportional to x^2, which might lead one to believe that collisions between one CO_2 and two H_2O molecules are extremely effective. However, the explanation is probably different (see below), since this term does not appear if D_2O is used instead of H_2O.

---

[1] R. A. Walker, T. D. Rossing, and S. Legvold, *Natl. Advisory Comm. Aeronaut., Tech. Notes* **3210** (1954).

[2] H. Knötzel and L. Knötzel, *Ann. Physik* [6] **2**, 393 (1948).

To sum up, there is no sign of any effect of triple collisions in nearly ideal gases.

Bourgin[3] had already tried to explain the apparently overlarge efficiency by "cluster formation," analogous to our exponential factor. Tuesday and Boudart[4] give a different interpretation. They point out that the vibration frequency of the oxygen molecule (wave number, 1580 cm^{-1}; characteristic temperature, $\vartheta = 2230$ °K) and the frequency of a bending vibration of the water molecule (wave number, 1595 cm^{-1}; $\vartheta = 2252$ °K) are nearly alike. One should therefore expect a very efficient transfer of a vibration quantum from oxygen to water (resonance transfer, Sec. 67). The deactivation of the oxygen molecule occurs *most easily*, therefore, by transfering the internal energy not to translation, but to a bending vibration of the water molecule. However, the opposite process is equally easy. Boudart writes the following reaction equation, with rate constants. (A star implies vibrational excitation; due to the high ϑ, only the first excited state need be considered.)

$$O_2{}^* + O_2 \underset{k_{01}}{\overset{k_{10}}{\rightleftarrows}} O_2 + O_2. \tag{40–8}$$

This is the usual transfer of vibrational to translational energy in oxygen.

$$O_2{}^* + H_2O \underset{k_{02}}{\overset{k_{20}}{\rightleftarrows}} O_2 + H_2O. \tag{40–8′}$$

This is the usual de-excitation by the impurity, water (mole fraction X), where transfer of vibrational energy of O_2 to translational energy of H_2O occurs. The corresponding processes for water are

$$H_2O^* + H_2O \underset{k_{04}}{\overset{k_{40}}{\rightleftarrows}} H_2O + H_2O \tag{40–8″}$$

and

$$H_2O^* + O_2 \underset{k_{05}}{\overset{k_{50}}{\rightleftarrows}} H_2O + O_2. \tag{40–8‴}$$

---

[3] G. Bourgin, *Phys. Rev.* **50**, 355 (1936).

[4] C. S. Tuesday and M. Boudart, Tech. Note 7, Contract AF 33 (038) –23976, Princeton Univ., January, 1955.

These describe the deactivation of excited water by the transfer of its vibrational energy into translational energy of either water or oxygen.

Finally, we have the resonance process

$$O_2^* + H_2O \underset{k_{03}}{\overset{k_{30}}{\rightleftarrows}} O_2 + H_2O^*. \qquad (40\text{–}8'''')$$

We will call the mole fractions of O_2, H_2O, O_2^*, and H_2O^*: $1 - X, X, x_1$, and x_2; the latter two are negligible compared to X, and X is small compared to unity. N is the number of molecules per cubic centimeter. It should be said here that the notation is that of Sec. 27, not that of Sec. 19, the bimolecular nature of the process being explicitly stated, so that the rate of Eq. (40–8'''') is, for example

$$N^2 \, [k_{30}x_1X - k_{03}(1 - X)x_2].$$

Boudart brings the equations only into the form of Eq. (19–6), the rest of the calculation proceeding as in Sec. 19. Then the reaction equation for excited O_2^* is

$$-N\frac{dx_1}{dt} = N^2(x_1 - x_1^0)\,\{k_{10}(1 - X) + k_{20}X + k_{30}\,X\} - N^2k_{03}(1 - X)\,(x_2 - x_2^0) \qquad (40\text{–}9)$$

the excitation reactions in Eqs. (40–8) to (40–8''') being neglected. The amount of x_2 is even smaller than that of x_1 and therefore adjusts itself very quickly, so that dx_2/dt is put equal to zero. (This procedure, of putting the concentration change of intermediates equal to zero, is customary in chemical kinetics.) One then gets

$$k_{03}(x_2 - x_2^0)\,(1 - X) + k_{40}(x_2 - x_2^0)X + k_{50}(x_2 - x_2^0)\,(1 - X) - k_{30}X(x_1 - x_1^0) = 0 \quad (40\text{–}10)$$

or

$$x_2 - x_2^0 = \frac{k_{30}X(x_1 - x_1^0)}{(k_{03} + k_{50})\,(1 - X) + k_{40}X} = \frac{k_{30}X(x_1 - x_1^0)}{(k_{03} + k_{50}) - (k_{03} + k_{50} - k_{40})X}. \qquad (40\text{–}10')$$

Inserting Eq. (40–10′) in Eq. (40–9), one has

$$-\frac{dx_1}{dt} = (x_1 - x_1^0)N\left\{k_{10}(1-X) + k_{20}X + k_{30}X\left[1 - \frac{k_{03}(1-X)}{k_{03}(1-X) + k_{50} + (k_{40}-k_{50})X}\right]\right\}$$

$$= (x_1 - x_1^0)N\left\{k_{10} + (k_{20}-k_{10})X + \frac{k_{30}X\,[(k_{40}-k_{50})X + k_{50}]}{(k_{03}+k_{50}) - (k_{03}+k_{50}-k_{40})X}\right\}$$

$$= (x_1 - x_1^0)N\left\{k_{10} + \left(k_{20} - k_{10} + \frac{k_{30}\,k_{50}}{k_{03}+k_{50}-(k_{03}+k_{50}-k_{40})X}\right)X + \frac{k_{30}(k_{40}-k_{50})X^2}{k_{03}+k_{50}-(k_{03}+k_{50}-k_{40})X}\right\}. \quad (40\text{–}11)$$

Therefore

$$\frac{1}{\tau} = Nk_{10} + N\left[k_{20} - k_{10} + \frac{k_{30}k_{50}}{k_{03}+k_{50}-(k_{03}+k_{50}-k_{40})X}\right]X + N\frac{k_{30}(k_{40}-k_{50})}{k_{03}+k_{50}-(k_{03}+k_{50}-k_{40})X}X^2. \quad (40\text{–}12)$$

This is of the required form, provided

$$k_{03} + k_{50} \gg |k_{03} + k_{50} - k_{40}|X$$

or

$$(k_{03} + k_{50})\,(1 - X) \gg k_{40}X.$$

Boudart assumes $k_{03} = k_{30} \gg k_{40}X$ (X being smaller than 0.02), $k_{20} = k_{50}$, and $k_{20} > k_{10}$ (experimental result). Then Eq. (40–12) can be simplified to

$$\frac{1}{\tau} = Nk_{10} + N(k_{20} + k_{50})X + N(k_{40} - k_{50})X^2. \quad (40\text{–}13)$$

(Boudart has k_{40} instead of $k_{40} - k_{50}$, because he uses our $X/(1 - X)$ as mole fraction.)

From his experiments, Boudart then concludes

$$Nk_{20} = Nk_{50} = 1.077 \times 10^5\,\mathrm{sec^{-1}\,atm^{-1}}$$

$$Nk_{40} - Nk_{50} = 7.037 \times 10^8\,\mathrm{sec^{-1}\,atm^{-1}}.$$

For D_2O, the resonance condition is not fulfilled, the bending vibration having the frequency 1178 cm^{-1}. While Eq. (40–12) is still valid, $k_{03} \neq k_{30}$ and both are not very large compared to $k_{40}X$, and the complete equation must be used. Assuming that k_{20}, k_{40}, and k_{50} are the same for D_2O as for H_2O, Tuesday and Boudart find for D_2O

$$Nk_{30} = 2.72 \times 10^6 \text{ sec}^{-1}\text{ atm}^{-1} \qquad Nk_{03} = 1.62 \times 10^6 \text{ sec}^{-1}\text{ atm}^{-1}.$$

41. Additional Absorption in Mixtures

Any irreversible process occurring in a sound wave will produce additional absorption. There are two such processes in mixtures, one due to the existence of a density gradient, the other due to the presence of a temperature gradient. In the former, there is a resultant flow of molecules down the gradient. However, in a mixture, the lighter molecules will move faster than the heavier ones, and therefore there will be a tendency to unmixing, with a relatively higher concentration of the lighter molecules in the density (pressure) troughs and of the heavier molecules in the density (pressure) peaks. The temperature gradient will produce thermal diffusion, also leading to partial unmixing. However, for sufficiently high frequency, this unmixing will be out of phase with the pressure variation.

The additional absorption, due to unmixing, depends on frequency and pressure in the same manner as classical absorption, and can therefore be formally represented by a volume viscosity η''. In the expression for η'', one needs the γ of the mixture, given by

$$\gamma = 1 + R\,[(C_v)_A\,(1 - x) + (C_v)_B x]^{-1} \tag{41–1}$$

and the two constants D and D_T of diffusion and thermal diffusion, defined by the flow set up by diffusion at constant pressure

$$-D \operatorname{grad} x - D_T \operatorname{grad}(\ln T) = -D\left[\operatorname{grad} x + \frac{D_T}{D}\operatorname{grad}(\ln T)\right].$$

D is proportional to $1/p$, and D_T/D is independent of pressure and depends on composition x in such a manner that

$$D_T\,[D(1 - x)x]^{-1}$$

is always finite. Then

$$\eta'' = \frac{3}{4}\gamma\rho D\left[\frac{M_B - M_A}{(1 - x)M_A + xM_B} + \frac{\gamma - 1}{\gamma}\,\frac{1}{(1 - x)x}\,\frac{D_T}{D}\right]^2. \tag{41–2}$$

In practice, according to Kohler, η'' is appreciable only if one partner is H_2 or He, and the other is a heavier gas. In 50–50 He-A mixtures, the absorption is increased by a factor 1.9; even in 99–1 He-A mixtures, it is increased by a factor 1.3. On the other hand, for air, which is a N_2-O_2 mixture, α increases only by a factor 1.003.

The theory was developed by Rocard,[1] Meixner,[2] and Kohler,[3] whom we have followed.

[1] Y. Rocard, "Propagation et Absorption du son." Herrmann, Paris, 1933.

[2] J. Meixner, *Ann. Physik* [5] **43**, 470 (1943).

[3] M. Kohler, *Z. Physik* **127**, 40 (1949).

V. Experimental Methods to Determine Velocity and Absorption of Ultrasonic Waves in Gases

42. Methods for Low Frequencies

(*a*) *Velocity and Absorption: The Kundt's Tube*[1]

In a Kundt's tube, the diameter is much smaller than the wave length. The source is a microphone at one end; the receiver is at the other end of the tube. Even if the diameter of the microphone is smaller than that of the tube, the wave is nearly plane within a short distance from it. The source and receiver have a flat sensitivity curve in the region of interest. The frequency is varied; the resonance frequency gives the velocity, the width of the resonance curve the loss. The latter is mainly determined by viscosity and heat loss at the wall; calling for the moment

$$g = \frac{1}{r}\sqrt{\frac{\eta}{2\rho}}\left[1 + (\gamma - 1)\sqrt{[\mathrm{Eu}]\frac{C_v}{M\gamma}}\right]$$

with r representing the radius of the tube; and [Eu], the Eucken number, the apparent absorption coefficient due to wall losses is given by

$$k'' \frac{g}{\mathfrak{V}_0}\sqrt{\omega}\,.$$

Any added absorption would have a different dependence on ω;[2] only an absorption due to a very long τ would be noticeable besides the loss on the wall.

The apparent velocity is

$$\mathfrak{V} = \mathfrak{V}_0\left(1 - \frac{k'g}{\sqrt{\omega}}\right)$$

---

[1] G. G. Sherrat and E. Griffiths, *Proc. Roy. Soc.* **A147**, 292 (1934).

[2] H. Knötzel and L. Knötzel, *Ann. Physik* [6] **2**, 393 (1948).

and k' and k'' are best determined by standardization with a known gas (argon, for example). The method can give data of high accuracy. Here and in the following method the frequency (not f/p) should be below the low frequency cutoff of the lowest nonplanar mode of tube vibration, i.e.

$$f < 0.5861 \frac{\mathfrak{V}}{2r} .$$

(b) Absorption Only: The Traveling Wave Tube

Angona[3] has used progressive waves at low frequencies in a tube of 1.7 cm diameter, which is plugged with Pyrex wool at both ends to prevent reflection. The source is a ribbon loudspeaker, working between 2 and 10 kc. The source can be moved along the tube by an external magnet. A condenser microphone is mounted at a fixed position. One works at pressures of 3 to 300 mm Hg, which permits covering a large f/p range. For low pressure, the loss on the walls increases only as $p^{-1/2}$, while the absorption within the gas increases as p^{-1} (as long as $\omega\tau \ll 1$). The uncertainty in $\alpha\lambda$ seems to be 0.005 to 0.01, which amounts to 10% for low absorption and to 2.5% at high absorption.

(c) Absorption Only: The Reverberation Method

This method was first used by Kneser and Knudsen.[4] A closed vessel is excited acoustically and the loss of the energy observed. The loss is made up of two parts: the volume loss, which is the interesting part, given by αV, and the surface loss σA. These are separated by using several vessels with different volume to surface ratio.

One can measure the loss in two ways: by exciting the vessel once (or repeatedly) and measuring the exponential decay of the amplitude with time, or by having a continuous source of sound and a steady state. In the former case, one does not need to know the absolute sound intensity.

In the latter method, the sound intensity produced in unit time is equal to that lost, so that an absolute measurement of absorption would require an absolute measurement of sound energy produced and of absolute intensity. Instead, the measurement is made relative to a calibrating gas; with constant sound source, the loss factor is inversely proportional to the steady state sound intensity.

---

[3] F. Angona, *J. Acoust. Soc. Am.* **25**, 1111 (1954).

[4] H. O. Kneser and V. O. Knudsen, *Ann. Physik* [5] **21**, 682 (1934).

Knudsen[5] uses a fan to distribute the sound intensity uniformly over the vessel.

Edmonds and Lamb[6] have measured the decay time in a cylindrical vessel (9.8 cm diameter, 60 cm length) in which the wall losses can be calculated in good agreement with experiment. "Classical" absorption is too low for measurement, but that in cyclopropane can be measured easily in the range of 3—20 kc/atm.

43. The Ultrasonic Interferometer

(*a*) *General*

The ultrasonic interferometer, first used by Pierce,[1] uses plane waves in a cavity, usually cylindrical. The source is a vibrating quartz crystal, although Pierce[1] has also used magnetostrictive rods. There are two main forms, single-crystal and double-crystal instruments. The former uses the reaction of a standing wave system on the source crystal, the standing wave system being determined by a reflector at the other end of the cavity. The latter uses a separate receiver crystal, at the end of the cavity opposite the source. The instrument has been highly refined, particularly by Hubbard.[2,3] Its general theory closely parallels that of a transmission line with loss, the one-crystal instrument corresponding to a measurement at the input-point, the two crystal interferometer to a measurement at the terminal point. The details of the theory have been developed by Hubbard,[3] Borgnis,[3a] and Solov'ev.[3b]

The phenomenon on which both velocity and absorption measurements depend is the appearance of a dip in the current, a "crevasse," when the gas column is in resonance.

There are some general precautions which have to be taken for best performance of the interferometer.

---

[5] V. O. Knudsen, *J. Acoust. Soc. Am.* **5**, 112 (1933).

[6] P. D. Edmonds and J. Lamb, *Proc. Phys. Soc.* (*London*) **71**, 17 (1958).

[1] G. W. Pierce, *Proc. Am. Acad. Arts Sci.* **60**, 271 (1925).

[2] J. C. Hubbard and A. L. Loomis, *J. Opt. Soc. Am.* **17**, 295 (1928); *Phys. Rev.* **36**, 1668 (1930).

[3] J. C. Hubbard, *Phys. Rev.* **38**, 1011 (1931); **41**, 523 (1932); **46**, 525 (1934).

[3a] F. E. Borgnis, *J. Acoust. Soc. Am.* **24**, 19 (1952).

[3b] V. A. Solov'ev, *Soviet Phys. Acoustics* **1956**, **2**, 301 (1957).

Too high an amplitude would produce local heating of the gas, particularly near the crystal, and distortion of the wave form (see Sec. 33). In general these effects are believed to be unimportant if no more than 0.1 volts is applied to the crystal. Quartz crystals usually have many resonance frequencies. Crystals of the same nominal frequency differ from each other; one has to be chosen in which the selected frequency is sufficiently isolated on both sides from neighboring resonances.

Next, the reflector and the radiating surfaces should be exactly parallel.[4] The variation in normal distance over the surface should be less than a half wave length of green light. Misalignment broadens the crevasse, makes it asymmetric, or even produces secondary crevasses.[5]

The waves should be plane waves. For this it is necessary for the diameter of the crystal to be large compared with the acoustical wave length; e.g., in air the wave length is 1.6 mm for 200 kc and 0.16 mm for 2 mc. A diameter of 100 wave lengths would be 16 cm for 200 kc, 1.6 cm for 2 Mc. Accordingly, 200 kc is about the low frequency limit for precision measurements. There are two different arrangements possible: crystal and reflector in a much wider vessel; or reflector fully filling the cross section of the cylindrical vessel (and gliding in it) and the crystal fully covering the other end, e.g., resting lightly on the upper end.

In the latter case, one can analyze the standing wave system into different modes as in a cylindrical wave guide. The lowest mode represents plane waves, higher modes more complicated waves with different phase velocity. Krasnooshkin[6] and Stewart and Stewart[7] have treated the result of the superposition of different modes, which results in variation of the distance between crevasses (and therefore of the apparent wave length) with crevasse number. Whether higher modes are present depends on the way of excitation, i.e., on the shape of vibration of the crystal. If the latter acted like a rigid piston filling the cylindrical interferometer, only the lowest mode (plane waves) would be excited. Hubbard always believed that his method of laying a very well polished crystal with very light pressure on the upper, open end of the interferometer guaranteed such a behavior. Some unpublished measurements of Townsend seemed to confirm this; they gave

---

[4] J. C. Hubbard, *Am. J. Phys.* 8, 207–211 (1940); note particularly p. 211.

[5] R. S. Alleman, *J. Acoust. Soc. Am.* **10**, 88 (1938); **13**, 23 (1941); *Phys. Rev.* **55**, 87 (1939).

[6] P. E. Krasnooshkin, *Phys. Rev.* **65**, 190 (1944).

[7] J. L. Stewart and E. S. Stewart, *J. Acoust. Soc. Am.* **24**, 22 (1952).

the same velocity in air with a diameter of 7 wave lengths as with a diameter of 100 wave lengths.

Van Itterbeek and Verhaegen[8a] have pointed out that one can test the presence of other modes in absorption measurements by plotting α against $1/p$ (linear scale). One should get a straight line in the region where $\omega\tau < 1$, a line which should go through the origin. The height at which the experimental line cuts the positive ordinate axis is a measure of the strength of the other modes. In the case of these authors, at 500 kc, this effect increases the absorption in He by about 0.01, or about 20% at 1 atm, 2.5% at 0.25 atm.

Another requirement is extreme electrical stability. Particularly when the measurements are made by hand, it might take nearly an hour to measure a crevasse, so that the drift should be no more than 2 cycles in 2 mc per hr. If automatic registration is used, much less time is needed and the requirements on stability are not as high.[8b]

Finally, the gas handling system, particularly at low pressure, must be well designed. If the influence of traces of impurities is investigated, adsorption or desorption in long tubes may be important and a flow system with analysis at the exit may be desirable.

(*b*) *Velocity Measurement:*

In principle, this is simple, since the crevasses are half a wave length distant from each other.

In practice one can use only a few frequencies. Apart from the harmonics of a crystal, one needs a different crystal for each frequency. It is much easier to change the pressure, since the dispersion and the absorption per wave length depend only on ω/p.

To get an idea about the accuracy required for velocity measurements to determine the effective specific heat, consider the following:

Assume we have a dispersion curve due to a single relaxation time, and we approach a constant value of $\mathfrak{V}$, either at the low frequency end or at the high frequency end. The question arises as how accurately $\mathfrak{V}$ must be measured to be sure that there is not another relaxation process, connected with a small C', either at much lower or much higher frequencies. Call the limiting specific heat $\bar{C}_v$ (this may be the static specific heat, important at the low frequency end, or 5/2 R for linear, 3 R for nonlinear molecules

---

[8a] A. van Itterbeek and L. Verhaegen, *Nature* **167**, 477 (1951).

[8b] M. C. Henderson and L. Peselnick, *J. Acoust. Soc. Am.* **29**, 1074 (1957).

at the high frequency end). Call the real part of the effective specific heat at the frequency used $\bar{C}_v + R\delta$. Then

$$\mathfrak{V}^2 = \gamma \frac{RT}{M} = \frac{R + \bar{C}_v + R\delta}{\bar{C}_v + R\delta} \frac{RT}{M} = \frac{RT}{M}\left(1 + \frac{R}{\bar{C}_v + R\delta}\right)$$

$$= \frac{RT}{M}\left[\left(1 + \frac{R}{\bar{C}_v}\right) - \left(\frac{R}{\bar{C}_v}\right)^2 \delta\right] = \bar{\gamma}\frac{RT}{M}\left(1 - \frac{R}{\bar{C}_v}\frac{R}{\bar{C}_p}\delta\right). \quad (43\text{–}1)$$

The relative change in velocity is, therefore

$$\frac{\Delta\mathfrak{V}}{\mathfrak{V}} = -\frac{1}{2}\frac{(\bar{\gamma}-1)^2}{\bar{\gamma}}\delta \quad (43\text{–}2)$$

with

$$\bar{\gamma} = \frac{R + \bar{C}_v}{\bar{C}_v}.$$

Accordingly, if a linear molecule still has, near the upper frequency limit, a vibrational energy of 0.1 R left, i.e., has a $C_v = 2.6\,R$, $\bar{\gamma} = 1.4$, $\delta = 0.1$, then

$$\frac{\Delta\mathfrak{V}}{\mathfrak{V}_\infty} = -\frac{(0.4)^2}{2 \times 1.4}0.1 = -0.006.$$

If $\mathfrak{V}$ is of the order of 300 m/sec. this means that $\mathfrak{V}$ is 1.8 m/sec below its final value. In other words, present methods (see below) do not permit detection of less than 0.02 R.

It is more probable that, in a polyatomic molecule, one or more vibrations with high frequency have a very long relaxation time, so that the corresponding process of relaxation would lie far below (or at much higher pressures) than the range of measurements made. In this case one gets an apparently constant velocity $\mathfrak{V}_0'$, which is somewhat higher than the true limiting velocity $\mathfrak{V}_0$.

Assume a molecule with $\bar{C}_v = 18\,R$. Then $\bar{\gamma} = 19/18 = 1.055$

$$\frac{\Delta\mathfrak{V}}{\mathfrak{V}_0} = 0.0015\,(-\delta).$$

In this case the lowest detectable specific heat deviation would be about R.

The width of the crevasses depends on the absorption. At low absorption they are very narrow; at high absorption they are quite broad.

It is exceedingly difficult fo fix the position of the very narrow crevasse at low absorption exactly. By fixing two points on both sides of the crevasse, which give the same galvanometer deflection, and taking the mean of the positions of these two points as the position of the crevasse, the accuracy is greatly increased.[9, 10]

For small absorption the accuracy ought to be determined by that of the screw. A Brown and Sharp micrometer screw has 40 turns to the inch and 250 divisions per turn, so that one division corresponds to 0.0025 mm. If one can measure the crevasses over a distance of 1 cm, the margin of error in the velocity measurements[11] ought to be 1 in 4000. Even in the best circumstances[7] the accuracy has not been better than half this value, and often the margin of error is not lower than 1 in 1000.

In principle, one would be able to use the interferometer up to 20 mc, if it were not for the absorption.

When the absorption is high, the accuracy of the velocity measurements is much less. If $\alpha\lambda$ is 0.06 one might not be able to see more than 4 or 5 peaks, and these peaks are so flat that their position cannot be determined to better than 1/30 of a half wave length, so that the velocity is only known to 1% or even less. Absorption measurements, on the other hand, are more accurate for larger absorption.

For low absorption, there are two methods. The first measures the width of the crevasse and the ratio of the current in the depth of the crevasse to the current that would be there if the crystal were replaced by an equivalent capacitance. This is difficult to do when the crevasse is very narrow and the measurements are made by hand, since it requires extreme frequency stability. Also, the crevasse must be symmetric. The measurement must be done at different reflector distances, since one determines the total loss and reflection losses are included.

The other method requires a plotting of crevasse depths and current outside the crevasse over a number of reflector positions, and the determination of the envelopes, which again requires high stability.

The data on small absorption given in the literature vary widely. The older measurements often gave results several times too high. A conspicuous example is He, for which results several times the classical value were found. This worried the theoretical physicists for several years until improved measurements in the early 1950's, by Greenspan[12] and by van Itterbeek and Verhaegen,[8] cleared the matter up (see Sec. 47).

---

[9] M. Grabau, *J. Acoust. Soc. Am.* **5**, 1 (1933).

[10] D. Sette, A. Busala, and J. C. Hubbard, *J. Chem. Phys.* **23**, 787 (1955).

[11] This requires that T be constant to 1 in 2000, or 0.1° at room temperature.

[12] M. Greenspan, *J. Acoust. Soc. Am.* **22**, 568 (1950).

When the absorption is large, its measurement is much easier. One then uses the second method described above, with simplifications due to Stewart and Stewart[7] and to Fox and Hunter.[13] The accuracy is probably better than 10%; this is probably still good down to $\alpha\lambda$ as low as 0.03. On the whole it is still difficult to judge at face value the accuracy of any given absorption measurement made with the interferometer.

Greenspan[12] and Greenspan and Thompson[14] use a two-crystal interferometer, one crystal serving as emitter, the other as receiver. The instrument is used at high absorption (100–200 Mc/atm) so that the standing wave ratio is negligible. The results for absorption are very good. The velocity is determined by pulsing.

44. Miscellaneous Methods

(*a*) *The Optical Method*

This is an application of a method first developed for liquids and used for gases by Grobe.[1] The alternate compressions and rarefactions of the gas in a progressive sound wave act as an optical grating for a light beam passing at right angles through the sound beam. The grating distance (acoustic wave length) determines the position of the first order spectrum, the sound intensity its brightness. From the former one gets the sound velocity; from the latter, if measured for different positions from the sound source, the absorption. The disadvantage of the method lies in the necessity of using high-intensity sound waves, with the danger of distortion of the wave form (Sec. 33) and local heating. Petersen[2] has decreased the necessary sound intensity by the use of higher gas pressures (10 atm at 4 mc).

(*b*) *The Pulse Method*

The pulse method was originally developed for the ultrasonic investigation of liquids (see Chapter IX). It has been successfully applied to gases by Wight[3] at Brown University in combination with method (a) of sec. 46.

---

[13] F. E. Fox and J. L. Hunter, *Proc. I.R.E.* (*Inst. Radio Engrs.*) **36**, 1500 (1948).
[14] M. Greenspan and M. C. Thompson, *J. Acoust. Soc. Am.* **25**, 92 (1953).

[1] H. Grobe, *Physik. Z.* **39**, **333** (1938).

[2] O. Petersen, *Physik. Z.* **41**, 29 (1940).

[3] H. M. Wight, *J. Acoust. Soc. Am.* **28**, 459 (1956).

45. Aerodynamical Methods

(a) *The Jet Method*[1]

Kantrowitz[2, 3] has developed a method for the direct measurement of relaxation times in gases. The physical principle is as follows:

Consider a gas emerging as a jet from a high-pressure tank through a nozzle. The kinetic energy is acquired from the internal energy of the gas and results in a temperature drop. If the nozzle is long enough, the expansion is sufficiently slow that all degrees of freedom participate, and the static specific heat C_p governs the process. If now the jet is stopped, the deceleration lasting for a time t, the kinetic energy of the jet is changed back to thermal energy. If t is large compared to τ, all degrees of freedom can again follow, the process is again governed by the static value C_p, and the end temperature and pressure are equal to the original (tank) temperature and pressure. If, on the other hand, t is small compared to τ, only the external degrees of freedom are active during the stoppage and compression, the specific heat $C_p - C'$ is effective, and immediately after the gas is stopped the temperature (stagnation temperature) is higher and the pressure (stagnation pressure) is lower than are the corresponding initial quantities. This is then followed during a time interval of order τ by an irreversible process of adjustment between external and internal degrees of freedom, during which the temperature drops to the initial temperature, the gas contracts, and the pressure remains constant.

The time of stoppage of the gas jet t depends on the size of the obstacle (e.g., the diameter d of the Pitot tube), and has the order of magnitude d/u. To give a more detailed calculation, one can distinguish (according to Griffith[4]) three regions: I, that of expansion; II, that of stoppage of the jet; III, that of irreversible adjustment.

One has in the first region

$$C_p(T_0 - T_{\text{I}}) = \frac{M}{2} u^2 \tag{45–1}$$

---

[1] Section 45(a) is reprinted from Section H 15, pp. 684, 685, and part of 686 in Karl F. Herzfeld, Relaxation Phenomena in Gases *In* "Thermodynamics and Physics of Matter" (F. D. Rossini, ed.), Princeton Univ. Press, Princeton, New Jersey, 1955.

[2] A. Kantrowitz, *J. Chem. Phys.* **14**, 150 (1946).

[3] P. W. Huber and A. Kantrowitz, *J. Chem. Phys.* **15**, 275 (1947).

[4] W. Griffith, *J. Appl. Phys.* **21**, 1319 (1950).

and

$$p_0^{(1-\gamma)/\gamma}\, T_0 = p_{\mathrm{I}}^{(1-\gamma)/\gamma}\, T_{\mathrm{I}} \tag{45–2}$$

with

$$\gamma = 1 + \frac{R}{C_v}\cdot \tag{45–3}$$

In region II

$$\frac{M}{2}\, u^2 = (C_p)_{\mathrm{eff}}(T_{\mathrm{II}} - T_{\mathrm{I}}) \tag{45–1′}$$

$$p_{\mathrm{I}}^{(1-\gamma')/\gamma'}\, T_{\mathrm{I}} = p_{\mathrm{II}}^{(1-\gamma')/\gamma'}\, T_{\mathrm{II}} \tag{45–2′}$$

with

$$\gamma' = 1 + \frac{R}{(C_v)_{\mathrm{eff}}}\cdot \tag{45–3′}$$

One has from Eqs. (45–1) and (45–1′)

$$C_p T_0 + [(C_p)_{\mathrm{eff}} - C_p] T_{\mathrm{I}} = (C_p)_{\mathrm{eff}} T_{\mathrm{II}}. \tag{45–4}$$

Eliminating T_{I} and T_{II} with the help of Eqs. (45–2) and (45–2′) and introducing the abbreviation

$$g = \frac{C_p}{(C_p)_{\mathrm{eff}}} - 1$$

one gets

$$\ln\frac{p_{\mathrm{II}}}{p_0} = \frac{g}{1+g}\ln\frac{p_I}{p_0} + \frac{\gamma}{(\gamma-1)\,(1+g)}\ln\left[1 + g - g\left(\frac{p_I}{p_0}\right)^{(\gamma-1)/\gamma}\right]. \tag{45–5}$$

This is always negative for $p_{\mathrm{I}} < p_0$.

For small values of g, one has

$$\frac{p_0 - p_{\mathrm{II}}}{p_0} = g\left\{\ln\frac{p_0}{p_I} - \frac{\gamma}{\gamma-1}\left[1 - \left(\frac{p_I}{p_0}\right)^{(\gamma-1)/\gamma}\right]\right\}. \tag{45–5′}$$

The difference between the tank pressure, p_0, and the stagnation pressure at the Pitot tube, p_{II}, is measured and gives g.

Up to now the process has been isentropic. It is followed by adjustment between the degrees of freedom, so that the whole thermal energy is again distributed over C_p, i.e.

$$C_p T_{\text{III}} = C_p T_0 \qquad T_{\text{III}} = T_0.$$

Since this occurs at constant pressure, an entropy change is involved equal to

$$\Delta S = R \ln \frac{p_0}{p_{\text{II}}}, \tag{45–6}$$

since the temperature dependent terms in the entropy are equal

$$C_p \ln T_{\text{III}} = C_p \ln T_0.$$

The next problem is to connect t and therefore $(C_p)_{\text{eff}}$ with the hydrodynamic flow. Griffith assumed a cylindrical Pitot tube, with an opening equal to 0.620 of the outer diameter d and with a flat ending. Graphical integration of the flow problem showed that the left side of Eq. (45–5) is only a function of the dimensionless quantity:

$$\frac{C_p - C'}{C_p} \tau \frac{u}{d}.$$

with u the speed of the jet. See Eq. (45–1).
One then gets the values in Table 45–1.

TABLE 45–1

PRESSURE DIFFERENCE IN STOPPED JETS

$\frac{C_p - C'}{C_p} \tau \frac{u}{d}$	0.1	0.33	1	3	10
$\frac{p_0 - p_{\text{II}}}{p_0}$	0.0828	0.226	0.480	0.723	0.908

In Griffith's experiments, Pitot tubes made from glass tubing were used with diameters between 0.007 in. and 0.024 in. The nozzles were 1/2 in. long with 0.07 or 0.04 in. diam of the exit, and with flow speeds of about 120 m/sec.

(b) The Shock Wave Method

This is based on the fundamental, theoretical work of Bethe and Teller.[5] It was first put into experimental practice by Slawsky's group[6,7] at the Naval Ordnance Laboratory, and shortly thereafter by Bleakney's co-workers[8,9] at Princeton. The measurements have been refined by Resler.[10] When a shock travels down a shock tube in a monatomic gas, the gas behind the shock—which itself has a thickness of only a few mean free paths—is adiabatically compressed, resulting in a higher density and temperature. A Mach-Zehnder interferometer which is sensitive to changes in refractive index and therefore to changes in density shows an abrupt change of density behind the shock, the density remaining constant afterward (until heat conduction to the walls intervenes).

If, however, the gas has internal degrees of freedom which take some time for adjustment, the external degrees of freedom alone are affected directly behind the shock, and the temperature increase is as large as it would be if the specific heat were $C_p - C'$. The energy then leaks into the internal degrees of freedom, the temperature goes down, and the density increases correspondingly. Finally, the density and temperature which correspond to the static value C_p are reached. The curvature of the interference fringes indicates how $(C_p)_{\text{eff}}$ varies with distance behind the shock and, therefore, if the shock speed is known, with time. This permits calculation of the relaxation time. Since very high temperatures can be reached in strong shocks (these depend on the ratio of the initial pressures on the two sides of the shock, and on γ) one can measure τ at temperatures so high that no other method is applicable.

Hornig and his co-workers[11] at Brown University reflect light from the shock front, instead of using an interferometer. The intensity of the reflected light depends on the thickness of the transition zone as compared to the wave length of light λ. This method is suited for short relaxation times,

---

[5] H. Bethe and E. Teller, Aberdeen Proving Ground Rept. No. X, **117** (1941).

[6] E. F. Smiley, E. H. Winkler, and Z. Slawsky, *J. Chem. Phys.* **20**, 923 (1952).

[7] E. F. Smiley and E. H. Winkler, *J. Chem. Phys.* **22**, 2018 (1954).

[8] W. Griffith, *Phys. Rev.* **87**, 234 (1952).

[9] V. H. Blackman, Princeton Univ. Tech. Rept. II, 20, May (1955).

[10] E. L. Resler, Jr. and M. Scheibe, *J. Acoust. Soc. Am.* **27**, 932 (1955).

[11] E. F. Greene, G. R. Cowan, and D. F. Hornig, *J. Chem. Phys.* **19**, 427 (1951).

e.g., those of rotational degrees of freedom, since the transition zone is then short. They assume a density distribution of the form

$$\rho = \rho_1 + (\rho_2 - \rho_1)\,(1 + e^{-4x/L})^{-1}.$$

If φ is the angle of incidence, the reflection coefficient is proportional to

$$(1 + \tan^4 \varphi)\left(\frac{L}{2\lambda}\cos\varphi\right)^2 \left[\sinh\left(\pi^2 \frac{L}{\lambda}\cos\varphi\right)\right]^{-2}.$$

46. Direct Methods for Measuring Absorption and Relaxation Time

This section describes three methods, two for the direct measurement of absorption, the third for the direct measurement of some relaxation times. These three methods cannot properly be put under any of the previous headings.

(a) Parker *et al.*[1] have an emitter and receiver, not large compared to the wave length, so that the waves are not plane. The frequency used is 60–70 kc, the distance about 60 cm. At one atm pressure the absorption is assumed negligible and the received signal measured as function of distance is determined by the geometry. It is now assumed that the geometry of the waves remains the same when the pressure is lowered, and that the greater decrease in the signal with distance is due to increased absorption, because of the larger values of ω/p. The instrument is useful for the range 20 to 50 Mc/atm.

(b) Another method uses the "quartz wind." A beam of plane progressive waves carries a linear momentum of $I/\mathfrak{B}$ per cm^2, analogous to the case of light. If the energy $I\alpha dx$ is absorbed in a layer of unit cross section and dx thickness, the momentum $I/\mathfrak{B}\,\alpha dx$ is taken out of the beam and transferred to the material so that a body force of amount $\alpha\, I/\mathfrak{B}$ per unit volume is exerted on the fluid. A flow may then be set up according to the hydrodynamical equations, just as when any other body force, such as gravity, acts. One can either measure the pressure difference or the flow velocity.[2] The latter is proportional to the force and inversely proportional to the viscous resistance, i.e. proportional to α/η or, by formally introducing the bulk viscosity, proportional to $(4/3\,\eta + \eta')/\eta$ or to $4/3 + \eta'/\eta$. This

---

[1] J. G. Parker, C. E. Adams, and R. M. Stavseth, *J. Acoust. Soc. Am.* **25**, 263 (1953).

[2] H. Medwin, *J. Acoust. Soc. Am.* **26**, 332 (1954).

would include the effect of heat conductivity in η'. The theory was first developed in detail by Eckart;[3] Cady had earlier given a presentation similar to the one given here, which was discussed and elaborated by Fox and Herzfeld;[4] and Nyborg,[5] Westervelt,[6] and Raney, *et al.*[7] have clarified the problem further.

(c) An ingenious method was developed and tested by Gorelik[8] and Slobodskaya[9] and rediscovered independently by Cottrell.[10] It measures the relaxation time for an individual degree of freedom, i.e., the time it takes for its excitation energy to appear as translational energy, but it is limited to those vibrations which are optically active, i.e., absorb (infrared) light. To measure the relaxation time for an individual vibration, infrared light of the proper frequency is sent into the test vessel. This is periodically chopped. The energy absorbed as vibrational excitation is then partly transferred to translational energy, which makes itself felt as increased pressure. The test vessel is equipped with pressure-sensitive microphones, and one measures the time delay between light absorption and pressure increase (phase difference between the periodic chopper and the periodic pressure variation). Recently, the method has been used by Jacox and Bauer[11].

---

[3] C. Eckart, *Phys. Rev.* **73**, 68 (1948).

[4] F. E. Fox and K. F. Herzfeld, *Phys. Rev.* **78**, 156 (1950).

[5] W. L. Nyborg, *J. Acoust. Soc. Am.* **24**, 119 (1952); **25**, 68, 189(A), 938 (1953).

[6] P. J. Westervelt, *J. Acoust. Soc. Am.* **23**, 312 (1951); **25**, 60, 193(A), 951, 1123 (1953).

[7] W. P. Raney, J. Corelli, and P. J. Westervelt, *J. Acoust. Soc. Am.* **26**, 1006 (1954).

[8] G. Gorelik, *Compt. rend. acad. sci. U. R. S. S.* **54**, 779 (1946).

[9] P. V. Slobodskaya, *Izvest. Akad. Nauk. S. S. S. R. Ser. Fiz.* **12**, 656 (1948).

[10] T. L. Cottrell, *Trans. Faraday Soc.* **46**, 1025 (1950).

[11] M. E. Jacox and S. H. Bauer, *J. Phys. Chem.* **61**, 833 (1957).

VI. Experimental Results in Molecules Without Electronic Excitation

A. Translation

47. Translational Relaxation in Monatomic Gases

Since monatomic gases have no internal degrees of freedom, only "classical" absorption and dispersion should exist (see Secs. 7 and 36). The earlier measurements of absorption at low frequency for neon and argon gave the classical value,[1] but those for helium showed values two to three times as great. This was quite inexplicable from the theoretical standpoint. The hypothesis was made that this may be due to the formation of double molecules. However, if this formation occurs in helium, it should occur to an even greater degree in neon and argon.

Finally it was shown by van Itterbeek and Verhaegen[2] and by Greenspan[3] that the previous results were due to experimental difficulties; improved measurements did give the results predicted by theory.

In Fig. 47–1, the discrete marks show the recent measurements of Greenspan for the rare gases; the ordinate is $\mathfrak{V}_0/\mathfrak{V}$ $(= \beta/\beta_0)$ and $\alpha\mathfrak{V}_0/\omega$, the abscissa the Reynolds number [Re]; see Sec. 7, Eq. (7–20). Low [Re] are high ω/p; high [Re], low values of ω/p. The right side of the figure shows a straight part of the full curve for $\alpha\mathfrak{V}_0/\omega$. This part represents the theoretical expression (7–17), and fits the experimental results well. When [Re] becomes smaller, the effects predicted by Lucas and Truesdell (Sec. 7) become noticeable. According to Greenspan,[3] Eq. (7–21) takes, for [Eu] = 2.5, the following form

$$\left(\frac{\mathfrak{V}_0}{\mathfrak{V}} - i\alpha\frac{\mathfrak{V}_0}{\omega}\right)^2 = [\mathrm{Re}]\,\{(36\,[\mathrm{Re}]^2 - 49 + 60\,i\,[\mathrm{Re}])^{1/2} - 6\,[\mathrm{Re}] - 23\,i\}\,\{40 - 18\,i\,[\mathrm{Re}]\}^{-1}. \qquad (47\text{–}1)$$

---

[1] H. H. Keller, *Physik. Z.* **41**, 386 (1940).

[2] A. van Itterbeek and L. Verhaegen, *Nature* **167**, 478 (1951).

[3] M. Greenspan, *J. Acoust. Soc. Am.* **22**, 568 (1950); **28**, 664 (1956).

The solution of this equation is plotted as the continuous line in Fig. 47–1. However, when the wave length becomes comparable with the mean free path Λ, one should expect that the Stokes-Navier equations, which describe a continuous medium, and Eq. (47–1), which is based on them, would not represent the process exactly.

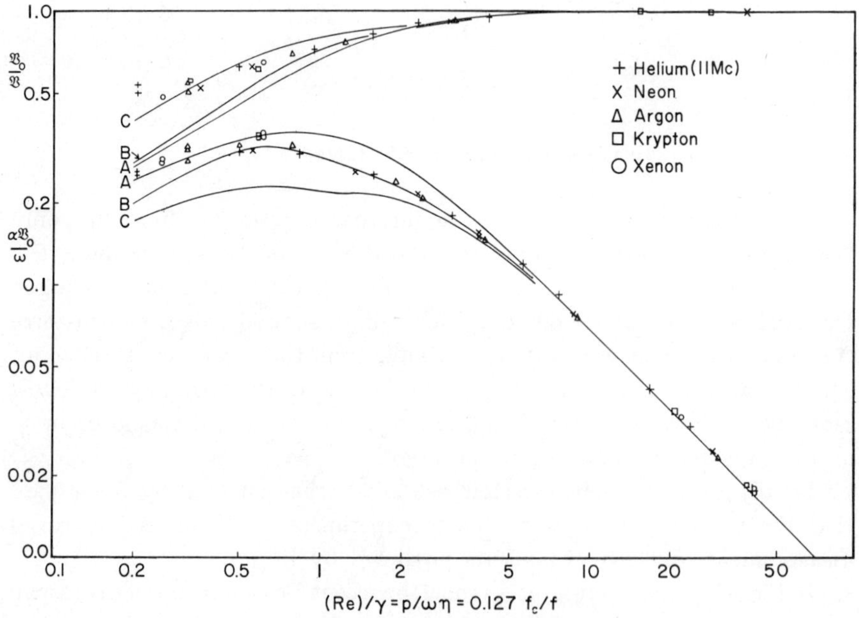

FIG. 47–1. Combined dispersion and absorption curves for the rare gases, drawn on a reduced scale. The top three curves represent $\mathfrak{V}_0/\mathfrak{V}$; the bottom three curves show $\alpha\ \mathfrak{V}_0/\omega$. All data are from Greenspan. Curves A are the theoretical curves according to the Stokes-Navier equation (Truesdell's theory), Curves B are calculated according to the Burnett equations using Uhlenbeck's calculations, and Curves C also includes the next term ("super-Burnett" theory). See M. Greenspan, *J. Acoust. Soc. Am.* **28**, 644 (1956).

Boltzmann's fundamental equation of gas theory is solved by a series proceeding according to powers of Λ. If only the zeroth and first powers are kept, one gets an equation like Eq. (36–6), from which the Stokes-Navier equations can be deduced. If one has to keep higher powers of Λ in the distribution function, one gets additional terms in the equations of motion and heat flow. In the one-dimensional case, the "viscous" force has the form

$$-\frac{4}{3}\eta\frac{\partial u}{\partial x}-\frac{2}{3}b_2\frac{\partial^2 p}{\partial x^2}+\frac{2}{3}b_3\frac{\partial^2 T}{\partial x^2} \tag{47–2}$$

and the heat flow is

$$-\lambda\frac{\partial T}{\partial x}+\frac{2}{3}b_1\frac{\partial^2 u}{\partial x^2}. \tag{47–3}$$

Here b_1, b_2, and b_3 are new constants.[4] (Uhlenbeck and Chang write w_2 for b_2; w_3 for b_3T; ϑ_2T, and ϑ_4 for b_1.)

Equations (47–2) and (47–3) amount to approximately

$$\eta=\eta_0\left\{1-\frac{1}{2}i\omega\frac{\rho_0}{\eta_0}\left[b_2-\frac{RT}{pC_p}b_3\right]\right\}$$

$$=\eta_0\left\{1-\frac{1}{2}i\omega\frac{M}{\eta_0}\left[\frac{pb_2}{RT}-\frac{1}{C_p}b_3\right]\right\}.$$

$$\lambda=\lambda_0\left\{1+\frac{2}{3\lambda_0}i\omega\, b_1\frac{C_v}{RT}\right\}.$$

Wang Chang and Uhlenbeck[4] have made calculations for different laws of interaction between two molecules.[5] The results for the propagation constant appear in the form of an infinite determinant. If one tries to develop the result into a series, the first term of which gives the Stokes-Navier terms, and the next terms those of Eqs. (47–2) and (47–3), the convergence turns out to be very bad. On the other hand, if one solves the determinant numerically, one gets much better results. According to an oral communication from Greenspan and Uhlenbeck, the calculation has been made for Maxwellian molecules (repulsive interaction energy $\sim 1/r^4$) using a 10×10 determinant.

It is seen that the experimental data deviate from the Stokes-Navier curve as soon as this curve deviates from a straight line (i.e., as soon as the Lucas-Truesdell calculations become significant), and follow pretty well the new Uhlenbeck curve. At very high ω/p (low [Re]) the experimental results seem to return to the Stokes-Navier curve. For this, there is no explanation.

---

[4] C. S. Wang Chang and G. E. Uhlenbeck, Rept. CM-433 UMH3-F, February, 1948; C. S. Wang Chang, Rept. CM-467 UMH-3-F, May, 1948, Applied Physics Laboratory, Johns Hopkins University, Baltimore, Maryland.

[5] J. de Boer and A. Michels, *Physica* **5**, 945 (1938); **6**, 409 (1939).

The expressions (47–2) and (47–3) were first proposed by Brillouin,[6] Jones,[7] and Rocard;[8] Burnett[9] then calculated the coefficients for hard molecules. Further extensions were made by Herzfeld,[10] who first applied the result to ultrasonic waves. This was done later independently by Primakoff[11] and Tsien and Schamberg,[12] the former correcting a mistake of Herzfeld's.

Experiments on argon have also been made by Boyer[13] down to [Re] = 3.8. They have not yet been compared with Greenspan's new data.

B. Rotation

48. Methods to Determine Rotational Relaxation Time

In all known cases, the rotational relaxation time is quite short, much shorter than the vibrational relaxation time (or times) in the same molecule.

There are three ways open to determine it.

(a) One can measure a dispersion curve. Since, from the preceding, no vibrational degree of freedom can follow at frequencies where the rotational dispersion sets in, the "low-frequency" velocity, which gives the horizontal part of the dispersion curve after the vibrations cannot follow any more, while the rotational degrees of freedom are still in equilibrium, will correspond to a velocity

$$\mathfrak{V}^2 = \frac{7}{5}\frac{RT}{M} \tag{48–1}$$

for linear molecules, and

$$\mathfrak{V}^2 = \frac{8}{6}\frac{RT}{M} \tag{48–2}$$

for nonlinear molecules.

---

[6] M. Brillouin, *Ann. chim. et phys.* **20**, 440 (1900).
[7] J. E. Jones, *Phil. Trans. Roy. Soc. London* **A223**, 1 (1923).
[8] Y. Rocard, *Ann. phys.* [10] **8**, 1 (1927).
[9] D. Burnett, *Proc. London Math. Soc.* **40**, 382 (1935).
[10] K. F. Herzfeld, *Ann. Physik* [5] **23**, 465 (1935).
[11] H. Primakoff, *J. Acoust. Soc. Am.* **14**, 14 (1942).
[12] H. S. Tsien and H. Schamberg, *J. Acoust. Soc. Am.* **18**, 334 (1946).
[13] R. A. Boyer, *J. Acoust. Soc. Am.* **23**, 176 (1951).

The dispersion region which follows will in general probably have a shape different from Eq. (13–5), since the calculations of Sec. 19 do not apply to rotational states and different transitions have different relaxation times. In default of anything better, one usually takes the midpoint of the dispersion curve as determining the rotational relaxation time. If only a few rotational states are important, as in H_2 or D_2, one may, by making measurements at different temperatures, be able to separate the contributions of different transitions, as Rhodes[1] has shown (at lower temperatures, only the transition $0 \longleftrightarrow 2$ is important).

At frequencies so high that even the rotational transitions cannot follow, the curve should again become horizontal, all molecules obeying the expression for monatomic gases

$$\mathfrak{V}^2 = \frac{5}{3} \frac{RT}{M}. \tag{48–3}$$

However, this might occur at such high frequencies that the dispersion of the *translational* degrees of freedom already overlaps, i.e., at frequencies so high that the Lucas-Truesdell effect (Sec. 7) and the discrete structure of the gas become important, as in monatomic gases (Sec. 47). This will occur if Z_{rot} is only a few times larger than unity, and would complicate the theory very much. In fact, this is one of the few cases where it is really important to consider the interaction of different mechanisms of absorption, as Hunt[2] would require in general. This has not yet been done.[3]

In the case of molecules with free internal rotation, like hexane (see Sec. 54), it might not be true, as assumed above, that the rotational relaxation time is much shorter than all other internal ones.

Except for H_2, HD, D_2, and OH, the rotational relaxation time seems to be $\sim 10^{-9}$ sec or shorter at atmospheric pressure, i.e., the midpoint of the dispersion curve lies higher than 100 mc/atm. This necessitates the use of rather low pressures in the acoustic interferometer.

(b) A different method consists of measuring the absorption in a region where the exchange of vibrational energy cannot follow any more and where, therefore, the contribution of the vibrational degrees of freedom can be

---

[1] J. E. Rhodes, *Phys. Rev.* **70**, 91, 932 (1946).

[2] V. F. Hunt, *J. Acoust. Soc. Am.* **27**, 1019 (1955).

[3] J. J. Markham, R. T. Beyer, and R. B. Lindsay, *Revs. Modern Phys.* **23**, 353 (1951), have made a beginning in this direction.

neglected, while the rotational degrees of freedom are in (near) equilibrium, i.e., in the region before rotational dispersion sets in. Then one has, for linear molecules, according to Eq. (38–6)

$$\alpha/\alpha_{\text{class}} = 1 + 0.067\, Z_{\text{rot}} \tag{48–4}$$

provided the rotational specific heat has its full value R.

Unfortunately this method needs a high accuracy of measurement. An absolute error of 0.2 in $\alpha/\alpha_{\text{class}}$ changes Z_{rot} by 3.

(c) Finally one can measure τ directly with the jet or of the shock wave method.

49. Results for Rotational Relaxation

(a) *Hydrogen and Deuterium*

The ϑ for H_2 is 5958 °K; for D_2, 4211 °K; at room temperature the vibrational specific heats are so low that their contribution to absorption can be neglected and any absorption above the classical must be due to rotational relaxation.

The τ_c for H_2 is 0.3×10^{-10} sec at 90 °K and 0.7×10^{-10} sec at 296 °K. The numbers for D_2 are larger by a factor $\sqrt{2}$.

The particular interest of hydrogen and deuterium lies in the fact that the moment of inertia is smaller than in other molecules and, as a result, the rotational energy jumps are larger. For this reason, the rotational relaxation time is longer than for other molecules. Hydrogen has the further property that it is a mixture of parahydrogen (nuclear spins antiparallel), which has only even numbered rotational states, and orthohydrogen (spins parallel), which has only odd numbered rotational states. One can prepare pure parahydrogen, and by comparing with normal hydrogen (a mixture of 1/4 parahydrogen and 3/4 orthohydrogen) get at the behavior of the orthohydrogen. In this way the relaxation of different rotational states may be measured separately.[1]

1. Absorption. The delay in the exchange of rotational and translational energy was first detected by van Itterbeek and his collaborators[2] in the

---

[1] J. E. Rhodes, *Phys. Rev.* **70**, 91, 932 (1946).

[2] A. van Itterbeek and P. Mariens, *Physica* **4**, 609 (1937); A. van Itterbeek and L. Thys, *Physica* **5**, 889 (1938).

case of these gases. They used an interferometer at 0.6 Mc between 1 and 0.4 atm, and found $\alpha/\alpha_{\text{class}} \sim 20$ for H_2 and ~ 10 for D_2. Unfortunately, their first measurements gave the wrong variation with p. This has been corrected in a newer paper by van Itterbeek and Verhaegen,[3] who found $\alpha \sim 1/p$, as it should (this is in the region in which $\alpha/\alpha_{\text{class}}$ is constant). E. S. Stewart[4] has extended the absorption measurements to higher frequencies, where $\alpha/\alpha_{\text{class}}$ should decrease [like $(1 + \omega^2\tau^2)^{-1}$]. This is found, but her data scatter widely. Later, E. S. Stewart and J. L. Stewart[5] made careful absorption measurements for H_2 and D_2 at 0° C, with an accuracy of about 20%. The data follow a theoretical single relaxation curve up to near the maximum of $\alpha'\lambda$, but then stay above the theoretical curve, due to the second, shorter relaxation time, in agreement with Rhodes' argument.

The maximum of $\alpha'\lambda$ has a value of 0.27 in both cases, corresponding to a C'/R of 0.98 ± 0.04.

2. Dispersion. E. S. Stewart and J. L. Stewart[6] succeeded for the first time in carrying velocity measurements through a rotational dispersion region, thereby proving that the excess absorption in hydrogen is in fact due to relaxation of rotational energy. They used an interferometer at 3.9 and 6.2 Mc, with a pressure between 1 and 0.5 atm.

Rhodes tried to separate the relaxation times of different rotational transitions. He assumed that in p-hydrogen at 197 °K, only the transition between the states 0 and 2 is involved; this gives a dispersion curve with a simple τ, according to Eq. (13–6). At 298 °K, one has the three states $j = 0, 2, 4$. He then treats the dispersion curve as a superposition of two simple ones.

Rhodes assumes that the 0 to 2 transition has a longer relaxation time than the 2 to 4 transition, which seems improbable since a larger change of kinetic energy is involved in the latter case. He interprets his dispersion measurements in this sense and finds, at 298.4°K, the midpoint frequencies $f'' = 7.2$ Mc/atm for the 0 to 2 transition, and 20 Mc/atm for the 2 to 4 transition. (These cannot be simply exchanged, since the contributions to the specific heat of the different rotational states enter into the calculation.)

---

[3] A. van Itterbeek and L. Verhaegen, *Nature* **167**, 478 (1951).

[4] E. S. Swomley Stewart, Ph. D. Dissertation, Johns Hopkins University, Baltimore, Maryland, 1946.

[5] E. S. Stewart and J. L. Stewart, *J. Acoust. Soc. Am.* **24**, 194 (1952).

[6] E. S. Stewart, J. L. Stewart, and J. C. Hubbard, *Phys. Rev.* **68**, 231 (1945); E. S. Stewart, *ibid.* **69**, 632 (1946); J. L. Stewart and E. S. Stewart, *J. Acoust. Soc. Am.* **20**, 585 (1948).

3. Huber and Kantrowitz[7] measured τ directly with the jet method. Table 49–1 shows the numerical results for rotational relaxation in H_2 and D_2. For the meaning of f'' and f''', see Sec. 18.

TABLE 49–1

RELAXATION OF ROTATIONAL ENERGY IN H_2 AND D_2

Gas	$n-H_2$		$p-H_2$		$n-H_2$	
T(°K)	79.5	90	79.5	90	288	309.5
Reference	3	3	3	3	2	7
α/α_{class}	8.8	12	13	18	20	28
C'/R	0.103	0.158			0.960	0.977
τ				2.5×10^{-8}	2×10^{-8}	2.8×10^{-8}
Z	560	540		360	300	400

Gas	$n-H_2$			D_2		
T(°K)	273	273	273	273	273	273
Reference	5	5	5	5	5	5
f''	11			13		
f''' (Mc/atm)		11			13	
α/α_{class}			25			15
τ	2.3×10^{-8}	2.1×10^{-8}		2×10^{-8}	1.8×10^{-8}	
Z*	350	305	375	210	190	225

* There is some indication[5] that water vapor decreases Z for rotation as it does for vibration.

(b) *Nitrogen and Oxygen*

Measurements of α (and therefore α/α_{class}) in N_2 at relatively low frequency have been made by Keller[8] with the optical method, Zmuda[9] with the interferometer, and Parker, Adams, and Stavseth[10] by Method 46(a). Zmuda and Boyer[11] also investigated dispersion. The square of the velocity should

[7] P. W. Huber and A. Kantrowitz, *J. Chem. Phys.* **15**, 275 (1947).

[8] H. H. Keller, *Physik. Z.* **41**, 386 (1940).

[9] A. J. Zmuda, *J. Acoust. Soc. Am.* **23**, 472 (1951).

[10] J. G. Parker, C. E. Adams, and R. M. Stavseth, *J. Acoust. Soc. Am.* **25**, 263 (1953).

[11] R. A. Boyer, *J. Acoust. Soc. Am.* **23**, 176 (1951).

change by a factor $5/3 : 7/5 = 1.19$. Zmuda reached less than one-third of this at 109 Mc/atm. At the beginning of the dispersion curve there is good agreement with the values calculated from the absorption ratio; at higher frequencies, the curve is much steeper than expected (if it were flatter, this could have been understood by the presence of a distribution of τ values for different rotational states). Whether this increased steepness (also found by Thaler for O_2, see below) is due to the onset of translational dispersion or to equipment errors at very low pressures is unknown. Boyer's measurements agree well with Zmuda's. Greene *et al.*[12] have used light reflection from a shock wave in nitrogen to measure the thickness of the transition layer; see Sec. 45(*b*). The results are shown in Table 49–2. For the meaning of f'' and f''' see Sec. 18.

TABLE 49–2

ROTATIONAL RELAXATION IN N_2 AND O_2
(*d* means dispersion measurement; *a*, absorption measurement)

Gas	N_2					O_2				
Reference	8	9	10	11	12	13	13	13	11	10
T(°C)	18–22	29	20–21	0		30	30	30	0	21–22
α/α_{class}	1.3	1.4	1.24			3.6				1.19
f'' (Mc/atm)				300						
f''' (Mc/atm)							38*a*	50*d*	114	
Z	4.5	6	3.6	6.2	20	40	40	35	16	3

In oxygen, Thaler[13] measured α and the velocity as functions of ω/p in the interferometer. From his data, there are three ways of calculating Z: from α/α_{class} at low frequency, from the frequency at which $\alpha/\alpha_{class} - 1$ has fallen to one-half of the low-frequency value, and from the dispersion curve. Of course, the absorption measurements scatter appreciably. However, as Table 49–2 shows, the results of the three methods agree very well. There are three difficulties with these numbers, however. Parker *et al.* got a much lower Z, one that is of the same order as for N_2; one cannot see theoretically why the Z for O_2 should be so much higher; and the velocities found by Thaler for high ω/p correspond to a γ even larger than 5/3, which would

[12] E. F. Greene, G. R. Cowan, and D. F. Hornig, *J. Chem. Phys.* **19**, 427 (1951).

[13] W. J. Thaler, *J. Acoust. Soc. Am.* **24**, 15 (1952).

mean the mixing in of translational dispersion. Thaler's dispersion curve is steeper than one which would correspond to a single relaxation time, as is Zmuda's. Boyer's velocity measurements give a Z between those of Thaler and of Parker *et al.*; he also gets velocities with an apparent γ larger than 5/3. Thaler's measurements indicate that 10% water vapor may shorten τ. Connor[13a] found with the interferometer that $Z = 13$. It now appears that in the original interferometer gas pressure equilibrium was not established rapidly enough, so that Thaler and Ener *et al.*[18] found values for Z which were too high.

(c) *Air*

Some of the oldest absorption measurements (Neklepajew[14] and Abello[15]) were made on air; its absorption coefficient was found higher than the classical value. More recent investigations were made by Sivian[16] and confirmed by Evans and Bazley.[17] It was found that the coefficient of amplitude absorption, at frequencies high above the vibrational relaxation frequency, is given, at 30° C, by

$$\alpha = 16.8 \times 10^{-14} f^2 \text{ cm}^{-1}.$$

Since the classical value is $12.4 \times 10^{-14} f^2$, one has $\alpha/\alpha_{\text{class}} = 1.36$, or $Z = 5.4$.

Ener *et al.*[18] find $\alpha/\alpha_{\text{class}} = 2.4$, or $Z = 21$. The dispersion (which gets too steep at very low pressures, just as found by Zmuda and Thaler) has its midpoint at 116 Mc/atm, or $\tau = 2.29 \times 10^{-9}$ sec and $Z = 16$.

It is of some interest to consider at this point a mixture of two gases A and B, which have the same relaxing specific heat C' and the same C_v. We take the frequency sufficiently low that α/f^2 is constant. Assume first that molecules A are only deactivated by collisions with other molecules A,

---

[13a] J. V. Connor, *J. Acoust. Soc. Am.* **30**, 297 (1958).

[14] N. Neklepajew, *Ann. Physik* [4] **35**, 175 (1911).

[15] T. B. Abello, *Proc. Natl. Acad. Sci U. S.* **13**, 699 (1927).

[16] L. J. Sivian, *J. Acoust. Soc. Am.* **19**, 914 (1947).

[17] E. J. Evans and E. N. Bazley, *Acustica* **6**, 238 (1956).

[18] C. Ener, A. F. Gabrysh, and J. C. Hubbard, *J. Acoust. Soc. Am.* **24**, 474 (1952).

and molecules B only by collisions with other molecules B. If the gas mixture is at a pressure p, then gas A contributes to the absorption of the mixture just as much absorption as it had *alone* at pressure p, since the relaxation time is increased by a factor $1/x$ and the contribution of A to the specific heat is the fraction x. A similar statement is true for B, which has the mole fraction $1 - x$. Accordingly, if there is no deactivation $A - B$, the absorption of the gas mixture at pressure p ought to be the sum of the absorptions of pure A at p and of pure B at p. Any additional absorption due to unmixing (Sec. **41**) is neglected. Therefore, the absorption of the mixture cannot be *more* than the sum of that of the pure gases separately at p, and any amount less than that sum which it may be is due to deactivations in collisions $A - B$. Unfortunately, in the above case the data are not sufficiently certain to draw conclusions.

(*d*) *Ammonia*

Keller[8] found $\alpha/\alpha_{\text{class}} = 1.67$; one now has to use an equation for non-linear molecules, which gives $Z = 9$.

C. Vibration

50. Oxygen, Nitrogen, Air

In these gases, the characteristic vibrational temperature is high. Therefore, the specific heat at room temperature is very small and dispersion can be found only by refined methods. At higher temperatures, C' increases; Shilling and Partington[1] found at 3 kc and 1273 °K a smaller specific heat for both O_2 and N_2 than the static one. Henry[2] was the first to interpret their results as due to relaxation. Measurements by Bender[3] at 100 °C give values far different from the above.

---

[1] W. G. Shilling and J. R. Partington, *Phil. Mag.* [7] **3**, 273 (1927).

[2] P. S. H. Henry, *Nature* **129**, 200 (1932).

[3] D. Bender, *Ann. Physik* [5] **38**, 199 (1940).

V. H. Blackman[4] has determined the relaxation time in a wide interval of elevated temperatures with the shock tube. From what was said earlier, low-temperature measurements—with correspondingly long relaxation times—are quite difficult. For oxygen at room temperature, the first studies were made by Kneser[5] and Knudsen[6] with the reverberation method; these included studies of the influence of impurities. The data were greatly improved by Knötzel and Knötzel,[7] who used the Kundt's tube. They found as the frequency for the absorption maximum in the presence of the mole fraction x of water vapor

$$f' = 40 + 195(1000\,x) + 132(1000\,x)^2 \text{ cycles/sec.}$$

The quadratic term has been explained by Boudart (see Sec. 40). For NH_3 as impurity, the expression is

$$f' = 60 + 1220(1000\,x).$$

Because of the small value of C', f' and f'' (τ' and τ'') are identical. The difference between the (extrapolated) values 40 and 60 is due to experimental uncertainty.

In N_2, the measurements at lowest temperature are those by Huber and Kantrowitz[8] with the jet method at 550 °K (with a 0.05% water content) and of Lukasik and Young,[9] who use a resonant cavity and measure the width of the resonance curve. According to their extrapolated curve, the relaxation times of Huber and Kantrowitz for nitrogen containing water are probably four times smaller than for dry nitrogen. The results are shown in Tables 50–1 and 50–2. All the times in Table 50–1 refer to nitrogen under 1 atm pressure at temperature T. Table 50–2 gives similar data for oxygen.

---

[4] V. H. Blackman, Vibrational relaxation in O_2 and N_2, Tech. Rept. II-20 N 6 ori-105 II. Princeton University, Princeton, New Jersey, May, 1955.

[5] H. O. Kneser, *J. Acoust. Soc. Am.* **5**, 122 (1933); H. O. Kneser and V. O. Knudsen, *Ann. Physik* [5] **21**, 682 (1934).

[6] V. O. Knudsen, *J. Acoust. Soc. Am.* **5**, 112 (1933); V. O. Knudsen and L. Obert, *J. Acoust. Soc. Am.* **7**, 249 (1936); *Phys. Rev.* **47**, 256 (1933).

[7] H. Knötzel and L. Knötzel, *Ann. Physik* [6] **2**, 393 (1948).

[8] P. W. Huber and A. Kantrowitz, *J. Chem. Phys.* **15**, 275 (1947).

[9] S. J. Lukasik and J. E. Young, *J. Chem. Phys.* **27**, 1149 (1957).

[10] Thermal properties of gases, *Natl. Bur. Standards (U. S.) Circ.* N564 (1955).

TABLE 50–1

VIBRATIONAL RELAXATION TIME IN N_2; $\vartheta = 3336\ °K$

T(°K)	C'/R	τ_c	τ	Z	Reference
300	0.0019	1.4×10^{-10}	$>0.05\times 10^{-3}$	$>0.4\times 10^{6}$	1, 2, 10
550	0.087	2.1	$5.9\ \times 10^{-3}$	2.8×10^{7}	8, 10
681	0.183	2.5	$3.0\ \times 10^{-3}$	1.2×10^{7}	8, 10
763	0.248	2.6	$2.6\ \times 10^{-3}$	1.0×10^{7}	8, 10
778	0.263	2.6	1.76×10^{-3}	6.5×10^{6}	9, 10
1020	0.446	3.2	1.44×10^{-3}	4.5×10^{6}	9, 10
1168	0.548	3.5	7.96×10^{-4}	2.3×10^{6}	9, 10
1273	0.595	3.6	$1.5\ \times 10^{-4}$	4.2×10^{5}	1, 2, 10
3480	0.989	6.9	$1.9\ \times 10^{-5}$	28,000	4, 10
3910	1.015	7.7	$1.5\ \times 10^{-5}$	20,000	4, 10
4200	1.027	8.1	$1.0\ \times 10^{-5}$	12,000	4, 10
4630	1.045	8.4	$7\ \ \times 10^{-6}$	8300	4, 10
5540	1.08	9.6×10^{-10}	$4.6\ \times 10^{-6}$	4800	4, 10

TABLE 50–2

VIBRATIONAL RELAXATION TIME FOR OXYGEN; $\vartheta = 2228\ °K$

T(°K)	C'/R	τ_c	τ	Z	Reference
288	0.028	1.6×10^{-10}	3.18×10^{-3}	2×10^{7}	7, 10
1173	0.780	4.4	$1.1\ \times 10^{-4}$	250,000	1, 2, 10
1260	0.815	4.4	$2\ \ \times 10^{-5}$	44,000	4, 10
1640	0.940	5.3	$1\ \ \times 10^{-5}$	19,000	4, 10
1910	1.017	5.8	$7\ \ \times 10^{-6}$	12,000	4, 10
2370	1.143	6.8	$4\ \ \times 10^{-6}$	5900	4, 10
2870	1.272	7.8×10^{-10}	$1.4\ \times 10^{-6}$	1800	4. 10

It has been shown by Knudsen[6] and by Kneser and Knudsen[5] that the absorption in air (except at very high frequency) is due to the oxygen in the air, nitrogen having too small a C'. By mixing pure oxygen with varying amounts of nitrogen and measuring the shift in the frequency of maximum absorption, Kneser and Knudsen believed they had shown that an O_2-N_2 collision is more efficient than an O_2-O_2 collision in deactivating oxygen; Z was found to be 100,000. However, according to Blackman,[4] in the range

$1800° - 2400°$ K, a nitrogen molecule is only about 60% as efficient as an oxygen molecule in deactivating oxygen. Whether this means that the order of efficiency changes with temperature or, what is more probable, that the early measurements could not with certainty decide such effects, is still unknown.

51. Other Diatomic Molecules

(a) *Chlorine*

Eucken and Becker[1] investigated the dispersion in chlorine; the gas was washed in water to remove HCl, then dried with $CaCl_2$, concentrated sulfuric acid, and P_2O_5. Smiley and Winkler[2] made shock tube measurements at higher temperatures. In Table 51–1 the results are shown; τ_c is calculated using Kohler's equation, Eq. (36–3), with η at higher temperatures according to the Hirschfelder tables.

TABLE 51–1

RELAXATION TIMES IN Cl_2

T(°C)	$\tau_c \times 10^{10}$ sec	$\tau \times 10^6$ sec	Z	Reference
−32	0.88	6.3	72,000	1
18	1.05	4.2	40,000	1
74	1.24	2.6	20,000	1
142	1.46	1.6	11,000	1
300	2.08	0.7	3400	2
380	2.3	0.4	1700	2
640	3.0	0.14	470	2
1200	4.3	0.08	200	2

Eucken and Becker have also measured the effect of different impurities on τ. That of water vapor is very strong but, astonishingly, Z increases with increasing T.

---

[1] A. Eucken and R. Becker, *Z. physik. Chem.* **B27**, 235 (1935).

[2] E. F. Smiley and E. H. Winkler, *J. Chem. Phys.* **22**, 2018 (1954).

(b) *Carbon Monoxide*

Since $\vartheta = 3080°$ C and $C' = 2.9 \times 10^{-3} R$ at 292° C, one should not expect measurable dispersion or absorption except at very low frequencies. Sherrat and Griffiths[3] used an interferometer at 7.9 and 27.4 kc at elevated temperatures. Table 51–2 shows their results. This is an improbably small variation with temperature.

TABLE 51–2

RELAXATION IN CO

T(°C)	$\tau_c \times 10^{10}$ sec	$\tau \times 10^6$ sec	Z
1000	4.7	10	21,000
1400	5.6	11.5	21,000
1800	6.2	10	16,000

Van Itterbeek and Mariens[4] have measured the absorption of well-dried CO in the interferometer at between 18° and 19° C. At 0.85 atm and 304 kc, they find $\alpha/\alpha_{\text{class}} = 4$, which would give $Z = 15{,}000$. However, their α is nearly independent of p down to 0.34 atm. Bender[5] finds, at 127° C, $\tau = 1.5 \times 10^{-7}$ sec and $Z = 860$, which looks very improbable experimentally in view of the other results, and theoretically because of the high ϑ.

(c) *Nitric Oxide*

In this gas there is an additional contribution to the specific heat besides the vibrational one, namely, that due to spin orientation parallel or antiparallel to the rotation of the molecule as a whole. The latter ought to be 0.1 R at 298 °K, as compared to a vibrational specific heat of 0.0085 R. Kneser[6] estimates that $\tau \sim 0.8 \times 10^{-6}$ sec, while Bender's[5] data at higher temperatures do not seem reliable.

---

[3] G. G. Sherrat and E. Griffiths, *Proc. Roy. Soc.* **A147**, 292 (1934).

[4] A. van Itterbeek and P. Mariens, *Physica* **4**, 609 (1937).

[5] D. Bender, *Ann. Physik* [5] **38**, 199 (1940).

[6] H. O. Kneser, *Ann. Physik* [5] **39**, 261 (1941).

52. Linear Triatomic Molecules

(a) *Vibrations*

Linear symmetric triatomic molecules (CO_2, CS_2) have the following internal vibrations:

A bending vibration, which is doubly degenerate (two directions of polarization), optically active (i.e., gives infrared absorption), and has the lowest frequency.

A totally symmetric longitudinal vibration, in which the central atom is at rest while the outer atoms move in phase in or out. This is optically inactive (appears only in the Raman effect) and has an intermediate frequency.

An asymmetric longitudinal or valence bond vibration, in which the center atom moves in the opposite direction from that of the two end atoms, which keep at constant distance from each other. This vibration is optically active and has the highest frequency.

In nonsymmetric molecules (COS, N_2O), the qualitative description of the vibration is the same except that the second vibration is not totally symmetric, i.e., the center atom is not quite at rest and the amplitudes of the two outer atoms are not quite equal, causing this vibration to give infrared absorption.

In the third vibration, the distance between the outer atoms does not remain constant.

(b) *Carbon Dioxide*

Ultrasonic dispersion was first discovered by Pierce[1] in CO_2; excess absorption in a gas was found first in CO_2 (and air) by Abello.[2] Since then, a large number of investigations have been devoted to CO_2, although the values for τ differ by a factor of from 3 to 5, perhaps because of variations in water content, since τ is very sensitive to H_2O as an impurity (see below). For this reason it has been suggested that the longest τ is nearest to that of pure CO_2.

The first complete dispersion curve was measured in CO_2 by Kneser,[3] although he must have had an appreciable amount of water present. Richards

---

[1] G. W. Pierce, *Proc. Am. Acad. Arts Sci.* **60**, 271 (1925).

[2] T. B. Abello, *Proc. Natl. Acad. Sci.* (*U.S.*) **13**, 699 (1927).

[3] H. O. Kneser, *Ann. Physik* [5] **11**, 777 (1931); [5] **12**, 1015 (1932).

and Reid[4] measured dispersion; Leonard,[5] both dispersion and absorption; the results from these two types of measurement fit together well. Other dispersion measurements are due to Eucken and Becker,[6] Eucken and Nümann,[7] and Küchler[8]—who went to higher temperatures— and to Metter.[9]

The absorption was investigated by Fricke,[10] Frick,[11] and van Itterbeek and Mariens.[12, 13] Angona[14] dried his gas for 48 hr over P_2O_5. His data fit the theoretical curve well with only a few points lying 10% below it at low frequency.

Buschmann and Schäfer[15] attempted to decide between excitation in parallel and in series (Secs. 21 and 22) by making careful observations on dispersion, not realizing that the two assumptions give the same dependence on ω/p. They find two relaxation times, which they ascribe to the bending and to the totally symmetric vibration.

Pielemeier *et al.*[16] also believe they have found two relaxation times, by extrapolating the results found in the presence of water vapor to dry CO_2.

Gustavson[17] and Griffith[18] have measured τ directly with the impact tube and Smiley and Winkler[19] have used the shock tube for the determination of τ at high temperatures. Plotted logarithmically against $T^{-1/3}$ this gives a fairly straight line (see Secs. 56 and 60) represented by

$$\ln \tau = 82.8\, T^{-1/3} + \text{const} = \frac{3}{2}\left(\frac{168000}{T}\right)^{1/3} + \text{const}$$

---

[4] W. T. Richards and J. A. Reid, *J. Chem. Phys.* **2**, 193 (1934).

[5] R. W. Leonard, *J. Acoust. Soc. Am.* **12**, 241 (1940).

[6] A. Eucken and R. Becker, *Z. physik. Chem.* (*Leipzig*) **B27**, 235 (1935).

[7] A. Eucken and E. Nümann, *Z. physik. Chem. (Leipzig)* **B36**, 163 (1937).

[8] L. Küchler, *Z. physik. Chem.* (*Leipzig*) **B41**, 199 (1938).

[9] I. M. Metter, *Physik. Z. Sowjetunion* **12**, 233 (1937).

[10] E. F. Fricke, *J. Acoust. Soc. Am.* **12**, 245 (1940).

[11] R. H. Frick, Ph. D. Dissertation, University of California at Los Angeles, California, 1942.

[12] A. van Itterbeek and P. Mariens, *Physica* **4**, 609 (1937).

[13] A. van Itterbeek, P. de Bruyn, and P. Mariens, *Physica* **6**, 511 (1939).

[14] F. A. Angona, *J. Acoust. Soc. Am.* **25**, 1116 (1954).

[15] K. F. Buschmann and K. Schäfer, *Z. physik. Chem.* **B50**, 73 (1941).

[16] W. H. Pielemeier, H. L. Saxton, and D. Telfair, *J. Chem. Phys.* **8**, 106 (1940).

[17] M. Gustavson, Ph. D. Dissertation, Cornell University, Ithaca, New York, 1952.

[18] W. Griffith, *J. Appl. Phys.* **21**, 1319 (1950).

[19] E. F. Smiley and E. H. Winkler, *J. Chem. Phys.* **22**, 2018 (1954).

which, when extrapolated to room temperature, gives good agreement with Angona's value.

TABLE 52–1

RELAXATION TIME IN CO_2

(*d* means dispersion measurement; *a*, absorption measurement)
The brackets indicate the presence of two relaxation times

T(°C)	$\tau \times 10^6$ sec	Z*	Reference
30	4.5	30,000	4*d*
25	5.9–6.8	38,000–57,000	5*a*
23	10.26	90,000	10*a*
	8.9	75,000	11*a*
18.3	12.3	105,000	13*a*
30.6	10.9	95,000	13*a*
40.3	8.7	71,000	13*a*
49.4	6.8	53,000	13*a*
23	6.61	57,500	14*a*
−32	9.3	90,000†	6*d*
18	5.7	51,000†	6*d*
20	6	50,000†	7*d*
74	4.5	36,000†	6*d*
100	4.5	29,000†	7*d*
142.5	1.6	9,000†	6*d*
200	3.2	17,000†	7*d*
200	3.6	19,000†	8*d*
400	2.2	9,000	7*d*
400	2.0	8,000	8*d*
0		51,300	9*d*
21	{1.53	14,000	15*d*
21	6.9}	60,000	15*d*
90	{1.44	12,600	15*d*
90	5.8}	50,000	15*d*
28	{3.1	27,000	16
28	3.7}	32,000	16
	{1.6	14,000	20
	7}	63,000	20
	2.5	22,000	17
20	6.95	60,000	18
100	3.5	24,000	19
250	0.9	4,800	19
760	0.09	280	19

* The Z values have been recalculated with $\tau_c = 1.15 \times 10^{-10}$ sec at 300 °K and 1 atm.

† These are the original values given by the respective authors. Some are $(k_{10}\tau_c)^{-1}$ instead of $[(k_{10} - k_{01})\tau_c]^{-1}$.

Slobodskaya[20] was able to determine separately the relaxation times for the bending vibration and the asymmetric valence bond vibration by the method of Sec. 46(c). (The totally symmetric vibration cannot be excited optically.)

Both the measurements of Richards and Reid[4] and those of Gutowski[21] have followed the dispersion curve to sufficiently high ω/p values, so that $\mathfrak{V}$ is constant at the theoretical value $(4/3\ RT/M)^{1/2}$.

The bending vibration has $\vartheta = 959\ °K$ with a specific heat, at $300\ °K$, of $C_1' = 2 \times 0.454\ R = 0.908\ R$; the totally symmetric vibration has $\vartheta = 1920\ °K$ with $C_2' = 0.069\ R$; and the asymmetric vibration has $\vartheta = 3380\ °K$ with $C_3' = 1.57 \times 10^{-3}\ R$, or a total $C' = 0.979\ R$.

The results of the measurements are shown in Table 52–1.

Knudsen and Fricke[22] have investigated the effect of impurities on $1/\tau$ or f'''. They find it strictly proportional to the concentration. In particular, the effect of water vapor is strong. As mentioned earlier, Pielemeier et al. find two absorption peaks, with different sensitivity to water vapor, given by

$$1/\tau = 2.7 \times 10^5 + 3.8 \times 10^8\ x$$
$$1/\tau = 3.2 \times 10^5 + 9 \times 10^7\ x.$$

Table 52–2 shows the data.

TABLE 52–2

EFFECT OF 1 MOLE % OF IMPURITIES ON f''' OF CO_2

Impurity	$\Delta f'''$	$Z_{CO_2-H_2O}$	Reference
H_2O		105	7
H_2O		34	6
H_2O		60	9
H_2O	660	44	13
H_2O	143, 604	48	15
H_2O	740	40	21
H_2O	920	50	22*
H_2	155		22
CH_3OH	550		22
C_3H_7OH	1100		22
$C_6H_5CH_3$	1780		22

* The numbers have been changed under the assumption that Knudsen and Fricke used weight percents for H_2O.

[20] P. V. Slobodskaya, Izvest. Akad. Nauk S. S. S. R. Ser. Fiz. 12, 656 (1948).

[21] F. A. Gutowski, J. Acoust. Soc. Am. 28, 478 (1956).

[22] V. O. Knudsen and E. Fricke, J. Acoust. Soc. Am. 9, 273 (1938); 10, 89 (1938); 12, 255 (1940).

Sette and Hubbard[23] find, in dispersion measurements, the relative effect of H_2O and D_2O to have a ratio of 1.5 : 1. Although the shape of their dispersion curve at high frequency cannot be reconciled with either a single or with a double relaxation time and disagrees with Gutowski's results,[21] the ratio 2 : 1 has been found by van Itterbeek and Mariens[13] by absorption measurements, in reasonable agreement with Sette and Hubbard.

(c) Carbon Oxysulfide and Carbon Disulfide

These gases have been investigated by Fricke; Richards and Reid have measured the dispersion in CS_2 (Fig. 52–1) and Angona the absorption

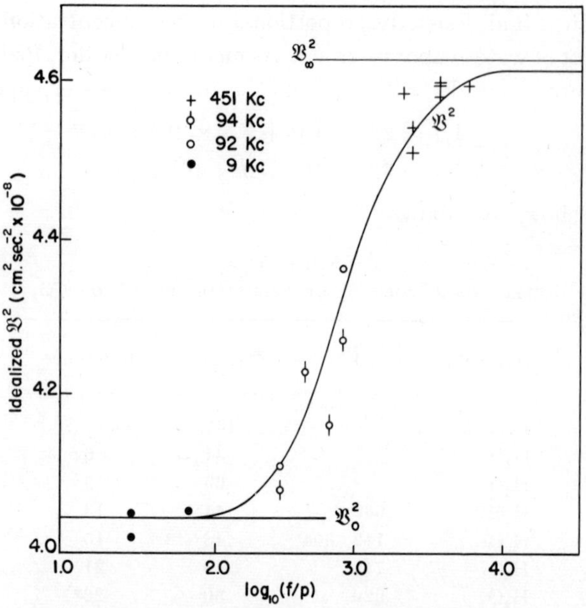

FIG. 52–1. Dispersion in CS_2 vapor according to Richards and Reid. The fully drawn curve is the theoretical curve according to single relaxation theory; the horizontal lines are the theoretical limiting velocities.

(Fig. 52–2). The latter dried his gas in the same way as CO_2. Eucken and Aybar[24] have measured τ for COS at different temperatures both in dispersion

[23] D. Sette and J. C. Hubbard, *J. Acoust. Soc. Am.* **25**, 994 (1953).

[24] A. Eucken and S. Aybar, *Z. physik. Chem. (Leipzig)* **B46**, 195 (1940).

TABLE 52–3

VIBRATIONAL CHARACTERISTIC TEMPERATURES AND SPECIFIC HEATS FOR COS AND CS_2

Gas		Bending vibration	Asymmetric longitudinal vibration	Symmetric vibration
COS	ϑ	758	1370	2988
	C'/R	2×0.602	0.221	4.7×10^{-3}
CS_2	ϑ	570	1043	2190
	C'/R	2×0.747	0.397	0.036

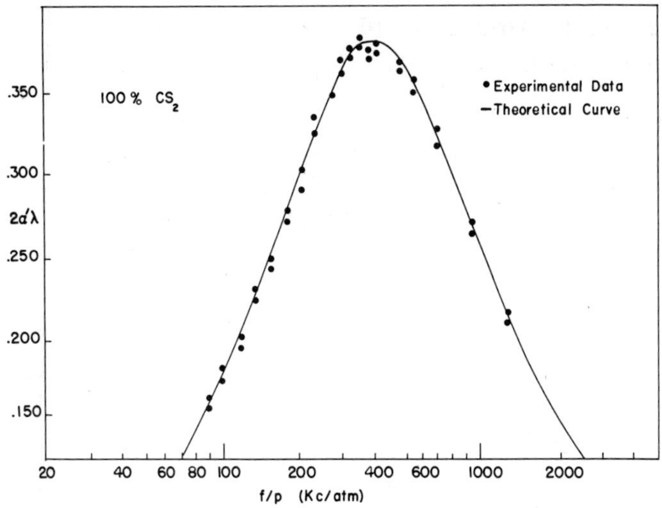

FIG. 52–2. Absorption of energy per wave length, $2\alpha'\lambda$, for CS_2 according to Angona. The fully drawn curve is the theoretical curve according to single relaxation theory.

TABLE 52–4

RELAXATION TIMES IN COS AND CS_2

(*a* means absorption measurement)

Gas	T(°C)	$\tau\times 10^6$ sec	Z	Reference
COS	23	0.86	9,600	10
COS	20	1.67	17,700	24*a*
COS	100	1.24	10,300	24*a*
COS	109	1.17	9,800	24*d*
COS	202	1.00	6,600	24*a*
CS_2	23	0.70	8,700	10
CS_2	30	0.52	6,550	4
CS_2	23	0.73	9,200	14

and absorption. Table 52–3 shows the vibrational characteristic temperatures and specific heats at 300 °K, while Table 52–4 gives the experimental data for COS and CS_2.

(d) Nitrous Oxide

This gas has been measured by Fricke in absorption,[10] by Buschmann and Schäfer[15] and by Walker *et al.*[25] in dispersion, and by Wight[26] in absorption. Buschmann and Schäfer also measured the temperature dependence of Z, and Wight[26] the effect of water vapor, as did Knudsen and Fricke.

The vibrational data are: $\vartheta = 847°$, 1850°, 3200 °K; at 300 °K, $C'/R = 2 \times 0.536$, 0.082, 2.6×10^{-3}, or a total $C' = 1.157\ R$.

The results are given in Table 52–5.

TABLE 52–5

RELAXATION TIME IN N_2O

(*d* means dispersion measurement; *a*, absorption measurement)

T(°C)	$\tau \times 10^6$ sec	Z*	Reference
23	1.55	11,800	10
	0.93	8,500	25
21	1.19	10,000	26
−56.2	2.3	28,000	15
−25.5	1.5	12,500	15
3	0.95	6,800	15
19	0.84	5,600	15
73	0.64	3,800	15
20	0.92	7,500†	7*d*
20	0.96	7,800†	7*a*
20	0.87	7,000†	7*a*
100	0.69	4,500†	7*d*
200	0.63	3,300†	7*d*
200	0.64	3,350†	7*a*
300	0.56	2,500†	7*d*
400	0.54	2,100†	7*d*

* The Z values have been recalculated with $\tau_c = 1.15 \times 10^{-10}$ sec at 300 °K and 1 atm.

† These are the original values given by the respective authors. Some are $(k_{10}\tau_c)^{-1}$ instead of $[(k_{10} - k_{01})\tau_c]^{-1}$.

---

25 R. A. Walker, T. D. Rossing, and S. Legvold, *Natl. Advisory Com. Aeronaut. Tech. Notes* 3210 (1954).

26 H. M. Wight, *J. Acoust. Soc. Am.* 28, 459 (1956).

According to Wight the frequency of maximum absorption is shifted 210 kc by 1% H_2O, 142 kc by 1% D_2O. The ratio is nearly that found for CO_2.

53. Nonlinear Triatomic Molecules and Four Atomic Molecules

(a) *Water Vapor and Sulfur Dioxide*

These molecules form isosceles triangles, with three modes of vibration each. One mode is essentially transversal, with the atom at the apex (O or S) nearly at rest, and the motion like that of opening and closing scissors. This has the lowest frequency ($\vartheta = 2294°$, $C' = 0.029\ R$ at 300 °K for H_2O; $\vartheta = 752°$, $C' = 0.609\ R$ for SO_2). In the other modes, the end atoms (H, O) move nearly but not exactly along the valence bonds; in one mode in phase, in the other in opposite phases. The motion of the apex atom is small. The corresponding values for H_2O are $\vartheta = 5117°$, $5400°$; and for SO_2 are $\vartheta = 1656°$, $C' = 0.223\ R$ and $\vartheta = 1956°$, $C' = 0.064\ R$. The total vibrational specific heat for SO_2 at 300 °K is $C' = 0.896\ R$.

Huber and Kantrowitz[1] have investigated water with the jet method at higher temperatures; the same method was applied by Griffith[2] to SO_2. Fricke[3] made ultrasonic absorption measurements on this gas. The results are shown in Table 53–1.

TABLE 53–1
RELAXATION TIME IN H_2O AND SO_2

Gas	T(°C)	τ(sec)	Z	Reference
H_2O	213	3.7×10^{-8}	400	1
H_2O	312	$2.6,\ 3.1\times 10^{-8}$	260, 310	1
H_2O	433	2.1×10^{-8}	190	1
SO_2	20	3.7×10^{-7}	1500	2
SO_2	23	1.81×10^{-7}	1900	3

Lambert and Salter[4] have measured the dispersion of SO_2 at 20° C, 102° C, and 200° C and found for all three temperatures that the dispersion curve could not be represented by a single relaxation time. Table 53–2 gives their results, which are calculated from curves for $(C_v)_{\text{eff}}$.

[1] P. W. Huber and A. Kantrowitz, *J. Chem. Phys.* **15**, 275 (1947).
[2] W. Griffith, *J. Appl. Phys.* **21**, 1319 (1950).
[3] E. F. Fricke, *J. Acoust. Soc. Am.* **12**, 245 (1940).
[4] J. D. Lambert and R. Salter, *Proc. Roy. Soc.* **A243**, 78 (1957).

TABLE 53–2
RELAXATION IN SO_2

T(°C)	C_1'/R	τ_1 (sec)	Z_1	C_2'/R	τ_2 (sec)	Z_2
20	0.595	5.6×10^{-8}	390	0.17	56×10^{-8}	2390
102	0.725	8.9×10^{-8}	530	0.39	89×10^{-8}	3130
200	0.81	5.0×10^{-8}	300	0.67	50×10^{-8}	1500

According to Boudart,[5] it follows from his experiments on the deactivation of O_2 by water vapor (Sec. 40) that the deactivation of an excited water molecule by another water molecule has a relaxation time given by

$$\frac{1}{\tau} = Nk_{40} = 7.04 \times 10^8 \text{ atm}^{-1} \text{ sec}^{-1}$$

see Eq. (40–8″), or $\tau = 1.42 \times 10^{-9}$ sec. This is fast compared to the values of Huber and Kantrowitz.

(*b*) *Ammonia*

This molecule, a pyramid with N at the apex, has three transversal (bending) and three valence bond vibrations. The former have $\vartheta = 1370°$ ($C' = 0.211\ R$ at 300 °K) and $\vartheta = 2340°$ (degenerate, $C' = 2 \times 0.025\ R$); the latter, $\vartheta = 4620°$ (degenerate) and $\vartheta = 4790°$. The valence bond vibrations do not contribute appreciably to C' at 300 °K.

Dispersion measurements by Buschmann and Schäfer[6] seem to indicate two relaxation times. (See Table 53–3.)

TABLE 53–3
RELAXATION TIME IN NH_3
The brackets indicate the presence of two relaxation times

T(°C)	τ(sec)	Z	Reference
20	1.2×10^{-7}	1,300	2
40	1.8×10^{-7}	{ 1,700	6
40	14.5×10^{-7}	13,600 }	6
100		{ 620	6
100		2,500 }	6

[5] C. S. Tuesday and M. Boudart, Technical Note 7, Contract AF 33(038)-23976, Princeton University, Princeton, New Jersey, January, 1955.

[6] K. F. Buschmann and K. Schäfer, *Z. physik. Chem.* **B50**, 73 (1941).

54. Large Molecules

This section gives a list of those molecules in which relaxation times have been determined. The results are listed in Tables 54–1, 54–2, and 54–3. Fig. 54–1 illustrates dispersion in CCl_4. The following explanations should be made.

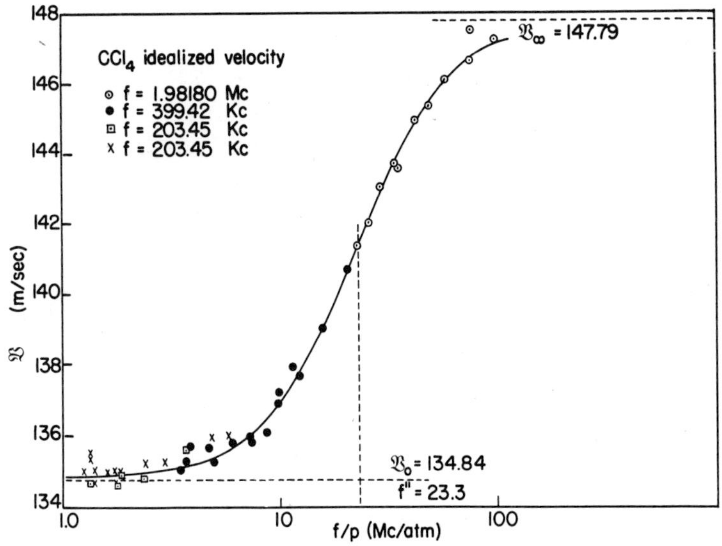

FIG. 54–1. Dispersion in carbon tetrachloride, corrected to the ideal gas state, according to Busala, Hubbard, and Sette. The absolute value of the limiting velocities is calculated theoretically from the specific heats.

Those Z which are not in parentheses are calculated by using Eq. (36–3) for the time between collisions. The Z in parentheses are not calculated this way but are quoted directly from the author. The last four columns indicate how far the measurements show whether there might be an additional relaxation time outside the range investigated. $(C_v/R)_{0\mathrm{calc}}$ is normally obtained from the knowledge of molecular vibrations, except for the data from Refs. 1 and 3, which should be checked for the source. In the last two columns $(C_v/R)_{\mathrm{obs}}$ is either calculated, if tables for the velocities are given, or estimated, if only drawings are shown; h indicates that the curve is already horizontal, nh that it is nearly horizontal. For the jet measurements (Ref. 4), such data cannot be given, nor can they be given for the absorption measurements.

TABLE 54–1
METHYL ALCOHOL AND HYDROCARBONS

Gas	T (°C)	$\tau \times 10^8$ sec	Z	$(C_v/R)_{0\,calc}$	$(C_v/R)_{\infty\,calc}$	Highest $(C_v/R)_{obs}$	Lowest $(C_v/R)_{obs}$	Reference
CH_3OH (methyl alcohol)	32	2.27	220	5.27	3.00	5.27 *h*		1
C_6H_6 (benzene)	30	5	270	9.45	3.00	8.17 *nh*	3.02	2
	96	15	1070		3.00			3
	117	13.3	950	12.2	3.00	13	7.5	3
	165	11.8	840					3
C_2H_6 (ethane)	20	0.524	52	5.25	3.00	5.4 *h*	4.6	3
	14	0.3	30					4
C_3H_8 (propane)	20	<1	<90	7.65		7.9		3
	20	<0.7	<60					4
C_3H_6 (cyclopropane)	18	36.4	4000	5.5	3.00	5.25 *h*	3.2 *h*	3
	100	27	2570	7.5	3.00	7.4 *h*	3 *h*	3
C_4H_{10} (butane)	20	1.8						4
C_6H_{14} (*n*-hexane)	100	<1	<90	19.7		17.5–19		4
	35	0.65	130	17.6		17.6		17
C_6H_{12} (cyclohexane)	100	<1	<90	15.8–16.2	3.00	14–16		3
C_2H_4 (ethylene)	30	23.8	2240					5
C_3H_6 (propylene)	20	<0.6	<50					4
C_4H_6 (butadiene)	20	<1.3						4
C_6H_{10} (cyclohexene)	100	<1	<90	15.3	3.00	14		3

TABLE 54–2
HALOGENATED METHANES

Gas	T (°C)	$\tau \times 10^8$ sec	Z	$(C_v/R)_{0\,\text{calc}}$	$(C_v/R)_{\infty\,\text{calc}}$	Highest $(C_v/R)_{obs}$	Lowest $(C_v/R)_{obs}$	Reference
CH_4	109	107	8400		3.00			6
	15	48	4800	3.03	3.00			4
CH_3F	100	320		4.07	3.00		3.1 *h*	7
CH_2F_2	100	5.5		4.88	3.00	4.9 ± 0.10	3.7	7
	27	3.0		4.17	3.00			8
CHF_3	100	42		6.04	3.00			7
	27	47.9		5.40	3.00		3.03 *nh*	8
CF_4	100	66		7.4	3.00		3.72	7
	27	75.6		6.49	3.00		3.07 *nh*	8
	20	76			3.00			9
CH_3Cl	100	18		4.55	3.00	4.7 *h*	2.9 *h*	7
	27	20.4		3.93	3.00	4.13 *nh*	3.04 *h*	8
	30	18.5		3.94	3.00	3.89	3.03	10
	22	20.2			3.00			4
CH_2Cl_2	100	8.4		5.94	3.00	5.9 ± 0.3 *h*	3.7	7
	30	9.46		5.21	(3.86)	5.14 ± 0.7 *nh*		10
		0.195		(3.86)	3.00		3.4 steep	
$CHCl_3$	100	<2.8		7.85	3.00			7
	30	1.35		6.97	3.00	6.46	3.22	10
CCl_4	100	8.3		9.84	3.00	9.8 ± 0.2 *nh*	5.5 ± 0.5	7
	30	2.08		9.12	3.00	8.70	3.12	10
CH_3Br	100	10		4.76	3.00	4.76 ± 0.15 *h*	3.3	7
	30	7.5		4.14	3.00			8
CH_3I	100	4.5		4.98	3.00	4.98 sloping		7
$CHClF_2$	27	9.5			3.00			8
	21	10		6.02	3.00			4
CCl_3F	27	4.0		8.35	3.00			8
$CBrClF_2$	27	5.0		8.15	3.00			8
CH_2ClF	27	1.0		4.75	3.00			8
$CClF_3$	27	23.9		7.10	3.00			8
$CHCl_2F$	27	2.5		6.40	3.00	6.45 *h*		8
CCl_2F_2	27	7.8		7.34	3.00			8
	19	9						4
CBr_2F_2	27	2.9		8.30	3.00			8
$CBrF_3$	27	19.6		7.95	3.00			8

TABLE 54–3
SUBSTITUTED ETHANES AND ETHYLENES

Gas	T (°C)	$\tau \times 10^8$ sec	Z	$(C_v/R)_0$ calc	$(C_v/R)_\infty$ calc	Highest $(C_v/R)_{obs}$	Lowest $(C_v/R)_{obs}$	Reference
C_2H_4O (ethylene oxide) *	23	35.6	5000					11
$Cl_2HC_2H_3$ (1,1 dichloro-ethane)	30	(36) 0.535		9.417		7.848 h	4.008	12
$ClH_2C_2ClH_2$ (1,2 dichloro-ethane)	30	(6.6) 0.425		9.152		8.968 (8.523 h)	4.483	12
ClHCCClH (dichloro-ethylene)								
cis	34.7	0.6		6.98	3.00	6.3 h	(3.8 nh)	13
trans	34.7	0.6		7.16	3.00	6.5 h	(3.7)	13
SF_6	30	58.9	4680	10.938	3.00	8.197	3.00–3.06 h	14

* Absorption measurements. $C' = 1.564\ R$ and $C - C' = 3.185\ R$ were used.

Cheng[2] has also made absorption measurements on benzene, the data scattering badly. Angona[11] has determined τ for ethylene oxide by absorption measurements only.

Ubbelohde and his co-workers[15 16] have extended the measurements of τ for ethylene, $H_2C = CH_2$, over a wider temperature range. They also tested the effectiveness of other hydrocarbons as impurities and found that those which have a chain of groups with free rotation around the bond joining them are particularly effective ("wrestling collisions"). This is in agreement with the failure of Lambert and Rowlinson[3] to find dispersion in n-hexane at 100° C. Klose[17] has found, at 40° C, such a dispersion with $\tau = 7 \times 10^{-9}$ sec.

Lambert and Rowlinson[3] have investigated cyclohexene, acetonitrile, acetaldehyde, and acetone and diethyl ether without finding dispersion (upper range 5—8 Mc/atm except for the second and third, where it was 20 Mc/atm). Fogg and Lambert[18] measured relaxation times for alkene halides, but in only three cases (which are included in Table 54–3) did the measurements seem extensive enough to make τ reliable. Matta and Richardson[19] have found dispersion in ethylene, ethyl ether and acetaldehyde (the latter contrary to Lambert and Rowlinson[3]). Other measurements in vapors were made by Railston[20] and Jatkar.[21]

---

[1] C. Ener, A. Busala, and J. C. Hubbard, *J. Chem. Phys.* **23**, 155 (1955).

[2] L. Cheng, *J. Chem. Phys.* **19**, 693 (1951).

[3] J. D. Lambert and J. S. Rowlinson, *Proc. Roy. Soc.* **A204**, 424 (1951).

[4] W. Griffith, *J. Appl. Phys.* **21**, 1319 (1950).

[5] W. T. Richards and J. A. Reid, *J. Chem. Phys.* **2**, 206 (1934).

[6] A. Eucken and S. Aybar, *Z. physik. Chem.* (*Leipzig*) **B46**, 195 (1940).

[7] P. G. T. Fogg, P. A. Hanks, and J. D. Lambert, *Proc. Roy. Soc.* **A219**, 490 (1953).

[8] T. D. Rossing and S. Legvold, *J. Chem. Phys.* **23**, 1118 (1955).

[9] W. H. Byers, *J. Chem. Phys.* **11**, 348 (1943).

[10] D. Sette, A. Busala, and J. C. Hubbard, *J. Chem. Phys.* **23**, 787 (1955).

[11] F. A. Angona, *J. Acoust. Soc. Am.* **25**, 1116 (1953).

[12] T. S. Rao and J. C. Hubbard, *J. Acoust. Soc. Am.* **27**, 321 (1955).

[13] A. Busala, D. Sette, and J. C. Hubbard, *J. Chem. Phys.* **20**, 1899 (1952).

[14] C. L. O'Connor, *J. Acoust. Soc. Am.* **26**, 361 (1954).

[15] J. C. McCoubrey, T. B. Parke, and A. R. Ubbelohde, *Proc. Roy. Soc.* **A223**, 155 (1954).

[16] W. D. McGrath and A. R. Ubbelohde, *Proc. Roy. Soc.* **A227**, 1 (1954).

[17] J. Klose, *J. Acoust. Soc. Am.* **30**, 605 (1958).

[18] P. G. T. Fogg and J. D. Lambert, *Proc. Roy. Soc.* **A232**, 537 (1955).

[19] K. Matta and E. R. Richardson, *J. Acoust. Soc. Am.* **23**, 581 (1951).

[20] W. Railston, *J. Acoust. Soc. Am.* **11**, 107 (1939).

[21] S. K. K. Jatkar and D. Lakshiminaravan, *J. Indian Inst. Sci.* **A23**, 1 (1946); **A28**, 1 (1948).

VII. Theory of Vibrational and Rotational Energy Exchange

55. Introductory Remarks

In ideal gases, the rate of energy exchange is proportional to the pressure for a given temperature, as we have seen. This proves that only pairs of molecules are involved. An energy transfer can only occur when the two molecules are very close together, i.e., in a collision. This knowledge makes the theoretical treatment for gases much simpler than for liquids, since the duration of a collision in an ideal gas is short compared to the time between collisions.

Kallmann and London[1] and O. K. Rice[2] gave early quantum theoretical treatments of the excitation process. Zener[3] investigated the energy transfer, both classically and quantum theoretically, and showed that collisions should be quite effective in the transfer of rotational energy and quite ineffective in the transfer of vibrational energy.

In the papers just cited, it is shown that the transition probability depends on the interaction energy between the molecules and on their relative velocity. However, the form of the interaction potential chosen was not close to that applicable to neutral molecules.

Landau and Teller[4] made a great step forward in the physical understanding of the process by discussing the process of energy transfer classically and pointing out the importance of Ehrenfest's adiabatic principle (see Sec. 56). They also assumed a much better interaction potential, and took Maxwell's distribution law of velocities into account. This allowed them to deduce the correct temperature dependence of the relaxation time; since they did not know the value of the constants in the interaction potential, they could not calculate the absolute values of τ.

In the following, it will first be shown how far one can get classically with Landau and Teller's assumptions (Sec. 56). Then the analogous quantum theoretical calculations will be developed, at first with simplifying assump-

---

[1] H. Kallmann and F. London, *Z. Physik. Chem.* **B2**, 207 (1929).

[2] O. K. Rice, *Phys. Rev.* **38**, 1943 (1931).

[3] C. Zener, *Phys. Rev.* **38**, 277 (1931); *Proc. Cambridge Phil. Soc.* **29**, 136 (1933).

[4] L. Landau and E. Teller, *Physik. Z. Sowjetunion* **10**, 34 (1936).

tions, which will then be dropped one by one. At the beginning, it will be assumed that we are dealing with a collision between a molecule BC and a monatomic molecule, A, and that this collision is head-on (Secs. 57 and 58). These assumptions are also made by Landau and Teller. Next, the restriction to head-on collisions is dropped (Secs. 60 to 62), but the orientation of the axis of BC during the collision is ignored. This amounts to a neglect of the effect of rotation on the transfer of vibrational energy. The combined transfer of vibrational and rotational energy into translational energy is then treated in Sec. 64. Finally, the possibility that A may also contain several atoms is at least partly taken into account (Sec. 65).

A point about notation should be remembered: k_{10} is the rate of deactivation (Sec. 19). The probability that a deactivation will occur during one collision is k_{10} divided by the number of collisions a molecule undergoes per second, or k_{10} multiplied by the time τ_c between collisions. The probability of deactivation is

$$k_{10}\tau_c = \frac{k_{10}}{k_{10} - k_{01}} (k_{10} - k_{01})\, \tau_c = \frac{1}{1-K} \frac{\tau_c}{\tau} = \frac{1}{1-K} Z^{-1}. \qquad (55\text{–}1)$$

If the rate of activation is slow compared with the rate of deactivation, the probability of deactivation is equal to $1/Z$.

It should be mentioned here that two other theories have been proposed: a resonance theory and a complex formation theory. The former, proposed fairly early, assumed that the maximum of $\alpha\lambda$ corresponds to a resonance with some internal vibration of the molecule. From our present knowledge, there are three objections against it, each of which is conclusive in itself:

(a) There are no internal vibrations of sufficiently low frequency inside a molecule, (b) the dispersion curve is quite different from those which occur in resonance phenomena (Sec. 9), and (c) the frequency at which the maximum occurs should be independent of the pressure, as long as the gas is ideal, instead of being $\sim p$.

The second theory, proposed by Rossing and Legvold,[5] assumes from numerical data the existence of a heat of activation for the process of deactivating or activating an internal vibration, so that

$$\tau = A\, e^{\varepsilon/kT} \qquad (55\text{–}2)$$

an assumption which Eucken and Becker[6] had made earlier. This might be interpreted in this manner: there is a potential hill between the two

[5] T. D. Rossing and S. Legvold, *J. Chem. Phys.* **23**, 1118 (1955).

[6] A. Eucken and R. Becker, *Z. physik. Chem.* **B20**, 467 (1933); **B27**, 219 (1934).

molecules, which only molecules having at least energy ε can pass. One must now distinguish between the two cases

$$\varepsilon > h\nu \quad \text{and} \quad \varepsilon < h\nu.$$

In the first case, which Rossing and Legvold assume, the hitting molecule A has, after passing the potential hill, enough energy to excite the molecule BC which it has hit by at least one additional quantum. The hitting molecule A, having lost this energy, is unable to get out over the hill until the vibrational energy is returned to it as kinetic energy; if the returned energy is just the one quantum it originally transferred to the vibration of BC, the collision is in effect elastic. If there is an appreciable chance that an additional quantum, which the hit molecule BC originally had, is added, a deactivation may take place. The ratio of the rates with which these two processes (deactivation and elastic collision) occur is not at all or not very temperature dependent. As for activation, if the hitting molecule A originally has a kinetic energy larger than $\varepsilon + h\nu$, the inverse process may take place, and the ratio of the rates of the processes of activation and deactivation is given correctly by Eq. (19–4). There is also a triple collision process possible, which alternately traps and frees the hitting molecule A while it is behind the potential hill.

If $\varepsilon < h\nu$, the description is similar, except that the hitting molecule A cannot, after the transit over the potential hill, transmit its energy to the vibrations of the molecule BC and need not wait until this energy comes back to it as kinetic energy.

The main trouble with this theory is that there is nothing in our knowledge of intermolecular forces—excluding the case of "chemical interaction"—to explain the existence of a potential hill, except for the low one due to centrifugal force.

Lukasik[7] has calculated the relaxation time for deactivation by radiation. This effect exists only in polar diatomic molecules and, for some modes of vibration, in polyatomic molecules, and is independent of pressure. Lukasik finds that for N_2O, OCS, and NO_2, $\tau = 0.04$ to 0.08 sec; and for HCl, $\tau = 3 \times 10^{-4}$ sec.

56. The Theory of Landau and Teller (Classical)

In the previous section, Ehrenfest's[1] principle was mentioned.

If one has a periodic motion and one changes a parameter, e.g., the strength of an external force, then one calls the process (nearly) adiabatic

[7] S. Lukasik, *J. Acoust. Soc. Am.* **28**, 455 (1956).

[1] P. Ehrenfest, *Koninkl. Ned. Akad. Wetenschap., Proc.* **16**, 591 (1914).

if the relative change of the parameter is small during a period of the motion, nonadiabatic if it is comparatively large during this time.

Ehrenfest showed that an adiabatic change does not affect the quantum numbers, i.e., at every moment the motion is the same as if the momentary value of the external force had persisted for a long time. In particular, if one brings the external potential back to its original value, the motion of the system, apart from a phase shift, is the same as if no change of potential had occurred at all.

On the other hand, if the change of force is relatively large during a period of the motion—which case is called nonadiabatic—quantum transitions may occur and, even if the potential returns to its earlier value, the system may be in a different state.

The classical analog, as discussed by Landau and Teller, is as follows. Consider the molecule BC, with atom C fixed in space, as if its mass were infinite, with A approaching along the direction BC to make a head-on hit. We are now considering *activation*, and therefore assume B originally at rest. We take two extreme types of interaction between B and A.

If B and A are hard elastic spheres, they interact only upon direct contact. Assume $m_B \geqslant m_A$. When A hits B, B will get a velocity directed toward C, and compress the "spring" between BC (i.e., run on against the intramolecular force which tries to keep the molecular size at a fixed value) until B is stopped. The "spring" will then expand again, accelerating B until, when B passes the equilibrium position—where it was hit by A—it has the same kinetic energy it received from A. A, however, has had the direction of its velocity reversed when it hit B, and by the time the half period of oscillation of BC is over, A is far enough away so that there is no possibility of A taking back any energy it had transferred to the vibration earlier. This is the extreme nonadiabatic situation, where energy transfer is highly efficient (though not 100% efficient; the efficiency depends upon the ratio of the masses).

The other extreme is that of a very "soft" force, i.e., one which changes slowly with distance and which has therefore a long range. This is the extreme adiabatic case. B and A start interacting with a weak force when they are still far apart. Because the force is weak, the acceleration of B (and deceleration of A) is small. As a consequence, the position of B is such during the process that the interaction force exerted on it by A toward C and the inner molecular force pushing it away from C are nearly in equilibrium; a moment comes when (nearly) all the kinetic energy A originally held is changed into potential energy of repulsion, repulsion between B and C and repulsion between B and A. Then both B and A are (nearly) at rest. The process is then reversed and B pushes A outward, with less and less force. When the distance between B and A has grown very large, A has received all its kinetic energy back and B has come to rest at its original equilibrium position, so that no energy remains in the vibration.

In this case, the efficiency of energy transfer is zero. Landau and Teller therefore conclude that the probability of energy transfer depends on (and increases with) the ratio of the period of vibration to the time of interaction.

The latter is put equal to a characteristic range of the forces divided by the molecular velocity. From this, they conclude that only short range forces are effective in producing transitions; since the repulsive intermolecular forces have shorter ranges than the attractive ones, they state that only the former need to be considered. It will turn out, however, that the attractive forces have an indirect influence (Sec. 59) on the transfer.

While the previous argument is concerned directly with activation, the rate of deactivation can be calculated from that of activation by Eqs. (19–12) and (19–13).

Landau and Teller's calculations will be somewhat amplified in the following.

If both the molecules BC and A move, only their relative velocity w matters. One has then to use the effective mass

$$\tilde{m} = \frac{m_A\, m_{BC}}{m_A + m_{BC}}\,. \tag{56–1}$$

The important ratio, time of interaction to period of vibration, mentioned above, is

$$\nu \frac{l'}{w}$$

where ν is the vibration frequency and l' the characteristic length.

Landau and Teller assume an exponential interaction law and deduce that the transition probability depends on this quantity in the following manner

$$\frac{1}{Z} = \frac{1}{Z_0{'}} \exp\left(-\frac{2\pi\nu l'}{w}\right). \tag{56–2}$$

($Z_0{'}$ is a pure number of order unity.) This has then to be averaged over the Maxwell distribution law of velocities w for the relative motion, which is

$$dN = N_0 w dw \,\frac{\tilde{m}}{kT} \exp\left(-\frac{\tilde{m}w^2}{2kT}\right). \tag{56–3}$$

This law is the distribution law for motion in one dimension (parallel to the line BC). It is not the law for the molecules contained in unit volume, but the law for the number hitting a unit area per second, and therefore contains an additional factor w which the former does not have. N_0 is the total number of molecules contained in unit volume.

The average probability of deactivation is then

$$\frac{1}{Z} = \frac{1}{Z_0'}\frac{1}{N_0}\int dN \exp\left(-\frac{2\pi\nu l'}{w}\right)$$

$$= \frac{1}{Z_0'}\frac{\tilde{m}}{kT}\int w\,dw \exp\left(-\frac{2\pi\nu l'}{w} - \frac{\tilde{m}w^2}{2kT}\right). \tag{56-4}$$

The preceding integral cannot be evaluated in closed form. An approximate evaluation is based on the following line of reasoning.

The probability of energy transfer increases strongly with increasing velocity w. On the other hand, the number of molecules with high velocity decreases strongly with increasing w. The product of these two factors will therefore have a maximum for some high velocity w_m. Only molecules with velocities near that of the maximum will play an important role. This argument is good only if the function falls steeply on both sides of the maximum. Since w occurs in the exponent, our function will have this character, and it is sufficient to look for the minimum of the absolute value of the exponent, which is negative.

The minimum of the exponent

$$\frac{2\pi\nu l'}{w} + \frac{\tilde{m}w^2}{2kT}$$

occurs at

$$-\frac{2\pi\nu l'}{w_m^{\,2}} + \frac{\tilde{m}w_m}{kT} = 0$$

or

$$\frac{\tilde{m}w_m^{\,2}}{2kT} = \frac{\pi\nu l'}{w_m} \tag{56-5}$$

or

$$w_m = \left(\frac{2\pi\nu l' kT}{\tilde{m}}\right)^{1/3}. \tag{56-5'}$$

In view of what has been said earlier, we develop the exponent around the minimum, while in the factors in front of the exponential, which do not vary rapidly with w, we use w_m. The exponent is

$$-\frac{2\pi\nu l'}{w}-\frac{\tilde{m}}{2}\frac{w^2}{kT}=-\frac{2\pi\nu l'}{w_m}-\frac{\tilde{m}}{2}\frac{w_m{}^2}{kT}-\frac{3}{2}\frac{\tilde{m}}{kT}(w-w_m)^2=-\frac{3}{2}\left(\frac{\varepsilon'}{kT}\right)^{1/3}-\frac{3}{2}\frac{\tilde{m}}{kT}(w-w_m)^2 \tag{56–6}$$

with the abbreviation

$$\varepsilon'=\tilde{m}(2\pi\nu l')^2. \tag{56–6′}$$

If the molecule were vibrating with the amplitude l', its energy would be $1/2\ \varepsilon'$.

It can be seen that the energy of relative motion E_m of a molecule which has the most favorable relative velocity w_m is, see Eq. (56—5)

$$E_m=\frac{1}{2}\tilde{m}\,w_m{}^2=\frac{1}{2}(\varepsilon')^{1/3}(kT)^{2/3} \tag{56–6″}$$

or

$$\frac{E_m}{kT}=\frac{1}{2}\left(\frac{\varepsilon'}{kT}\right)^{1/3}. \tag{56–6‴}$$

Inserting Eq. (56–6) in Eq. (56–4) and integrating over all the molecules with velocities near w_m one gets[2]

$$\frac{1}{Z}=\frac{1}{Z_0'}\frac{\tilde{m}}{kT}w_m\exp\left[-\frac{3}{2}\left(\frac{\varepsilon'}{kT}\right)^{1/3}\right]\int_{-\infty}^{\infty}dw\exp\left[-\frac{3}{2}\frac{\tilde{m}}{kT}(w-w_m)^2\right]$$

$$=\frac{1}{Z_0'}\frac{\tilde{m}}{kT}\left(\frac{\varepsilon'}{\tilde{m}}\right)^{1/6}\left(\frac{kT}{\tilde{m}}\right)^{1/3}\sqrt{\pi}\left(\frac{2kT}{3\tilde{m}}\right)^{1/2}\exp\left[-\frac{3}{2}\left(\frac{\varepsilon'}{kT}\right)^{1/3}\right]$$

$$=\frac{1}{Z_0'}\sqrt{\frac{2\pi}{3}}\left(\frac{\varepsilon'}{kT}\right)^{1/6}\exp\left[-\frac{3}{2}\left(\frac{\varepsilon'}{kT}\right)^{1/3}\right] \tag{56–7}$$

---

[2] One can see that ε'/kT is a measure of the degree of adiabasy, which latter is the decisive criterion, according to Sec. 55.

$$\frac{\tilde{m}}{kT}=\frac{2}{3}\frac{1}{\overline{w^2}}$$

$$\frac{\varepsilon'}{kT}=(2\pi\nu l')^2\frac{\tilde{m}}{kT}=(2\pi\nu l')^2\frac{2}{3}\frac{1}{\overline{w^2}}$$

$$\left(\frac{\varepsilon'}{kT}\right)^{1/2}=2\pi\sqrt{\frac{2}{3}}\frac{\nu l'}{\sqrt{\overline{w^2}}}=2\pi\sqrt{\frac{2}{3}}\frac{l'}{\sqrt{\overline{w^2}}}\frac{1}{\text{period}}=2\pi\sqrt{\frac{2}{3}\frac{\text{interaction time}}{\text{vibration period}}}.$$

where the integration has been extended from $-\infty$ to $+\infty$, because the wings for which Eq. (56–6) does not hold do not contribute appreciably to the integral.

57. Fundamental Quantum Consideration

The physical problem is the calculation of the probability of the excitation or de-excitation of the vibrations of a molecule BC by "hitting" molecules A. One does not consider a single molecule A, but a parallel stream of molecules A, falling on one molecule BC, which acts as a scatterer. We have only to consider the relative motion of BC and A, so that we can then consider BC (or rather the center of gravity of BC) as resting at the origin. If x_A, x_B, x_C are the momentary coordinates of the three atoms (treating them first as if they were all aligned along the x axis) and x_{BC} the coordinate of the center of gravity of BC, the internal vibration of the molecule is described by

$$x_B - x_C = \frac{m_B + m_C}{m_C}(x_B - x_{BC}) = X. \tag{57–1}$$

Call the distance of A from the center of gravity of BC: x

$$x = x_A - x_{BC} \tag{57–1'}$$

X and x will be used as the coordinates describing the internal motion of BC and the relative translational motion of A against BC, at least in the one-dimensional approximation.

Up to now, everything is common to classical and quantum theory.

We now associate a wave with a stream of particles—a plane wave with a parallel stream, a spherical wave with a stream divergent from a center.

The wave length is given by the de Broglie equation

$$\lambda = \frac{h}{p} \tag{57–2}$$

where

$$p = \tilde{m}w$$

is the linear momentum belonging to the relative velocity w. In Chapter VII, p will always be used for linear momentum. The other meaning of p —hydrostatic pressure—will not appear in this chapter.

From the plane wave falling on the scatterer BC, the latter will produce a scattered wave. This will follow from the necessity of satisfying the boundary conditions at the origin. (These are, essentially, that the wave cannot reach the center of gravity of BC.) The scattered wave will contain one (relatively strong) part with the original wave length (i.e., that belonging to the original linear momentum p_0), which is called the elastically scattered wave. The other parts will have modified wave lengths (changed p). They correspond to particles A which have produced an excitation and are called inelastically scattered waves. From the principle of conservation of energy one gets[1]

$$p_1 - p_0 = \sqrt{p_0^2 - 2\tilde{m}h\nu} - p_0 \tag{57-3}$$

if the energy transferred to excitation is just one vibrational quantum $h\nu$. (In the case of de-excitation, there is a plus sign in front of $2\tilde{m}h\nu$.)

Similarly, there will be some scattered waves with increased p, since in the stationary quantum description a BC has a finite probability of being in an excited state and of then being deactivated by the hit. (Such waves are occasionally called super elastic waves.)

In general, scattering problems cannot be solved exactly, but only by the method of perturbation. In the way the treatment has been outlined, this is a stationary (time-independent) state of perturbation. Assume for the moment that the scatterer BC has only two internal states of energy, ε_1 and ε_2. The molecules A which are scattered per second with unchanged energy $p_0^2/2\tilde{m}$, i.e., the ones which are elastically scattered, are the ones which have brought about neither excitation nor de-excitation.

Since perturbation calculations are mathematically permissible only if the perturbation is small, we can only consider cases where the fraction of excited molecules

$$\frac{n_2}{n_1 + n_2}$$

is small compared to unity, so that the number of molecules A scattered elastically per second is nearly equal to those scattered elastically *from the ground state.* One can replace the number of molecules scattered per second by those scattered elastically. The number of molecules A which are scattered per second with the diminished kinetic energy

$$\frac{p_0^2}{2m} - (\varepsilon_2 - \varepsilon_1)$$

is equal to the number of excitation processes.

---

[1] The value of $p_1 - p_0$ is largest for low p_0 and diminishes to $\pm\, \tilde{m}h\nu/p_0$ for large p_0.

Therefore, the ratio of the number scattered per second with energy $p_0^2/2\tilde{m} - (\varepsilon_2 - \varepsilon_1)$: number of all scattered per second is equal to the probability of excitation, or equal to unity divided by the number of collisions needed for excitation; or, the number of collisions needed for excitation is equal to the number of molecules A scattered elastically per second divided by the number of molecules A scattered with energy $p_0^2/2\tilde{m} - (\varepsilon_2 - \varepsilon_1)$ per second.

By a similar argument it follows that the number of collisions needed for de-excitation is equal to the number of molecules A scattered elastically by excited molecules BC per second divided by the number of molecules A scattered per second with kinetic energy $p_0^2/2\tilde{m} + (\varepsilon_2 - \varepsilon_1)$ by excited molecules BC.

It is further assumed that the number of molecules A scattered elastically per second by a given number of molecules BC is the same whether the molecules BC are excited or not.

If there are more than two states of excitation possible for BC, there is no change in the argument, provided all the energy-differences $\varepsilon_j - \varepsilon_s$ have different values. If the energy jumps are the same, as in the harmonic oscillator

$$\varepsilon_{j+1} - \varepsilon_j = h\nu$$

one must make the conditions such (the temperature so low) that only the first two levels are appreciably present, and, once k_{01} or k_{10} (Sec. 19) are calculated, proceed formally from there as in Sec. 19.

The next problem is the calculation of the fraction of particles scattered elastically.

A wave is described by a wave function ψ^A, containing the translational coordinate (x in the one-dimensional case, r later in the tridimensional case); $|\psi^A|^2$ gives the density (number of particles per unit volume)

$$w|\psi^A|^2 = \frac{p}{\tilde{m}} |\psi^A|^2 \tag{57–4}$$

the flow of particles per second through unit area in the direction of w (or p).

If the incident wave is represented by a plane wave of unit amplitude, this means one incident particle A per unit volume. The flow of particles per second per unit area is therefore given as

$$\frac{1}{\tilde{m}} p_0 |\psi_0^A|^2.$$

The scattered wave, in turn, will be, at large distances from the scatterer, a plane wave (one dimension) or a spherical wave (three dimensions). If we choose the scattered wave function $\psi_1{}^A$ with proper normalization, the flow per unit area per second will be

$$\frac{1}{m} p_1 |a_1|^2 |\psi_1{}^A|^2$$

where a_1 is an amplitude. The rate constant k_{01} is then

$$k_{01} = \frac{p_1}{p_0} |a_1|^2 \int |\psi_1{}^A|^2 dS \qquad (57\text{–}4')$$

where dS is an element of either a plane surface (integration over unit area) or a sphere (integration over the sphere). One now proceeds in the following manner:

One sets up an over-all unperturbed wave function

$$\Psi_0 = \psi_0{}^A(x)\psi_0{}^{BC}(X) \qquad (57\text{–}5)$$

the first factor being the translational wave function for the unperturbed, relative motion; the second factor, the unmodified vibrational wave function of molecule BC. The fact that the two are simply multiplied means that, on this approximation, the translation of A and the vibration of BC do not affect each other. Actually, this would not be too good an approximation. It is considerably improved if we include the elastically scattered wave in the lowest approximation, so that

$$\Psi_0 = (\psi_0{}^A + \psi_e{}^A)\psi_0{}^{BC}. \qquad (57\text{–}5')$$

Both $\psi_0{}^A$ and $\psi_e{}^A$ belong to the linear momentum p_0. To this, one now adds a wave function Ψ_1 for the inelastically scattered wave

$$\Psi_1 = a_1\psi_1{}^A(x)\psi_1{}^{BC}(X) \qquad (57\text{–}5'')$$

which contains a translational wave function $\psi_1{}^A$ belonging to the decreased linear momentum p_1, and the excited vibrational state $\psi_1{}^{BC}$. The complete wave function is then

$$\Psi_0 + \Psi_1 = (\psi_0{}^A + \psi_e{}^A)\psi_0{}^{BC} + a_1\psi_1{}^A\psi_1{}^{BC}. \qquad (57\text{–}6)$$

This complete wave function can no longer be regarded as the product of one wave function describing the translational motion of A and one describing the vibration of BC. This is a sign that the translational motion and the vibration have interacted.

Up to now, we have formulated our discussion in common for the one-dimensional and the three-dimensional case, except for the use of the letters x and r.

We will talk specifically first about the one-dimensional case. Our model is therefore really a plane of molecules BC, with axis normal to the plane (or two plates, separated by properly spaced springs) on which a stream of molecules A impinges normally.

In this case, the elastically reflected wave is also a plane wave, of (nearly) the same amplitude and the same wave length as the incident wave. The inelastically reflected wave is also plane, its amplitude given by

$$a_1 = \frac{4\pi\tilde{m}}{hp_1} H_{01}' \tag{57–7}$$

where H_{01}' is the "matrix element" of the interaction energy H', defined by

$$H_{01}' = \int \Psi_0{}^* H' \Psi_1 dx dX. \tag{57–7′}$$

The integration interval for both x and X goes from $-\infty$ to $+\infty$. If H' were independent of the vibrational coordinate, H_{01}' would be zero, because the two vibrational wave functions $\psi_0{}^{BC}$ and $\psi_1{}^{BC}$ are orthogonal. H' does depend on X if we assume that the interaction is between A and the two atoms B and C; in practice, because of the rapid decrease of interaction with distance between A and B, H' really depends on

$$x_A - x_B = x_A - x_{BC} - (x_B - x_{BC})$$

$$= x - \frac{m_C}{m_B + m_C} X \tag{57–8}$$

see Eq. (57–1). In general, the vibrational amplitude X is small compared to the interatomic distance x, so that one can develop

$$H'\left(x - \frac{m_C}{m_B + m_C} X\right) = H'(x) - \frac{m_C}{m_B + m_C} \frac{dH'}{dx} X. \tag{57–9}$$

If this is inserted in Eq. (57–7′), it is seen that the contribution of $H'(x)$ to the matrix element is zero; i.e., the part $H'(x)$ does not produce vibrational transitions. (However, it is used to calculate the best form of the wave function describing the elastically scattered wave and the primary wave near the scatterer; this was the innovation of Mott and Jackson, and is called the method of distorted waves.)

The second term in Eq. (57–9) does produce transitions. One can now split H_{01}' into two factors, one dependent only on the translation, the other only on the vibration.

$$H_{01}' = H_{01}'^{(\mathrm{tr})} H_{01}'^{(\mathrm{osc})} \tag{57–10}$$

$$H_{01}'^{(\mathrm{tr})} = l \int (\psi_0{}^A + \psi_e{}^A)^* \frac{dH'}{dx} \psi_1{}^A dx \tag{57–10′}$$

$$H_{01}'^{(\mathrm{osc})} = - \frac{m_C}{m_B + m_C} \frac{1}{l} \int \psi_0{}^{BC} X \psi_1{}^{BC} dX. \tag{57–10″}$$

The l is an arbitrary length introduced so as to make Eq. (57–10″) dimensionless, which gives Eq. (51–10′) the dimensions of an energy. From Eqs. (57–4′) and (57–7)

$$k_{01} = \left[\frac{4\pi \tilde{m}}{h\sqrt{p_0 p_1}} H_{01}'^{(\mathrm{tr})} \right]^2 [H_{01}'^{(\mathrm{osc})}]^2. \tag{57–10‴}$$

If molecule BC is a simple harmonic oscillator, then Eq. (57–10″) has the form of a "dipole" transition induced by an electomagnetic wave. It is well-known that only changes by one quantum number are then allowed, $j \rightleftarrows j+1$, which is what was used in Eq. (57–3). For the transition $0 \to 1$

$$H_{01}'^{(\mathrm{osc})} = - \frac{m_C}{m_B + m_C} \frac{1}{2\pi l} \left[\frac{h}{2\tilde{m}_{BC} \nu} \right]^{1/2}. \tag{57–11}$$

where

$$\tilde{m}_{BC} = \frac{m_B m_C}{m_B + m_C}.$$

Using the quantity ε', introduced in Eq. (56–6′), and $l' = 2\pi l$

$$H_{01}'^{(\mathrm{osc})} = - \frac{m_C}{m_B + m_C} \left[2\pi^2 \frac{\tilde{m}}{\tilde{m}_{BC}} \frac{h\nu}{\varepsilon'} \right]^{1/2} \tag{57–12}$$

and, finally

$$[H_{01}'^{(\mathrm{osc})}]^2 = \frac{1}{2} \frac{m_C{}^2 + m_B{}^2}{m_B m_C} \frac{m_A}{m_A + m_B + m_C} 2\pi^2 \frac{h\nu}{\varepsilon'} \tag{57–12′}$$

where the following transformation was made

$$\left(\frac{m_C}{m_B + m_C} \right)^2 \frac{\tilde{m}}{\tilde{m}_{BC}} = \frac{m_C{}^2}{(m_B + m_C)^2} \frac{m_A(m_B + m_C)}{m_A + m_B + m_C} \frac{m_B + m_C}{m_B m_C}$$

$$= \frac{m_A m_C}{m_B(m_A + m_B + m_C)} = \frac{M_A M_C}{M_B(M_A + M_B + M_C)}.$$

In the last expression, the mole masses M (molecular weights) have been substituted for the masses of one molecule m, since the fraction on the left contains equal powers of m in the numerator and denominator.

Since the molecule BC may with equal probability have the orientations CB or BC, we take finally the mean

$$\frac{1}{2}\left(\frac{M_C}{M_B}+\frac{M_B}{M_C}\right)\frac{M_A}{M_A+M_B+M_C}=\frac{1}{2}\,\frac{M_B^2+M_C^2}{M_BM_C}\,\frac{M_A}{M_A+M_B+M_C}.$$

The remaining task (in the one-dimensional approximation) is the calculation of $H_{01}^{\prime(\mathrm{tr})}$. It is clear that this factor must be mainly responsible for the wide variation in the values of Z found experimentally.

In the one-dimensional case, ψ_0^A, ψ_e^A, and ψ_1^A will all represent plane waves at large distances from BC; ψ_0^A, a wave running to the left, ψ_e^A and ψ_1^A, the elastically and the unelastically reflected waves running to the right. The product of two waves of different wave length integrated over an appreciable distance gives zero. Therefore, the region in which dH'/dx is small or constant does not contribute to the integral. Only the region in which dH'/dx is appreciable and varies considerably with x gives an appreciable contribution to $H_{01}^{\prime(\mathrm{tr})}$, since the wave length of ψ_0^A and ψ_e^A on the one side and of ψ_1^A on the other differ because of the energy jump.[2]

If the velocity is very high, one can use the so-called Born approximation by keeping the λ (i.e., both p_0 and p_1) independent of x, that is, by preserving the values of p_0 and p_1, which exist far way from BC, throughout the collision.

The method of distorted waves proceeds differently. It uses as zero order approximation the exact solutions that would exist in the absence of transitions. The incident plus the elastically reflected wave are then solutions of the Schroedinger equation

$$\frac{d^2}{dx^2}\psi^A+\frac{8\pi^2\tilde{m}}{h^2}\left[\frac{p_0^{\,2}}{2\tilde{m}}-H'(x)\right]\psi^A=0 \qquad (57\text{–}13)$$

where $p_0^{\,2}/2\tilde{m}$ is the kinetic energy *far away*. The boundary condition prescribes that ψ^A must be a plane wave of finite amplitude at $x=\infty$ and that the particles A do not penetrate the wall of BC's, i.e., that ψ^A is zero at $x=-\infty$.

---

[2] The closer the two wave lengths are, i.e., the less p_0 and p_1 differ relatively, the larger $(H_{01}^{\prime(\mathrm{tr})})^2$ and the transition probability will be. This is the quantum side of the Landau-Teller statement—that high molecular velocity is favorable for producing transitions, since it follows from Eq. (57–3) that the higher the p_0, the less p_0 and p_1 differ.

58. Inelastic Scattering for an Exponential Interaction Potential

For reasons which have been explained in Sec. 56, we will choose for H' a potential energy producing short range repulsive forces. Jackson and Mott selected, for mathematical simplicity, the expression[1]

$$H' = H_0' \exp(-x/l). \tag{58–1}$$

Introduce the abbreviation[2]

$$g = \frac{4\pi^2 pl}{h}. \tag{58–2}$$

As will be shown in Sec. 66, l is of the order 0.2 A.

Using the de Broglie wave length λ, g has the meaning

$$g = 2\pi \frac{2\pi l}{\lambda}.$$

The de Broglie wave length is, for a hydrogen molecule of mean thermal velocity at room temperature

$$\lambda = \frac{h}{mw} = \frac{6.6 \times 10^{-27}}{3.2 \times 10^{-24} \times 1.8 \times 10^5} = 1.1 \times 10^{-8}\,\text{cm} = 1.1\,\text{A}.$$

For heavier atoms or higher velocity, the wave length is even shorter. For the above data then, g is ~ 7; for heavier atoms or higher velocities even larger. Jackson and Mott integrate the Schroedinger equation, Eq. (57–13), with the interaction potential, Eq. (58–1), and form the matrix element, Eq. (57–10′), with the following result[3]

$$\frac{4\pi\tilde{m}}{h\sqrt{p_1 p_0}} H_{01}'^{(\text{tr})} \tag{58–3}$$

$$= \frac{h}{\sqrt{p_0 p_1}} \frac{1}{8\pi^3 l} (g_1^2 - g_0^2) \sqrt{g_0 g_1} (\sinh g_0 \sinh g_1)^{1/2} [\cosh g_1 - \cosh g_0]^{-1}.$$

---

[1] J. M. Jackson and N. F. Mott, *Proc. Roy. Soc.* **A 137**, 703 (1932). They write a instead of $1/l$.

[2] Jackson and Mott's g has π instead of our π^2.

[3] To this, the incident and the reflected (elastically scattered) wave contribute equal parts.

There, sinh and cosh are the hyperbolic sine and cosine

$$\sinh g \text{ (or } \cosh g) = \frac{1}{2}(e^{g} \mp e^{-g}).$$

In view of the previous calculation of g, it is clear that e^{-g} can be neglected next to unity, and

$$\sinh g = \cosh g = \frac{1}{2} e^{g}.$$

Therefore

$$[\sinh g_0 \sinh g_1]^{1/2} [\cosh g_1 - \cosh g_0]^{-1} = \left[\exp \frac{g_0 + g_1}{2}\right] [e^{g_1} - e^{g_0}]^{-1}$$

$$= \left[\exp\left(\frac{g_0 + g_1}{2} - g_1\right) [1 - e^{g_0 - g_1}]^{-1}. \qquad (58\text{–}4)$$

The square of Eq. (58–4) which will be needed is, therefore

$$[\exp(g_0 - g_1)] [1 - e^{g_0 - g_1}]^{-2}. \qquad (58\text{–}4')$$

Furthermore

$$\frac{h}{\sqrt{p_0 p_1}} \frac{1}{8\pi^3 l} \sqrt{g_0 g_1} = \frac{4\pi^2 l}{h} \frac{h}{8\pi^3 l} = \frac{1}{2\pi}$$

$$g_1{}^2 - g_0{}^2 = \left(\frac{4\pi^2 l}{h}\right)^2 (p_1{}^2 - p_0{}^2) = \mp \left(\frac{4\pi^2 l}{h}\right)^2 2\tilde{m}h\nu$$

$$= \mp 2 \frac{16\pi^4 \tilde{m} \nu^2 l^2}{h\nu} = \mp 2 \frac{\varepsilon'}{h\nu}.$$

One has, therefore

$$\frac{4\pi\tilde{m}}{h\sqrt{p_0 p_1}} H_{01}{}'^{(\text{tr})} = \mp \frac{\varepsilon'}{\pi h\nu} \exp\left(\frac{g_0 - g_1}{2}\right) [1 - e^{g_0 - g_1}]^{-1}. \qquad (58\text{–}5)$$

It is easily seen that this expression is independent of the sign of $g_0 - g_1$. If we select the sign as $-|g_0 - g_1|$ we can neglect the exponential in the denominator compared to unity, provided that not only g_0 but also the difference $|g_0 - g_1|$ is large compared to unity. Equation (58–4′) then has the approximate form

$$\exp(-|g_0 - g_1|) = \exp\left(-\frac{4\pi^2 l}{h} |p_0 - p_1|\right). \qquad (58\text{–}4'')$$

We now use the expression in Eq. (57–3) and develop to include three terms

$$p_0 - p_1 = p_0 - p_0\left[1 \mp \frac{\tilde{m}h\nu}{p_0{}^2} - \frac{1}{2}\left(\frac{\tilde{m}h\nu}{p_0{}^2}\right)^2\right] \tag{58–5'}$$

$$= \pm \frac{\tilde{m}h\nu}{p_0}\left[1 \pm \frac{\tilde{m}h\nu}{2p_0{}^2}\right] = \pm \frac{h\nu}{w_0}\left[1 \pm \frac{h\nu}{2\tilde{m}w_0{}^2}\right].$$

Here the upper sign is to be chosen for activation, the lower for deactivation. Accordingly

$$\frac{1}{p_0 p_1}\left[\frac{4\pi\tilde{m}}{h} H'^{(\mathrm{tr})}\right]^2 = \left(\frac{\varepsilon'}{\pi h\nu}\right)^2 \exp\left[-\frac{4\pi^2 l\nu}{w_0} \mp \frac{4\pi^2 l\nu}{2\tilde{m}w_0{}^3} h\nu\right]. \tag{58–6}$$

Omit for the moment the second term in the exponent; it is seen that the expression is of the same form as the Landau-Teller expression, Eq. (56–2), provided one identifies their l' with $2\pi l$, as has been done earlier.

In direct analogy to Eq. (56–7), this leads, by Maxwells distribution law to

$$\frac{1}{p_0 p_1}\left[\frac{4\pi\tilde{m}}{h} H'^{(\mathrm{tr})}\right]^2 = \frac{1}{\pi^2}\left(\frac{\varepsilon'}{h\nu}\right)^2 \sqrt{\frac{2\pi}{3}}\left(\frac{\varepsilon'}{kT}\right)^{1/6} \exp\left[-\frac{3}{2}\left(\frac{\varepsilon'}{kT}\right)^{1/3}\right]. \tag{58–7}$$

Finally, the factor, recently neglected

$$\exp\left[\mp \frac{4\pi^2 l\nu}{2\tilde{m}w_0{}^3} h\nu\right]$$

has to be evaluated. In it, the velocity for the most efficient collisions will be chosen. According to Eq. (56–5)

$$\frac{4\pi^2 l\nu}{\tilde{m}w^3} = \frac{1}{kT}$$

so that this factor is equal to $\exp(\mp h\nu/2kT)$. This results in the relationship

$$[H_{01}{}'^{(\mathrm{tr})}]^2 : [H_{10}{}'^{(\mathrm{tr})}]^2 = e^{-h\nu/kT} \tag{58.8}$$

and since the oscillatory matrix element, Eq. (57–11), is the same for activation and deactivation, one gets

$$k_{01} : k_{10} = e^{-h\nu/kT} \tag{58–8'}$$

as one should, according to Eqs. (19–12) and (19–13).

It brings the numbers into a more convenient range if one introduces characteristic temperatures, instead of energies. First, as usual, one writes

$$\vartheta = \frac{h\nu}{k} = 1.440\,\tilde{\nu} \tag{58–9}$$

$\tilde{\nu}$ in wave numbers. Next

$$\vartheta' = \frac{\varepsilon'}{k} = \frac{16\pi^4 \tilde{m} l^2 \nu^2}{k} = 0.8153\, M\, \vartheta^2 l^2 \tag{58–9'}$$

where M is the usual molecular weight, and l is in A. In this notation, one has

$$\frac{1}{Z_{\text{osc}}} = \frac{1}{2}\frac{M_B{}^2 + M_C{}^2}{M_B M_C} \frac{M_A}{M_A + M_B + M_C} 2\pi^2 \frac{\vartheta}{\vartheta'} \tag{58–10}$$

$$\frac{1}{Z_{\text{tr}}'} = \frac{1}{p_0 p_1}\left[\frac{4\pi\tilde{m}}{h} H_{10}{}'^{(\text{tr})}\right]^2$$

$$= \frac{1}{\pi^2}\sqrt{\frac{2\pi}{3}}\left(\frac{\vartheta'}{\vartheta}\right)^2\left(\frac{\vartheta'}{T}\right)^{1/6} \exp\left[-\frac{3}{2}\left(\frac{\vartheta'}{T}\right)^{1/3} + \frac{\vartheta}{2T}\right] \tag{58–11}$$

and

$$k_{10} = \frac{1}{Z_0}\frac{1}{Z_{\text{osc}}}\frac{1}{Z_{\text{tr}}'} \tag{58–12}$$

where Z_0 is a geometrical factor, which might be estimated as 3.

Furthermore, one has, see Eq. (19–17)

$$\frac{1}{\tau} = k_{10} - k_{01} = k_{10}\,(1 - e^{-\vartheta/T}). \tag{58–13}$$

Define

$$Z = \frac{\tau}{\tau_c}. \tag{58–14}$$

Then, under our present assumptions, there is one collision per second (a flow of one particle per second per unit area, with every particle colliding with the "wall"), so that $\tau_c = 1$. Therefore[4]

$$Z = Z_0 Z_{\text{osc}} Z_{\text{tr}}'\,(1 - e^{-\vartheta/T})^{-1}. \tag{58–15}$$

---

[4] The last factor was neglected in the papers by Slawsky, Schwartz, and Herzfeld.

Because only molecules with a kinetic energy considerably larger than $h\nu$ transfer energy efficiently, our formulas do not make it clear that those molecules with kinetic energy below $h\nu$ cannot produce excitation at all, however inefficiently. The problem has been treated by B. Widom.[5]

59. Introduction of a Better Interaction Potential

The exponential interaction Eq. (58–1), is very convenient for mathematical treatment, and possibly even correct for the repulsion. However, a large number[1] of gas theoretical calculations have recently been made with the Lennard-Jones expression[2]

$$H'' = 4\varepsilon\left[\left(\frac{r_0}{r}\right)^{12} - \left(\frac{r_0}{r}\right)^{6}\right]. \tag{59–1}$$

The negative term represents the attraction; here, the sixth power can be theoretically understood. The repulsive potential is much steeper, and the twelfth power has been chosen for mathematical convenience. Hirschfelder and his co-workers[1] have used measurements of viscosity and of its variation with temperature to determine the constants ε and r_0 for a large number of gases.

We show in Fig. 59–1 a curve which gives both the potential energy H'' and the total energy, plotted against r (or x).

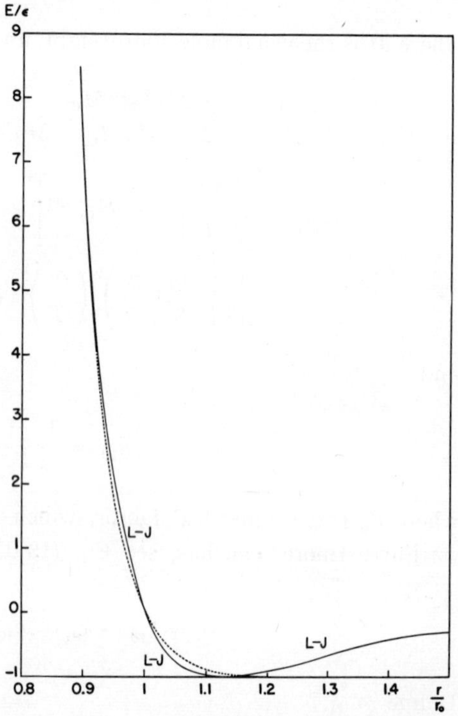

FIG. 59–1. Comparison of energies of interaction. The solid curve represents the Lennard-Jones equation, the dotted curve the exponential equation $-\varepsilon + H_{00} \exp(-r/l)$, with $r_0/l = 20.4$.

---

[5] B. Widom, *J. Chem. Phys.* **23**, 2377 (1955).

[1] J. O. Hirschfelder, C. F. Curtiss, and R. B. Bird, "Molecular Theory of Gases and Liquids." Wiley, New York, 1954.

[2] J. E. Lennard-Jones, *Proc. Roy. Soc.* **A106**, 441 (1924).

If a molecule A comes from infinity with a kinetic energy of relative motion E, this remains the constant value of its total energy. Its motion can therefore be presented by a horizontal line at height E. At any distance r to the right of r_0, it has acquired potential energy H'' (which is negative) and its kinetic energy is given by $E - H''$ (larger than E), a quantity given by the vertical distance of the line E from the curve H''. At r_0 the potential energy is again 0, and the particle again has its original kinetic energy E. Closer than r_0 the particle runs up against a repulsive force and loses kinetic energy. When, finally, the point r_c is reached, at which the potential energy curve is cut by the horizontal line E, all the original kinetic energy has been changed into potential energy, the particle stops and, in the case of an elastic collision, the motion is inverted.

Schwartz *et al.*[3] have made the transition from the potential energy, Eq. (59–1), to the exponential form, Eq. (58–1), by fitting an exponential curve to the former.

Let us first consider Eq. (59–1) a little closer. The stopping point r_c for a particle coming from infinity with the (original) kinetic energy of relative motion E is

$$E = 4\varepsilon\left\{\left(\frac{r_0}{r_c}\right)^{12} - \left(\frac{r_0}{r_c}\right)^{6}\right\}. \tag{59–2}$$

Considering this as a quadratic equation for $(r_0/r_c)^6$, one has

$$\left(\frac{r_0}{r_c}\right)^6 = \frac{1}{2}\left[1 + \sqrt{\frac{E}{\varepsilon} + 1}\right] \tag{59–3}$$

the minus sign which occurs as a possibility in a quadratic equation having been omitted, since it gives negative values to the left side.

From Eq. (59–3)

$$\frac{r_0}{r_c} = \left\{\frac{1}{2}\left[1 + \sqrt{\frac{E}{\varepsilon} + 1}\right]\right\}^{1/6}. \tag{59–3′}$$

Furthermore, the slope of the curve at r_c is

$$\begin{aligned} -\frac{dH''}{dr} &= \frac{4\varepsilon}{r_c}\left\{12\left(\frac{r_0}{r_c}\right)^{12} - 6\left(\frac{r_0}{r_c}\right)^{6}\right\} = \frac{4\varepsilon}{r_c}\left\{12\left(\frac{r_0}{r_c}\right)^{12} - 12\left(\frac{r_0}{r_c}\right)^{6} + 6\left(\frac{r_0}{r_c}\right)^{6}\right\} \\ &= \frac{1}{r_c}\left\{12\,E + 6 \times 4\varepsilon \times \frac{1}{2}\left[1 + \sqrt{\frac{E}{\varepsilon} + 1}\right]\right\} \\ &= \frac{12\varepsilon}{r_c}\left[\frac{E}{\varepsilon} + 1 + \sqrt{\frac{E}{\varepsilon} + 1}\right] \end{aligned} \tag{59–4}$$

[3] R. N. Schwartz, Z. I. Slawsky, and K. F. Herzfeld, *J. Chem. Phys.* **20**, 1591 (1952).

or

$$-\frac{r_c}{12}\left[1+\sqrt{\frac{\varepsilon}{E+\varepsilon}}\right]^{-1}\frac{dH''}{dr}=E+\varepsilon. \quad (59\text{–}4')$$

Since the differential equation for an exponential curve would be

$$-l\frac{dH'}{dr}=H' \quad (59\text{–}5)$$

and since the Lennard-Jones curve goes to a negative minimum of $-\varepsilon$, one sees that an exponential curve which could be substituted for a Lennard-Jones potential along the steep part must have its horizontal asymptote at $H'=-\varepsilon$. The exponential curve

$$H'=H_0'\,e^{-r/l}-\varepsilon \quad (59\text{–}6)$$

has two constants, H_0' and l, to be determined. This still leaves several ways to choose these constants so that the exponential curve will represent the important part of the Lennard-Jones potential. In all cases the point of fitting is that for the most effective energy of collision, E_m, see Eq. (56–6″), at the distance r_c.

Furthermore, in all methods the potential energy is made to cut the potential energy curve of Lennard-Jones at r_c, so that

$$E_m=[H_0'\exp(-r_c/l)]-\varepsilon$$

or

$$E_m+\varepsilon=H_0'\exp(-r_c/l). \quad (59\text{–}7)$$

The difference comes in the second equation.

Method A is the original method of Schwartz *et al.*[3] Here, the exponential curve is made *tangent* to the Lennard-Jones curve at r_c, so that, see Eqs. (59–4) and (59–7)

$$-\frac{1}{l}H_0'\exp\left(-\frac{r_c}{l}\right)=-\frac{1}{l}(E_m+\varepsilon)=-\frac{12\varepsilon}{r_c}\left[\frac{E_m}{\varepsilon}+1+\sqrt{\frac{E_m}{\varepsilon}+1}\right]$$

or

$$\frac{r_c}{l}=\frac{r_c}{r_0}\frac{r_0}{l}=12\left[1+\left(\frac{E_m}{\varepsilon}+1\right)^{-1/2}\right] \quad (59\text{–}8)$$

or, using Eqs. (59–3′) and (59–8), one gets as second equation:

$$\frac{r_0}{l}=12\left[\frac{1}{2}\left(1+\sqrt{\frac{E_m}{\varepsilon}+1}\right)\right]^{1/6}\left[1+\left(\frac{E_m}{\varepsilon}+1\right)^{-1/2}\right]. \quad (59\text{–}8')$$

The numerical results are shown in Table 59–1.

Method B. De Wette and Slawsky[4] have pointed out that it is easier to require that the two curves have *two* points in common, instead of requiring that at the one common point r_c they also have the same slope, as *Method A* does. Accordingly, *Method B* keeps Eqs. (59–7) and (59–3′), but substitutes for Eq. (59–8) the requirement that the point $E = 0$ and $r = r_0$ be common.

Therefore, from Eq. (59–6)

$$0 = \left[H_0' \exp\left(-\frac{r_0}{l}\right)\right] - \varepsilon \tag{59–9}$$

or

$$\varepsilon = H_0' \exp\left(-\frac{r_0}{l}\right). \tag{59–9′}$$

TABLE 59–1

r_0/r_c AND r_0/l AS FUNCTIONS OF E_m/ε

E_m/ε	r_0/r_c	*Method A*, r_0/l	*Method B*, r_0/l
0	1	24	24
1.25	1.0377	20.75	22.32
3	1.070	19.26	21.2
5.25	1.0978	18.44	20.6
8	1.1225	17.96	20.1
15	1.165	17.48	19.58
24	1.2010	17.29	19.23
35	1.2322	17.25	19.02
63	1.2849	17.25	18.76
99	1.3286	17.54	18.63
120	1.3480	17.65	18.58
168	1.3831	17.87	18.52
224	1.4142	18.10	18.49
399	1.4797	18.65	18.48
728	1.5525	19.32	18.52

Divide Eq. (59–7) by Eq. (59–9′). Then

$$\frac{E_m + \varepsilon}{\varepsilon} = \exp\left(+\frac{r_0 - r_c}{l}\right) \tag{59–10}$$

[4] F. W. de Wette and Z. I. Slawsky, *Physica* **20**, 1169 (1954).

or

$$\ln\left(\frac{E_m}{\varepsilon}+1\right)=\frac{r_0-r_c}{l}=\frac{r_0}{l}\left(1-\frac{r_c}{r_0}\right). \tag{59–10′}$$

Again using (59–3′), one has in *Method B*

$$\frac{r_0}{l}=\left[\ln\left(\frac{E_m}{\varepsilon}+1\right)\right]\left\{1-\left[\frac{1}{2}\left(1+\sqrt{\frac{E_m}{\varepsilon}+1}\right)\right]^{-1/6}\right\}. \tag{59–10″}$$

Numerical results are again shown in Table 59–1.

It is seen that *Method A* gives a broad, nearly constant minimum range of 17.25 to 17.54 when E_m/ε varies from about 10 to about 100, while *Method B* gives a nearly constant minimum range of 18.76 to 18.48 when E_m/ε lies between 63 and 729.

Method C. In the original papers[3] the spirit of *Method A* was followed, but the formulas used were

$$\left(\frac{r_0}{r_c}\right)^6=\frac{1}{2}+\frac{1}{2}\sqrt{\frac{E_m}{\varepsilon}+2} \tag{59–11}$$

or

$$E=4\varepsilon\left\{\left(\frac{r_0}{r}\right)^{12}-\left(\frac{r_0}{r}\right)^{6}\right\}-\varepsilon \tag{59–11′}$$

i.e., the Lennard-Jones curve was lowered by the amount ε.

In our notation, the equation for l is

$$\frac{r_c}{l}=12\,\{2\varepsilon+E_m+\sqrt{\varepsilon}\,\sqrt{2\varepsilon+E_m}\}\,(\varepsilon+E_m)^{-1}. \tag{59–11″}$$

This means that the equation of the exponential curve is

$$E=H_{00}'\,e^{-r/l}-\varepsilon$$

i.e., it is tangent for $r=\infty$ to the Lennard-Jones curve, both being horizontal at $-\varepsilon$.

Method C leads in general to smaller l and Z than either *Methods A* or *B*, and will not be used further.

The appearance of the attractive forces, as expressed by the fact that not H' but $H' + \varepsilon$ is an exponential function, affects not only the value of l, but also directly affects the transition probability $k_{10} = |a_1|^2 p_1/p_0$ by the appearance of a factor $e^{\varepsilon/kT}$ in Eq. (58–11), or a factor $e^{-\varepsilon/kT}$ which has to be included in the expression for Z. This factor can be deduced in two different ways. However, both lead to essentially the same result.

(a) One may assume the validity of Maxwell's distribution law for velocities at the point $r_{\min}$. This assumption includes among the molecules A those which have been captured in the potential valley surrounding $r_{\min}$ by collisions.

In that case the velocity w in Eq. (56–2) is the local w at the place $r_{\min}$, and the calculation in Sec. 56 concerning the integration over the Maxwell distribution law remains unchanged. However, the local density of molecules A is larger by $e^{\varepsilon/kT}$ than the density outside. Therefore, the number of collisions is correspondingly greater, and Z should have a factor $e^{-\varepsilon/kT}$, since τ_c refers to collisions at the outside density.

(b) One assumes that equilibrium is not established in the potential valley but only outside. If we than call w the velocity of the molecule A before interaction with BC becomes effective, the Maxwell distribution law ought to be written with w, but in the exponent of Eq. (56–2) the velocity at $r_{\min}$ ought to appear, i.e., $\sqrt{w^2 + 2\varepsilon/\tilde{m}}$. The exponent to be minimized is now, see Sec. 56

$$2\pi\nu l'\left(w^2 + \frac{2\varepsilon}{\tilde{m}}\right)^{-1/2} + \frac{\tilde{m}}{2kT}w^2 \tag{59–12}$$

giving the condition

$$-2\pi\nu l'\left(w^2 + \frac{2\varepsilon}{\tilde{m}}\right)^{-3/2} w + \frac{\tilde{m}}{kT}w = 0 \tag{59–12'}$$

or

$$\frac{2\pi\nu l' kT}{\tilde{m}} = \left(w^2 + \frac{2\varepsilon}{\tilde{m}}\right)^{3/2} \tag{59–12''}$$

$$\left(\frac{2\pi\nu l' kT}{\tilde{m}}\right)^{2/3} - \frac{2\varepsilon}{\tilde{m}} = w^2. \tag{59–12'''}$$

The exponent at its minimum value is then

$$-\frac{3}{2}\left(\frac{\varepsilon'}{kT}\right)^{1/3} + \frac{\varepsilon}{kT}. \tag{59–13}$$

Also, the factor in front of the exponential $(\tilde{m}/kT)^{1/2}\,w$, which formerly led to the factor $(\varepsilon'/kT)^{1/6}$ in front of the exponential in the expression Eq. (58–7) for $(\ldots H'^{\text{tr}})^2$, now produces the factor

$$\left(\frac{\varepsilon'}{kT}\right)^{1/6}\left[1-\frac{2\varepsilon}{kT}\left(\frac{kT}{\varepsilon'}\right)^{1/3}\right]^{1/2}. \tag{59–13'}$$

The correction in brackets is completely negligible under most conditions. The physical reason that both assumptions (a) and (b) give practically the same result is, of course, that their difference lies only in the molecules captured in the potential valley, which (a) takes into account and (b) does not; these molecules have velocities so low that they are extremely inefficient in inducing jumps.

Therefore, the over-all result is that the expression for Z ought to be multiplied by $e^{-\varepsilon/kT}$, i.e., Eq. (58–11) should be divided by

$$\begin{aligned}&(1-e^{-h\nu/kT})^{-1}\,e^{-\varepsilon/kT}\\ &=(1-e^{-\vartheta/T})^{-1}\,e^{-\varepsilon/kT}.\end{aligned} \tag{59–14}$$

One sees, therefore, that Landau and Teller's[5] argument, that only the short range, repulsive forces determine the transitions, is correct only in a limited sense. It is true that the short range forces alone determine the transition probability directly. Since this quantity is, however, very sensitive to the velocity with which the molecules collide, and since the long range, attractive forces influence the value of the relative velocity at the critical distances, they exert an appreciable indirect influence.

De Wette and Slawsky[4] have tested this argument in a careful theoretical investigation of two cases in which the long range forces are strong, namely, dipole-dipole interaction in the case of two HCl molecules and quadrupole-quadrupole interaction in the case of two CO molecules. They divide the interaction into a long range (adiabatic) and a short range (nonadiabatic) interaction, and find the influence of both, separately, on the relative motion of the molecules, ψ_A, see Eqs. (57–5), and on the perturbation which leads to transitions. The resulting equations, which are exact, are more complicated than those used by Jackson and Mott,[6] but, as modified by Slawsky, Schwartz, and Herzfeld,[3] lead to them with sufficient approximation. It is confirmed that the effect of the long range forces is confined to the "acceleration" effect, which produces the factor exp (ε/RT).

---

[5] L. Landau and E. Teller, *Physik. Z. Sowjetunion* **10**, 34 (1936).

[6] J. M. Jackson and N. F. Mott, *Proc. Roy. Soc.* **A137**, 703 (1932).

Historically, there was a time interval of about 10 to 15 years between the work[7] of Landau and Teller and attempts to use their ideas to calculate a large number of relaxation times. A paper by Slawsky *et al.*[8] outlined the quantum theoretical treatment elaborated on in Sec. 57 and stimulated further work in this country and Europe. The paper by Slawsky *et al.*[3] was the first one to give numerical results for Z from a priori calculations. However, Takayanagi[9] published the same theoretical results simultaneously or even a little earlier, but without as many numerical data.

It should be stated that the paper by Slawsky *et al.*[3] did not contain, in the expression of the probability, the factor

$$e^{h\nu/2kT+\varepsilon/kT}\,(1 - e^{-h\nu/kT})$$

and the mass factors in front of the expression. Furthermore, it should be stated that the following relation exists between the notation in Slawsky *et al.*[3] and the present book: Slawsky *et al.* use $\sigma^{1/3}$; the present book uses $3/2\,(\varepsilon')^{1/3}$. Slawsky *et al.* use σ; the present book uses $27/8\,\varepsilon'$.

60. Tridimensional Case

In dealing with the tridimensional case, we treat the molecule at first as spherically symmetric, i.e., as if the vibration were a symmetrical increase and decrease in size of a sphere. The relative motion of the molecules is then described by three coordinates r; $\mu = \cos\chi$, χ being the geographical latitude, and φ the geographical longitude, instead of the single coordinate x. Due to our assumption of spherical symmetry (which neglects rotation of the molecule) nothing will depend on φ, and everything will have cylindrical symmetry around the direction of incidence, which will be taken as the polar axis. This assumption is not necessary, but simplifies the calculations. The Schrödinger equation for the relative motion Eq. (57–13) is then replaced by

$$\frac{1}{r^2}\frac{\partial}{\partial r}\,r^2\,\frac{\partial\psi_A}{\partial r} + \frac{1}{r^2}\frac{\partial}{\partial\mu}\,(1-\mu^2)\,\frac{\partial}{\partial\mu}\,\psi_A + \frac{8\pi^2\tilde{m}}{h^2}\,[E - H'(r)]\psi_A = 0. \qquad (60\text{–}1)$$

---

[7] Their paper was followed by H. Bethe and E. Teller, Rept. X–117, Aberdeen Proving Ground, Md., 1941, but this was not widely available.

[8] Z. I. Slawsky, F. W. de Wette, and S. R. de Groot, *Koninkl. Vlaam. Acad. Wetenschap., Letter. en Schone Kunsten Belg., Colloq. Ultrasonore Trillingen, Brussels, 1951,* p. 82.

[9] K. Takayanagi, *Progr. Theoret. Phys. Japan* 8, 111 (1952).

This equation is partially solved by writing[1]

$$\psi_A = \frac{1}{r} f_j(r) P_j(\mu). \tag{60–2}$$

Here P_j is a Legendre polynomial of order j which describes the angle dependence of the solution. As examples

$$P_0 = 1$$

$$P_1 = \mu = \cos \chi$$

$$P_2 = \frac{1}{2} (3\mu^2 - 1).$$

The P_j are orthogonal to each other when integrated over the surface of a sphere. Equation (60–2) describes a spherical wave, and the factor $1/r$ provides the well-known decrease of amplitude with distance.

A calculation which will not be reproduced here shows that the motion described by Eq. (60–2) has an angular momentum, the square of which is given by

$$\left(\frac{h}{2\pi}\right)^2 j(j+1).$$

In general a scattered wave will be a superposition of partial waves, each of the form of Eq. (60–2), so that

$$\psi_A = \frac{1}{r} \sum_j f_j(r) P_j(\mu) \tag{60–2'}$$

and one is able to represent any given angle dependence (for a fixed r) in this form.

If one now inserts Eq. (60–2) in Eq. (60–1), one gets

$$\frac{d^2}{dr^2} f_j + \frac{8\pi^2 \tilde{m}}{h^2} \left[E - H'(r) - \frac{h^2}{8\pi^2 \tilde{m}} \frac{j(j+1)}{r^2} \right] f_j = 0 \tag{60–3}$$

since P_j obeys the equation

$$\frac{d}{d\mu} (1 - \mu^2) \frac{dP_j}{d\mu} + j(j+1) P_j(\mu) = 0.$$

---

[1] H. Margenau and G. E. W. Murphy, "The Mathematics of Physics and Chemistry." Van Nostrand, New York, 1943.

This means that the equation which f_j obeys in the three-dimensional case is the same as that which ψ_A obeys in the one-dimensional case, Eq. (57–13), except for the fact that to the potential energy $H'(r)$ is added the quasi-potential energy due to the centrifugal force, namely

$$\varepsilon_j = \frac{h^2}{8\pi^2 \tilde{m}} \frac{j(j+1)}{r^2} = \frac{1}{2\,\tilde{m}r^2} \times \text{(square of angular momentum)}. \qquad (60\text{–}4)$$

A similar expression is valid in the classical calculation, where for circular motion the centrifugal *force* is

$$\frac{\tilde{m}w^2}{r} = \frac{1}{\tilde{m}} \frac{(\tilde{m}wr)^2}{r^3} = \frac{1}{\tilde{m}r^3} \times \text{(square of angular momentum)}.$$

One cannot integrate Eq. (60–3) by a known expression if $H'(r)$ is taken as an exponential function. However, the following argument leads to an approximate solution. We first note that the quasipotential energy of the centrifugal force

$$\varepsilon_j = \frac{h^2}{8\pi\tilde{m}} j(j+1) \frac{1}{r^2}$$

varies slowly compared to the intermolecular repulsive force, and should therefore not affect quantum jumps directly. Secondly, we note that it is possible to integrate Eq. (60–3) exactly if the repulsive force H' corresponds to a hard sphere, i.e., is zero at distances larger than r_0, and infinite at distances smaller than r_0. The corresponding one-dimensional case without centrifugal term is that of a reflection on a hard wall, which gives the solution as a certain function $\bar{F}(2\pi p^0 x/h)$. The solution for the corresponding tridimensional case, namely, the scattering by a hard sphere, is[2] the *same* function (with r instead of x)

$$f = \bar{F}\left(\frac{2\pi}{h} pr\right)$$

except that now the linear momentum p does not have the constant value p^0 everywhere that it has at infinity, but instead varies slowly with position, being governed by the principle of conservation of energy

$$E = \frac{(p^0)^2}{2\tilde{m}} = \frac{p^2}{2\tilde{m}} + \frac{h^2}{8\pi^2\tilde{m}} \frac{j(j+1)}{r^2}$$

---

[2] N. F. Mott and H. S. W. Massey, "The Theory of Atomic Collisions." 2nd ed., Chapter VII. Oxford Univ. Press. New York, 1949.

or

$$p^2 = (p^0)^2 - \left(\frac{h}{2\pi}\right)^2 \frac{j(j+1)}{r^2}. \tag{60–5}$$

Therefore, the quantity $p = h/\lambda$ (λ is the de Broglie wave length) which enters f is the local, adiabatically varying linear momentum. Head-on collisions, $j = 0$, give the one-dimensional solution exactly.

Since for the transition the force exerted at the shortest approach $r = r_c$ is decisive, we are going to use the following approximation:[3] We assume that the only influence of the long range forces, attractive and centrifugal, lies in a shift of the effective collision velocity from w^0 to w

$$w^2 = (w^0)^2 - \left(\frac{h}{2\pi\tilde{m}}\right)^2 \frac{j(j+1)}{r_c^2} + \frac{2\varepsilon}{\tilde{m}} = (w^0)^2 + \frac{2}{\tilde{m}}(\varepsilon - \varepsilon_j). \tag{60–6}$$

In this argument it is essential that all potential and quasipotential energies disappear at infinite distance.

The effect described by Eq. (60–6) is of the same kind as that which has been taken into account in Sec. 59, where it has been shown that the effect lies in producing a factor $e^{-\varepsilon/kT}$ in Z; see Eq. (59–14). By the same argument, the presence of the two kinds of long range forces just described produces the factor $e^{(\varepsilon_j - \varepsilon)/kT}$ in Z instead of $e^{-\varepsilon/kT}$ alone. All the preceding has led us only to the unperturbed wave functions, without considering transitions.

61. Discussion of Scattering

In this section the mathematical theory of scattering by a particle having the interaction energy, Eq. (58–1), will be discussed. The result of this section will be used from Sec. 62 on, but Sec. 61 itself may be omitted when reading the book.

This section is concerned with the application of the calculations Jackson and Mott[1] made for the one-dimensional case to the tridimensional situation. We then introduce a function F_j, which is a solution of the differential equations (60–3) and (61–1), and which corresponds to the situation in which there is no quantum jump, i.e., in which the particle has the same energy at great distance, whether coming in or going out.

---

[3] R. N. Schwartz and K. F. Herzfeld, *J. Chem. Phys.* **22**, 767 (1954).

[1] J. M. Jackson and N. F. Mott, *Proc. Roy. Soc.* **A137**, 703 (1932).

The differential equation for F can be written in the following form

$$\frac{d^2}{dr^2}F + \left[\left(\frac{2\pi p}{h}\right)^2 - \frac{8\pi^2\tilde{m}}{h^2}H_0'\,e^{-r/l}\right]F = 0 \tag{61–1}$$

where p is p_0 or p_+ according to Eqs. (60–5) and (60–6). In the next two sections the index "plus" on p (and later Q) refers to activation, the index "minus" to deactivation while the index zero refers to the unchanged momentum.

Introducing as a new variable

$$y = 2l\sqrt{\frac{8\pi^2\tilde{m}H_0'}{h^2}}\,e^{-r/2l} = \sqrt{\frac{2}{\pi^2}\frac{\varepsilon' H_0'}{(h\nu)^2}}\,e^{-r/2l}$$

$$= \frac{1}{\pi\vartheta}\sqrt{2\vartheta'\frac{H_0'}{k}}\,e^{-r/2l} \tag{61–2}$$

$$q = \frac{4\pi}{h}pl = \frac{g}{\pi} \tag{61–2'}$$

(this is the same g as in Eq. (58–2); the letter q will not be used in this sense elsewhere), one has

$$\frac{d^2F}{dy^2} + \frac{1}{y}\frac{dF}{dy} + \left(\frac{q^2}{y^2} - 1\right)F = 0. \tag{61–3}$$

This is Bessel's equation, for an argument iy and index iq, so that the general solution for F is

$$F = bI_{iq}(iy) + cI_{-iq}(-iy) \tag{61–4}$$

with I the usual Bessel function.

From Eq. (61–2), we see that the limiting values of y are

$$r = 0 \qquad y_0 = \frac{1}{\pi\vartheta}\sqrt{2\vartheta'\frac{H_0'}{k}} \tag{61–5}$$

$$r = \infty \qquad y = 0. \tag{61–5'}$$

In the one-dimensional case, one has x instead of r, and the limit, instead of $r = 0$, is $x = -\infty$, $y = \infty$. However, numerically there is no appreciable difference between y_0 as given above and $y = \infty$. To prove this, one needs an estimate of the appropriate H_0'. The exponential curve has been fitted at the point r_c, where the potential energy is equal to the far away kinetic energy at its most effective value. From Eq. (56–6'''), therefore, one has

$$-4\varepsilon\left[\left(\frac{r_0}{r_c}\right)^6-\left(\frac{r_0}{r_c}\right)^{12}\right]=\frac{1}{2}(\varepsilon')^{1/3}(kT)^{2/3} \tag{61–6}$$

or

$$\left(\frac{r_0}{r_c}\right)^{12}-\left(\frac{r_0}{r_c}\right)^6=\frac{1}{8\varepsilon}(\varepsilon')^{1/3}(kT)^{2/3}. \tag{61–6'}$$

Numerical evaluation shows (Table 59–1) that

$$0.75\,r_0 \leqslant r_c < r_0.$$

Since the exponential curve is fitted at r_c and $(\tilde{m}/2)(w_{\max})^2$, H_0' is determined by

$$\varepsilon+\frac{1}{2}(\varepsilon')^{1/3}(kT)^{2/3}=H_0'\,e^{-r_c/l} \tag{61–7}$$

or

$$\frac{H_0'}{k}\,e^{-r_c/l}=\frac{1}{2}(\vartheta')^{1/3}\,T^{2/3}+\frac{\varepsilon}{k}. \tag{61–7'}$$

Therefore, neglecting ε/k in the preceding, Eq. (61–5) is

$$y_0=\frac{1}{\pi\vartheta}\left[\vartheta'(\vartheta')^{1/3}\,T^{2/3}\right]^{1/2}e^{r_c/2l}$$

$$=\frac{1}{\pi\vartheta}(\vartheta')^{2/3}\,T^{1/3}\,e^{r_c/2l}=\frac{1}{\pi}\frac{T}{\vartheta}\left(\frac{\vartheta'}{T}\right)^{2/3}e^{r_c/2l}. \tag{61–8}$$

From the data given in Table 59–1, $8 < r_c/2l < 11$, and the factor in front of the exponential might vary from 3 to 60. Accordingly, $y_0 > 9000$.

We next discuss the behavior of the Bessel function for large r (small y). One has, in general[2]

$$I_n(x)=\left(\frac{x}{2}\right)^n\frac{1}{n!}\sum_s(-1)^s\frac{1}{s!}\left(\frac{x}{2}\right)^{2s}\frac{1}{(n+1)\ldots(n+s)}. \tag{61–9}$$

For small x, this is $(1/n!)\,(x/2)^n$.

---

[2] E. Jahncke and F. Emde, "Tables of Functions." 4th ed., p. 128. Dover, New York, 1945.

Accordingly, for large r, i.e., small y

$$I_{iq}(iy) = \frac{1}{(iq)!}\left(\frac{iy}{2}\right)^{iq}. \tag{61–10}$$

Inserting the value of y, write $i = e^{i\pi/2}$ and use the values of the factorial for large q

$$(iq)! = \left(\frac{\pi q}{\sinh \pi q}\right)^{1/2} e^{i\eta'} = \left(\frac{g}{\sinh g}\right)^{1/2} e^{i\eta'} \tag{61–11}$$

$$\eta' = \frac{\pi}{4} + q(\ln q - 1) - \frac{1}{12q}. \tag{61–11'}$$

Then

$$I_{-iq}(-iy) = e^{i\eta}\left(e^{-g}\frac{\sinh g}{g}\right)^{1/2} e^{iqr/2l}$$

$$= e^{i\eta}\left(e^{-g}\frac{\sinh g}{g}\right)^{1/2} \exp\left(i\frac{2\pi p}{h}r\right) \tag{61–12}$$

(for large r) with the phase factor η

$$-\eta = -\frac{\pi}{4} + q\left\{\ln\left[\frac{1}{2\pi\vartheta}\left(2\vartheta'\frac{H_0'}{k}\right)^{1/2} q^{-1}\right] + 1\right\} + \frac{1}{12q}. \tag{61–12'}$$

Similarly, for large r

$$I_{iq}(iy) = e^{-i\eta} e^{-g}\left(\frac{\sinh g}{g}\right)^{1/2} \exp\left(-i\frac{2\pi p}{h}r\right) \tag{61–13}$$

with the same η.

Accordingly, the solution, Eq. (61–4), is the superposition of an incoming, convergent wave and an outgoing, divergent wave, and the problem remains of determining the constant coefficients b and c.

In the one-dimensional case, where x replaces r, we have for $p = p_0$ a primary wave of amplitude unity; namely, at large x

$$\exp\left(i\frac{2\pi p_0}{h}x\right).$$

Accordingly, b is then

$$\sqrt{\frac{g}{\sinh g}e^{g}} \tag{61–14}$$

(a common phase factor does not matter).

The part $cI_{iq}(iy)$ represents the elastically reflected wave, for which the amplitude has to be chosen so that the resultant wave motion at $x = -\infty$, $y = 0$, is zero. The corresponding combination, with this choice of c, has at large positive distances from the wall twice the amplitude of the incoming wave. The expression, valid for all values of x, which fulfills these conditions; namely

$$F_0 = \left(\frac{g\, e^g}{\sinh g}\right)^{1/2} \left\{\frac{c}{b} I_{-iq}(-iy) + I_{iq}(iy)\right\} \tag{61–15}$$

is written by Jackson and Mott as

$$F_0 = \frac{2}{\pi} (g \sinh g)^{1/2} K_{iq}(y). \tag{61–15'}$$

K is a function which, of course, also satisfies Eq. (61–3) and becomes, for large x

$$K_{iq}(y) = \frac{\pi}{2} (g \sinh g)^{-1/2} \left\{\exp i\left(\frac{2\pi p}{h} x + \eta\right) + \exp - i\left(\frac{2\pi p}{h} x + \eta\right)\right\} \tag{61–15''}$$

i.e., $c = b$; so that

$$F_0 = \exp i\left(\frac{2\pi p}{h} x + \eta\right) + \exp - i\left(\frac{2\pi p}{h} x + \eta\right) = 2 \cos\left(\frac{2\pi p}{h} x + \eta\right) \tag{61–16}$$

for large x. The superposition of the primary and the elastically reflected wave (both plane at large, positive x) gives twice the amplitude of the primary wave (factor 2 on right).

Going now to the tridimensional case, we must require that $F_0 = 0$ at $r = 0$, $y = y_0$, because in the expression (60–2) there is an r in the denominator. In other words, the elastically reflected wave has an amplitude and phase such that it prevents the superposition of the primary wave and the elastically reflected wave from becoming infinite at the origin. This means that the ratio c/b must be so determined that

$$F_0(r = 0) = b\left\{\frac{c}{b} I_{-iq}(-iy_0) + I_{iq}(iy_0)\right\} = 0. \tag{61–17}$$

However, we have seen previously that y_0 is so large that we can replace y_0 in Eq. (61–17) by infinity, so that instead of Eq. (61–17) the same condition can be written as in the one-dimensional case, i.e.

$$F_0 = b' \frac{2}{\pi} (g \sinh g)^{1/2} K_{iq}(y) \tag{61–18}$$

which, for large r, small y, takes the form

$$F_0 = b' e^{i\eta} \left\{ \exp\left(i \frac{2\pi p}{h} r \right) + \exp - i \left(\frac{2\pi p}{h} r + 2\eta \right) \right\}. \tag{61–18'}$$

The next step is to write the equation for the incoming wave. This is, at large r, a plane wave, which can be represented for large r by

$$\exp i \left(\frac{2\pi p}{h} r \cos \chi \right) = \frac{h}{2\pi r} \sum_j (2j+1) \frac{1}{2ip} \left[\exp i \left(\frac{2\pi p}{h} r \right) - (-1)^j \exp - i \left(\frac{2\pi p}{h} r \right) \right] P_j. \tag{61–19}$$

Using the fact that the primary wave also satisfies the wave equation (61–1), and using Eqs. (61–12) and (61–13), we have, for the incoming wave alone, for all r

$$\frac{h}{2\pi r} \sum_j (2j+1) \frac{1}{2ip} \left(\frac{g\, e^g}{\sinh g} \right)^{1/2} \{ e^{-i\eta} I_{iq}(iy) - (-1)^j e^{i\eta} I_{-iq}(-iy) \} P_j. \tag{61–20}$$

To this a scattered wave has to be added, which may be written

$$\frac{h}{2\pi r} \sum_j (2j+1) \frac{1}{2ip} c_j' \left(\frac{g\, e^g}{\sinh g} \right)^{1/2} I_{iq}(iy) P_j. \tag{61–21}$$

The primary wave and the elastically scattered wave together must give a wave function which is finite at $r = 0$. This condition determines the c'. However, we have no need to calculate these explicitly. We know that the result, for the sum of the primary and the elastically scattered wave, i.e., for the whole wave function which has an unchanged p_0, is

$$\psi_A{}^0 = \frac{h}{2\pi r} \sum (2j+1) \frac{1}{i\pi p_j} (g \sinh g)^{1/2} e^{-i\eta} K_{iq}(y) P_j. \tag{61–22}$$

This makes, at large r, the $\exp i(2\pi p/h)r$ terms (which appear only in the primary wave) in Eqs. (61–19) and (61–22) the same according to Eq. (61–15″), and gives a finite $\psi_A{}^0$ at $r = 0$.

Next, we have to calculate the inelastically scattered wave which Eq. (61–22) produces. Because Legendre functions P with different j are orthogonal to each other, each term in Eq. (61–22) with a given P_j produces a definite inelastically scattered partial wave with the same P_j no matter what terms with other P_s are present, so that each inelastically scattered partial wave of index j can be calculated by itself.

Jackson and Mott's results can now be taken over directly. They show that for a primary wave and elastically scattered wave given by

$$\psi_A{}^0 = \frac{2}{\pi}\,(g \sinh g)^{1/2}\, K_{iq}(y)$$

see Eq. (61–15′), the amplitude of the scattered one-dimensional wave is given by the product of the right side of Eq. (57–11), the right side of Eq. (58–5), and $\sqrt{p_0/p_+}$. Call the product of the right sides of Eqs. (58–6) and (57–12′) $\bar{Q}$.

$$\bar{Q} = \text{right side of Eq. (58–6) multiplied by the right side of Eq. (57–12′)}. \tag{61–23}$$

Then the square of the amplitude of the one-dimensional scattered wave is $\bar{Q}(p_0/p_+)$. The inelastic scattering cross section is $\bar{Q}$, since the number of primary particles crossing the unit area per second is $p_0/\tilde{m}$, and the number of inelastically scattered particles crossing the unit area per second is $\bar{Q}(p_0/p_+)p_+/\tilde{m}$.

For the tridimensional case it follows that the primary wave plus the elastically scattered wave with an amplitude given by, see Eq. (61–22)

$$\frac{h}{2\pi r}\,(2j+1)\,\frac{1}{i\pi p_0}\,(g \sinh g)^{1/2}\, e^{-i\eta}\, K_{iq}(y)\, P_j \tag{61–24}$$

produces an inelastically scattered wave of amplitude

$$\frac{h}{2\pi r}\,(2j+1)\,\frac{1}{2ip_0}\, e^{-i\eta}\left(\bar{Q}\,\frac{p_0}{p_+}\right)^{1/2} P_j. \tag{61–25}$$

62. Conclusion of the Tridimensional Calculation

In the preceding section it has been shown that the amplitude of the wave scattered inelastically with the angle distribution given by the Legendre function P_j is given by

$$\frac{h}{2\pi r}\,\frac{2j+1}{2ip_0}\,e^{-i\eta}\left(\bar{Q}_j\,\frac{p_0}{p_+}\right)^{1/2} P_j$$

This refers to a stream of incoming particles numbering $p_0/\tilde{m}$ per second and unit area. The total number of particles of the above kind, scattered inelastically per second, is the square of the above expression, integrated over the area of a sphere of radius r, and multiplied by their speed $p_+/\tilde{m}$. This is

$$\frac{p_+}{\tilde{m}}\left[\frac{h(2j+1)}{2\pi r\cdot 2p_0}\right]^2 \bar{Q}_j\,\frac{p_0}{p_+}\,2\pi r^2\int P_j{}^2 d\mu \tag{62–1}$$

$$\int P_j{}^2 d\mu = \frac{2}{2j+1} \tag{62–2}$$

The ratio of the number, Eq. (62–1), to the number of particles coming in per unit area can be called the partial inelastic scattering cross section, Q_j

$$\begin{aligned} Q_j &= \frac{p_+}{p_0}\,\frac{h^2}{4\pi^2 r^2}\,\frac{(2j+1)^2}{4p_0{}^2}\,\bar{Q}\,\frac{p_0}{p_+}\,2\pi r^2\,\frac{2}{2j+1} \\ &= (2j+1)\,\frac{h^2}{4\pi p_0{}^2}\,\bar{Q}. \end{aligned} \tag{62–3}$$

We next have to average over all velocities of the incoming molecules, but now the tridimensional Maxwell distribution has to be taken, instead of the one-dimensional expression, Eq. (56–3)

$$\frac{dN}{N_0} = \frac{\tilde{m}w^2}{2kT}\,\frac{\tilde{m}w}{kT}\exp\left(-\frac{\tilde{m}w^2}{2kT}\right)dw. \tag{62–4}$$

Therefore

$$\begin{aligned} (Q_j)_{\text{av}} &= \frac{h^2}{4\pi}(2j+1)\int\frac{1}{p^2}\,\frac{\tilde{m}w^2}{2kT}\,\bar{Q}\,\frac{\tilde{m}w}{kT}\exp\left(-\frac{\tilde{m}w^2}{2kT}\right)dw \\ &= \frac{h^2}{8\pi\tilde{m}kT}(2j+1)\int\bar{Q}\,\frac{\tilde{m}w}{kT}\exp\left(-\frac{\tilde{m}w^2}{2kT}\right)dw. \end{aligned} \tag{62–5}$$

The integral in the last line, however, is exactly $(\bar{Q})_{\text{av}}$ for the one-dimensional case, so that

$$(Q_j)_{\text{av}} = \frac{h^2}{8\pi \tilde{m} kT} (2j + 1) (\bar{Q})_{\text{av}}. \tag{62–6}$$

Up to now, the effect of the centrifugal quasipotential energy has not been taken into account. However, it had been shown in Sec. 60 that the effect of this quasipotential is to add a factor $e^{-\varepsilon_j/kT}$ to the expression for the transition probability. Therefore

$$(Q)_{\text{av}} = \frac{h^2}{8\pi \tilde{m} kT} (\bar{Q})_{\text{av}} \sum_j (2j + 1)\, e^{-\varepsilon_j/kT} \tag{62–7}$$

$$\varepsilon_j = \frac{h^2}{8\pi^2 \tilde{m} r_c^2} j\,(j + 1). \tag{62–7′}$$

If the different levels of the rotational energy lie close enough together, one can replace the summation by an integration

$$\sum (2j + 1)\, e^{-\varepsilon_j/kT} = \int_0^\infty e^{-\varepsilon_j/kT} (2j + 1)\, dj$$

$$= \frac{8\pi^2 \tilde{m} r_c^2}{h^2} \int_0^\infty e^{-\varepsilon_j/kT}\, d\varepsilon_j = \frac{8\pi^2 \tilde{m} r_c^2}{h^2} kT \tag{62–8}$$

so that

$$(Q)_{\text{av}} = \pi r_c^2 (\bar{Q})_{\text{av}}. \tag{62–9}$$

The calculations in Eq. (62–8) are subject to two limitations. To permit the integration, the energy level differences must be small enough. The sum is simply the quantum theoretical value of the partition function of a rigid rotator, with a moment of inertia equal to $\tilde{m} r_c^2$ (see Mayer and Mayer,[1] p. 450, who call this quantity Q_{jm}). The integral is the classical value of this function, which Mayer and Mayer call σ^{-1}. The ratio of the two, in Mayer and Mayer's notation σQ_{jm}, is a factor with which the expression

[1] J. E. Mayer and M. G. Mayer, "Introduction to Statistical Mechanics." Wiley, New York, 1940.

(62–9) for Q should be multiplied. From Table A IX. 5 in Ref. 1, one can calculate the correction factor for Q as follows:

σ^{-1},	classical partition function	50	10	6.7	5	2	1	0.5
σQ_{jm},	correction factor	1.000	1.005	1.01	1.07	1.165	1.42	2.11

Then σ^{-1}, the classical partition function, may be rewritten

$$\frac{8\pi^2\tilde{m}}{h^2} r_c^2 kT = \frac{1}{2\pi^2} \frac{16\pi^4 \tilde{m} \nu^2 l^2}{(h\nu)^2} kT \left(\frac{r_c}{l}\right)^2 = \frac{\vartheta' T}{\vartheta^2} \frac{1}{2\pi^2} \left(\frac{r_c}{l}\right)^2. \tag{62–10}$$

Since r_c/l lies between 12 and 24, we have σ^{-1} equal to between 8 and 30 $\vartheta' T/\vartheta^2$, so that in most cases the expression (62–8) is quite good.

On the other hand, if the centrifugal force is too large, it causes a repulsive potential hill even farther out than the energy minimum.[2] If this hill is higher than

$$E_m = \frac{1}{2} (\varepsilon')^{1/3} (kT)^{2/3}$$

see Eq. (56–6″), the molecules of that energy collide with the potential hill, and never get close enough to interact with the vibration.

The condition for the existence of the hill is, for a particular j

$$\frac{d}{dr} \left\{ \frac{h^2 j(j+1)}{8\pi^2 \tilde{m} r^2} - 4\varepsilon \left(\frac{r_0}{r}\right)^6 \right\} = 0$$

or

$$\frac{h^2 j(j+1)}{8\pi^2 \tilde{m} r_0^2} = 12\varepsilon \left(\frac{r_0}{r}\right)^4 \tag{62–11}$$

which must be fulfilled for $r > (2)^{1/6} r_0$, the minimum of the Lennard-Jones potential. Therefore

$$\frac{h^2 j(j+1)}{8\pi^2 \tilde{m} r_0^2} > 6 \sqrt[3]{2}\, \varepsilon. \tag{62–11″}$$

Furthermore, for the hill to be troublesome, one must have the stronger condition

$$\frac{h^2 j(j+1)}{8\pi^2 \tilde{m} r^2} > E_m \tag{62–11‴}$$

---

[2] R. N. Schwartz and K. F. Herzfeld, *J. Chem. Phys.* **22**, 767 (1954).

or, with Eq. (62–11)

$$\frac{h^2 j(j+1)}{8\pi^2 \tilde{m} r_0^2}\left[\frac{h^2 j(j+1)}{8\pi^2 \tilde{m} r_0^2 \cdot 12\varepsilon}\right]^{1/2} > E_m$$

or

$$\frac{h^2}{8\pi^2 \tilde{m} r_0^2} j(j+1) > E_m^{2/3}(12\varepsilon)^{1/3} = (3\varepsilon)^{1/3}(\varepsilon')^{2/9}(kT)^{4/9}. \qquad (62\text{–}12)$$

If this quantity, divided by kT, is large, the corresponding j do not contribute appreciably to the integral and may be ignored. The condition for a possible hill to be unimportant is therefore

$$(3\varepsilon)^{1/3}(\varepsilon')^{2/9}(kT)^{-5/9} > 1$$

or

$$\left(3\frac{\varepsilon}{k}\right)^3 (\vartheta')^2 > T^5. \qquad (62\text{–}13)$$

To resume discussion of Eq. (62–9) we may write further

$$(Q)_{\text{av}} = \pi r_0^2 \left(\frac{r_c}{r_0}\right)^2 (\bar{Q})_{\text{av}} \qquad (62\text{–}9')$$

where r_c/r_0 can be found from Table 59–1. $(Q)_{\text{av}}$ is the fraction of the molecules passing through a unit area which activate—or, with proper $(\bar{Q})$, deactivate. The number of activations per N scatterers per second, when there is one hitting molecule A per unit volume, is, therefore

$$(Q)_{\text{av}} N \bar{W}_r = \pi r_0^2 N \bar{W}_r \left(\frac{r_c}{r_0}\right)^2 (\bar{Q})_{\text{av}}$$

$\bar{W}_r$ being the mean relative thermal speed; i.e., if τ is the average relaxation time

$$\frac{1}{\tau} = (Q^-)_{\text{av}}(1 - e^{-\vartheta/T}) N\bar{W}_r = \pi r_0^2 N \bar{W}_r \left(\frac{r_c}{r_0}\right)^2 (\bar{Q}^-)_{\text{av}}(1 - e^{-\vartheta/T}) \qquad (62\text{–}13)$$

Q^- being the cross section for deactivation, and Eq. (19–17) having been used. The quantity $\pi r_0^2 N \bar{W}_r$ is, apart from a numerical factor, $1/\tau_c$. This factor is equal to

$$\left\{1.271 \times \frac{4}{5} Y(2,2)\right\}^{-1} = \{1.017\, Y(2,2)\}^{-1}$$

where $Y(2,2)$ is a function of kT/ε, which decreases monotonously with that quantity and which is tabulated by Hirschfelder *et al.*[3]

For the range $0.70 \leqslant kT/\varepsilon \leqslant 10$, $Y(2,2)$ can be represented within 2% by a Sutherland correction

$$Y(2,2) = 0.76\left(1 + 1.1\,\frac{\varepsilon}{kT}\right). \tag{62–14}$$

For $kT/\varepsilon < 0.7$ and for $kT/\varepsilon > 10$, $Y(2,2)$ is smaller than given by Eq. (62–14).

Finally

$$\frac{\tau}{\tau_c} = Z = 1.017\ Y(2,2)\left(\frac{r_0}{r_c}\right)^2 \{(\bar{Q}^-)_{\rm av}\,(1 - e^{-\vartheta/T})\}^{-1}. \tag{62–15}$$

Therefore

$$Z = 1.017\left(\frac{r_0}{r_c}\right)^2 Y(2,2)\,(1 - e^{-\vartheta/T})^{-1}\,(\bar{Q}_{\rm av})^{-1}$$

$$= 1.017\left(\frac{r_0}{r_c}\right)^2 Z_0 Z_{\rm osc} Z_{\rm tr}'\ Y(2,2)\ e^{-\varepsilon/kT}\,(1 - e^{-\vartheta/T})^{-1} \tag{62–16}$$

with the abbreviations of Eq. (58–11); namely

$$Z_{\rm osc} = \frac{M_B M_C(M_A + M_B + M_C)}{(M_B{}^2 + M_C{}^2)M_A}\,\frac{1}{\pi^2}\,\frac{\vartheta'}{\vartheta} \tag{62–16′}$$

$$Z_{\rm tr}' = \pi^2\left(\frac{\vartheta}{\vartheta'}\right)^2 \sqrt{\frac{3}{2\pi}}\left(\frac{T}{\vartheta'}\right)^{1/6} \exp\left[\frac{3}{2}\left(\frac{\vartheta'}{T}\right)^{1/3} - \frac{\vartheta}{2T}\right]. \tag{62–16″}$$

The preceding equations[4] were developed by Schwartz and Herzfeld.[2] In their first paper, a factor 4 was omitted from the expression for Q. This was corrected later[5] at the suggestion of Dr. F. Tanczos. The decisive step,

---

[3] J. O. Hirschfelder, C. F. Curtiss, and R. B. Bird, "Molecular Theory of Gases and Liquids." Wiley, New York, 1954.

[4] One can approach the equation in a slightly different form by dividing Eq. (62–9) by the average cross section for elastic collisions $(Q_{\rm el})_{\rm av}$. Then the fraction of (activating or deactivating) collisions is

$$(Q)_{av}/(Q_{el})_{av}$$

and

$$\frac{1}{Z} = [(Q^-)_{av}/(Q_{el})_{av}]\,(1 - e^{-\vartheta/T}).$$

[5] K. F. Herzfeld, *in* "Thermodynamics and Physics of Matter" (F. D. Rossini, ed.), Chapter 4. Princeton Univ. Press, Princeton, New Jersey, 1955.

that of replacing the quasipotential energy of the centrifugal force by a constant—by replacing r^2 by r_c^2 in Eq. (60–6)—was, however, first taken by Takayanagi.[6] In our calculation, no interaction with rotation was assumed; i.e., the molecules were replaced by spheres which could change their size, subject to Hooke's law force. Takayanagi[7] has taken the dependence of the potential on the mutual orientation of the molecules into account which, of course, introduces rotational transitions, and vibrational transitions where part of the energy comes from or goes into rotational excitation. Takayanagi and Kaneko[8] have also discussed de-excitation of the oxygen vibration by helium, with rotational transitions involved. This will be brought up again in Sec. 64. Curtiss and Adler[9] developed the general equations, taking into account all possible combinations of transitions without, however, assuming any form for the potential or making numerical calculations. Widom and Bauer[10] compared in a detailed calculation the classical and quantum treatment of the de-excitation process.

63. Some Numerical Data. Effect of Molecular Frequency on Low Frequency Absorption

The purpose of Tables 63–1 to 63–4 is to give the reader a feeling of the order of magnitude of the quantities involved.

TABLE 63–1

ϑ' in °K for $l = 0.2$ A

M	$\vartheta = 300$	$\vartheta = 600$	$\vartheta = 1200$	$\vartheta = 1800$	$\vartheta = 2400$
1	2935	1.17×10^4	4.70×10^4	1.06×10^5	1.88×10^5
10	2.94×10^4	1.17×10^5	4.70×10^5	1.06×10^6	1.88×10^6
20	5.87×10^4	2.35×10^5	9.39×10^5	2.11×10^6	3.76×10^6
40	1.17×10^5	4.70×10^5	1.88×10^6	4.23×10^6	7.51×10^6
80	2.35×10^5	9.39×10^5	3.76×10^6	8.45×10^6	1.50×10^7

---

[6] K. Takayanagi, *Progr. Theoret. Phys. Japan* 8, 111, 497 (1952).

[7] K. Takayanagi, *Progr. Theoret. Phys. Japan* **11**, 557 (1954).

[8] K. Takayanagi and S. Kaneko, *Sci. Rept. Saitama Univ. Ser. A*, **1**, 111 (1954).

[9] C. F. Curtiss and F. T. Adler, *J. Chem. Phys.* **20**, 249 (1952).

[10] B. Widom and S. H. Bauer, *J. Chem. Phys.* **21**, 1670 (1953).

TABLE 63–2*

E_m/k for 300 °K, $l = 0.2$ A

M	$\vartheta = 300$	$\vartheta = 600$	$\vartheta = 1200$	$\vartheta = 1800$	$\vartheta = 2400$
1	641.6	1020	1620	2120	2566
10	1380	2200	2490	4565	5560
20	1740	2765	4400	5750	6980
40	2200	3490	5540	7245	8795

* At 600 °K, these values have to be multiplied by 1.587; at 1200 °K by 2.52; at 1800 °K by 3.302; and at 2400 °K by 4.

TABLE 63–3

Z_{osc}; Eq. (62–16′), $l = 0.2$ A

M	$\vartheta = 300$	$\vartheta = 600$	$\vartheta = 1200$	$\vartheta = 1800$	$\vartheta = 2400$
1	0.991	1.98	3.97	5.95	7.93
10	9.913	19.83	39.65	59.48	79.30
20	19.83	39.65	79.30	—	—
40	39.65	79.30	158.60	—	—

TABLE 63–4

Z_{tr}'; Eq. (62–16″), $l = 0.2$ A

M	$\vartheta = 300$	$\vartheta = 600$	$\vartheta = 1200$	$\vartheta = 1800$	$\vartheta = 2400$
1	2.41	3.15	12.44	47.13	285
10	0.666	7.67	958	8.03×10^4	5.29×10^6
20	0.895	31.4	1.20×10^4	6.95×10^6	1.55×10^9
40	1.92	240	1.32×10^6	—	—

Since the theory developed is a perturbation theory which is valid only when the fraction of inelastic collisions is small, i.e., when Z is large, the low numbers in Tables 63–1 to 63–4 have no meaning.

One can see from Table 63–4 how fast Z_{tr}' increases with increasing ϑ and M, i.e., with the amount of energy to be exchanged with the translational motion, and with the time of interaction which, everything else being constant, is proportional to $\sqrt{M}$.

The temperature dependence of Z, as it follows from Eq. (62–16), is

$$\frac{1}{Z}dZ = \left[-\frac{1}{2}\left(\frac{\vartheta'}{T}\right)^{\frac{1}{3}} + \frac{1}{6} + \left(\frac{\vartheta}{2} + \frac{\varepsilon}{k}\right)\frac{1}{T} + \frac{\vartheta}{T}(e^{\vartheta/T} - 1)^{-1}\right]\frac{dT}{T}. \tag{63–1}$$

The last term in this expression goes from zero at low temperatures (ϑ/T is large) to unity at high temperatures. It follows that the temperature coefficient could only be positive if

$$\left(\frac{\vartheta}{2} + \frac{\varepsilon}{k}\right)\frac{1}{T} + \frac{7}{6} > \frac{1}{2}\left(\frac{\vartheta'}{T}\right)^{\frac{1}{3}}. \tag{63–2}$$

This can happen in two cases: (a) at extremely low temperatures, since lowering the temperature increases the left side more than the right; or (b) for very large ε. In this case the temperature coefficient may be positive at low temperatures, zero when the right side of Eq. (63–1) is zero, and negative, as usual, at higher temperatures.

An example for the usual case is given below for an imaginary diatomic gas with $M = 10$, $\vartheta = 1200$, $\varepsilon/k = 100$, $Z_0 = 3$, and $l = 0.2$ A.

T	300	600	1200	2400
Z	11,300	1340	200	51

In the preceding, l has been kept constant. An error in l affects Z as follows

$$\frac{dZ}{Z} = \left[\left(\frac{\vartheta'}{T}\right)^{\frac{1}{3}} - \frac{7}{3}\right]\frac{dl}{l}. \tag{63–3}$$

If l depends appreciably on T, which would be through

$$\frac{dl}{dT} = \frac{dl}{dE_m}\frac{dE_m}{dT} = \frac{2}{3}\frac{E_m}{\varepsilon}\frac{1}{T}\frac{dl}{dE_m/\varepsilon}$$

one would have to add to Eq. (63–1) the term

$$\left[\left(\frac{\vartheta'}{T}\right)^{\frac{1}{3}} - \frac{7}{3}\right]\frac{2E_m}{3\varepsilon}\frac{1}{l}\frac{dl}{dE_m/\varepsilon}\frac{dT}{T} \tag{63–4}$$

the quantity $E_m/\varepsilon\,(1/l)\,dl/dE_m/\varepsilon$ being governed by the equations of Sec. 59.

It follows from Eq. (63–3) that, for example, for $(\vartheta'/T)^{1/3} = 10$, an error of 1% in l affects Z by 8%.

Going back to the equations of Sec. 14, one might wonder how the low-frequency absorption of a gas varies with the ϑ of the vibration, since with increasing ϑ, τ (or Z) increases, while C' decreases. To illustrate the low frequency absorption coefficient as a function of ϑ, we show the case of an imaginary diatomic gas, where $M = 10$, $l = 0.2$ A, $\varepsilon/k = 100$ and $T = 300°$ for varying ϑ.

ϑ	300	600	1200	1800	2400
$2\alpha'\mathfrak{B}/\omega^2\tau_c$	0.8	37	310	15,000	42,000

Assuming $\tau_c = 1.5 \times 10^{-10}$ sec, $\alpha'\mathfrak{B}/\omega^2$ falls to half its value at 50 Mc for $\vartheta = 300$, at 60 cycles for $\vartheta = 2400$. Therefore the effect of large ϑ will be negligible in the ultrasonic range at room temperature.

64. Simultaneous Transitions in Rotational, Vibrational, and Translational Energy

We now take up a problem we have ignored previously; namely, that during the transfer of a vibrational quantum, jumps occur at the same time in the rotational quantum number J and the corresponding "magnetic" quantum number m. These are accompanied by jumps in the orbital quantum number j of the relative motion (and the corresponding magnetic quantum number), so as to keep the total angular momentum constant. To simplify the calculation, we will first consider the collision of a homonuclear diatomic molecule BB with a monatomic molecule A. The first step is to find the part of the interaction energy which depends on the orientation of BB. If one assumes, with Jackson and Howarth[1] and de Boer,[2] that the atoms of B act on A independently (which is the assumption made in Sec. 57 for the vibration), one gets as interaction energy[3,4]

$$H = H^0\left[\exp\left(-\frac{r_1}{l}\right) + \exp\left(-\frac{r_2}{l}\right)\right] \tag{64–1}$$

where r_1 and r_2 are the distances of the two atoms B from A. Calling r the distance of the center BB from A; Γ, the angle between the molecular

---

[1] J. M. Jackson and A. Howarth, *Proc. Roy. Soc.* **A152**, 515 (1935).
[2] J. de Boer, *Physica* **9**, 363 (1942).
[3] J. C. Beckerle, *J. Chem. Phys.* **21**, 2034 (1953).
[4] R. Brout, *J. Chem. Phys.* **22**, 934 (1954).

axis and the vector r; X, the vibration amplitude; and L, the equilibrium distance BB, one has

$$r_1{}^2 = r^2 + \frac{1}{4}(L+X)^2 - 2r \times \frac{1}{2}(L+X)\cos\Gamma \tag{64–2}$$

$$r_2{}^2 = r^2 + \frac{1}{4}(L+X)^2 + 2r \times \frac{1}{2}(L+X)\cos\Gamma. \tag{64–2′}$$

Assuming $r > L/2$, one can develop Eq. (64–2) and finds

$$r_1 = r - \frac{1}{2}(L+X)\cos\Gamma \tag{64–3}$$

$$r_2 = r + \frac{1}{2}(L+X)\cos\Gamma. \tag{64–3′}$$

$X/2l$ is surely small compared to unity, even if $L/2l$ is not. The interaction energy is then

$$\begin{aligned} H &= H^0 e^{-r/l}\left[\exp\left(\frac{L}{2l}\cos\Gamma\right)\left(1+\frac{X}{2l}\cos\Gamma\right)+\exp\left(-\frac{L}{2l}\cos\Gamma\right)\left(1-\frac{X}{2l}\cos\Gamma\right)\right] \\ &= 2H^0 e^{-r/l}\cosh\left(\frac{L}{2l}\cos\Gamma\right)+2H^0 e^{-r/l}\frac{X}{2l}\cos\Gamma\sinh\left(\frac{L}{2l}\cos\Gamma\right) \\ &= 2H^0 e^{-r/l}+2H^0 e^{-r/l}\left[\cosh\left(\frac{L}{2l}\cos\Gamma\right)-1\right]+ \\ &\qquad 2H^0 e^{-r/l}\frac{X}{2l}\left[\cos\Gamma\sinh\left(\frac{L}{2l}\cos\Gamma\right)\right]. \end{aligned} \tag{64–4}$$

The first term represents the unperturbed interaction which determines the translational motion; the second produces pure rotational transitions (Sec. 69); the third, the transitions involving vibrations and rotations.

We now enlarge a term in the wave function from the form in Eqs. (57–5′) and (60–2) by a rotational term ψ_J to

$$\frac{1}{r}f(r)S_j\,\psi^{BB}_{\text{osc}}\,\psi_J = \frac{1}{r}f(r)S_j\,\psi_{\text{osc}}\,S_J \tag{64–5}$$

where the S are normalized spherical harmonics of order j (for the relative motion) and order J (for the rotational motion). The j and J include the magnetic quantum number. The corresponding amplitude a, Eq. (57–7), for an inelastically scattered particle characterized by a prime, is then

$$\frac{hp_1}{4\pi\tilde{m}} a = \int \frac{1}{r} f'(r) H^0 e^{-r/l} \frac{1}{r} f(r) r^2 dr \int \psi'_{\text{osc}} \frac{X}{2l} \psi_{\text{osc}} dX$$

$$\iint S_j'^* \, S_J'^* \left[2 \sinh \left(\frac{L}{2l} \cos \Gamma \right) \cos \Gamma \right] S_j \, S_J \, d\Omega \, d\Omega' \tag{64–6}$$

where $d\Omega$ and $d\Omega'$ are the elements of steric angle for relative motion and rotation. The probabilities of transition result from the square of a; see Eq. (57–4′).

We assume that the energy difference involved in the rotational jump is so small compared to $h\nu$ that its influence on the translational motion can be neglected. The transition probability is then given by Eq. (58–12)

$$|a|^2 \frac{p_1}{p_0} = \frac{1}{Z_{\text{tr}}'} \frac{1}{Z_{\text{osc}}} e^{\varepsilon/kT} \left(1 - e^{-\vartheta/T}\right)$$

$$\left| \iint S_j'^* \, S_J'^* \left[2 \sinh \left(\frac{L}{2l} \cos \Gamma \right) \cos \Gamma \right] S_j \, S_J \, d\Omega \, d\Omega' \right|^2 \tag{64–7}$$

where Z_{tr}' and Z_{osc} are the same numbers as before.

In the previous calculations, the sum over all the values of j, J, j', and J', properly weighted, were set $1/Z_0 = 1/3$. We first keep a fixed state of origin j, J, and sum over all possible end states j', J'. This gives the simple result[5]

$$\iint S_j^* \, S_J^* \left[2 \sinh \left(\frac{L}{2l} \cos \Gamma \right) \cos \Gamma \right]^2 S_j \, S_J \, d\Omega \, d\Omega'. \tag{64–8}$$

If we now put the z axis in the direction of the incoming beam

$$S_j = (2\pi N_j)^{-1/2} \, P_j \tag{64–9}$$

---

[5] If one has any quantity H, the integral—see, for example, Eq. (57–7′)—

$$\int \psi_s^* H \psi_j d\tau$$

is called the $s-j$th matrix element of H and written H_{sj}. The rules of matrix multiplication give

$$\sum_s H_{js}^* H_{sj} = (H^2)_{jj}$$

with

$$(H^2)_{jj} = \int \psi_j^* H^2 \psi_j d\tau.$$

while

$$S_J = (2\pi N_J^{(m)})^{-1/2} P_J^{(m)} e^{\pm im\varphi} \tag{64–9'}$$

where N_j and $N_J^{(m)}$ are the normalizing factors.

Abbreviate now, with Mayer and Mayer[6]

$$\sigma_1 = \frac{h^2}{8\pi^2 \tilde{m}\, r_c^2 kT} \qquad \sigma_2 = \frac{h^2}{8\pi^2 IkT}.$$

According to Eqs. (62–1), (62–7), and (62–8), the contribution of a term with $N_j^{-1/2} P_j$ is weighted by the factor

$$(2j+1)\,\sigma_1 \exp\,[-\sigma_1 j(j+1)].$$

Similarly, the probability of a state J, m, is given by

$$2\sigma_2 \exp\,[-\sigma_2 J(J+1)]$$

with J even. The elements of steric angle are

$$d\Omega = \sin\vartheta d\vartheta d\varphi \qquad d\Omega' = \sin\chi d\chi d\varphi'.$$

Therefore

$$\frac{1}{Z_0} = 2\sigma_1\sigma_2 \iint \sum_j (2j+1) \exp\,[-\sigma_1 j(j+1)]\, \frac{1}{2\pi N_j}$$
$$P_j^2 \sin\vartheta d\vartheta d\varphi \iint \sum_J \exp\,[-\sigma_2 J(J+1)] \tag{64–10}$$
$$\sum_m \frac{1}{2\pi N_J^{(m)}} (P_J^{(m)})^2 \sin\chi d\chi d\varphi' \left[2\sinh\left(\frac{L}{2}\cos\Gamma\right)\cos\Gamma\right]^2.$$

One can now make use of the following theorem[7–9]

$$\sum_m \frac{1}{N_J^{(m)}} (P_J^{(m)})^2 = \frac{2J+1}{2} \tag{64–11}$$

for every value of the argument.

---

[6] J. E. Mayer and M. G. Mayer, "Introduction to Statistical Mechanics." Wiley, New York, 1940.

[7] This theorem is used, for example, to prove that closed subshells in atoms have spherical symmetry.

[8] A. Unsöld, *Ann. Physik* [4] 82, 355 (1927).

[9] A. Sommerfeld, "Atombau und Spectrallinien," 2 nd ed., Vol. 2, p. 145. Vieweg, Braunschweig, 1939.

This leaves, in Eq. (64–10), only

$$2\sigma_2 \sum \frac{2J+1}{2} \exp\left[-\sigma_2 J(J+1)\right]$$

as dependent on J. If σ_2 is sufficiently small compared to unity[10] (which means that the first rotational jump is small compared to kT and that the most probable rotational level has a J which is large compared to unity), one can replace the sum by an integral, and has, with good approximation

$$2\sigma_2 \frac{1}{4} \int (2J+1) \exp\left[-\sigma_2 J(J+1)\right] dJ = \frac{1}{2}.$$

Therefore, Eq. (64–10) finally has the form

$$\frac{1}{Z_0} = \frac{1}{2}\sigma_1 \sum_j (2j+1) \exp\left[-\sigma_1 j(j+1)\right] \tag{64–12}$$

$$\frac{1}{N_j} \iint \sin\vartheta\, d\vartheta\, (P_j)^2 \frac{d\varphi}{2\pi} \sin\chi\, d\chi\, \frac{d\varphi'}{2\pi} \left[2\sinh\left(\frac{L}{2l}\cos\Gamma\right)\cos\Gamma\right]^2 .$$

Furthermore, by writing φ'' for $\varphi' - \varphi$ in Eq. (64–12), one integration over $d\varphi/2\pi$ can be performed and will give unity.

One can now try two extreme approximations.

(a) One can replace $\sinh(L/2l \cos\Gamma)$ by the first power of the series development, $(L/2l)\cos\Gamma$, so that the interaction term is

$$\left(\frac{L}{l}\right)^2 \cos^4\Gamma.$$

(b) One can assume that $L/2l \gg 1$, so that the sinh has appreciable value only near $\cos\Gamma = \pm 1$.

We will first treat case (a). Then

$$\begin{aligned} \cos^4\Gamma &= [\cos\vartheta\cos\chi + \sin\vartheta\sin\chi\cos(\varphi'-\varphi)]^4 \\ &= (\cos\vartheta\cos\chi)^4 + 4(\cos\vartheta\cos\chi)^3 \sin\vartheta\sin\chi\cos(\varphi'-\varphi) + \\ &\quad 6[\cos\vartheta\cos\chi\sin\vartheta\sin\chi\cos(\varphi'-\varphi)]^2 + \\ &\quad 4\cos\vartheta\cos\chi[\sin\vartheta\sin\chi\cos(\varphi'-\varphi)]^3 + [\sin\vartheta\sin\chi\cos(\varphi'-\varphi)]^4. \end{aligned} \tag{64–13}$$

[10] This is not necessary for the result. If $\sigma_2 > 1$, the factor in front is not $2\sigma_2$.

The integration over φ' drops out the odd powers of $\cos(\varphi - \varphi')$, and gives (together with the normalization factor $1/2\pi$) $1/2$ for the square, and $3/8$ for the 4th power. Therefore

$$\frac{1}{2\pi}\int d\varphi \frac{1}{2\pi}\int d\varphi' \cos^4 \Gamma = (\cos\vartheta\cos\chi)^4 + \tag{64–13'}$$

$$3(\cos\vartheta\cos\chi\sin\vartheta\sin\chi)^2 + \frac{3}{8}(\sin\vartheta\sin\chi)^4$$

$$= \cos^4\vartheta\cos^4\chi + 3(\cos^2\vartheta - \cos^4\vartheta)(\cos^2\chi - \cos^4\chi) +$$

$$\frac{3}{8}(1 - 2\cos^2\vartheta + \cos^4\vartheta)(1 - 2\cos^2\chi + \cos^4\chi).$$

One then has, after integrating over χ

$$\frac{1}{Z_0} = \frac{2}{5}\left(\frac{L}{l}\right)^2 \sigma_1 \sum (2j+1)\exp[-\sigma_1 j(j+1)]\frac{1}{N_j}\int (P_j)^2 \sin\vartheta\, d\vartheta.$$

$$\frac{1}{Z_0} = \left(\frac{L}{l}\right)^2 \frac{2}{5}\sigma_1 \sum (2j+1)\exp[-\sigma_1 j(j+1)] = \frac{2}{5}\left(\frac{L}{l}\right)^2$$

$$Z_0 = 2.5\left(\frac{l}{L}\right)^2. \tag{64–14}$$

We turn to case (b), with $L \gg l$, and take as the zero order scattering interaction in Eq. (64–4) the expression

$$H^0 \exp - \left(\frac{r}{l} - \frac{L}{2l}\right) = (H^0 e^{L/2l})\, e^{-r/l} \tag{64–4'}$$

This implies that even the elastic scattering is done by the nearest atom. Otherwise Z_0 would have an additional factor $\exp(-L/l)$. The perturbation energy then contains the factor

$$\cos\Gamma\, e^{-L/2l}\, 2\cosh\left(\frac{L}{2l}\cos\Gamma\right) = \cos\Gamma \exp\left[\frac{L}{2l}(\cos\Gamma - 1)\right] + \ldots$$

which is appreciable only if $\cos\Gamma$ is near unity (or, for the other term in cosh, near -1), which means physically that the molecular axis is pointing at the hitting particle A. This is physically plausible. Therefore, we can put

$$\chi = \vartheta + \delta$$

$$\cos\Gamma = \cos\vartheta\cos(\vartheta+\delta) + \sin\vartheta\sin(\vartheta+\delta)\cos\varphi''$$

and treat δ and $\varphi'' = \varphi' - \varphi$ as small quantities of the first order. Then

$$\cos\Gamma = \cos\vartheta\left[\left(1-\frac{\delta^2}{2}\right)\cos\vartheta - \delta\sin\vartheta\right] + \tag{64–15}$$

$$\sin\vartheta\left[\left(1-\frac{\delta^2}{2}\right)\sin\vartheta + \delta\cos\vartheta\right]\left[1-\frac{(\varphi'')^2}{2}\right]$$

$$= [\cos^2\vartheta + \sin^2\vartheta]\left(1-\frac{\delta^2}{2}\right) - \sin^2\vartheta\,\frac{(\varphi'')^2}{2} = 1 - \frac{1}{2}[\delta^2 + (\varphi'')^2\sin^2\vartheta].$$

Accordingly

$$H'' = \cos\Gamma\, 2\cosh\left(\frac{L}{2l}\cos\Gamma\right) \times e^{-L/2l} = \exp\left\{-\frac{L}{4l}[\delta^2 + (\varphi'')^2\sin^2\vartheta]\right\} \tag{64–16}$$

with a second, similar term at $\chi = -\vartheta + \delta$.

Therefore, Eq. (64–12) takes the form ($\sin\chi d\chi = \sin\vartheta d\delta$)

$$\frac{1}{Z_0} = \frac{1}{2}\sigma_1 \sum (2j+1)\exp[-\sigma_1 j(j+1)]\frac{1}{N_j}\int \sin^2\vartheta d\vartheta\,(P_j)^2 \tag{64–17}$$

$$\iint d\delta\,\frac{d\varphi''}{2\pi}\exp\left\{-\frac{L}{2l}[\delta^2 + (\varphi'')^2\sin^2\vartheta]\right\}.$$

Because of the steepness of the last exponential function one can extend the integrals from $-\infty$ to $+\infty$, getting

$$\int d\delta\exp\left(-\frac{L}{2l}\delta^2\right)\int\frac{d\varphi''}{2\pi}\exp\left[-\left(\frac{L}{2l}\sin^2\vartheta\right)(\varphi'')^2\right]$$

$$= \sqrt{\frac{2\pi l}{L}}\,\frac{1}{2\pi}\sqrt{\frac{2\pi l}{L\sin^2\vartheta}} = \frac{l}{L}\,\frac{1}{\sin\vartheta}.$$

Inserting this in Eq. (64–17), one finds

$$\frac{1}{Z_0} = \frac{1}{2}\left\{\sigma_1\sum(2j+1)\exp[-\sigma_1 j(j+1)]\frac{1}{N_j}\int\sin\vartheta d\vartheta\,(P_j)^2\right\} \times 2\,\frac{l}{L} = \frac{l}{L} \tag{64–17'}$$

the last factor 2 arising from the two favorable positions of the molecule, or

$$Z_0 = \frac{L}{l}. \tag{64–18}$$

In practice, L is neither very large nor very small compared to l, so that Eqs. (64–14) and (64–18) should result asymptotically, as required, and we write tentatively

$$Z_0 = 2.5\left(\frac{l}{L}\right)^2 + \frac{L}{l}. \qquad (64\text{–}19)$$

Some numerical results of Z_0 as a function of L/l are shown below.

L/l	1/2	1	2	3	4	5	10
Z_0	10.5	3.5	2.62	3.28	4.16	5.10	10.03

We next consider the transversal vibration of linear molecules of the type BCB, like CO_2 or CS_2.

If X_B and X_C are the amplitudes of vibration of B and C

$$X_B = -X\frac{M_C}{2M_B + M_C} \qquad X_C = +X\frac{2M_B}{2M_B + M_C}$$

one finds

$$r_C{}^2 = r^2 + X_C{}^2 - 2rX_C \sin\Gamma$$

$$r_B{}^2 = r^2 + 2r\left[\pm\frac{L}{2}\cos\Gamma - X_B\sin\Gamma\right] + \frac{L^2}{4} + X_B{}^2$$

and by developing

$$r_C = r - X_C\sin\Gamma$$

$$r_B = r \pm \frac{L}{2}\cos\Gamma - X_B\sin\Gamma.$$

We now have to assume that the atoms B and C have a common l. Then

$$H = e^{-r/l}\left\{H_C{}^0\left(1 - \frac{X_C}{l}\sin\Gamma\right) + 2\,H_B{}^0\cosh\left(\frac{L}{2}\cos\Gamma\right)\left(1 - \frac{X_B}{l}\sin\Gamma\right)\right\}$$

$$= [H_C{}^0 + 2H_B{}^0\,e^{L/2l}]\,e^{-r/l} + 2H_B{}^0\,e^{L/2l}\,e^{-r/l}\left[e^{-L/2l}\cosh\left(\frac{L}{2l}\cos\Gamma\right) - 1\right] -$$

$$\left[H_C{}^0\frac{X_C}{X} + 2H_B{}^0\,e^{L/2l}\frac{X_B}{X}\,e^{-L/2l}\cosh\left(\frac{L}{2l}\cos\Gamma\right)\right]\sin\Gamma\,\frac{X}{l}. \qquad (64\text{–}20)$$

In Eq. (64–20) the first term

$$(H_C{}^0 + 2H_B{}^0\, e^{L/2l})\, e^{-r/l}$$

is the unperturbed interaction energy, $H_C{}^0 + 2H_B{}^0\, e^{L/2l}$ being the quantity called $H_0{}'$ in Sec. 59. The second term induces pure rotational transitions, while vibrational-rotational transitions are due to the last term

$$H'' = \left[H_C{}^0 \frac{2M_B}{2M_B + M_C} - 2\,(H_B{}^0\, e^{L/2l}) \frac{M_C}{2M_B + M_C}\, e^{-L/2l} \cosh\left(\frac{L}{2l} \cos \Gamma\right)\right] \times \sin \Gamma\, e^{-r/l} \frac{X}{l}. \quad (64\text{–}21)$$

The quantity

$$\frac{\sin^2 \Gamma}{(H^0)^2}\left[H_C{}^0 \frac{2M_B}{2M_B + M_C} - 2H_B{}^0\, e^{L/2l} \frac{M_C}{2M_B + M_C}\, e^{-L/2l} \cosh\left(\frac{L}{2l} \cos \Gamma\right)\right]^2$$

plays the role of

$$\frac{1}{2}\left[\frac{(2M_B)^2}{(2M_B + M_C)^2} + \frac{M_C{}^2}{(2M_B + M_C)^2}\right]$$

in Eqs. (57–11) and (58–10). This factor is already included in Z_{osc}^{-1}. Therefore, the new factor which determines $Z_0{}^{-1}$ is

$$\frac{2 \sin^2 \Gamma}{4M_B{}^2 + M_C{}^2}\left[\frac{H_C{}^0}{H^0} 2M_B - 2\frac{H_B{}^0\, e^{L/2l}}{H^0} M_C\, e^{-L/2l} \cosh\left(\frac{L}{2} \cos \Gamma\right)\right]^2. \quad (64\text{–}22)$$

By squaring out, we have

$$\frac{8}{4M_B{}^2 + M_C{}^2}\left\{M_B{}^2 \left(\frac{H_C{}^0}{H^0}\right)^2 \sin^2 \Gamma - 2M_B M_C \frac{H_C{}^0}{H^0}\frac{H_B{}^0\, e^{L/2l}}{H^0} \sin^2 \Gamma \times \right. \quad (64\text{–}22')$$

$$\left. e^{-L/2l} \cosh\left(\frac{L}{2l} \cos \Gamma\right) + M_C{}^2 \left(\frac{H_B{}^0\, e^{L/2l}}{H^0}\right)^2 \sin^2 \Gamma \left[e^{-L/2l} \cosh\left(\frac{L}{2l} \cos \Gamma\right)\right]^2\right\}.$$

Introduce the abbreviation

$$\frac{H_B{}^0\, e^{L/2l}}{H_C{}^0} = h \quad (64\text{–}23)$$

or

$$\frac{H_C{}^0}{H^0} = \frac{1}{2h + 1}. \quad (64\text{–}23')$$

In a sense $L(2h/(2h+1))$ measures the ratio of the torque exerted by molecule A to the total force exerted by it.

From what has been said before, we get the following results if we insert Eq. (64–22′) in Eq. (64–12):

The first term in Eq. (64–22′) contains the factor

$$\sin^2 \Gamma = 1 - \cos^2 \Gamma = 1 - \cos^2 \vartheta \cos^2 \chi - 2 \cos \vartheta \sin \vartheta \cos \chi \sin \chi \cos \varphi'' - (1 - \cos^2 \vartheta)(1 - \cos^2 \chi) \cos^2 \varphi''.$$

The first summand, upon insertion in Eq. (64–12) and integration, gives 2. The rest gives, after integration over $\sin \chi \, d\chi (1/2\pi) d\varphi''$

$$-\frac{2}{3} \cos^2 \vartheta - (1 - \cos^2 \vartheta)\left(2 - \frac{2}{3}\right) \cdot \frac{1}{2} = -\frac{2}{3}.$$

Therefore, the over-all contribution to $1/Z_0$ of the first term in Eq. (64–22′) is

$$\frac{4}{3} \frac{4M_B{}^2}{4M_B{}^2 + M_C{}^2} \left(\frac{1}{2h+1}\right)^2. \tag{64–24}$$

The second and third terms contain exponentials which are appreciable only in the neighborhood of $\cos \Gamma = 1$, but in that neighborhood $\sin \Gamma$ is very small. Proceeding as in Eq. (64–15), one has

$$2\, e^{-L/2l} \cosh\left(\frac{L}{2l} \cos \Gamma\right) \sin^2 \Gamma = [\delta^2 + (\varphi'')^2 \sin^2 \vartheta] \exp\left\{-\frac{L}{4l} [\delta^2 + (\varphi'')^2 \sin^2 \vartheta]\right\}.$$

The integration over $\sin \chi d\chi (d\varphi''/2\pi)$ gives

$$\begin{aligned} \sin \vartheta \iint d\delta \frac{d\varphi''}{2\pi} [\delta^2 + (\varphi'')^2 \sin^2 \vartheta] \exp\left(-\frac{L}{4l}\delta^2\right) \exp\left[-\frac{L}{4l}(\varphi'')^2 \sin^2 \vartheta\right] \\ = \sin \vartheta \int d\delta \exp\left(-\frac{L}{4l}\delta^2\right) \frac{1}{2\pi} \sqrt{\frac{4\pi l}{L}} \frac{1}{\sin \vartheta} \left[\delta^2 + \frac{1}{2}\frac{4l}{L}\right] \qquad (64\text{–}24') \\ = \frac{1}{2\pi} \sqrt{\frac{4\pi l}{L}} \sqrt{\frac{4\pi l}{L}} \left[\frac{1}{2}\frac{4l}{L} + \frac{1}{2}\frac{4l}{L}\right] = \frac{1}{2}\left(\frac{4l}{L}\right)^2. \end{aligned}$$

This has to be multiplied by 2 to take care of the second term in cosh.

The third summand with $[2\, e^{-L/2l} \cosh(L/2l \cos \Gamma) \sin \Gamma]^2$ also gives the expression (64–23′), except that l replaces $2l$. The end result is

$$\frac{1}{Z_0} = \frac{4}{3}\frac{4M_B^2}{4M_B^2 + M_C^2}\frac{1}{(2h+1)^2} - 128\frac{M_B M_C}{4M_B^2 + M_C^2}\frac{h}{(2h+1)^2}\left(\frac{l}{L}\right)^2 + 8\frac{M_C^2}{4M_B^2 + M_C^2}\left(\frac{h}{2h+1}\right)^2\left(\frac{l}{L}\right)^2. \quad (64\text{–}25)$$

The first term is largest, because the interaction with the center atom C does not depend strongly on the orientation of the molecule. Finally

$$Z_0 = \frac{3}{4}\left(1 + \frac{M_C^2}{4M_B^2}\right)(2h+1)^2\left\{1 - 6\left(\frac{l}{L}\right)^2\left[16\frac{M_C}{M_B}h - \frac{M_C^2}{M_B^2}h^2\right]\right\}^{-1}. \quad (64\text{–}25')$$

Apart from the known parameter l/L, Eq. (64–25′) contains (not counting the masses) as its only other parameter the unknown quantity h. No method is known to calculate this quantity with certainty.

One may try the probably incorrect assumption that the interaction energy of an atom is independent of the bonding and the chemical partner. In that case, one can calculate $H_B{}^0$ if the data for molecule BB are known. They shall be designated by primes. Then, from Eqs. (59–9) and (64–20), one has

$$2H_B{}^0 \exp\left(\frac{L'}{2l'} - \frac{r_0'}{l'}\right) = \varepsilon' \quad (64\text{–}26)$$

$$[H_C{}^0 + 2H_B{}^0 e^{L/2l}]\, e^{-r_0/l} = \varepsilon \quad (64\text{–}26')$$

so that

$$h = \frac{1}{2}\varepsilon'\left[\varepsilon \exp\left(\frac{2r_0 - L}{2l} - \frac{2r_0' - L'}{2l'}\right) - \varepsilon'\right]^{-1}. \quad (64\text{–}26'')$$

Using, for example, for CO_2 and O_2 the values of l from the data of Table 66–5, one gets a negative h—which is impossible—by this method. In the absence of anything better, we may put $h = 1$. For the values of l/L which occur and lie between 1/4 and 1/7 one does not make a big error by setting in Eq. (64–25′) $\{\ \} = 1$, so that

$$Z_0 = \frac{3}{4}\left(1 + \frac{M_C^2}{4M_B^2}\right)9\left(\frac{2h+1}{3}\right)^2 = 6.75\left(1 + \frac{M_C^2}{4M_B^2}\right)\left(\frac{2h+1}{3}\right)^2. \quad (64\text{–}27)$$

Curtiss and Adler[11] have given general equations for combined translational-rotational-vibrational transitions, but have not made numerical calculations.

---

[11] C. F. Curtiss and F. T. Adler, *J. Chem. Phys.* **20**, 249 (1952).

Aroeste[12] has made a direct calculation for F_2O (a triangular molecule), the results of which agree only roughly with the above. He simplifies the calculation by taking the molecule as a plane rotator, and the collisions as one-dimensional. The incoming beam is represented as a plane wave (Born approximation), not as a wave distorted by the interaction potential. Because no development in a series is made, the azimuthal quantum number changes by more than 1 or 2, depending on the characteristic vibration affected. At least for a particular energy of the incoming particles, the total probabilities for combined rotational-translational transitions are one to three times those of pure vibrational transitions.

Takayanagi and Kaneko[13] have treated the collision between an oxygen molecule and a helium atom, including combined vibrational-rotational-translational transitions. The interaction potential is set equal to

$$H = (100.9 + 101.8\, P_2 + 89.04\, X\, P_2 + 44.52\, X)\, e^{-r/l}$$
$$l = 0.4630\, \text{Å}$$

(i.e., more than twice the value used by us).

The first term determines the distorted waves, the second gives rotational-translational transitions, the last term vibrational-translational transitions, and the third term the combined vibrational-rotational-translational transitions.

The method of calculating the vibrational and translational factors is very close[14] to that used in Sec. 62, except that the energy transferred may not be $h\nu$, but might include a change of rotational energy. The authors find numerically for a transition in which the vibrational quantum number goes from $1 \to 0$

Rotational Transition	Probability in Relative Numbers
$J \to J\ (J = 10)$ (no rotational change)	1
$J \to J + 2\ (10 \to 12)$	0.27
$J \to J - 2\ (10 \to 8)$	0.22

that is, the vibrational-rotational-translational transitions are 0.49 times the pure vibrational-translational ones; the Z value is reduced by the factor $1.49^{-1} \sim 2/3$. This ratio will depend upon J, but seems to be nearly independent of ϑ, l, and T.

---

[12] H. Aroeste, *J. Chem. Phys.* **21**, 870 (1953).

[13] K. Takayanagi and S. Kaneko, *Sci. Rept. Saitoma Univ. Ser. A* **1**, 111 (1954).

[14] Except that the authors use the one-dimensional Maxwell distribution, Eq. (56–3), and omit $Z_0 = 3$.

65. Polyatomic Molecules. More Than One Vibration Is Involved. Complex Collisions

(a) *Normal Vibrations*

For diatomic molecules, the factor in the cross section depending on the vibration is [see Eq. (57–10″)]

$$\left[\frac{m_C}{m_B + m_C}\frac{1}{l}\int \psi_i^{BC}\, X\, \psi_j^{BC}\, dX\right]^2. \tag{65–1}$$

Here X is the amplitude of vibration in the radial direction of the atom B; later, half the sum of this expression for atoms B and C are taken.

In polyatomic molecules, the atoms do not vibrate independently of each other, but the motion can be analyzed into independent normal vibrations,[1,2] which are described by normal coordinates q_s, so that

$$q_s = q_s^0 \cos 2\pi\nu_s(t - t_s'). \tag{65–2}$$

There are three times as many normal coordinates as atoms. However, three of these describe the motion of the center of mass, and three more (or two for a linear molecule) the rotation of the molecule as a whole. If x_j, y_j, z_j are the coordinates of the jth atom, the amplitude of the vibration in the $x,y,z,$ direction is given by

$$\Delta x_j = \sum_s a_{js} q_s \tag{65–3}$$

$$\Delta y_j = \sum_s b_{js} q_s \tag{65–3′}$$

$$\Delta z_j = \sum c_{js} q_s. \tag{65–3″}$$

The a, b, and c, are pure numbers.

The square array

$$\begin{matrix} a_{11}\, b_{11}\, c_{11} & a_{21} \cdots \\ a_{12}\, b_{12}\, c_{12} \cdots & \end{matrix}$$

---

[1] E. B. Wilson, Jr., C. Decius, and P. C. Cross, "Molecular Vibrations." McGraw-Hill, New York, 1955.

[2] R. N. Schwartz, Z. I. Slawsky, and K. F. Herzfeld, *J. Chem. Phys.* **20**, 1591 (1952).

is called an orthogonal matrix; there are certain relations among the a, b, and c. The square of the amplitude in the radial direction, Δr_j, is then given by

$$(\Delta r_j)^2 = \sum_s \sum_k (a_{js}a_{jk} + b_{js}b_{jk} + c_{js}c_{jk})q_s q_k. \tag{65–4}$$

If we consider only one transition, e.g., for the sth vibration from quantum number one to quantum number zero, then

$$(a_{js}{}^2 + b_{js}{}^2 + c_{js}{}^2)\left[\int \frac{1}{l}\, \psi_1 q_s \psi_0 dq_s\right]^2 = (a_{js}{}^2 + b_{js}{}^2 + c_{js}{}^2)\frac{h}{8\pi^2 m_s l^2 \nu_s} \tag{65–5}$$

takes the place of Eq. (57–12′).

In this expression, m_s is the effective mass connected with the vibration ν_s. To determine this quantity, we write the total kinetic energy which is the sum of the kinetic energy of all the atoms

$$\text{kinetic energy} = \frac{1}{2}\sum_j m_j\,[(\Delta\dot{x}_j)^2 + (\Delta\dot{y}_j)^2 + (\Delta\dot{z}_j)^2] = \frac{1}{2}\sum_s m_s \dot{q}_s{}^2. \tag{65–6}$$

Equation (65–6) is really the definition of m_s, the mass associated with the normal vibrations.

Differentiating Eq. (65–3) with respect to the time and squaring, one has for the middle term of Eq. (65–6)

$$\frac{1}{2}\sum_j m_j \sum_s (a_{js}{}^2 + b_{js}{}^2 + c_{js}{}^2)\,\dot{q}_s{}^2 \tag{65–6′}$$

or, rearranging

$$\frac{1}{2}\sum_s m_s \dot{q}_s{}^2 = \frac{1}{2}\sum_s \dot{q}_s{}^2 \sum_j m_j\,(a_{js}{}^2 + b_{js}{}^2 + c_{js}{}^2). \tag{65–6″}$$

The q_s, i.e., the a, b, c in Eq. (65–3), are determined in such a manner that no mixed terms $\dot{q}_s\dot{q}_k$ appear in Eq. (65–6′). Since the q_s and, therefore, the $\dot{q}_s$, are independent of each other, Eq. (65–6″) can only be fulfilled by making the coefficient of each $\dot{q}_s{}^2$ the same on both sides, i.e.

$$m_s = \sum_j m_j\,(a_{js}{}^2 + b_{js}{}^2 + c_{js}{}^2). \tag{65–7}$$

The sum is to be extended over all atoms.

Finally, Eq. (65–5) has to be summed over all surface atoms. If there are n' of these, one has, replacing Eq. (58–10)

$$Z_{\text{osc},s}{}^{-1} = 2\pi^2 \frac{\tilde{M}}{M_s} \frac{\vartheta_s}{\vartheta_s'} \frac{1}{n'} \sum_{\substack{\text{surface}\\ \text{atoms}}} (a_{js}{}^2 + b_{js}{}^2 + c_{js}{}^2). \qquad (65\text{–}8)$$

It is not always easy to find the coefficients a, b, and c.

(*b*) *The Idea of Complex Collisions*[2]

The theory developed in the preceding sections involves only quantum jumps of a single quantum. This was a consequence of the fact that in the vibrational part of the transition probability, Eq. (57–10″), only the first power of the vibrational coordinate X enters.

It follows from the numerical calculation, as can be seen from Tables 63–1 and 63–3, that the transition probability strongly decreases and Z_{tr} strongly increases with the energy $h\nu$ which has to be transferred to or from the translational energy, since ε' is proportional to $(h\nu)^2$ or ϑ^2. For that reason, complex collisions may become very important in many cases. These are collisions in which the energy to be exchanged with the translational degrees of freedom is diminished at the cost of increasing the number of vibrational quanta involved. There are two particular types of cases in which this occurs:

1. One has, for example, a diatomic gas with a vibrational characteristic temperature ϑ_1, and an impurity with a characteristic vibrational temperature $\vartheta_2 < \vartheta_1$. In a straightforward deactivation by the impurity, an energy $h\nu_1 = k\vartheta_1$ would have to be transferred to translational energy. Instead, in the complex process, the substrate loses a quantum $h\nu_1$, while in the collision the impurity molecule is excited and gains the quantum $h\nu_2$, and only the difference $h\nu_1 - h\nu_2$ is changed into translational energy. This complex process may be much faster than the direct one.

2. Even more important is the case of polyatomic molecules, which have many vibrational frequencies, $\nu_1, \nu_2 \cdots$ If only single quantum processes existed, these would each have to be de-excited separately by collisions, i.e., we would have exactly the process of de-excitation in parallel discussed in Sec. 21. However, in larger molecules the frequencies —and the separate relaxation times—are spread over a large range, so that, for example, a frequency with $\vartheta = 800$ would essentially have a Z of the order of magnitude of that of chlorine, as compared to Z values in the

hundreds (see Tables 54–1, 54–2, and 54–3). Here again the complex collision takes over in a process in which the vibrational energy of the kth vibration, $h\nu_k$, is not directly changed into translational energy, but the part $h\nu_s$ where $h\nu_s < h\nu_k$ is used to excite the sth vibration (in the same molecule or in the collision partner) by one quantum, and only the difference $h\nu_k - h\nu_s$ is transformed into translational energy.

Since the energy transferred to translation is (writing 1, 2 for s, k)

$$\pm h(\nu_1 - \nu_2) = \pm k(\vartheta_1 - \vartheta_2)$$

one gets the following result for Z_{tr}

$$Z_{\mathrm{tr}} = \pi^2 \sqrt{\frac{3}{2\pi}} \left(\frac{T}{\vartheta_{12}'}\right)^{1/6} \left(\frac{\vartheta_1 - \vartheta_2}{\vartheta_{12}'}\right)^2 \exp\left[\frac{3}{2}\left(\frac{\vartheta_{12}'}{T}\right)^{1/3} \mp \frac{\vartheta_1 - \vartheta_2}{2T} - \frac{\varepsilon}{T}\right] \tag{65–9}$$

if one follows through the calculation of Secs. 58 and 62, and defines

$$\begin{aligned} k\vartheta_{12}' &= 16\pi^4 \tilde{m}_{12} l^2 (\nu_1 - \nu_2)^2 \\ &= k\, 0.8153\, \tilde{m}_{12} l^2 (\vartheta_1 - \vartheta_2)^2. \end{aligned} \tag{65–10}$$

(c) Exact Resonance

If $\nu_1 = \nu_2$, no transfer from or to translational energy is needed. Then, in Eqs. (58–3) and (58–5), $g_i = g_j$, and the approximations used there are not valid. Instead, a direct calculation must be made. One finds

$$\lim_{g_i = g_j} \frac{g_j^2 - g_i^2}{\cosh g_j - \cosh g_i} = 4g\, e^{-g}$$

and

$$\frac{4\pi\tilde{m}}{hp} H_{\mathrm{tr}}' = 4\pi \frac{pl}{h}. \tag{65–11}$$

The average value of the square of Eq. (65–11)

$$(Z_{\mathrm{tr}})^{-1} = \left(\frac{4\pi\tilde{m}}{hp} H_{\mathrm{tr}}'\right)^2_{\mathrm{av}} = \frac{16\pi^2 l^2}{h^2} p_{\mathrm{av}}^2 \tag{65–11'}$$

is given by the fact that in collisions

$$p_{\mathrm{av}}^2 = 2\tilde{m} \cdot 2kT.$$

(The average energy of gas molecules passing through an area per second is larger by $1/2\,kT$ than that of the molecules contained in a volume.)

Therefore, Eq. (65–9) has to be replaced in this case by

$$Z_{\mathrm{tr}}{}^{-1} = \frac{64\pi^2 \tilde{m} l^2\, kT}{h^2} = \frac{4}{\pi^2}\frac{\vartheta' T}{\vartheta^2}\,. \tag{65–12}$$

This should be multiplied by $e^{\varepsilon/kT}$.

For intermediate cases where neither $g_i = g_j$ nor $|g_j - g_i| \gg 1$, one can smoothly interpolate between Eqs. (65–9) and (65–12), as Dr. F. Tanczos has pointed out. One may question why, when no exchange of kinetic energy is involved, a translational transition probability like Eq. (65–11′) and, consequently, p^2, enters into the picture at all. The reason is as follows: If the molecules were not in relative motion, but were coupled by an interaction energy $H'(r)\,[X_1 - X_2]^2/l^2$, with r constant, this interaction energy would only result in a slight shift of the vibrational frequencies, but the two molecules would continue to behave as simple harmonic oscillators, and no transitions would occur. Such transitions occur only because r varies with time.

(*d*) *Diatomic Gas with Diatomic Impurity*

The exponent in the exponential potential of interaction between the diatomic gas molecule (1) and the impurity (2) is now

$$\frac{1}{l}\left[r - \beta_1\left(\frac{m_C}{m_C + m_B}\right)_1 \Delta r_1 - \beta_2\left(\frac{m_C}{m_C + m_B}\right)_2 \Delta r_2\right]$$

where β_1, β_2 are direction cosines. The process in which the molecule (1) loses one quantum and the impurity (2) gains one quantum arises from the term

$$\frac{1}{2}\frac{d^2H'}{dr^2}\left[\beta_1\left(\frac{m_C}{m_C + m_B}\right)_1 \Delta r_1 + \beta_2\left(\frac{m_C}{m_C + m_B}\right)_2 \Delta r_2\right]^2.$$

If this is squared out, there are terms with $(\Delta r_1)^2$ and $(\Delta r_2)^2$. These simply give two quantum jumps each in molecules 1 and 2, respectively, and are of no interest now. The complex jumps arise from the double product

$$\frac{1}{2}\frac{d^2H'}{dr^2}\, 2\beta_1\beta_2 \left(\frac{m_C}{m_C + m_B}\right)_1 \left(\frac{m_C}{m_C + m_B}\right)_2 \Delta r_1 \Delta r_2 \tag{65–13}$$

and lead, if one follows the procedure of Sec. 57 exactly, to a vibrational Z_{osc}

$$Z_{osc} = \frac{1}{4\pi^4}\left(\frac{4M_B M_C}{M_B^2 + M_C^2}\right)_1 \left(\frac{4M_B M_C}{M_B^2 + M_C^2}\right)_2 \frac{\vartheta_1'}{\vartheta_1}\frac{\vartheta_2'}{\vartheta_2} \tag{65–14}$$

$$Z_0 = \overline{\beta_1^2 \beta_2^2} = 9. \tag{65–14'}$$

Here, ϑ_1' and ϑ_2' are the ϑ' for the pure gases, but with the common l.

(e) Complex Collisions in Polyatomic Molecules

The exponent in the potential interaction now looks as follows

$$\frac{1}{l}(r - \Delta r_j)$$

and the corresponding energy term is

$$+\frac{1}{2}\frac{d^2H'}{dr^2}(\Delta r_j)^2.$$

Taking the proper average over all the atoms and using Eq. (65–4), one has

$$\frac{1}{2}\frac{d^2H'}{dr^2}\sum_s \sum_k (a_{js}a_{jk} + b_{js}b_{jk} + c_{js}c_{jk})\, q_s q_k. \tag{65–15}$$

For a particular complex transition, involving the pair of normal vibrations q_1, q_2, this gives

$$\frac{1}{2}\frac{d^2H'}{dr^2}\, 2\,(a_{j1}a_{j2} + b_{j1}b_{j2} + c_{j1}c_{j2})\, q_1 q_2 \tag{65–15'}$$

(the factor 2 arises because s, k may be 1, 2 or 2, 1).

If one follows the calculation through and takes the proper average over the surface atoms

$$Z_{osc} = \frac{1}{4\pi^4}\, n' \left[\sum_{\substack{\text{surface}\\ \text{atoms}}} (a_{j1}a_{j2} + b_{j1}b_{j2} + c_{j1}c_{j2})^2\right]^{-1} \frac{m_1 m_2}{\tilde{m}^2}\frac{\vartheta_1'}{\vartheta_1}\frac{\vartheta_2'}{\vartheta_2}. \tag{65–16}$$

Here, ϑ_1' and ϑ_2' are calculated with the common $\tilde{m}$.

66. Numerical Results for Diatomic and Linear Triatomic Molecules

(a) *The Molecular Constants Used*

In this section the theoretical calculations for Z (or τ) will be compared with the experimental data. Since the molecular force constants are taken from viscosity measurements, we will have to decide which method to adopt for the calculation of l, the range of the exponential repulsion (see Sec. 59). The choice can only be made from this over-all comparison.

We first compile, from Hirschfelder's book,[1] the data used. These data are shown in Table 66–1.

TABLE 66–1
DATA FOR MOLECULAR COLLISIONS

Molecular pair	r_0, A	ε/k(°K)	$\tilde{M}$	ϑ(°K)
N_2-N_2	3.681	91.5	14	3380
N_2-H_2	3.325	55.2	1.87	3380
O_2-O_2	3.433	113.2	16	2230
O_2-H_2	3.201	62.4	1.88	2230
O_2-N_2	3.557	102	14.93	2230
Cl_2-Cl_2	4.115	357	35.46	810
Cl_2-He	3.41	46.4	3.78	810
Cl_2-N_2	3.898	181	20	810
Br_2-Br_2	4.268	520	80	470
CO_2	3.996	190	22	959
COS	4.13	335	30	758
CS_2	4.438	488	38	570

For pairs of unlike molecules, r_0 has been taken as the arithmetical mean and ε as the geometrical mean of the corresponding two values for the pure gases.

It should be noted that an increase in r_0 and an increase in ε affect η in the same direction, so that one may have the same η if one increases r_0 and decreases ε. Only by measuring the temperature dependence can the two quantities be separated.

---

[1] J. O. Hirschfelder, C. F. Curtiss, and R. B. Bird, "Molecular Theory of Gases and Liquids." Wiley, New York, 1954.

However, the effect on τ of a change of r_0 and ε is opposite, an increase in r_0 increasing τ, and an increase in ε decreasing τ. For example, let us assume that, due to a faulty measurement of $d\eta/dT$, ε for CS_2 is 10% too small. To get the correct value of η, one has to decrease r_0 (and therefore l) by 3%. From Eq. (63–3), this means an increase of Z by 27%, while the direct effect of the change decreases it by 18%, resulting in an over-all increase of 9%.

(b) *The Number of Collisions at Elevated Temperatures*

If the viscosity is known, the number of collisions can be calculated from Eq. (36–3). However, at elevated temperatures, η may not be known. Under these circumstances, the formulas and tables developed by Hirschfelder and his collaborators for the calculation of η (starting from the data relating to η at moderate temperatures) are used. Table 66–2 shows the results.

TABLE 66–2

TIME BETWEEN COLLISIONS IN 10^{-10} SEC FOR 1 ATM

$T^{-1/3}$	T (°K)	CO_2	Cl_2	O_2	N_2
0.1514	288	1.15	1.03	1.51	1.36
0.1181	600	2.1			2.29
0.1	1000	3.10	3.30	3.67	2.66
0.09	1372		4.12	4.45	3.88
0.08	1953		5.24	5.71	4.95
0.07	2912			7.35	6.40
0.06	4630				8.65

$T^{-1/3}$ is listed because the experimental papers on shock waves often use this quantity as abscissa.

The next table, Table 66–3, gives the measured τ and the Z calculated from it and from the data of Table 66–2. The experimental τ are interpolated visually to the selected T values, which may involve errors of 20%. The data at room temperature are taken from Secs. 50, 51, and 52. The value of τ (and Z) for N_2 at 550 °K is fairly uncertain and is therefore put in parenthesis.

TABLE 66–3

EXPERIMENTAL τ AND Z AT ELEVATED TEMPERATURES

Gas	T (°K)	τ	Z
O_2	288	3.18×10^{-3}	2.1×10^{7}
	1372	15×10^{-6}	36000
	1953	7×10^{-6}	12000
	2912	1.3×10^{-6}	1800
N_2	550	(24×10^{-3})	1.1×10^{8}
	778	1.8×10^{-3}	6.5×10^{6}
	1020	1.4×10^{-3}	4.5×10^{6}
	1168	8.0×10^{-4}	2.3×10^{6}
	3640	18×10^{-6}	24000
	4630	7×10^{-6}	8000
CO_2	288	2.5×10^{-6}	22000
	600	$(6\pm 2)\times 10^{-7}$	3000
	1000	$(9\pm 3)\times 10^{-8}$	300
Cl_2	288	3.5×10^{-6}	34000
	1000	$(1.8\pm 0.3)\times 10^{-7}$	550
	1372	$(8.5\pm 4)\times 10^{-8}$	200

(c) *Calculations with Method A and Method B*

We next compare the experimental results with the theory; l is calculated according to Method A or B of Sec. 59. For Z, Eqs. (62–13), (62–13′). and (62–13″) are used, with Z_0 equal to 3. This is called Z'.

TABLE 66–4

COMPARISON OF THEORETICAL AND EXPERIMENTAL Z' (METHOD A)

Gas	T(°K)	E_m/ε	r_0/l	l, A	$\vartheta'\times 10^{-6}$	Z'_{calc}	Z_{exp}
O_2	288	25.88	17.29	0.1986	2.604	6.80×10^{8}	2.1×10^{7}
O_2	1372	70.76	17.25	0.1995	2.617	82400	36000
O_2	1953	89.02	17.44	0.1968	2.560	15200	12000
O_2	2912	112.2	17.65	0.1945	2.500	2780	1800
N_2	550	66.1	17.26	0.2117	5.842	1.2×10^{10}	1.1×10^{8}
N_2	3640	226.8	18.11	0.2033	5.387	27800	24000
N_2	4630	264.9	18.24	0.2018	5.311	9350	8000
Cl_2	288	5.96	18.31	0.225	0.926	578000	34000
Cl_2	1000	14.23	17.50	0.235	1.049	4900	550
Cl_2	1372	17.63	17.41	0.236	1.060	1650	200
CO_2	300	11.42	17.63	0.2267	0.8475	118000	22000
CO_2	600	17.86	17.41	0.2295	0.8690	6100	3000
CO_2	1000	25.24	17.28	0.2313	0.8820	915	300

Gas	T(°K)	E_m/ε	r_0/l	l, A	$\vartheta' \times 10^{-6}$	Z'_{calc}	Z_{exp}
N_2O	273	8.068	17.96	0.2160	0.6002	24200	8400
N_2O	473	11.75	17.71	0.2190	0.6173	3870	3300
N_2O	673	15.00	17.48	0.2219	0.6337	1200	2100
O_2-H_2	288	22.90	17.30	0.1850	0.2680	4680	20000
Cl_2-He	288	22.04	17.35	0.196	0.0780	6950	900
Cl_2-N_2	288	9.824	17.79	0.2241	0.5300	73500	43000
COS	288	5.815	18.34	0.225	0.7817	30000	9600
CS_2	288	3.841	18.93	0.2344	0.5532	4800	8000

TABLE 66–5

COMPARISON OF THEORETICAL AND EXPERIMENTAL Z' (METHOD B)

Gas	T(°K)	E_m/ε	r_0/l	l, A	$\vartheta' \times 10^{-6}$	Z'_{calc}	Z_{exp}
O_2	288	25.35	19.21	0.1787	2.072	7.30×10^7	2.1×10^7
O_2	1372	71.33	18.73	0.1833	2.179	20600	36000
O_2	1953	90.5	18.66	0.1840	2.196	6400	12000
O_2	2912	118.6	18.57	0.1849	2.217	1900	1800
N_2	550	62.82	18.76	0.1963	5.023	7.61×10^8	1.1×10^8
N_2	778	79.39	18.68	0.1971	5.066	7.30×10^7	6.5×10^6
N_2	1020	95.20	18.64	0.1974	5.082	1.22×10^7	4.5×10^6
N_2	1168	103.3	18.62	0.1976	5.093	3.03×10^6	2.3×10^6
N_2	3640	223.7	18.49	0.1991	5.169	23000	24000
N_2	4630	262.6	18.49	0.1991	5.169	8400	8000
Cl_2	288	5.57	20.55	0.1998	0.7575	180000	34000
Cl_2	1000	13.15	19.65	0.2090	0.8284	2100	550
Cl_2	1372	16.32	19.50	0.2106	0.8412	780	200
CO_2	300	10.30	19.87	0.2011	0.6672	33000	22000
CO_2	600	16.56	19.50	0.2049	0.6927	2300	3000
CO_2	1000	23.47	19.25	0.2076	0.7107	440	300
N_2O	273	7.46	20.20	0.1920	0.4745	10900	8400
N_2O	473	10.88	19.89	0.1950	0.4894	1500	3300
N_2O	673	13.87	19.66	0.1973	0.5009	520	2100
Br_2	300	3.634	20.92	0.2040	0.5997	37500	—
O_2-H_2	288	21.27	19.32	0.1657	0.2149	2150	20000
Cl_2-He	288	18.67	19.40	0.1757	0.0624	1790	900
Cl_2-N_2	288	9.093	19.98	0.2001	0.4300	24300	43000
COS	288	5.372	20.59	0.2006	0.5655	8800	9600
CS_2	288	3.415	21.07	0.2106	0.4464	1800	8000
O_2-N_2	1953	90.7	18.66	0.1842	2.200	1.003*	2.5†

* $(Z'O_2\text{-}O_2/Z'O_2\text{-}N_2)_{calc}$.

† $(ZO_2\text{-}O_2/ZO_2\text{-}N_2)_{exp}$.

A rough review of the data is shown in Table 66–6.

TABLE 66–6
Z'_{calc}/Z_{exp}

Gas	T (°K)	Method A	Method B
O_2	288	32.5	3.45
O_2	1372	2.29	0.58
O_2	1953	1.27	0.53
O_2	2912	1.54	1.05
N_2	550	110	7
N_2	778	—	11
N_2	1020	—	2.7
N_2	1168	—	7
N_2	3640	1.16	0.96
N_2	4630	1.17	1.05
Cl_2	288	17	5.3
Cl_2	1000	8.9	3.9
Cl_2	1372	8.25	3.9
CO_2	300	5.4	1.5
CO_2	600	2.0	0.77
CO_2	1000	3.05	1.47
N_2O	273	2.86	1.3
N_2O	473	1.17	0.45
N_2O	673	0.57	0.25
O_2-H_2	288	0.235	0.107
Cl_2-He	288	7.7	2.0
Cl_2-N_2	288	1.7	0.56
COS	288	3.1	0.92
CS_2	288	0.60	0.225

On the whole, one gets the impression that Method B gives the better results, and this will be chosen from now on.

(d) Replacement of Steric Factor 3 by Taking Account of Simultaneous Rotational Transitions

Using the equations of Sec. 64, one finds, from Eq. (64–19), the results given in Tables 66–7 and 66–8.

TABLE 66–7
METHOD *A*

Gas	T (°K)	Z_{calc}	Z_{calc}/Z_{exp}
O_2	288	124×10^7	58
O_2	1372	1.5×10^5	4.17
O_2	1953	28000	2.33
O_2	2912	4730	2.63
N_2	550	2200×10^7	200
N_2	3640	54800	2.28
N_2	4630	19500	2.31
Cl_2	288	1.7×10^6	49
Cl_2	1000	13800	25
Cl_2	1372	4620	23.1
O_2-H_2	288	8560	0.43
Cl_2-He	288	20700	23
Cl_2-N_2	288	215000	5

TABLE 66–8
METHOD *B*

Gas	T (°K)	Z_{calc}	Z_{calc}/Z_{exp}
O_2	288	14.8×10^7	7.0
O_2	1372	41000	1.14
O_2	1953	12700	1.06
O_2	2912	3700	2.05
N_2	550	1.41×10^9	13
N_2	778	1.29×10^8	20
N_2	1020	2.26×10^7	5
N_2	1168	5.59×10^6	2.2
N_2	3640	42500	1.77
N_2	4630	15500	1.94
Cl_2	288	600000	17.7
Cl_2	1000	6680	12.1
Cl_2	1372	2400	12
Br_2	300	114000	—
O_2-H_2	288	4400	0.22
Cl_2-He	288	5850	6.5
Cl_2-N_2	288	80000	1.9
$(Z_{O_2\text{-}O_2}/Z_{O_2\text{-}N_2})_{calc}$	1953	1.075	

(e) *Triatomic Molecules*

For the triatomic molecules one gets, with the { } in Eq. (64–25′) set equal to unity, the results shown in Tables 66–9 and 66–10.

TABLE 66–9
METHOD *A*

Gas	T (°K)	$Z_{calc}\left(\frac{3}{2h+1}\right)^2$	$(Z_{calc}/Z_{exp})\left(\frac{3}{2h+1}\right)^2$
CO_2	300	343000	15.6
CO_2	600	17700	5.9
CO_2	1000	660	8.9
N_2O	273	75000	8.9
N_2O	473	12000	3.6
N_2O	673	3700	1.76
COS	288	81300	8.5
CS_2	288	12900	1.61

TABLE 66–10
METHOD *B*

Gas	T (°K)	$Z_{calc}\left(\frac{3}{2h+1}\right)^2$	$(Z_{calc}/Z_{exp})\left(\frac{3}{2h+1}\right)^2$
CO_2	300	96000	4.37
CO_2	600	6700	2.3
CO_2	1000	1280	4.3
N_2O	273	33800	4.0
N_2O	473	4600	1.4
N_2O	673	1610	0.77
COS	288	23900	2.5
CS_2	288	4840	0.61

(f) *General Discussion*

There are 17 data on diatomic molecules for Method B. Five of these give a ratio Z_{calc}/Z_{exp} between 20 and 10; three, a ratio between 10 and 5;

seven, between 3 and 1; and two, a ratio between 0.4 and 0.2. Furthermore, there are eight data on triatomic molecules where the calculated Z contains an unknown constant h. If the latter is put equal to unity, six of the ratios lie between 4.4 and 1 and two between 0.8 and 0.6.

One has a general impression that[2] for large Z the theoretical values of Z are too large; for small Z, too small. One might think that this is due to the failure of the Lennard-Jones expression, Eq. (59–1), at high energies. But the relative position of the effective collisions on the potential energy curve is measured by E_m/ε, and the deviations do not have a simple connection with E_m/ε. Z_{calc}/Z_{exp} is near unity for CO_2 (E_m/ε 10 to 20) and for O_2 and N_2 at high temperatures (E_m/ε 70 to 260). For O_2 and Cl_2 at room temperature, the ratio is 7 to 20 (E_m/ε 25 and 5.6); for CS_2 it is low ($E_m/\varepsilon = 3.4$).

It should be emphasized again that there is *no* adjustable constant in the theory.

It is possible to calculate backward an interaction energy which would give exactly the experimental Z. Z is very sensitive to the shape of the energy curve. For example, to get the exact experimental value for O_2 at 288°, one has to change, at $E/\varepsilon = 22.6$, r/r_0 from 0.8359 to 0.8444.

Several authors have assumed without further justification that $l \sim 1 - 2$A and then have pointed out correctly that this gives far too small a probability. Tables 66–4 and 66–5 show instead that $l = 0.16 - 0.24$ A. This range agrees remarkably well with the l one gets if one represents the repulsive potential between rare gas atoms by an exponential expression calculated from quantum theory. Slater[3] finds that for He-He, $l = 0.2183$ A. Bleick and Mayer[4] find that for Ne-Ne, $l = 0.2091$ A.

67. Further Numerical Discussion of the Effect of Impurities, of Complex Collisions, and of Exact Resonance

The strong effect of water vapor on the τ of CO_2 and other gases was recognized early (see Secs. 51 and 52), but could not be explained for a long time. Widom and Bauer[1] gave a detailed treatment of the CO_2-H_2O mixture, comparing the classical and quantum theoretical treatment. They could explain the results by essentially assuming an exceptionally large ε/k. (The effect of H_2O on O_2 is a special case; see later in this section.) Although

---

[2] See however, T. L. Cottrell, *Trans. Faraday Soc.* **54**, 1098 (1958).

[3] J. C. Slater, *Phys. Rev.* **32**, 349 (1928).

[4] W. E. Bleick and J. E. Mayer, *J. Chem. Phys.* **2**, 252 (1934).

[1] B. Widom and S. H. Bauer, *J. Chem. Phys.* **21**, 1670 (1953).

for such a large ε/k the approximations of our theory are not valid, it is worthwhile to see what one would get. For the calculation, one replaces the whole field of the H_2O molecule, which contains a dipole contribution, by a Lennard-Jones field, with $r_0 = 3.282$, $\varepsilon/k = 417$, but uses as the interaction ε/k not the geometrical mean, but the much higher value 1200. One then gets the following results for CO_2-H_2O at 300 °K: E_m/ε, 1.181; r_0/l, 22.4; l, 0.1624 A; ϑ', 252,700; Z_{calc}, 83; and Z_{exp}, 120.

Eucken[2] found that the Z for CO_2-H_2O decreases with rising temperature, as usual, but then reaches a minimum and increases with further increase of temperature. There is no theoretical explanation for such behavior.

For two cases tested, Eqs. (65–9) and (65–14) do not fit at all, inasmuch as the experimental Z are much lower than the theoretical. One case is O_2 with CO as impurity. O_2-CO at 288°, computed by Method B, gives: E_m/ε, 12.44; r_0/l, 19.77; l, 0.1776 A; ϑ', 2.582×10^5; Z_0, 9; (Z_{osc}) O_2, 106; (Z_{osc}) CO, 121; Z_{tr}, 1360; Z_{calc}, 1.6×10^8; Z_{exp}, 8000.

The second case is that of Cl_2-CO, where the formulas do not give any indication that CO should be efficient as deactivator, while the experiment[2] gives $Z = 230$.

Slawsky[3] had suggested as explanation in the latter case the chemical affinity between Cl_2 and CO, due to the possible formation of phosgene Cl_2CO, since such an affinity should give high efficiency, according to Franck and Eucken.[4] Whether such an explanation is applicable to the case O_2-CO is unknown.

For exact resonance, $\vartheta_1 = \vartheta_2$, the expression is Eqs. (65–12) and (65–14)

$$Z = Z_0 Z_{\text{osc}} Z_{\text{tr}} = Z_0 \left(\frac{4\,M_B M_C}{M_B{}^2 + M_C{}^2}\right)_1 \left(\frac{4\,M_B M_C}{M_B{}^2 + M_C{}^2}\right)_2 \frac{1}{16\,\pi^2} \frac{\vartheta_1{}'}{\vartheta} \frac{\vartheta_2{}'}{\vartheta} \frac{\vartheta^2}{\vartheta_{12}{}'T} e^{-\varepsilon/kT}. \tag{67–1}$$

In this case, $\vartheta_1{}'$, $\vartheta_2{}'$, and $\vartheta_{12}{}'$ differ only by the relative masses they contain

$$\vartheta_1{}' : \vartheta_2{}' : \vartheta_{12}{}' = \tfrac{1}{2}\,(m_B + m_C)_1 : \tfrac{1}{2}\,(m_B + m_C)_2 : \tilde{m}. \tag{67–2}$$

Therefore

$$Z = Z_0 \frac{1}{4\,\pi^2} \left[\frac{(M_B + M_C) M_B M_C}{M_B{}^2 + M_C{}^2}\right]_1 \left[\frac{(M_B + M_C) M_B M_C}{M_B{}^2 + M_C{}^2}\right]_2 \frac{1}{\tilde{M}^2} \frac{\vartheta_{12}{}'}{T} e^{-\varepsilon/kT}. \tag{67–3}$$

---

[2] A. Eucken and R. Becker, *Z. physik. Chem.* *B* **27**, 235 (1934).
[3] Z. I. Slawsky, private communication.
[4] J. Franck and A. Eucken, *Z. physik. Chem.* *B* **20**, 460 (1933).

A particular simple case is the one in which molecule 1 is the same kind as molecule 2. Then this expression governs the rate of adjustment of the internal distribution function, Eq. (67–3) being the number of collisions needed for one molecule to make the transition $1 \rightarrow 0$ and the other the transition $0 \rightarrow 1$.

For the transition $j \rightarrow j-1,\ i \rightarrow i+1$, Eq. (67–3) has to be divided by $j(i+1)$.

If the two molecules are the same kind

$$\tilde{M} = \tfrac{1}{2}(M_B + M_C)$$

and[5]

$$Z = \frac{Z_0}{\pi^2}\left(\frac{M_B M_C}{M_B{}^2 + M_C{}^2}\right)^2 \frac{\vartheta_{12}'}{T} e^{-\varepsilon/kT}. \tag{67–3'}$$

This means, for example, that at $T = 288°$, the Z for exchange of internal energy between like molecules for O_2 is 124 Z_0; for Cl_2, 20 Z_0; and for CO_2, 30 Z_0.

It follows from the above that the equilibrium between the different vibrational states needs far fewer collisions—and is therefore established much faster—than that between translation and vibration.[6]

The only case in which the formulas given for exact resonance can be tested is that of the collision between O_2 and H_2O, if Boudart's explanation[7]

---

[5] The question arises here as to what l to take, i.e., what value of E_m/ε. Fortunately, since ϑ' appears only as factor and not as exponent, the result does not depend critically on the choice of l. One might choose $E_m/\varepsilon = 2kT/\varepsilon$ or, more crudely, equal to zero, which gives $r_0/l = 24$.

[6] One can show that the equation giving the change in occupation numbers due to collisions which only transfer single quanta between molecules of the same kind is ($\bar{\varepsilon}$ is the average vibrational energy per molecule)

$$-\tau \frac{dN_j}{dt} = N_{j+1} - \frac{h\nu}{\bar{\varepsilon} + h\nu} N_j - \left[N_j - \frac{h\nu}{\bar{\varepsilon} + h\nu} N_{j-1}\right] \tag{67–4}$$

where

$$\tau = Z\left(1 + \frac{\bar{\varepsilon}}{h\nu}\right)\tau_c.$$

Shuler and Montroll have shown how to solve Eq. (67–4). See K. E. Shuler and E. Montroll, *J. Chem. Phys.* **26**, 454 (1957).

[7] C. S. Tuesday and M. Boudart, Tech. Note 7, Contract AF 33(038)–23976, Princeton University, Princeton, New Jersey, January, 1955.

for the quadratic dependence of τ^{-1} on water content is right. Water vapor has, as mentoned before, a dipole moment, and the Lennard-Jones potential fits badly. Nonetheless, we will use

$$r_0 = \tfrac{1}{2}(3.433 + 3.282) = 3.357$$

and

$$\frac{\varepsilon}{k} = \sqrt{110 \times \frac{1}{1.1} 459} = 214.2$$

since 459 is the Sutherland constant in the range 300°—400 °K and 1.1 ε/k is approximately equal to the Sutherland constant. One gets $r_0/l = 21.0$, $l = 0.16$ A, $\vartheta' = 1.226 \times 10^6$, $Z_{\text{calc}} = 15.3\, Z_0 \sim 140$ and $Z_{\text{exp}} \sim 2000$.

68. Polyatomic Molecules: Methane and Chlorinated Methanes

The most complicated molecules which have been treated by the methods described in the preceding are methane and the four chlorinated methanes, for which the experimental data have been given in Sec. 54. The work involved is so great that it is not likely that even more complex molecules will be investigated without a compelling motive.

Tanczos[1] had to use the Krieger potential,[2] which explicitly includes a dipole contribution, for the dipole molecules CH_3Cl, CH_2Cl_2, and $CHCl_3$.

TABLE 68-1
EQUIVALENT EXPONENTIAL INTERACTION FOR METHANE AND CHLORINATED METHANES; METHOD C, $T = 300$ °K

Gas	r_0, A	r_0/l	l, A
CH_4	3.832	18.5	0.208
CH_3Cl	4.332	26.6	0.164
CH_2Cl_2	4.913	24.1	0.204
$CHCl_3$	5.117	23.3	0.219
CCl_4	5.528	22.9	0.241

[1] F. Tanczos, Catholic Univ. Ph. D. Dissertation, Washington, D.C., 1956. *J. Chem. Phys.* **25**, 439 (1956).

[2] F. I. Krieger, The Viscosity of Polar Gases, Project Rand. Rept. R. M 646, July 1, 1951.

As we shall see, the relaxation times come out too long, as compared with experiment. If a straight Lennard-Jones potential had been used, the values of τ would have been further increased by the factors 19.2, 1.81, and 1.56. The resulting l-values are shown in Table 68–1. They were calculated with Method C, Eq. (59–11″), of Sec. 59.

Next, the geometrical constants and effective masses of the normal modes were calculated. Table 68–2 shows the values for the hydrogen and chlorine atoms which form the surface of the molecule.

TABLE 68–2

CALCULATED VALUES OF THE SQUARED COEFFICIENTS RELATING ATOMIC CARTESIAN COORDINATES TO NORMAL COORDINATES (m IS MEASURED IN ATOMIC UNITS)*

Gas	a	ν (cm^{-1})	C_a'/R	$\frac{1}{m_H}\sum_H (a_{Ha}^2 + b_{Ha}^2 + c_{Ha}^2)$	$\frac{1}{m_{Cl}}\sum_{Cl} (a_{Cla}^2 + b_{Cla}^2 + c_{Cla}^2)$
CH_4	2	1499	0.0827	0.9921	—
	1	1306	0.2359	0.8504	
CH_3Cl	4	1455	0.0961	0.9632	0
	3	1355	0.0671	0.8650	0
	2	1015	0.3823	0.8246	0.0004
	1	732	0.4026	0.0987	0.0083
CH_2Cl_2	7	1423	0.0536	0.9126	0
	6	1260	0.0911	0.9190	0.0005
	5	1151	0.1280	0.9890	0.0110
	4	899	0.2632	0.6752	0.0006
	3	737	0.3943	0.0228	0.0064
	2	702	0.4273	0.1027	0.0078
	1	283	0,8629	0.0129	0.0250
$CHCl_3$	5	1211	0.1954	0.9705	0.0004
	4	760	0.7474	0.0112	0.0054
	3	670	0.4585	0.0627	0.0075
	2	363	0.7866	0.0128	0.0238
	1	261	1.7643	0.0057	0.0262
CCl_4	4	776	1.0784	—	0.0043
	3	458	0.6850	—	0.0282
	2	314	2.5033	—	0.0261
	1	218	1.8312	—	0.0282

* To compare with the expressions of Sec. 65, particularly Eq. (65–5), note that H or Cl takes the role of the first index, a that of the second.

Finally, the equations for the rates were set up as follows (we use a notation consistent with that in this book, but differing from Tanczos).

The notation

$$\bar{k}_{10}(a) \qquad [\text{Tanczos } MP_{10}(a)]$$

designates the quantity k_{10} for the vibration a, which corresponds to the deactivation of the first excited state by one quantum and the transfer of its energy to translation, and which is given by the reciprocal of Eq. (62–16).

The quantity, e.g.

$$\tau_c \bar{k}_{02}^{10}(a,b) \qquad [\text{Tanczos } P_{02}^{10}(a,b)]$$

is the probability per collision of the complex process in which vibration a goes from a state of one quantum to a state of zero quantum, vibration b from no quantum to a state containing two quanta, and the energy $h\nu_a - 2\,h\nu_b$ is transferred to the translational degrees of freedom.

Define now the following quantities

$$\frac{1}{\tau_{aa}} = (1 - e^{-\vartheta_a/T}) \Big\{ \bar{k}_{10}(a) + \sum_b g_b\,(1 - e^{-\vartheta_b/T})^{-1} \cdot \\ [\bar{k}_{01}^{10}\,(ab) + 2\,(1 - e^{-\vartheta_b/T})^{-1}\,\bar{k}_{02}^{10}\,(ab) + 2\,e^{-\vartheta_b/T}\,\bar{k}_{01}^{20}(ab)] \Big\} \tag{68–1}$$

$$\frac{1}{\tau_{ab}} = g_b \frac{\vartheta_b}{\vartheta_a} (1 - e^{-\vartheta_b/T})^{-1} \{ (1 - e^{-\vartheta_a/T})\,[\bar{k}_{01}^{10}\,(ab) + 2\,\bar{k}_{02}^{10}\,(ab)] + \\ 2\,e^{-\vartheta_a/T}\,\bar{k}_{01}^{20}\,(ab) \}. \tag{68–2}$$

The g_b are the degeneracies of the states b.

Tanczos calls $1/\tau_{aa} : k_{aa}$, $1/\tau_{ab} : k_{ab}$, and $1/\tau_c : M$. The rate equations are then

$$\frac{dT_a}{dt} = \frac{1}{\tau_{aa}} (T_{\text{tr}} - T_a) - \sum_{b \neq a} \frac{1}{\tau_{ab}} (T_{\text{tr}} - T_b). \tag{68–3}$$

The left side of Eq. (68–3) may be written as

$$\frac{dT_{\text{tr}}}{dt} - \frac{d}{dt} (T_{\text{tr}} - T_a).$$

If everything is proportional to $e^{i\omega t}$, one has

$$T_{\text{tr}} - T_0 = \left(1 + \frac{1}{i\omega\tau_{aa}}\right) (T_{\text{tr}} - T_a) - \sum_{b \neq a} \frac{1}{i\omega\tau_{ab}} (T_{\text{tr}} - T_b) \tag{68–4}$$

or

$$1 = \left(1 + \frac{1}{i\omega\tau_{aa}}\right)\left(1 - \frac{dT_a}{dT_{\text{tr}}}\right) - \sum_{b \neq a} \frac{1}{i\omega\tau_{ab}}\left(1 - \frac{dT_b}{dT_{\text{tr}}}\right). \qquad (68\text{–}4')$$

Since the effective specific heat is, see Eq. (20–1)

$$(C_p)_{\text{eff}} = C_p - \sum_s C_s'\left(1 - \frac{dT_s}{dT_{tr}}\right)$$

one needs to solve Eq. (68–4′) and represent $\mathfrak{V}^2/\mathfrak{V}_0^2$ as the sum of relaxation terms, as described in Secs. 23 and 24. The results are given in Table 68–3.

TABLE 68–3
Calculated Constants for Terms of Appreciable Value in the Dispersion Equation, Eq. (21–6)

Gas	i	$\dfrac{RC_i''}{C_v\tilde{C}_p}$	$\tau_i''(10^{-6}\,\text{sec})$
CH_4	1	0.0245	2.864
	2	0.0001	0.0016
CH_3Cl	1	0.0600	0.1733
	2	0.0036	0.0043
CH_2Cl_2	1	0.0627	0.0123
	2	0.0015	0.1120
	3	0.0547	1.367
$CHCl_3$	1	0.1342	0.0363
	2	0.0007	0.1886
	3	0.0306	1.983
CCl_4	1	0.1854	0.0537
	2	0.0001	0.0839
	3	0.0135	~1000

Table 68–4 shows the effective relaxation time τ'', i. e. the τ_i'' of Table 68–3 belonging to the largest C_i'', and compares it with $\bar{\tau}''$, the time calculated according to Section 62 for direct collisions with the vibration of lowest ϑ. The agreement is fair. Of course this would give no clue to the possible existence of additional relaxation frequencies.

TABLE 68–4

COMPARISON OF CALCULATED EFFECTIVE RELAXATION TIME* τ'' WITH SIMPLE ENERGY EXCHANGE WITH TRANSLATION $\bar{\tau}''$

Gas	C''/R	τ''	$\bar{\tau}''$
CH_4	0.318	2.86	2.43
CH_3Cl	0.908	0.173	0.116
CH_2Cl_2	0.863	0.0123	0.0167
$CHCl_3$	2.550	0.0363	0.0388
CCl_4	5.020	0.0537	0.0332

* These values are in 10^{-6} sec.

TABLE 68–5

CALCULATED AND EXPERIMENTAL VALUES OF f'', THE MIDPOINT OF THE DISPERSION CURVE FOR METHANE AND CHLORINATED METHANES, AT 30 °C; f'' IN Mc

Gas	f''_{calc}	f''_{exp}	Reference
CH_4	0.055	0.123	3
CH_3Cl	0.93	1.13	4
		0.64	5*
		1.04	6*
CH_2Cl_2	0.12, 13	2.27, 105	4
		1.4	5*
$CHCl_3$	3.4	27.3	4
		4.1	5*
CCl_4	2.6	23.3	4
		1.4	5*

* Data transposed to 30 °C.

Finally, Table 68–5 shows the theoretical and experimental frequencies for the inflection points of the dispersion curves, f''. It is seen that the

---

[3] A. Eucken and S. Aybar, *Z. physik. Chem.* **B46**, 195 (1940).
[4] D. Sette, A. Busala, and J. C. Hubbard, *J. Chem. Phys.* **23**, 787 (1955).
[5] P. G. T. Fogg, P. A. Hanks, and J. D. Lambert, *Proc. Roy. Soc.* **A219**, 490 (1953).
[6] T. D. Rossing and S. Legvold, *J. Chem. Phys.* **23**, 1118 (1955).

theory gives a good picture of the character of the individual curves and shows moderate numerical agreement for CH_4 and CH_3Cl, but for the other molecules the theoretical frequencies are too low by a factor 8–10. The data of Fogg *et al.*[5] were reduced to 303°C by the use of the present theory. This resulted in a factor 1.38. Inoue and Takahashi[7] have also calculated τ for CH_4 and find 7.6×10^{-5} sec.

Dickens and Linnett[8] have applied a similar procedure to the calculation of the dispersion curve of SO_2. In agreement with the results of Lambert and Salter (Sec. 53) the curves show two distinct relaxation times, but the calculated relaxation times are 5 to 10 times longer than the observed ones, as is the case for Tanczos' theory. The short relaxation time corresponds to the relaxation of the mode with $\vartheta = 752$, the long τ to that of the modes with $\vartheta = 1656$ and 1956.

69. Theory of Exchange of Rotational and Translational Energy

This subject was first treated in a general way by Zener,[1] who predicted a high efficiency for these transitions. Later, Roy and Rose[2] investigated the problem further.

The basic assumptions[3,4] are those made in Sec. 64, namely, that each atom of the molecule BB exerts central forces on the hitting molecule A. Accordingly, the part of the interaction energy which induces transitions between rotational and translational energy is given by the middle term of Eq. (64–4), as follows

$$2\,H^0\left[\cosh\left(\frac{L}{2\,l}\cos\Gamma\right)-1\right]e^{-r/l}$$

or better (see Eq. 64–4′)

$$2\,H^0\,e^{L/2l}\left[e^{-L/2l}\cosh\left(\frac{L}{2\,l}\cos\Gamma\right)-1\right]e^{-r/l}. \tag{69–1}$$

Beckerle[5] has compared this expression with the direct quantum theoretical calculations of Margenau[6] for H_2, and finds that these are better represented

---

[7] T. Inoue and T. Takahashi, *Phys. Soc. Japan* **10**, 208 (1935).
[8] P. G. D. Dickens and J. W. Linnett, *Proc. Roy. Soc.* **A243**, 84 (1957).
[1] C. Zener, *Phys. Rev.* **37**, 556 (1931).
[2] A. S. Roy and M. E. Rose, *Proc. Roy. Soc.* **A149**, 511 (1935).
[3] J. M. Jackson and A. Howarth, *Proc. Roy. Soc.* **A152**, 515 (1935).
[4] J. de Boer, *Physica* **9**, 363 (1942).
[5] J. C. Beckerle, *J. Chem. Phys.* **21**, 2034 (1953).
[6] H. Margenau, *Phys. Rev.* **64**, 131 (1943).

by a formula like Eq. (64–4), if for L a value only equal to 0.488 times the distance H-H is used[7] (it is true that this is the more complicated case of the interaction of *two* diatomic molecules).

Beckerle solved the problem for the case of a plane rotator, treating it as a one-dimensional scattering problem. Because the H_2 molecule has equal ends, only jumps by even numbers of the rotational quantum number J are allowed. Integration over the Maxwell distribution was performed numerically for H_2 and D_2.

Brout[8] makes a power development of the hyperbolic cosines in Eq. (64–4) and breaks off at the second term

$$H = 2\,H^0\,e^{-r/l}\left\{1 + \frac{1}{2}\left(\frac{L}{2\,l}\right)^2 \cos^2 \Gamma\right\} \tag{69–2}$$

but treats the problem for three dimensions. Both he and Beckerle use distorted wave functions for the calculation, "distorted" by the unperturbed exponential interaction energy; see the first term in Eq. (69–2). Equation (69–2) is rewritten, using the Legendre function P_2

$$P_2 = \tfrac{3}{2}\cos^2 \Gamma - \tfrac{1}{2}$$

$$\begin{aligned} H &= 2\,H^0\,e^{-r/l}\left\{1 + \frac{L^2}{24\,l^2} + \frac{L^2}{12\,l^2}\,P_2\right\} \\ &= 2\,H^0\left(1 + \frac{L^2}{24\,l^2}\right)e^{-r/l}\left\{1 + \frac{L^2}{12\,l^2}\left(1 + \frac{L^2}{24\,l^2}\right)^{-1} P_2\right\} \\ &= H^{00}\,e^{-r/l}\,\{1 + \Lambda P_2\}. \end{aligned} \tag{69–3}$$

The rotational states of the molecule are characterized by two quantum numbers, J (orbital angular momentum) and m (projection of J on the direction of the incoming molecules). The result is again a product of two factors, one involving the rotational change, which depends appreciably on the change in m; and one involving the translational change, which is assumed to depend little on the change in m.

The final result is

$$Z_{2-0} = 329 \qquad Z_{3-1} = 338$$

in fairly good agreement with experiment.

---

[7] Brout[8] gets nearly the same value for $L/2l$ (1.30) as Beckerle (1.13). However, he uses the distance L between the H atoms, because his l (0.283A) is nearly twice that of Beckerle (0.162A).

[8] R. Brout, *J. Chem. Phys.* **22**, 934 (1954).

The rotational energy values of a simple rotator are

$$E_{\text{rot}} = \frac{h^2}{8\,\pi^2[I]} J(J+1) = k\vartheta_r J(J+1) \tag{69–4}$$

$$\vartheta_r = \frac{h^2}{8\,\pi^2[I]k}\,. \tag{69–4'}$$

Here $[I]$ is the moment of inertia and J the rotational quantum number.

The energy change in a transition from J to $J-2$ is

$$\Delta E_{\text{rot}} = k\vartheta_r\{J(J+1) - (J-2)(J-1)\} = 4\,k\vartheta_r\,(J-\tfrac{1}{2}). \tag{69–5}$$

H_2 and D_2 have a particularly small moment of inertia. The ϑ_r is 85 for H_2, so that the transition $2 \to 0$ involves a $\Delta E = 510\,k$, larger than the kT at room temperature. Correspondingly, the transition probabilities are small and there is no difficulty in treating inelastic collisions by first-order perturbation methods. This will probably apply also to other molecules of composition HB (B being any atom), such as HCl and OH, where the rotation is essentially one of H atoms around a heavy atom. However, other molecules have much smaller ϑ_r values: such as N_2, 2.8; CO, 2.7; and Cl_2, 0.35. For such molecules the energy difference for a transition at the most probable values of J, $J \sim \sqrt{T/(2\,\vartheta_r)}$, is approximately

$$\Delta E_{\text{rot}} = \sqrt{8\,\frac{\vartheta_r}{T}}\,kT \tag{69–5'}$$

or generally small compared to kT. (For molecules with different ends 8 must be replaced by 2.)

Accordingly, Beckerle's and others attempts to make calculations for other molecules failed. When the probability of an inelastic collision is not small, the first approximation of a perturbation calculation is insufficient. Physically, this means that one also has to consider multiple processes during a single collision, like

$$J \to J' \to J$$

where at the end the system is in the original state; or

$$J \to J'' \to J'$$

where the state J' is reached in a roundabout way, i.e., by means of processes like the Raman effect.

Brout[9] has attempted to extend his work from H_2 to other molecules, basing his formulas on the experience with H_2. He assumes that only processes where the "magnetic quantum number" m remains unchanged are important, and that the probability for processes $J \to J - 2$, $m \to m$ is independent of the value of m. The interaction energy is written in the form of Eq. (64–1).

Calling the original and final linear momenta of the hitting atom A p and p', one has

$$p^2 = 2\,\tilde{m}E \tag{69–6}$$

and

$$p'^2 = 2\,\tilde{m}\,(E - \Delta E_{\mathrm{rot}}) = 2\,\tilde{m}\,\{E - 4\,k\vartheta_r\,(J - \tfrac{1}{2})\} \tag{69–6'}$$

where E is the original kinetic energy of A.

The cross section Q_J for the transition $J \to J - 2$ is then

$$Q_J = \pi l^2\,800\,\Lambda^2 \left(\frac{2\,\pi l}{h}\right)^4 pp'^3 \left\{(p^2 - p'^2)^2 \left(\frac{2\,\pi l}{h}\right)^4 + 2\,(p^2 + p'^2)\left(\frac{2\,\pi l}{h}\right)^2 + 1\right\}^{-2} \cdot \left[\frac{(2\,J - 3)^2}{4} \int P_J P_2 P_{J-2}\, d(\cos\Gamma)\right]^2. \tag{69–7}$$

For $J > 5$ (which is true for the J values of appreciable probability in most molecules) the last factor can be replaced by $1/7$. The product πl^2 has the dimensions of a cross section; the other factors are dimensionless. A quantity like $2\pi lp/h$ is equal to 2π times the number of de Broglie waves contained in the distance l. The factor 800 in Eq. (69–7) is empirical, determined by fitting this simplified formula to the exact calculation for H_2.

Using Eq. (69–6), one has, for $J > 5$

$$Q_J = \pi l^2 \cdot 112\,\Lambda^2 \left(\frac{8\,\pi^2 \tilde{m} E l^2}{h^2}\right)^2 \left[1 - \frac{4\,k\vartheta_r}{E}\,(J - \tfrac{1}{2})\right]^{\frac{3}{2}} \cdot \left\{\left[\frac{32\,\pi^2 \tilde{m} l^2 k\vartheta_r}{h^2}\,(J - \tfrac{1}{2})\right]^2 + \frac{32\,\pi^2 \tilde{m} l^2 E}{h^2}\left[1 - \frac{2\,k\vartheta_r}{E}\,(J - \tfrac{1}{2})\right] + 1\right\}^{-2}. \tag{69–8}$$

Numerically, for most molecules and at reasonable temperatures, $J(k\vartheta_r/E)$ is small (for the most probable rotational state, this is approximately $\sqrt{T/2\vartheta_r}\,k\vartheta_r/E$. In the denominator, the middle term seems to be the largest, and the first term may or may not be large compared to unity. Then

$$Q_J = \pi l^2\, 7\,\Lambda^2 \left\{1 + \frac{32\,\pi^2 \tilde{m} l^2}{h^2} \frac{(k\vartheta_r)^2}{E}\,(J - \tfrac{1}{2})^2\right\}^{-2}. \tag{69–9}$$

---

[9] R. Brout, *J. Chem. Phys.* **22**, 1189 (1954).

For the most probable J and with $E = 2kT$, the last bracket is

$$\left\{1 + \frac{8\,\pi^2 \tilde{m} l^2}{h^2}\, k\vartheta_r\right\}^{-2}.$$

One sees that Q_J is independent[10] of the temperature and of J, and with $l \sim 1/18\, r_0$

$$Q_J = \pi r_0{}^2 \frac{\Lambda^2}{45}. \qquad (69\text{–}9')$$

This is smaller than the experiment seems to indicate.

In the theories described next, both molecules are considered as diatomic (instead of one being considered a smooth, spherical atom).

The first theory of that kind was developed on a classical basis by Jeans,[11] who used as molecular model smooth spheres, with the center of mass different from the center of the sphere. While this model may look unrealistic, Gioumousis[12] has pointed out that HD is a case in point, if one can treat H_2 as a sphere. Jeans finds

$$\tau_{\text{rot}} = \frac{9}{20}\left(\frac{r'}{\delta}\right)^2 1.016\, \tau_c \qquad (69\text{–}10)$$

where r' is the radius of gyration and δ the distance of the center of mass from the center of the sphere.

Pidduck[13] has considered molecules with a rough surface, so that on collision the relative velocities at the point of contact are reversed. According to Kohler,[14]

$\frac{\eta'}{\eta} = \frac{11}{30}$, and since from Eq. (38–4) $\frac{\eta'}{\eta} = \frac{1}{1.271}\,\frac{2}{5} Z$ it follows that $Z = 1.17$.

Takayanagi[15] assumes the interaction energy to be of exponential form, acting between each pair of atoms (one in each molecule). This is then

[10] For sufficiently large J, the energy difference is proportional to J, Eq. (69–5), and the most important J is $\sim \sqrt{T}$. However, the average molecular velocity is also proportional to $\sqrt{T}$, and therefore $\Delta E/w$, see Eq. (56–2), is independent of T.

[11] J. J. Jeans, "The Dynamical Theory of Gases," p. 104. Cambridge Univ. Press, London, 1904.

[12] G. Gioumousis, University of Wisconsin Naval Research Lab. Rept., NSF Grant G 994, November 4, 1955.

[13] F. B. Pidduck, *Proc. Roy. Soc.* **A101**, 101 (1922).

[14] M. Kohler, *Z. Physik* **125**, 715 (1948).

[15] K. Takayanagi, *Progr. Theoret. Phys.* (*Kyoto*) **8**, 497 (1952).

developed into a power series of powers of L/r; In a later paper,[16] other terms in this development are discussed. Takayanagi[17] applies his calculations to H_2, making approximations somewhat similar to those in Sec. 60; he expresses these by saying that only head-on collisions are considered. His result agrees with experiment within a factor 2. Takayanagi and Kishimoto[17] return to a calculation of rotational transitions in hydrogen, using for the translational factor the Jackson-Mott expression (Sec. 60). For the three processes $2 \to 0$, $J \to J$; $4 \to 2$, $J \to J$; and $4 \to 2$, $0 \to 2$ they find for the relative cross sections ($T = 298.4$ °K, $J = 0$) $1 : 0.46 : 0.19$; $Z_{\text{rot}} = 100$ for the first process. A calculated curve for C_{eff} is shifted by a factor of 4 to higher frequencies, as compared to the experiment.

In reference 16 these calculations are taken up again, close attention being paid to the fact that particles of the same kind are indistinguishable in quantum theory, their behavior depending upon whether they obey Bose-Einstein or Fermi-Dirac statistics. Since, however, molecules in different or differently oriented (different magnetic quantum number m) rotational states are considered different, the effect is, in general, only important when only a few states are occupied, i.e., when $\vartheta_r > T$.

The author then develops the semiclassical method which uses, as orbit of the translational motion, the classical motion under the action of a potential, which is the smoothed-out mean over the internal (rotational) states of the molecule. The rotational states are then subjected to a time-dependent potential. No new numerical calculations are made.

Gioumousis[12] has treated rotational transitions with a method which is, in general, similar to the one used by Takayanagi, although more detailed.[18]

The formulas are then applied to the model of a hard molecule, nearly spherical, the surface of which is given by the equation

$$R = R_0 + R_1 \cos \beta. \tag{69–11}$$

In particular, collisions between H_2 (spherical) and HD (center of mass shifted, see above) are calculated. The "shape" of HD is calculated to be

$$R = 2.93 \times 10^{-8} + 0.125 \times 10^{-8} \cos \beta \text{ cm}.$$

---

[16] K. Takayanagi, *Progr. Theoret. Phys.* (*Kyoto*) **11**, 557 (1954).

[17] K. Takayanagi and T. Kishimoto, *Progr. Theoret. Phys. Japan* **9**, 578 (1953); **10**, 369 (1953).

[18] Originally, the orientations of the molecules are characterized by angles (which are also contained in the rotational wave functions) over which one must integrate. In the outcome, the state is characterized by quantum numbers and the angles have disappeared. This is somewhat similar to the fact that, in Eq. (62–7), a summation over j appears instead of an integration over space.

The result for the cross section Q for the transition $0 \rightarrow 1$ in HD is given in Table 69–1 for different initial relative translational energies, expressed as kT.

TABLE 69–1

$Q_{0\rightarrow 1}$ IN $(\text{A})^2$, H_2-HD COLLISION; ELASTIC CROSS SECTION, $26.97(\text{A})^2$

T (°K)	140	170	300	800
$Q_{0\rightarrow 1}$	0.169	0.679	3.091	11.519

70. Energy Transfer and the Kinetics of Chemical Gas Reactions[1-3]

Unimolecular decompositions in which the molecule needs a minimum energy before it can react are the only ones which go slow enough to be measured. This energy, which is many (15 to 20) times kT, must therefore be furnished first to the molecule which is to react. Supply through radiant energy is too slow, so collisions with other molecules are the only source of the energy necessary for decomposition. The energy supply process is a second-order reaction because the number of collisions occurring per second in a unit volume is proportional to the square of the number of molecules. The actual decomposition of molecules, once they have sufficient energy, is a first-order reaction, i.e., it is proportional to the first power of the number of sufficiently excited molecules. Therefore, the processes of energy supply and of actual decomposition present two reactions in series. In such a case, the rate of the over-all reaction—the measured rate—is determined by the slower of the two processes, which forms a bottleneck.[4]

If the actual decomposition is the slower process, most of the molecules acquiring sufficient energy for decomposition by collisions lose it again in ensuing collisions before they decompose. In this case, the number of molecules with sufficient energy is practically equal to the equilibrium number—a temperature dependent, pressure independent, fraction of the

---

[1] Section 70 is mainly a reprint of Section H, 35, pages 724, 725, 726, 727, and part of 728 by Karl F. Herzfeld, *in* "Thermodynamics and Physics of Matter" (F. D. Rossini, ed.). Princeton Univ. Press, Princeton, New Jersey, 1955.

[2] K. Laidler, "Chemical Kinetics." McGraw-Hill, New York, 1950.

[3] H. J. Schumacher, "Chemische Gasreaktionen." Steinkopf, Dresden, 1938.

[4] In the case of two reactions in parallel, the over-all rate is determined by the *faster* of the two. For the details of the theory presented above see the book by K. Laidler;[2] for the experimental data see the book by Schumacher.[3]

total number of molecules—and a given fraction of these decompose per second. The over-all reaction is therefore unimolecular (first order). If, on the other hand, the supply of energy is the much slower process, then practically all molecules decompose in a very short time after they have acquired sufficient energy, and the collisions are so far apart that practically all molecules of sufficient energy have decomposed when the collision after the activating collision is due. Therefore, practically no molecules lose their activation energy by a deactivating collision. In this case, the over-all rate is equal to the rate of activating collisions, i.e., is bimolecular or, for a given temperature, proportional to the square of the pressure.

Since the activation-deactivation process is proportional to the square of the pressure, the actual decomposition to the first power, it follows that at sufficiently low pressures the activation process must be the slower one and that therefore the over-all process must be bimolecular. At high pressures the activation process must be the faster one and therefore the over-all rate must be monomolecular.

If one then follows the rate and finds it monomolecular at higher pressures, the monomolecular rate constant k_2 means that during dt the fraction k_2dt of molecules decomposes. If at lower pressures the rate constant decreases, it means that the rate of activation is now comparable to the decomposition rate. In particular, when the apparent monomolecular rate constant has fallen to $k_2/2$, it means that during dt the fraction of molecules which acquire sufficient energy by collision is k_2dt. Half of these decompose, and half are deactivated by collision.

Thus, knowing experimentally the rate at which molecules acquire sufficient energy, one can calculate Z, the efficiency of energy transfer.

There is still another point to be considered.[5] From the standpoint of classical physics, the question may be formulated as follows: One is interested in the probability of any particular vibration or bond having an energy larger than a prescribed energy E_0 (per mole), E_0 being larger than RT. The different degrees of freedom of vibration would have an average energy RT. The whole energy of the molecule migrates from time to time, either into a particular bond by interference, or into a particular vibration by the nonlinear coupling terms. The larger the numbers of degrees of freedom, the smaller the energy the last collision has to add to bring the total energy above E_0.

---

[5] F. A. Lindemann, *Trans. Faraday Soc.* **17**, 598 (1922).

A more precise statement comes from the theory of probability, according to which the probability of getting a certain high energy is greater, the greater the number of ways of making it up. Mathematically, the statement is as follows: Consider a molecule with s degrees of vibrational freedom. The fraction of molecules in which the total vibrational energy is larger than E_0 is

$$\frac{1}{(s-1)!}\left(\frac{E_0}{RT}\right)^{s-1} e^{-E_0/RT}. \tag{70–1}$$

If one assumes that it takes Z collisions to take away sufficient energy to make the molecule chemically inactive, then among N molecules the number of deactivation processes per second is, in equilibrium

$$\frac{1}{Z\tau_c}\frac{N}{(s-1)!}\left(\frac{E_0}{RT}\right)^{s-1} e^{-E_0/RT}. \tag{70–2}$$

This is also the rate of production of activated molecules. If the rate of the decomposition is put equal to $Ae^{-E_0/RT}$, where A is the so-called frequency factor of the unimolecular reaction, then we have, at the pressure at which the high pressure rate constant has fallen to half its former value

$$\frac{1}{2Z}\left(\frac{1}{\tau_c}\right)_{1/2}\frac{1}{(s-1)!}\left(\frac{E_0}{RT}\right)^{s-1} e^{-E_0/RT} = Ae^{-E_0/RT}. \tag{70–3}$$

There are more elaborate theories by Kassel[6] and by Rice and Ramsperger,[7] which assume a dependence of A on the energy of the reacting molecule. However, they do not change the order of magnitude of Eq. (70–3).

Experimentally it has been found that the rate constants of some monomolecular reactions decrease at low pressure, which is in agreement with the theory. In such cases, the admixture of a foreign gas very often restores the monomolecular rate constant to the value it had at higher pressures, or at least diminishes the drop. H_2 and He seem to be particularly effective. All this can be understood from the theory. Unfortunately, the interpretation is less certain than might be wished, because in the case of many apparently monomolecular reactions it is doubtful whether they really occur in a single step or whether they are chain reactions (or even occur at the wall).

---

[6] L. Kassel, *Chem. Revs.* **10**, 14 (1932).

[7] O. K. Rice and H. C. Ramsperger, *J. Am. Chem. Soc.* **49**, 1617 (1927).

Table 70–1 shows relative values for $1/Z$.

TABLE 70–1

EFFICIENCY OF COLLISION PARTNERS COMPARED TO THE PURE GAS

Decomposition of	Temperature (°C)	Impurity						Reference
		He	A	N_2	O_2	H_2O	CO_2	
F_2O	250	0.40	0.52	1.01	1.13			8
F_2O_2	−37	0.07	0.40	0.21	1.2		0.45	9
N_2O	653	0.66	0.20	0.24	0.23	1.5	1.32	10
Azomethane CH_2-N_2-CH_2	310	0.07		0.21	0.37	0.46	0.25	10a

For F_2O the reaction is bimolecular in the whole pressure range, which means that the process of supplying energy is rate determining. Since the molecule is triangular, it has three vibrational degrees of freedom. All three of them, with $Z \cong 1$, are needed to make the rate of production of activated molecules equal to the measured reaction rate.

F_2O_2 has six vibrational degrees of freedom. To represent the change of reaction rate constant (at −37°C it falls to half its high-pressure value at about 50 mm Hg), one needs all six degrees of freedom, again with $Z \cong 1$.

For N_2O, which is linear, Volmer calculates Z for several assumptions concerning the number s of cooperating degrees of freedom: for $s = 4$, $Z = 1700$; for $s = 3$, $Z = 190$; and for $s = 2$, $Z = 12$. Only the order of magnitude of these numbers is to be considered. Patat and Bartholomé[11] argue in favor of the last of these values, with the following arguments.

From sound absorption measurements, Eucken and Jaaks[12] had found the following Z numbers for H_2O as impurity in N_2O (see Sec. 52): at 20° C, $Z = 60$; at 195° C, $Z = 10$. Therefore, they conclude that at 635° C, Z must surely be smaller, say, $Z \cong 5$. However, according to Table 70-1, Z for $N_2O = 1.5\,Z\,(H_2O)$, and therefore $2 < Z(N_2O) < 8$ at 635° C.

[8] W. H. Koblitz and H. J. Schumacher, *Z. physik. Chem.* **B25**, 283 (1934).
[9] H. J. Schumacher and P. Frisch, *Z. physik. Chem.* **B37**, 1 (1937).
[10] M. Volmer and H. Fröhlich, *Z. physik. Chem.* **B19**, 85 (1931).
[10a] O. K. Rice and D. V. Sickman, *J. Am. Chem. Soc.* **57**, 1384 (1935).
[11] E. Patat and E. Bartholomé, *Z. physik. Chem.* **B32**, 396 (1936).
[12] A. Eucken and H. Jaaks, *Z. physik. Chem.* **B30**, 85 (1935).

Measurements have also been made on NO_2Cl.[13] Since the decomposition of azomethane and of many organic compounds involves radical chains, we will not try to draw conclusions as to collision efficiencies here. A considerable amount of work has been done on that subject, particularly by Hinshelwood and his collaborators. It should be noted in this connection that in some of those organic reactions where the rate constant decreases at low initial pressure, the rate constant does not change while the reaction progresses, although the amount of initial substance is diminishing. This is usually explained by saying that the products of the reaction have efficiency equal to that of the original substance. Such a statement, however, is astonishing in view of the different behavior of different substances as shown in ultrasonic absorption as well as in the above inorganic reactions. There seems to be nothing in the structure of the decomposition products, as compared with the initial substance, to give them equal efficiency in energy transfer. This increases the suspicion that the effect of pressure here lies in the complication of the chemical mechanism. No measurements of the effect of helium admixtures on the rate of unimolecular organic reactions have been made in the low-pressure region, where the rate constant of the pure substance falls off. Patat and Bartholomé[11] point out that in pure gases transfer of excitation energy from a particular vibration in one molecule to the corresponding vibration in a colliding molecule—with no change in translation energy—does not show up in ultrasonics at all. On the other hand, in chemical reactions, where it is a matter of total energy in a molecule, these "resonance transfers" do matter. If the transfer of energy between translation and vibration is inefficient, but the resonance transfer between vibrations is very efficient, then the large Z found in ultrasonics and the low Z found in reaction rates are compatible.

In a pure gas, then, the rate of acquisition of the necessary energy for reactions seems to be as follows if, in approximation, we treat the vibration as harmonic and talk about one degree of freedom only. Let n' be the number of quanta necessary for reaction, so that

$$n'h\nu = E'/N_A$$

is the heat of activation. Then the fastest process in which E' is reached is the collision of one molecule with $n' - 1$ quanta with a molecule with s quanta, and the activation process is $n' - 1 \rightarrow n'$, $s \rightarrow s - 1$. To calculate the rate at which this occurs, call N_s the number of molecules per cc with

[13] H. J. Schumacher and P. Sprenger, *Z. physik. Chem.* **B12**, 115 (1931).

s quanta, N' those with $n' - 1$ quanta, and N the total number of molecules per cc. The total number of processes $n' - 1 \to n'$ per cc and second is then, from Eq. (65–12)

$$N' \cdot n' \, (\Sigma s N_s) \, (Z^0)^{-1} \, 4\pi^2 \left[\frac{M_B{}^2 + M_C{}^2}{M_{BC}{}^2} \right]^2 \frac{T}{\vartheta'} \frac{1}{\tau_c N} \, e^{\varepsilon/kT}. \tag{70–4}$$

Now

$$\sum sN_s = \frac{1}{h\nu} \sum sh\nu N_s = \frac{1}{h\nu} \frac{h\nu}{e^{\vartheta/T} - 1} N = Ne^{-\vartheta/T} \, (1 - e^{-\vartheta/T})^{-1}. \tag{70–5}$$

Near equilibrium

$$N' = N \, (1 - e^{-\vartheta/T})^{-1} \exp\left[- (n' - 1) \frac{\vartheta}{T} \right] = Ne^{-E'/RT} \, (1 - e^{-\vartheta/T})^{-1} \, e^{\vartheta/T}. \tag{70–5'}$$

Therefore, the rate is

$$\frac{N}{\tau_c} e^{-E'/kT} \, (1 - e^{-\vartheta/T})^{-2} \, (Z^0)^{-1} \, \pi^2 \left(\frac{M_B{}^2 + M_C{}^2}{M_{BC}{}^2} \right)^2 \frac{T}{\vartheta'} \, e^{\varepsilon/kT}. \tag{70–6}$$

If $\vartheta \sim 600$, $T = 600°$, $\vartheta' = 300{,}000$, $\varepsilon/k = 200$, and $M_B = M_C$, the factor of $e^{-E'/RT} N/\tau_c$ is $\sim (Z^0)^{-1} \, 1/40$. This seems too low by a factor $40 Z^0$ for F_2O and F_2O_2, although the theory should be developed in more detail for several degrees of internal freedom. The N_2O case does not seem to cause any difficulty.

The impurities also seem much more efficient than the data from ultrasonics should let one expect, since for the rare gases, and for N_2 or O_2, the explanation of Patat and Bartholomé is not applicable and for He, Z is usually ~ 100; for A, etc., much higher.

A related effect appears in the measurement of the recombination of atoms, which is possible in triple collisions (or on the wall) where the heat of formation may be removed by the third partner (or the wall). The most reliable measurements for the recombination of Br and I atoms in the presence of other gases have been made, after earlier attempts by others, by Rabinowitch and Wood.[14] They produced the atoms by photodissociation and measured optically the Br_2 or I_2 concentration in the stationary state.

---

[14] E. Rabinowitch and W. C. Wood, *J. Chem. Phys.* **4**, 497 (1936).

Table 70–2 gives[15] the fraction of the collisions between atoms which combine in the presence of 1 atm of the foreign gas, i.e., essentially $(b/12,300)Z$. This shows that Z is of the order of magnitude of 1. The same seems to be true for the recombination of two H atoms with H_2 as third partner, while H is only about one-tenth as efficient.[16]

TABLE 70–2
FRACTION OF ATOMIC COLLISIONS LEADING TO RECOMBINATION IN PRESENCE OF 1 ATM OF FOREIGN GAS

Foreign gas		He	A	H_2	N_2	O_2	CO_2	C_6H_6
Fraction of atomic collisions $\times 10^3$	Br	0.82	1.4	2.2	2.7	3.4	5.7	
	I	1.7	3.6	3.9	6.3	10	17	97

To sum up the results reported here, one finds high efficiency of some triple collisions in recombination reactions. For double collisions also the calculated efficiencies are much higher than usually found in ultrasonic experiments.

Since chemical reaction usually requires vibrational excitation to a high quantum number n, the vibrational relaxation times as determined by acoustics (which correspond to transitions $0 \rightleftarrows 1$) have to be divided by n.

For further details, see a discussion at the American Chemical Society meeting, September, 1956.[17,18]

71. Summary and Comparison of Theory and Experiment

The theory presented here for the calculation of the transfer of vibrational to translational energy suffers from two defects, named in (a) and (b) below.

(a) An approximation is made in which one calculates the translational wave function by replacing the long-range attractive potential and the long-range repulsive quasi-potential of the centrifugal force by a constant, which changes only the effective collision velocity. In the calculation of the transition probability these forces are completely omitted.

---

15 E. Rabinowitch, *Trans. Faraday Soc.* **33**, 283 (1937).
16 W. Steiner, *Trans. Faraday Soc.* **31**, 623 (1935).
17 G. B. Kistiakowsky, unpublished work.
18 K. F. Herzfeld, *J. Phys. Chem.* **61**, 844 (1957).

The reason for this approximation is only that it permits integration in closed form. Numerical integration for one case should be made—possibly on a machine—and the result compared with our approximation. It is true that this will involve a double integration, one over the angular momenta j and one over the energy according to a Maxwell distribution law.

(b) The calculation has been made for the collision of an atom A with a molecule (BB or BCB, etc.) but not for collision of a molecule BB with another BB. Here, the general expressions are available (Curtiss and Adler,[1]) but no actual calculations have been made. Polyatomic molecules have not been treated in detail as to simultaneous, translational-rotational-vibrational transitions.

(c) There does not seem to be much hope of getting an improved interaction energy from other sources. The transition probability is so sensitive to small changes in the interaction curve that it probably provides the best method of finding the exact shape of the curve for the interaction energy from measured relaxation times, once points (a) and (b) are cleared up. The formal procedure is such that one finds the ϑ' which gives the correct Z, then calculates l from ϑ' and r_c from l according to Eq. (59–10′). This then gives one a point on the curve E/ε, r_c/r_0.

The over-all result of the comparison is that the curve seems to get *slightly* less steep with increasing E/ε, although all molecules do not seem to have the same dependence. The decrease in steepness is in agreement with the measurements of Amdur[2] who, by using ion beams and neutralizing them, found in the range of 100 electron volts ($E/\varepsilon \sim 10^4$) the softer expression $(r_0/r)^{7.48}$.

(d) According to the Landau-Teller theory (Sec. 56) of which all the subsequent calculations are an elaboration, the efficiency of the collision decreases, for a given vibration, with the increase of the duration of the collision. However, it seems that this should not hold any more when this duration becomes very large and large molecules with complex structures are involved. We can then speak of the formation of an intermediate complex, and one might expect that, when this complex flies apart, the probability of the excitation being in either partner is of the same order of magnitude. There is some connection here with the importance of chemical affinity for high transfer probability, which is emphasized by Eucken and Franck.[3]

---

[1] C. F. Curtiss and F. T. Adler, *J. Chem. Phys.* **20**, 249 (1952).

[2] I. Amdur and H. Pearlman, *J. Chem. Phys.* **8**, 7, 998 (1940), **9**, 503 (1941).

[3] J. Franck and A. Eucken, *Z. physik. Chem.* **B20**, 460 (1933).

However, no detailed theory exists yet for this case, and neither does a theory exist for the gradual transition from the Landau-Teller case to this case.

(e) Taking due consideration of points (a), (b), and (c), the agreement between theory and experiment is in general satisfactory. There are several exceptions to this, mostly in cases in which two unequal molecules interact.

(1) CO, in collision with O_2 and Cl_2, is much more efficient than the theory presented here can explain. Franck and Eucken's[3] statement, that chemical affinity increases the efficiency in a collision, has not yet been put into a qualitative form.

(2) The high efficiency of H_2O can qualitatively be explained by a high interaction energy. However, this can not explain why the effectiveness of H_2O goes to a maximum and then decreases with increasing temperature, as found by Eucken.[4]

(3) The effectiveness of energy supply in chemical reactions may still be higher than can be explained by our calculations. A more detailed theory is needed.

(f) It is often stated that the collision with a different molecule is always more efficient than with a molecule of the same kind. However, there are exceptions; i.e., a collision of O_2, Cl_2, or CO_2 with krypton or xenon will surely be less efficient than with another O_2, Cl_2, or CO_2 molecule.

The collision with the foreign molecule will be more efficient if one of the following three conditions is fulfilled.

(1) $\tilde{M}l^2$ is smaller for such a collision, which will happen if the foreign molecule is either very light or very small (He, H_2).

(2) The ε/k is very high (CO_2-H_2O).

(3) A complex collision can take place, which is often the case for large molecules.

(g) The calculations for transfer of rotational energy to translational degrees of freedom are still unsatisfactory, except for H_2 and D_2.

[4] A. Eucken and R. Becker, *Z. physik. Chem.* **B27**, 235 (1934).

C. LIQUIDS

VIII. General Review of Ultrasonic Absorption and Dispersion in Liquids[1,2]

72. Classical Absorption

The equation of classical absorption of Sec. 7, Eq. (7–17), is applicable in liquids. Except for liquid metals which have high heat conductivity, the part played by heat conduction is small compared to that played by viscosity. This is shown in Table 72–1, due to Biquard.[3]

TABLE 72–1
CLASSICAL ABSORPTION, $\alpha_{\text{class}}/f^2 \times 10^{17}\ \text{cm}^{-1}$

Liquid	Viscosity	Heat conduction
Ethyl ether	8.48	0.49
Acetone	6.54	0.5
Chloroform	10.045	0.057
Benzene	8.36	0.3
Water	8.5	0.0064
Mercury[4]	1	4.1

It is noted that in the liquids of Table 72–1 $\alpha_{\text{class}}/f^2$ is a few times 10^{-17}, while in gases under standard conditions it is a few times 10^{-14}. These different values of $\eta/\rho\mathfrak{V}^3$ arise in the following manner:

(a) The η of the liquids is about 50 times larger (water, 0.01 poise; air, 1.8×10^{-4} poise).

(b) The sound velocity of the liquids is 4.5 times larger (water, 1500 m/sec; air, 333 m/sec). Therefore $\mathfrak{V}^3$ is about 90 times larger for the liquids, or $\eta/\mathfrak{V}^3$ has about half the value for the liquids that it has for the gases.

---

[1] For a general review of the data, methods of measurement, theories, and literature, see D. Sette, *Nuovo cimento* [9] **6**, Suppl. N1, 135 (1949).

[2] J. J. Markham, R. T. Beyer, and R. B. Lindsay, *Revs. Mod. Phys.* **23**, 353 (1951).

[3] P. Biquard, Thèses de doctorat, Paris 1935; *Ann. phys.* [11] **6**, 195 (1936).

[4] P. Riekmann, *Physik. Z.* **40**, 582 (1939).

(c) The ρ is 1000 to 300 times larger for the liquid; the ratio of ρ for liquid to gas is 1300 for water, 300 for benzene. This is the decisive factor.

73. Absorption of Ultrasonic Waves in Liquids: The Situation in 1948. Pinkerton's Classification of Liquids

Biquard[1] was the first to discover that an excess absorption exists in liquids, just as in gases. His pioneering researches were followed by many papers; due to the difficulties of measuring low values of the absorption—which occur particularly at low frequencies—some of the earlier data were faulty. As an example we have compiled in Fig. 73–1, following Teeter[2], all the

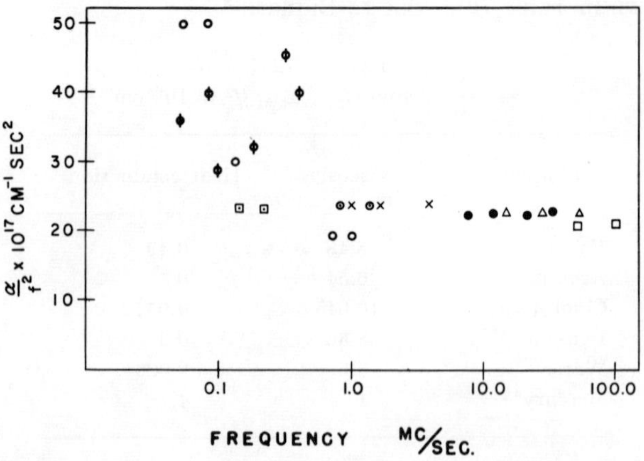

FIG. 73–1. α/f^2 vs frequency for water. ○, R. W. Leonard, *U.C.L.A. Tech. Rept. No.* **1**, June 1, 1950; ø, E. Skudrzyk, *Acta Phys. Austriaca* **2**, 148 (1948); ⊙, C. J. Moen, *J. Acoust. Soc. Am.* **23**, 62 (1951); ×, G. S. Verma, *J. Chem. Phys.* **18**, 1352 (1950); □, R. A. Rapuano, *Phys. Rev.* **72**, 78 (1947); ●, F. E. Fox and G. D. Rock, *Phys. Rev.* **70**, 68 (1946); and Δ, J. M. M. Pinkerton, *Nature* **160**, 128 (1947).

existing measurements for water. The rise of α/ω^2 at low frequencies is now known to be spurious. By 1948 it had been shown that the absorption values measured till then gave α/ω^2 independent of the frequency, which proves that the relaxation times involved are much shorter than $1/(2\pi$ times the frequency of the ultrasonic waves used).

[1] P. Biquard, *Compt. rend.* **193**, 226 (1931); **197**, 309 (1933).

[2] C. E. Teeter, Jr., *J. Acoust. Soc. Am.* **18**, 488 (1946).

Particularly important in the attempt to approach the relaxation region were papers by those who pushed the frequency limit up; for example, by Bär,[3] up to 80 mc; and by Rapuano,[4] up to about 200 mc. Since α/ω^2 was still found constant, this meant that $\tau < 10^{-9}$ sec. There were four exceptions to this rule, which did show a decrease of α/ω^2 with increasing frequency: CS_2, acetic acid,[5] methyl acetate,[1,3,6] and ethyl acetate.[7] However, the physicists felt entitled to be suspicious of these substances and to ascribe their exceptional behavior to chemical reactions.

As far as general theories for the excess absorption in liquids went, Kneser[8] proposed that thermal relaxation was responsible, just as in gases. This was widely accepted, particularly since excess absorption seemed to be nearly absent in liquid mercury[9] and in liquefied "permanent" gases, like O_2 and N_2. However, an exceptional substance was available to test the theory, namely, water.

Water has a density maximum at 4° C. Accordingly, it follows that at this temperature the expansion coefficient β is zero and, according to Eq. (4–9), so is Δ or $C_p - C_v$. However, Δ is a factor in the absorption which is due to thermal relaxation, which should therefore be absent in water at 4° C. To put it differently, according to Eq. (4–7) the temperature rise in adiabatic compression is absent—isothermal and adiabatic processes are identical—and since the temperature of the external degrees does not change, there is no occasion for any exchange of energy with the internal degrees of freedom.

Accordingly, at 4° C in water, the absorption should have the classical value.

Fox and Rock,[10] at the suggestion of J. C. Hubbard, measured the absorption in water between 2° and 40° C and found no peculiar behavior at 4° C. Instead, the ratio of $\alpha/\alpha_{\text{class}}$ remained nearly constant, equal to about 3, in the whole temperature range. This proved that in water in this temperature

---

[3] R. Bär, *Helv. Phys. Acta* **10**, 332 (1937).

[4] R. A. Rapuano, *Phys. Rev.* **72**, 78 (1947).

[5] P. Bazulin, *Compt. rend. acad. sci. U.R.S.S.* **3**, 285 (1936); *Zhur. Eksptl. i Teoret. Fiz.* **8**, 457 (1938).

[6] J. Claeys, J. Errera, and H. Sack, *Trans. Faraday Soc.* **33**, 136 (1937).

[7] R. T. Beyer and M. C. Smith, *J. Acoust. Soc. Am.* **18**, 424 (1946).

[8] H. O. Kneser, *Ann. Physik* [5] **32**, 277 (1938).

[9] P. Riekmann, *Physik. Z.* **40**, 582 (1939).

[10] F. E. Fox and G. D. Rock, *Phys. Rev.* **70**, 68 (1946).

range the excess absorption is not due to thermal relaxation. Herzfeld[11] had pointed this out earlier; if one uses the measured absorption and the very low values of Δ and C, one gets too long a τ.

Therefore, Fox and Rock assumed that the explanation must lie in a suggestion by Debye,[12] that the excess absorption is due to a structural relaxation. This means that the structure is pressure-dependent; when the pressure changes, it takes a time τ before the molecules assume the changed structure appropriate to the changed pressure.

In the meantime, it became possible to make much more accurate and less time-consuming absorption measurements in liquids, due to the introduction of pulse technique. This had first been invented by Biquard,[13] but war-time radar had trained many people in pulse techniques and put surplus equipment in the hands of university laboratories. Applications to ultrasonics were made almost simultaneously at the Massachusetts Institute of Technology[14] and at the University of Cambridge.[15] On the basis of the material so accumulated, Pinkerton[16] made a classification of liquids according to their ultrasonic absorption. The basis of this classification is shown in Table 73–1 (this is supplemented by some later measurements).

Accordingly, Pinkerton divided liquids into "normal liquids" (our Group I) and "abnormal liquids" (our Groups II and III).

The normal liquids are made up of monatomic liquids (Hg, A) and those which behave as monatomic liquids (liquid N_2, O_2, H_2). Their absorption is only slightly larger than the classical value.

The anomalous behavior of liquid helium (second sound) will not be discussed in this book.

The abnormal liquids fall into two groups. Group II contains a few inorganic liquids like CS_2 and the majority of organic liquids. It is characterized by a ratio of $\alpha/\alpha_{\text{class}}$ which may lie between 400 and 3, and by a positive temperature coefficient of absorption. Pinkerton assumes that the reason for the excess absorption in these liquids is the slow exchange of internal and external energy, as originally proposed by Kneser.[8] These liquids shall from here on be called "Kneser liquids."

---

[11] K. F. Herzfeld, *J. Acoust. Soc. Am.* **13**, 33 (1941).

[12] P. Debye, *Z. Elektrochem.* **45**, 174 (1939).

[13] P. Biquard, *Ann. phys.* [11] **6**, 195 (1936).

[14] J. R. Pellam and J. K. Galt, *J. Chem. Phys.* **14**, 608 (1946).

[15] J. M. M. Pinkerton, *Proc. Phys. Soc. London* **B 62**, 286 (1949).

[16] J. M. M. Pinkerton, *Proc. Phys. Soc. London* **B 62**, 129 (1949).

TABLE 73-1
ULTRASONIC ABSORPTION OF LIQUIDS

Liquid	T*	$10^{17}\ \alpha/f^2$	$\alpha/\alpha_{\text{class}}$	$1/\alpha(\partial\alpha/\partial T)$	Reference
		Group I			
Hg	300	6.1	1.2	—	9
A	85.2	10.1	1.0	—	17
N_2	73.9	10.6	1.1	—	17
O_2	87	8.6	1.2	0	17
O_2	60	8.6	1.0	0	17
H_2	17	5.6	1.0	—	17
		Group II			
CS_2	25	5800	1150	—	18
CH_3CH_2Br	10	62	6.2	0.010	14
CH_3I	2	247	24.7	0.0087	14
CH_3I	30	334	—	0.0087	14
CCl_4	23.5	533	26.6	—	14
C_2H_5I	2	40	3.3	—	14
CH_2Cl_2	25	1114	183	0.0116	19
CH_2Br_2	25	567	354	0.0071	19
CCl_2HCH_3	25	99.3	10.2	0.005	19
C_6H_6	22	800	100	0.011	14
C_6H_5Cl	25	148	15	0.0072	20
$C_6H_5NO_2$	24	79	5.6	0.0048	14
n-C_6H_{14}	21	77	7.7	—	14
		Group III			
H_2O	15	24	2.9	−0.036	10
CH_3OH	2	45	3.0	−0.011	14
n-C_3H_7OH	27.5	70	1.9	−0.0086	14
n-$C_5H_{11}OH$	28.6	106	1.8	−0.014	14
Glycerol	50	790	1.78	−0.05	21

* T for Group I is measured in degrees Kelvin; T for Groups II and III, in degrees Centigrade.

[17] J. K. Galt, *J. Chem. Phys.* **16**, 505 (1948); R. T. Beyer, *J. Chem. Phys.* **19**, 788 (1951).

[18] J. Lamb and J. H. Andreae, *Nature* **167**, 898 (1951).

[19] D. Sette, *J. Chem. Phys.* **19**, 1337 (1951).

[20] D. Sette, *Nuovo cimento* [9] Suppl. N 2 **7**, 318 (1950).

[21] R. Piccirelli and T. A. Litovitz, *J. Acoust. Soc. Am.* **29**, 1009 (1957).

The other group of anomalous liquids, our Group III, behaves very much like water. The chemists call them "associated" liquids. Although, since most have no density maximum and therefore no point at which the compression is isothermal, one cannot prove as directly as for water that the excess absorption is due to a structural change, this is assumed by Pinkerton.

The "associated liquids" are characterized by three properties. The ratio of the absorption coefficient to its classical value lies between three and unity (at low pressures), i.e., $8/3 \geqslant \eta'/\eta > 0$. This ratio, and therefore η'/η, is nearly independent of temperature (as first pointed out by Fox and Rock for water). As a consequence, the temperature coefficient of absorption is negative (since the decrease of η with increasing T is stronger than the other effects). Some data illustrating these points appear in Table 73–2.

TABLE 73–2

α/α_{class} AS FUNCTION OF TEMPERATURE

Liquid	T (°C)	$10^{17}\ \alpha/f^2$	α/α_{class}	η'/η
Water[15,22]	0	56.9	3.33	3.11
	5	44.1	3.29	3.05
	10	36.1	3.18	2.91
	15	29.6	3.09	2.79
	20	25.3	3.10	2.80
	30	19.1	3.10	2.80
	40	14.6	3.01	2.68
	50	11.99	3.01	2.68
	60	10.2	3.04	2.72
Ethanediol,[23]	43	82	1.68	0.91
30 Mc	31.5	120	1.70	0.93
	24.0	153	1.69	0.92
	15.8	213	1.71	0.95
	5.9	331	1.74	0.99
	−5.2	604	1.79	1.05
	−13.1	1010	1.78	1.04
	−19.4	1560	1.75	1.00

Even if the pressure is varied, α/α_{class} or η'/η varies less than α/f^2; see Table 73–3.

[22] J. M. M. Pinkerton, *Nature* **160**, 128 (1947).

[23] T. A. Litovitz, R. Higgs, and R. Meister, *J. Chem. Phys.* **22**, 1281 (1954).

TABLE 73-3

α/α_{class} AS FUNCTION OF PRESSURE FOR WATER,[24] 30° C

p (atm)	$10^{17}\ \alpha/f^2$	α/α_{class}	η'/η
0	18.5	3.01	2.68
500	15.4	2.91	2.55
1000	12.7	2.75	2.33
1500	11.1	2.64	2.18
2000	9.9	2.75	2.33

Pinkerton had originally introduced a second group of normal liquids, which have an absorption only slightly above the classical one, namely, very viscous liquids.[25] However, in the present state of our knowledge these seem rather to fit into the third group.

74. Developments Since 1948. Critical Review of Pinkerton's Classification

(a) As mentioned in Sec. 73, there were only four liquids known which showed a decided decrease of α/f^2 with increasing frequency and so gave an experimental indication of where the relaxation frequency is situated. In addition, Herzfeld[1] had calculated the average τ for other liquids, under condition that they were Kneser liquids. Since 1948, the following fundamental progress in the experimental knowledge of τ and of the nature of the excess absorption in liquids has been made:

(1) The recognition[2] that methyl acetate, ethyl acetate and[3] CS_2 are genuine Kneser liquids, and the direct determination of their τ.

(2) The discovery of minor absorption maxima in toluene[4,5] and in a number of other liquids by Lamb[2] and by Karpovich.[6] This was only made possible by a considerable increase in measuring accuracy.

---

[24] T. A. Litovitz and E. H. Carnevale, *J. Appl. Phys.* **26** ,816 (1955).

[25] J. L. Hunter, *J. Acoust. Soc. Am.* **13**, 36 (1941).

[1] K. F. Herzfeld, *J. Acoust. Soc. Am.* **13**, 33 (1941).

[2] J. H. Andreae, E. L. Heasall, and J. Lamb, *Proc. Phys. Soc. London* **B69**, 625 (1956).

[3] J. Lamb and J. H. Andreae, *Nature* **167**, 898 (1951).

[4] C. J. Moen, *J. Acoust. Soc. Am.* **23**, 62 (1951).

[5] R. T. Beyer, *J. Acoust. Soc. Am.* **27**, 1 (1955).

[6] J. Karpovich, *J. Chem. Phys.* **22**, 1767 (1954).

(3) The discovery by Pinkerton and Lamb[7,8] that the behavior of acetic acid (Sec. 73) is shared by other members of the series. They could not only measure the absorption curves, but could detect, for the first time, dispersion in a liquid. The relaxation processes involved are surely thermal, but their exact nature is still in dispute (see Sec. 116).

(4) The investigation of structural relaxation in associated liquids was initiated under the late F. E. Fox. Decisive for success was the idea that liquids of high viscosity should have a long relaxation time, which then falls into the measurable range. The details will be discussed in Chap. XII.

(b) If one reviews relaxation processes in polyatomic liquids and their bearing on Pinkerton's classification in the light of present knowledge, it is clear that all the processes suggested will give the same elementary form of the dispersion and absorption equation as function of the frequency, although the experimental results may require a superposition of several such processes with different relaxation times.

Experimentally one can decide about the nature of the relaxation process only from the numerical value of the constants involved (e.g., whether an absorption is too large or too small to be explained by the freezing out of the effect of an internal vibration), by their dependence on temperature and pressure, and by their behavior in mixtures.

The fundamental similarity of the equations is due to the fact that relaxation processes all consist of slow transitions between two (or more) states of the molecules or groups of molecules.

One can classify these transitions either by the nature of the state or by the causative agent for the transition. The first classification divides the states to be considered into internal states of the molecules and external states, i.e., structural states (since ideal gases have no structure, these latter processes appear there only in η).

The second classification divides the transitions according to whether they are caused by temperature changes, volume changes, or both. Since it is known both from experiment and from theory that the internal states are generally fairly insensitive to changes of volume, transitions between different internal states will be affected mainly by temperature changes alone. For the case of water at about 4° C, the structure change is affected only by volume changes. In general, structural transitions may be induced by both volume and temperature changes.

---

[7] J. Lamb and J. M. M. Pinkerton, *Proc. Roy. Soc.* **A199**, 114 (1949).

[8] J. Lamb and D. H. A. Huddart, *Trans. Faraday Soc.* **46**, 540 (1950).

If the relaxation process in acetic and propionic acids (and the acetates?) is the slow establishment of equilibrium between monomer and dimer, it can be considered both an internal change (as far as the dimer is concerned) and a structural one (as far as the monomers are concerned). Whereas the reaction is mainly affected by the temperature variation in the sound wave, the absorption should be strongly affected by dilution.

Since all the molecules concerned have both internal vibrations and some structure, one would expect them all to behave in some ways as Kneser liquids and in some ways as associated liquids. The distinction lies mainly in which effect predominates. The "associated liquids" are often made up of CH_3, CH_2, and OH groups which do not have a large vibrational specific heat (the absorption in C_6H_{14} is small); in addition, the presence of OH makes the energy exchange easy. On the other hand, the presence of hydrogen bonds makes the structural change slow.

75. Velocity of Sound Waves of Ultrahigh Frequency (UHF)

When light of optical wave length, λ_0, passes through a liquid which is transversed by Debye heat waves (sound waves of thermal energy), the light is reflected from the crests of the sound waves (higher liquid density). However, the reflection from a single crest is minute, and the effect becomes observable only if the reflections from subsequent crests are added by constructive interference, i.e., if the Bragg condition is fulfilled, with the wave length λ_s of the sound playing the role of the lattice distance

$$\lambda_0 = 2\,\lambda_s \cos\varphi. \tag{75–1}$$

Here, φ is the angle between the normals of light wave and sound wave.

However, the sound waves are moving with the velocity $\mathfrak{V}$ and accordingly produce a Doppler effect, splitting the optical line into a doublet

$$\pm\frac{\delta\lambda_0}{\lambda_0} = 2\frac{\mathfrak{V}}{c}\cos\varphi. \tag{75–2}$$

A determination of the splitting therefore permits a measurement of $\mathfrak{V}$ for sound waves of wave length $\lambda_0(2\cos\varphi)^{-1}$. However, since $\mathfrak{V}/c \sim 1/2 \times 10^{-5}$, $\delta\lambda_0 \sim 0.05$ Å; if the optical accuracy is 0.005 Å, this gives $\mathfrak{V}$ to 10%. Therefore, a Fabry-Perot interferometer must be used.

The theory was developed by Brillouin.[1]

---

[1] L. Brillouin, *Ann. phys.* [9] **17**, 88 (1922).

After a number of preliminary papers,[2] extensive measurements were made by Sunanda Bai[3] and Venketeswaran[4,5] and more recently by Fabelinski.[6,7] Some of the results are shownin Table 75–1.

TABLE 75–1
COMPARISON OF ULTRASONIC AND UHF VELOCITIES OF LIQUIDS;

Liquid	Ultrasonic $\mathfrak{B}_0$ m/sec	UHF $\mathfrak{B}$ m/sec	Reference
Benzene	1324	1470 ± 20	6
Carbon disulfide	1158	1265 ± 22	6
Carbon tetrachloride	920	1040 ± 27	6
Toluene	1324	1314 ± 34	6
Acetone	1190	1190 ± 40	6
Acetic acid	1144	1140 ± 35	6
Methylene chloride	1093	1245	7
Methylene bromide	963	1100	7
Chloroform	1001	~1200	7
Water	1492	1509 ± 25	5
Ethyl Alcohol	1150	1160 ± 25	5
Glycerol	1960	2500 ± 25	5
Castor Oil	1506	1626 ± 25	5

Venketeswaran[5] undertook the examination of liquids with high viscosity because he expected that at the acoustic frequencies involved the absorption would be so high that no regular wave would persist over even one wave length, and that therefore the Bragg effect would be missing. However, this was not the case; glycerine showed a sharp Doppler line. Sunanda Bai[8] measured the UHF velocity in benzene—*n*-heptane mixtures, which behave normally.

---

[2] B. V. Raghavendra Rao, *Nature* **139**, 885 (1937); *Proc. Indian Acad. Sci.* **A1**, 261, 473 (1935); **7**, 163 (1938).

[3] K. Sunanda Bai, *Proc. Indian Acad. Sci.* **A15**, 349 (1942).

[4] C. S. Venketeswaran, *Proc. Indian Acad. Sci.* **A15**, 371 (1942).

[5] C. S. Venketeswaran, *Proc. Indian Acad. Sci.* **A15**, 362 (1942).

[6] I. L. Fabelinski, Uspekhi Fiz. Nauk 63, Part 2, 355 (1957).

[7] I. L. Fabelinski, private communication, June 1958.

[8] K. Sunanda Bai, *Proc. Indian Acad. Sci.* **A18**, 210 (1943).

It is clear that the results of the UHF velocity measurements contradict the simple Stokes-Navier-Truesdell theory, since the frequency of the Debye waves involved ($\sim 10^{10}$ cycles/sec) is much higher than the generalized Lucas frequency (see Eq. 7–9′) and therefore the velocity increase should be considerable. On the other hand, the results correspond in general with those predicted by relaxation theory, although difficulties still exist. For the discussion we will have to anticipate numerical results from later sections.

We will discuss Kneser liquids first. Table 75–2 gives the following data: the relaxation time τ of the thermal relaxation from Table 95–1; γ_0 and γ_∞ (the latter at frequencies so high that C' is not involved) calculated from the data of Table 93–1; $(\gamma_\infty/\gamma_0)^{1/2}$, the ratio of the expected velocity; τ_s, the shear relaxation time, calculated approximately from $\eta = 10^{10}\,\tau_s$ (Sec. 100); and finally $(2\pi f_h)^{-1}$, the time corresponding to the UHF sonic waves observed optically.

TABLE 75–2

UHF AND RELAXATION DATA FOR KNESER LIQUIDS

Time in 10^{-10} sec

Liquid	τ	γ_0	γ_∞	$(\gamma_\infty/\gamma_0)^{1/2}$	τ_s	$(2\pi f_h)^{-1}$
CS_2	28.3	1.55	1.82	1.09	0.004	0.233
$CHCl_3$	1.30	1.52	1.90	1.12	0.009	0.233
CCl_4	1.26	1.46	2.16	1.22	0.009	0.233
C_6H_6	2.70	1.45	2.16	1.22	0.006	0.233

It is obvious that the frequencies of the UHF sonic waves are far above those of thermal relaxation, while they are far below those at which viscous relaxation occurs. One would therefore expect the velocity of the UHF sonic wave to be 9% for CS_2, 12% for $CHCl_3$ or 22% (for CCl_4 and C_6H_6) above the usual sound velocity.

The UHF data show these increases to be 9% for CS_2, 20% for $CHCl_3$, 13% for CCl_4, and 10% for C_6H_6. The data for CS_2 and $CHCl_3$ agree within experimental error with those values calculated in Table 75–2. (Note that the measured $CHCl_3$ values obtained by Fabelinski are approximate only). The UHF sonic velocities found for CCl_4 and C_6H_6 are definitely low. It is possible that at these ultra high frequencies not all the degrees of freedom have relaxed. (τ has been calculated on the assumption that all the degrees of freedom have the same relaxation time.)

The relaxation absorption in C_6H_6 in this region is independent of frequency with $\alpha \sim 5000\ cm^{-1}$, i.e., a decay to $1/e$ of the amplitude over a distance of 2×10^{-4} cm. Since half of the optical wave length in benzene is 1.6×10^{-5} cm, about 12 crests cooperate optically.

Next, two associated liquids, glycerol and *n*-propyl alcohol, are treated. Table 75–3 contains data estimated at 20° C. The relaxation time τ for glycerine is extrapolated from the data in Sec. 106 and the paper by Piccirelli and Litovitz;[7] for *n*-propyl alcohol, from the formula quoted previously for the calculation of τ_s. The next column contains the ratio of high frequency to low frequency velocity, the former calculated from a linear combination of compressional and shear modulus (see Secs. 110 and 111). The last column again gives the relevant times for the UHF velocity measurement.

TABLE 75–3
UHF DATA FOR TWO ASSOCIATED LIQUIDS
Time in 10^{-10} sec

Liquid	τ	$\mathfrak{B}_\infty/\mathfrak{B}_0$	$(2\pi f_h)^{-1}$
Glycerine	3.3	1.5	0.11
n-propyl alcohol	0.0002	1.33	0.22

It is obvious that the times corresponding to the frequencies of the Debye waves observed are much shorter than the compressional and shear relaxation time of glycerine, so that $\mathfrak{B}_\infty = 1.5\ \mathfrak{B}_0$ should be observed; actually, a value equal to $1.28\ \mathfrak{B}_0$ is found. For alcohol, $(2\pi f_h)^{-1}$ is much longer than τ_s, so that the velocity should be $\mathfrak{B}_0$, as is observed.

As for absorption in glycerine, one can estimate $\alpha\lambda = 0.066$, so that the amplitude falls by the factor $1/e$ in about 15 wave lengths; about that many crests should cooperate optically.

It should be pointed out that these waves are still 250 times longer than the limiting Debye waves.

We have replaced the often used word „hypersonics" by UHF to avoid confusion with the aerodynamic „hypersonic velocity."

[7] R. Piccirelli and T. A. Litovitz, *J. Acoust. Soc. Am.* **29**, 1009 (1957).

IX. Experimental Methods to Determine Dispersion and Absorption of Ultrasonic Waves in Liquids

76. Methods for Low Frequencies

As is the case in gases (see Sec. 42) the measurement of absorption at low frequencies is difficult owing to the smallness of the absorption coefficient at these frequencies. Also as in gases, the production of plane waves necessary for accurate interferometer work involves very bulky equipment. Two methods appear useful in this region.

Reverberation Method. The theory of this method has been described in Sec. 42. It is useful for both gases and liquids. The method has been extended with various modifications to liquids by Mulders,[1] Leonard,[2] Moen,[3] Kurtze and Tamm,[4] and Karpovich.[5]

The main difficulty of this method is the problem of separating the wall losses from the absorption losses. In this connection Karpovich's work is quite significant. He has shown that the wall loss correction is not only a function of the container dimensions but is also dependent on the loss in the liquid. Karpovich calibrated the liquid container with liquids of known absorption and in this manner obtained results good to within $\pm 5\%$.

Direct Measurement of Absorption. The "quartz wind" or acoustic streaming method has been used to measure absorption in liquids at 1.0 Mc by Piercy and Lamb.[6] Their experimental arrangement involves the use of a beam of progressive sound waves in a main tube and a small side tube which provides a return path for the streaming. The motion of small aluminum particles in the side tube is followed by means of a microscope, thus allowing a measurement of the streaming velocity in the smaller tube. The use of a small side tube allows "amplification" of the streaming velocity. Thus,

---

[1] C. E. Mulders, *Appl. Sci. Research* **B1**, 149 (1948).
[2] R. W. Leonard, *U.C.L.A. Tech. Rept. No. 1*, June 1, 1950.
[3] C. J. Moen, *J. Acoust. Soc. Am.* **23**, 62 (1951).
[4] G. Kurtze and K. Tamm, *Acoustica* **3**, 33 (1953).
[5] J. Karpovich, *J. Acoust. Soc. Am.* **26**, 819 (1955).
[6] J. E. Piercy and J. Lamb, *Proc. Roy. Soc.* **A226**, 43 (1954).

weakly absorbing liquids can be measured. At 1.0 Mc Piercy and Lamb have obtained results good to within 10% with liquids having an α as low as $2.4 \times 10^{-4}\ \text{cm}^{-1}$. This method promises to be of use at even lower frequencies. See also Sec. 46.

77. The Ultrasonic Interferometer

The ultrasonic interferometer (see Sec. 43) has been used extensively for the measurement of ultrasonic velocities in liquids. Fox[1] has considered in detail the theory of ultrasonic interferometry for liquid media and the differences which occur between gas and liquid interferometry. In gases the current in the associated electrical circuits of the crystal has a sharp peak when the reflector setting is a multiple of one-half wave lengths from the transducer, i.e., the *minimum* of the "crevasse," which is determined by the resonance of the quartz crystal, has a peak. In liquids in which there is no crevasse, one gets a dip in the current at reflector distances which are $(2n + 1)$ one-quarter wave lengths from the transducer.[2]

There is a considerable discrepancy to be found in the literature concerning the measurements of the velocity of sound using the interferometer technique. Many investigators were reporting "reproducibilities" of $\pm$ 0.1%, but the comparison of data from one investigator to another often showed discrepancies exceeding $\pm$ 0.1%. The possible reasons for disagreement are clearly summarized by Del Grosso and co-workers.[3] Assuming that the variables, such as frequency, temperature, purity of sample, and calibration of the distance-measuring device, have been adequately taken into account, the main source of error would be in the design of the interferometer. According to Del Grosso and co-workers, most of these errors are caused by diffraction, due to finite size of the source; excitation of Rayleigh modes, due to transverse vibrations of the crystal; and coherent radial reflections, and/or reflection of the primary beam from the walls of the container.

---

[1] F. E. Fox, *Phys. Rev.* **52**, 973 (1937); an improved method to find the absorption is due to J. L. Hunter and F. E. Fox, *J. Acoust. Soc. Am.* **22**, 238 (1950).

[2] The difference arises from the fact that $\rho\mathfrak{B}$, the radiation impedance of the medium, is much larger in the liquid. Accordingly, the reaction of the fluid column on the crystal, which is small for the gas, is quite large for the liquid. In the gas, the maximum current occurs when the reactive effect of the gas is zero at exact resonance and the resistive effect a maximum. For liquids, the minimum current occurs when the reactive effect is zero between resonance positions and the resistive effect is smallest. At high gas pressures, there will be a transition between the two cases.

[3] V. A. Del Grosso, E. J. Smura, and P. F. Fougere, *N.R.L. Rept. No. 4439*, December, 1954.

Del Grosso has reported that at frequencies of the order of 1.0 Mc, after taking proper precautions to eliminate the above-mentioned errors, velocity measurements accurate to 1 part in 30,000 are possible in low attenuating liquids and 1 part in 5000 in highly attenuating liquids. As in gases, the accuracy of the measurement decreases as the absorption increases. Furthermore, in highly viscous liquids in the megacycle range measurements become very difficult.

Fox[1] has also discussed the use of the interferometer in making absorption measurements in liquids and has pointed out the difficulties in this type of measurement. In general the interferometer has not proven useful in making attenuation measurements in liquids.

78. Pulse Methods

The application of ultrasonic pulse methods to liquids by Pellam and Galt[1] and Pinkerton[2] has had a tremendous impact on the study of ultrasonic propagation in liquids and solids. There are two main advantages of the pulse technique over continuous wave methods for the measurement of absorption. One is the elimination of standing waves. The other is the minimization of local heating effects because even with high peak powers the average energy and therefore the average heating effect of the radio frequency pulse is small.

A typical pulse reflection system works in the following way. Square electric pulses of from 1 to 50 μsec are used to modulate a radio frequency signal which drives a suitable transducer. The crystal emits a wave train containing anywhere from 10 to 100 cycles of the radio frequency signal. This acoustic pulse is received either by a second transducer or is first reflected and then arrives back at the emitting transducer where it is amplified and presented on the screen of a cathode ray oscilloscope.

Attenuation measurements over a range of frequency from 0.5 Mc to 300 Mc can be made reproducible to within $\pm$ 2% by comparing the reflected signal with the output of a calibrated standard signal generator tuned to the same frequency as the reflected signal or "echo".

There are many possible variations in the use of the pulse technique for velocity measurements, all of which give an accuracy of 0.1% in weakly attenuating liquids. One method[1] is to measure the change in time of arrival of the reflected echo as the path length is changed by some known amount.

---

[1] J. R. Pellam and J. K. Galt, *J. Chem. Phys.* **14**, 608 (1946).

[2] J. M. M. Pinkerton, *Proc. Phys. Soc. London* **B62**, 286 (1949).

The timing must be done electronically. This method is limited to liquids of small absorption.

An alternative method[3] of velocity measurement is to "beat" the reflected echo against a fixed signal of the same frequency. As the path length is changed the relative phase of the reflected echo and the fixed signal changes. Measurement of the number of in-phase "beats" occurring over a given change in path length of the echo allows one to calculate the wave length in the medium. This method has been used in liquids with absorption coefficients as high as $\alpha = 100\ \text{cm}^{-1}$. The accuracy of the velocity measurement in this high absorption region is about 1/2 to 1%.

Greenspan's[4] "direct method" claims an accuracy of 1 in 30 000, but this is still in dispute.

79. Mechanical Method: Radiation Pressure Measurements

Sound absorption measurements in liquids can be made by a mechanical method which is based on radiation pressure. A plane sound wave of intensity I carries with it a linear momentum of amount $I/\mathfrak{V}$ per second and unit area. If the total radiation flux Φ is taken out of the plane wave and either absorbed or scattered uniformly in all directions, the linear momentum $(1/\mathfrak{V})\,\Phi$ is taken out of the plane wave per second and transferred to the absorber or scatterer. This is equivalent to a force $\Phi/\mathfrak{V}$ acting on it in the direction of propagation. This pressure difference or radiation pressure is proportional to the ultrasonic intensity. Thus, a measurement of this quantity as a function of distance allows one to obtain the absorption coefficient.

Various mechanical arrangements have been used to measure this radiation pressure. For example, Fox and Rock[1] have allowed a horizontal ultrasonic beam to displace a plate or bead at the end of a long wire. If the sound beam is directed vertically upward as done by Claeys, *et al.*[2] and an object is suspended in the sound field, its apparent weight can be measured with and without the sound beam turned on.

There are severe limitations to the use of this method. In common with other continuous wave methods one must be very careful of the possible existence of standing waves and, even more so, of "acoustic streaming" (see Sec. 76). Lack of attention to this point caused large discrepancies in

---

[3] W. P. Mason, W. O. Baker, H. J. McSkimin, and J. H. Heiss, *Phys. Rev.* **73**, 1074 (1948).

[4] M. Greenspan and C. E. Tschiegg, *J. Research Natl. Bur. Standards* **59**, 249 (1957).

[1] F. E. Fox and G. D. Rock, *Phys. Rev.* **54**, 223 (1938); **70**, 68 (1946).

[2] J. Claeys, J. Errera, and H. Sack, *Trans. Faraday Soc.* **33**, 136 (1937).

the results of early investigators. Surface tension and other frictional-type forces also serve to limit the accuracy of the measurement. This is especially true in high viscosity liquids where the radiation pressure method is not useful.

At best this method is limited to low viscosity liquids at frequencies above about 10 Mc, where an accuracy of about $\pm 5\%$ can be obtained. Lower frequency measurements can be made only in highly attenuating liquids.

80. Optical Methods[1a]

The most practical optical method of measuring sound absorption is that based on the Debye-Sears effect.[1b] The successive compressions and rarefactions of a sound wave alter the index of refraction of the medium in which it travels. If a light wave traverses this beam of sound at right angles, the light effectively sees a sinusoidal diffraction grating and some of the light is diffracted away from the main beam. The amount of light diffracted is proportional to the intensity of the sound beam. A photocell can be used to detect the amount of light remaining in the main beam. The output of the photocell is measured as the light beam is moved to different distances from the source of the sound. From this information the absorption coefficient is calculated.

The limitations of this method are the following: A plane wave is necessary; thus, at low frequencies the method is not practical. Standing waves and multiple reflections from walls will lead to erroneous results. If the attenuation is too great this method cannot be used. The range of α in which the method appears to be applicable is from about 0.01 to 10 cm^{-1}. In this range the optical method is of an accuracy comparable to that of the pulse method. Because of the depth of the sound field, the exact theory is fairly complicated.

Method of Isochromates. Measurement of sound absorption in liquids has been accomplished by an optical technique known as the method of isochromates. The method was originally suggested by Hiedemann and Osterhammel.[2] When an ultrasonic wave is used as an optical grating, the intensity distribution of the light over the diffraction orders depends on the

---

[1a] See also Sec. **44**.

[1b] P. Debye and F. Sears, *Proc. Natl. Acad. Sci. U.S.* **18**, 409 (1932).

[2] K. Osterhammel, *Akust. Z.* **6**, 73 (1941).

intensity of the ultrasonic waves. However, the intensity of the diffracted light also depends on the length of the optical path in the field and on the wave length of the light. With white light, one obtains a color picture of the sound field in which lines of equal color—isochromates—represent lines of equal sound intensity. In practice, the absorption coefficient is obtained by measuring the distance of a given color (or intensity of sound) from the crystal for varying intensities of radiated power from the crystal, this latter quantity being monitored by measuring the current in the quartz transducer.

Measurements of absorption in liquids using this method have been made by Schreuer and Osterhammel[3] and Kammura.[4] The results indicate that an accuracy of $\pm$ 10% is attainable.

[3] E. Schreuer and K. Osterhammel, *Naturwissenschaften* **29**, 44 (1941).

[4] M. Kammura, *J. Acoust. Soc. Am.* **27**, 5 (1956).

X. Review of Theories of Liquids

81. Introduction

The theory of liquids will be reviewed in this chapter with a view toward understanding the values of the relaxation times τ and their dependence on temperature and pressure. This task will fall into two parts.

For Kneser liquids, one tries to see what quantity takes the role which τ_c, the time between collisions, plays in gases. This is apparently the only part of the problem which is associated with the liquid as a liquid; the rest has to do with internal processes in the molecule.

For monatomic and associated liquids, the task is essentially that of calculating the relaxation time of the structure, i.e., the time it takes the spatial distribution to take its equilibrium value when disturbed. In gases, no such time is considered; the closest analogue is the time $1.27\ \tau_c$, which is needed to adjust the Maxwell distribution of velocities (Sec. 36).

In monatomic liquids, where the molecules can be considered as spherical, the methods and results are somewhat different from those used for the associated liquids.

Both problems mentioned above are closely tied to the theory of viscosity. Two fundamentally different approaches to this problem, depending upon whether one treats the liquid as a compressed gas or as a highly disordered crystal[1], exist. In the first approach, one considers the motion as given and tries to calculate the stresses, defined as due to the transport of momentum. This approach tries to correct the gas kinetic formulas by considering the dense packing and shortened mean free path, and therefore introduces the time between collisions directly.

The second approach takes the stresses as given and tries to calculate the resulting motion. This is considered to consist mainly of molecular jumps over a potential hill separating possible locations of the molecule in the crystal, making it strongly temperature-dependent. The first approach does not assume a potential barrier.

Put differently, the motion of a molecule in a liquid can be divided into two parts, using the language of the "cell theory" (Secs. 84–86): a motion of

[1] J. Frenkel, "Kinetic Theory of Liquids," Oxford, Univ. Press, London and New York, 1946.

the molecule within the cell, and the diffusion of the molecule out of the cell. The first approach emphasizes the first kind of motion, the second approach the second kind.

In the next sections, there will be no attempt to present the theory of the liquid state, but only those features which are of importance to us for an understanding of concepts like viscosity or "collision" in this state.

A. The Number of Collisions

82. Connection with Internal Pressure. Theory of Jäger

Following van der Waals' theory liquids were first treated as gases of high density. Boltzmann[1] had given a theory of viscosity for nonideal gases consisting of hard molecules; Enskog[2] generalized this to molecules interacting according to power laws. However, neither calculation is valid to densities as high as those in the liquid state.

Jäger[3] made the following argument. Gas pressure is caused by the molecules carrying linear momentum—the component parallel to their thermal motion to the wall. Each molecule carries mW_3 to the wall in the $x - y$ plane with the speed W_3. In a condensed gas, the thermal pressure per molecule is much higher than $m\overline{W_3{}^2}$, not because a molecule carries more linear momentum—it does not—but because the linear momentum is not wholly carried with the speed W_3 of molecular transportation. Instead, it jumps, at each collision, approximately the distance of the molecular diameter. This ratio is expressed by the ratio of the "thermal pressure" in the liquid, $-(\partial U/\partial V - p) = [T(\partial p/\partial T)]_v$, to the kinetic pressure NkT of point molecules of the same number per volume.

In viscous laminar flow, the viscous stress arises because a molecule transports that component of excess momentum which is in the direction of macroscopic flow, carrying it normal to that flow, which is the direction of the gradient of the macroscopic velocity. If the flow is in the x direction, and the gradient in the z direction, the excess momentum carried is

$$m \frac{\partial w_1}{\partial z} r \cos\varphi \tag{82–1}$$

[1] L. Boltzmann, "Vorlesungen über Gastheorie," Vol. II, p. **143**. A. Barth Leipzig, 1899; H. C. Longuet-Higgins and J. A. Pople, *J. Chem. Phys.* **25,** 884, (1956).

[2] D. Enskog, *Kgl. Svenska Vetenskapsakad. Handbl.* **63,** No. 4, (1921).

[3] G. Jäger, *Sitzber. Akad. Wiss. Wien Math. naturw. Kl. Abt.* **111**, 697 (1902).

where r is the distance from the last collision (in the ideal gas the mean free path Λ), and φ the angle between the direction of travel and the z direction. This momentum is transported with the speed W_3.

Jäger now draws the analogy with the gas *pressure* and assumes that the deviation from the ideal gas equation for viscosity is due to the same cause as for the gas pressure, namely, increase in transport velocity in the same ratio; i.e.

$$T\left(\frac{\partial p}{\partial T}\right)_v : NkT = \eta : \frac{1}{3} Nm\bar{W}r \tag{82-2}$$

pressure ratio = viscosity ratio

or

$$\eta = \frac{1}{3}\frac{m}{k} r \left(\frac{\partial p}{\partial T}\right)_v \bar{W} = \frac{1}{3}\frac{M}{R} r \frac{\beta \bar{W}}{\kappa_T} \tag{82-3}$$

[see Eq. (4–2), setting $ds = 0$] where r is set equal to the average distance between molecules.

While this formula does not give too poor numerical results at room temperature, it does not show any reason for the experimental temperature dependence

$$\frac{\partial \ln \eta}{\partial T} = -\frac{E'}{RT^2}. \tag{82-4}$$

Numerical results are given in Table 82–1; r has been identified with r_0 (Sec. 59).

TABLE 82–1
VISCOSITY OF LIQUIDS CALCULATED FROM INTERNAL PRESSURE

Liquid	$CHCl_3$	CCl_4	C_6H_6	CS_2	H_2O (4°C)	CH_3OH (20° C)	Glycerine* (20° C)
$\eta_{exp} \times 100$	0.514	0.843	0.564	0.346	1.57	0.597	1490
$\eta_{calc} \times 100$	0.478	0.939	0.563	0.473	0	0.58	3.2

* It has been assumed that r_0 for glycerine is the value for methyl alcohol times $\sqrt[3]{3}$. From the densities, one would estimate $\sqrt[3]{2.17}$, which decreases the calculated value by 10%.

It is seen that the agreement is fairly good for the normal liquids and even for methyl alcohol, but that for water and glycerine, and probably for all highly viscous liquids, the theory gives absurd results.

If one tries to follow Jäger's ideas farther, one can, by treating the molecules as hard spheres of diameter r_0, proceed as follows:

Imagine a straight line, 1 cm long, drawn in the liquid. This line will be partly in the space between molecules and partly within a molecule. Let the line pass through N' molecules. A line drawn randomly through spheres of diameter d is, on the average, for the distance $d/2$ within a sphere. Therefore, this line passes for the fraction $N'(d/2)$ through molecules and for the fraction $1 - N'(d/2)$ through the space between the molecules. However, from Jäger's argument, the fraction of the path in which the linear momentum is transported through the space between molecules is

$$NkT\left[T\left(\frac{\partial p}{\partial T}\right)_v\right]^{-1}.$$

Therefore

$$1 - N'\frac{d}{2} = NkT\left[T\left(\frac{\partial p}{\partial T}\right)_v\right]^{-1} = Nk\frac{\kappa_T}{\beta}. \tag{82–5}$$

This is a small quantity, so that approximately

$$N'\frac{d}{2} = 1. \tag{82–6}$$

Then, the fraction of the line going through space between the molecules being given by Eq. (82–5), and N' being the number of molecules along the line, the average length of the line lying between two molecules—which we can identify with the mean free path—is

$$\frac{1}{N'}Nk\frac{\kappa_T}{\beta} = Nk\frac{\kappa_T}{\beta}\frac{d}{2} = \frac{\rho}{M}R\frac{\kappa_T}{2\beta}d.$$

We identify d with r_0.

The time between collisions is

$$\tau_c = \frac{\rho}{M}\frac{R}{\overline{W}}\frac{\kappa_T}{2\beta}r_0 = \frac{R}{2\beta M}\frac{\gamma_{\text{liquid}}}{\mathfrak{V}_{\text{liquid}}^2}\frac{r_0}{\overline{W}} = \frac{\gamma_{\text{liquid}}}{\gamma_{\text{gas}}}\left(\frac{\mathfrak{V}_{\text{gas}}}{\mathfrak{V}_{\text{liquid}}}\right)^2\frac{1}{2T\beta}\frac{r_0}{\overline{W}}. \tag{82–7}$$

Some computed collision times τ_c from Jäger's theory, are, for $CHCl_3$, 1.37×10^{-13} sec; for CCl_4, 0.86; for C_6H_6, 0.72; and for CS_2, 0.88×10^{-13} sec.

83. Heat Produced by Friction. Number of Collisions

The following calculations do not attempt to give a theory of the viscosity coefficient η. On the contrary, they attempt to calculate a "number of collisions" per second and unit volume, or the quantity N/τ_c, from the experimental η. One starts with a consideration of frictional heat. In the simplest viscous flow, the stress per unit area is

$$\eta \frac{\partial w_1}{\partial z}.$$

If the layer has the thickness h and the speed zero at the bottom, the speed at the top is

$$h \frac{\partial w_1}{\partial z}.$$

The upper solid plate, the motion of which keeps the laminar flow going, therefore does the following amount of work per unit area and time

$$\text{stress} \times \text{speed} = \eta \left(\frac{\partial w_1}{\partial z}\right)^2 h. \tag{83–1}$$

This produces frictional heat in the volume of size 1 cm$^2 \times h$ equal to this work, or per unit volume and unit time

$$\eta \left(\frac{\partial w_1}{\partial z}\right)^2. \tag{83–2}$$

The heat originates physically from the energy exchange between the molecules. In the elementary theory of η for the gas, it is assumed that a molecule coming from a distance Λ since its last collision has an energy (see Sec. 36)

$$\begin{aligned} \frac{m}{2}\left\{\left(W_1 + w_1 + \frac{\partial w_1}{\partial z} \Lambda \cos \varphi\right)^2 + W_2{}^2 + W_3{}^2\right\} \\ = \frac{m}{2}\{(W_1 + w_1)^2 + W_2{}^2 + W_3{}^2\} + \\ 2\,\frac{m}{2}(W_1 + w_1)\frac{\partial w_1}{\partial z}\Lambda \cos\varphi + \frac{m}{2}\left(\frac{\partial w_1}{\partial z}\right)^2 \Lambda^2 \cos^2\varphi. \end{aligned} \tag{83–3}$$

It then collides with molecules of the local kinetic energy

$$\frac{m}{2}\{(W_1 + w_1)^2 + W_2^2 + W_3^2\} \tag{83–3'}$$

and, in equalizing its energy, loses the amount

$$m(W_1 + w_1)\frac{\partial w_1}{\partial z}\Lambda\cos\varphi + \frac{m}{2}\left(\frac{\partial w_1}{\partial z}\right)^2\Lambda^2\cos^2\varphi. \tag{83–3''}$$

In averaging over molecules coming from all directions the first term drops out, because the average of $\cos\varphi$ is zero, but the second term does not (average of $\cos^2\varphi = 1/3$) and is the average friction heat produced per collision

$$\text{Average friction heat produced per collision} = \frac{m}{6}\left(\frac{\partial w_1}{\partial z}\right)^2\Lambda^2. \tag{83–4}$$

Since the number of collisions per unit time and volume is N/τ_c, one gets as friction heat produced per unit time and volume

$$\frac{N}{\tau_c}\frac{m}{6}\left(\frac{\partial w_1}{\partial z}\right)^2\Lambda^2 = \eta\left(\frac{\partial w_1}{\partial z}\right)^2 \tag{83–5}$$

or

$$\eta = \frac{Nm}{6}\frac{\Lambda^2}{\tau_c}. \tag{83–5'}$$

For ideal gases, this agrees with the usual elementary formula, except for a factor 1/2, since

$$\tau_c = \frac{\Lambda}{\overline{W}}. \tag{83–5''}$$

For the liquid, we take over this formula, assuming with Jäger that the molecule carried with it the flow velocity corresponding to the position of its center, at a distance r, where r is the average distance of the molecules. This is substituted for Λ, and

$$\eta = \frac{\rho r^2}{6\tau_c} \tag{83–6}$$

$$\tau_c = \frac{\rho r^2}{6\eta}. \tag{83–6'}$$

The collision times τ_c for several liquids are: for CH_2Cl_2, 1.37×10^{-13} sec.; for $CHCl_3$, 1.27; for CCl_4, 0.96; for C_6H_6, 0.72; for C_6H_{14}, 1.34; and for CS_2, 1.20×10^{-13} sec.

If one uses Jäger's formula, Eq. (82–3), for η in Eq. (83–6′), one gets exactly Eq. (82–7). However, Eq. (83–6′) does not presuppose hard molecules.

84. Cubic Cell Model. Available Volume

(a) *Cubic Cell Model*

Eyring and Hirschfelder[1] have proposed a simple cell model for rigid spheres of diameter d. The molecules are located in the center of a cube of side $(V/N_A)^{1/3}$. They can move from the center of the cube to each side the distance

$$\left(\frac{V}{N_A}\right)^{1/3} - d \tag{84–1}$$

in the direction parallel to the edges of the cube. The total possible motion is then twice as much (sum of motion to left and right) and the time between collisions is

$$\tau_c = \frac{2}{\bar{W}}\left[\left(\frac{V}{N_A}\right)^{1/3} - d\right]. \tag{84–2}$$

If d is identified with r_0, it is found that for several molecules Eq. (84–1) is negative. Nonetheless, τ_c has been calculated for liquids in which the value is positive. The results are given in the second line of Table 84–1.

Equation (84–1) implies a head-on collision. If one draws a straight line randomly through a sphere, the average length of the line is $d/2$; this is the average distance the momentum jumps in collision (Sec. 82). Therefore, we replace the previous equations by

$$\left(\frac{V}{N_A}\right)^{1/3} - \frac{d}{2} \tag{84–1′}$$

and

$$\tau_c = \frac{1}{\bar{W}}\left[2\left(\frac{V}{N_A}\right)^{1/3} - r_0\right]. \tag{84–2′}$$

The numerical results are given in the last line of Table 84–1.

---

[1] H. Eyring and J. O. Hirschfelder, *J. Phys. Chem.* **41**, 249 (1937).

TABLE 84–1
COLLISION TIMES FROM SIMPLE CELL THEORY

Liquid	CH_2Cl_2	$CHCl_3$	CCl_4	C_6H_6	C_6H_{14}	CS_2	CH_3OH
$\tau_c \times 10^{12}$ sec*				0.009	0.07	0.4	0.21
$\tau_c \times 10^{12}$ sec†	1.66	2.20	2.62	1.86	2.25	2.22	1.02

* Results from Eq. (84–2).
† Results from Eq. (84–2′).

(b) *The "Available Volume." Kittel's Formula*

Kittel[2] has developed a formula related to that of Jäger, Eq. (82–7), and based on a particular equation of state. Kittel introduces the concept of "available" volume V_a. For the particular equation of state used, one has

$$pV_a = 3NkT$$

(N = number of molecules per unit volume) but this equation will not be used here. Kittel writes

$$3\,\frac{\gamma_{\text{liquid}}}{\gamma_{\text{gas}}}\left(\frac{\mathfrak{V}_{\text{gas}}}{\mathfrak{V}_{\text{liquid}}}\right)^2 = \frac{V_a}{V}\,. \tag{84–3}$$

If one inserts

$$V = \frac{M}{\rho}$$

$$\mathfrak{V}_{\text{gas}}{}^2 = \gamma_{\text{gas}}\frac{RT}{M} = \gamma_{\text{gas}}\frac{\pi}{8}\,\bar{W}^2$$

$$\mathfrak{V}_{\text{liquid}}{}^2 = \gamma_{\text{liquid}}\frac{1}{\rho\kappa_T}$$

and puts

$$\tau_c = \frac{1}{\bar{W}}\left(\frac{V_a}{N_A}\right)^{1/3} \tag{84–4}$$

one gets

$$\tau_c = \left(\frac{3\pi}{8}\,\frac{M}{N_A}\,\frac{\kappa_T}{\bar{W}}\right)^{1/3}. \tag{84–5}$$

[2] C. Kittel, *J. Chem. Phys.* **14, 614 (1946)**.

The collision times, $\tau_c \times 10^{12}$ sec, calculated from the "available" volume are: for $CHCl_3$, 1.13; for CCl_4, 1.10; for C_6H_6, 0.81; for C_6H_{14}, 0.99; for CS_2, 0.80; and for CH_3OH, 0.54.

85. Spherical Cell Model. "Free Volume" According to Thermodynamics

Assume that the motions of the molecules in the liquid obey classical theory and that the internal motions of the molecule—including rotation—are the same in the liquid and in the vapor state; it does not matter whether they are classical or not. Then, strictly from statistical mechanics, one can define a free volume v_f of the liquid per molecule by

$$v_f \exp\left(\frac{H'}{RT}\right) = \frac{kT}{p} \tag{85–1}$$

where H' is the heat of evaporation and p is the vapor pressure. This idea of the free volume was first introduced by Herzfeld[1] and has been used extensively by Kincaid and Eyring.[2] Equation (85–1) can be rewritten

$$H' = RT \ln \frac{kT}{pv_f}. \tag{85–1'}$$

In equilibrium

$$H' - TS' = 0$$

so that

$$S' = R \ln \frac{kT}{pv_f} \tag{85–1''}$$

or

$$\ln v_f = \ln \frac{kT}{p} - \frac{S'}{R}. \tag{85–1'''}$$

It is now useful to introduce a quantity

$$v_f' = \frac{v_f}{e} \tag{85–2}$$

or

$$\ln v_f' = \ln \frac{kT}{p} - \frac{S'}{R} - 1. \tag{85–2'}$$

---

[1] K. F. Herzfeld, "Kinetische Theorie der Wärme." Braunschweig, 1924.

[2] J. F. Kincaid and H. Eyring, *J. Chem. Phys.* **6**, 620 (1938).

The term $R \ln e$ is often called the communal entropy and is due to the fact that a cell may be empty or it may be occupied by more than one molecule, as Kirkwood[3] has pointed out. One has, therefore

$$v_f' = \frac{kT}{p} \exp\left[-\frac{S'}{R} - 1\right]. \tag{85–3}$$

If, as happens, the table[4] carries S' as referred to standard pressure, Eq. (85–3) is

$$v_f' = 0.5 \times 10^{-22}\, T \exp\left(-\frac{S'}{R}\right). \tag{85–3'}$$

If S' is given at a temperature T_0 different from T, the desired temperature, one has

$$S'(T) = S'(T_0) + \int_{T_0}^{T} (C_{p\ \mathrm{vapor}} - C_{p\ \mathrm{liquid}}) \frac{dT}{T}$$

which can be approximated by

$$\begin{aligned} S'(T) &= S'(T_0) + R\left(4 + \frac{C'}{R} - \frac{C_{p\ \mathrm{liquid}}}{R}\right) \ln \frac{T}{T_0} \\ &= S'(T_0) - 6R \ln \frac{T}{T_0} \end{aligned} \tag{85–4}$$

assuming that the molecule in not linear, and using the results of Sec. 93. Up to now, there has been no simplification, apart from the slightly doubtful factor e.

We now consider v_f' as a sphere of diameter $2r$, in which the molecule moves, and assume as time between collisions

$$\begin{aligned} \tau_c = \frac{2r}{\overline{W}} = \frac{1}{\overline{W}}\left(\frac{6}{\pi} v_f'\right)^{1/3} &= \frac{1}{\overline{W}} 3.076 \times 10^{-7} \left(\frac{T}{300}\right)^{1/3} \left(\frac{1}{p_{\mathrm{atm}}}\right)^{1/3} \times \\ \exp\left(-\frac{S'}{3R}\right) &= \frac{1}{\overline{W}} 3.076 \times 10^{-7} \left(\frac{T}{300}\right)^{1/3} \left(\frac{1}{p_{\mathrm{atm}}}\right)^{1/3} \left(\frac{T}{T_0}\right)^{2} 10^{-0.07293\, S'(T_0)} \end{aligned} \tag{85–5}$$

with S' in cal/degree moles.

[3] J. G. Kirkwood, *J. Chem. Phys.* **18**, 380 (1950).

[4] Selected Values of Chemical Thermodynamical Properties. *Nat. Bur. Standards U.S. Circ.* **500** (1952).

The collision times τ_c calculated from the thermodynamic free volume, at 300 °K, are, for CH_3Br, 4.4×10^{-13} sec; for CH_2Cl_2, 2.84; for $CHCl_3$, 3.17; CCl_4, 3.56; $CHCl_2CH_3$, 2.40; CH_2ClCH_2Cl, 2.06; *cis*-$C_2H_2Cl_2$, 2.63; *trans*-$C_2H_2Cl_2$, 2.67; C_6H_6, 2.33; CS_2, 3.27; and CH_3OH, 0.81×10^{-13} sec.

86. Spherical Cell Model. The Motion Treated as Simple Harmonic Motion

Herzfeld[1] has used the "cell theory" of liquids[2] in the following manner: Each molecule is supposed to be in a spherical cell; on the average $\tilde{N}$ neighbors form the cell wall. The field produced by these neighbors is calculated as if the neighbors made up a uniform spherical shell. (The next "shell" does not appreciably contribute to the field, because of the rapid decay with distance.)

If the radius of the cell is r_1, and the molecule within the cell is at a distance R from the center of the cell, the interaction energy is

$$H' = 4\varepsilon \frac{\tilde{N}}{4\pi r_1{}^2} \int \left\{ \left[\frac{r_0{}^2}{r_1{}^2 + R^2 - 2r_1 R \cos\vartheta} \right]^6 - \left[\frac{r_0{}^2}{r_1{}^2 + R^2 - 2r_1 R \cos\vartheta} \right]^3 \right\} r_1{}^2 \sin\vartheta \, d\vartheta \, d\varphi \tag{86–1}$$

$$= \frac{4\varepsilon\tilde{N}}{4r_1 R} \left\{ \frac{r_0{}^{12}}{5} \left[\frac{1}{(r_1 - R)^{10}} - \frac{1}{(r_1 + R)^{10}} \right] - \frac{r_0{}^6}{2} \left[\frac{1}{(r_1 - R)^4} - \frac{1}{(r_1 + R)^4} \right] \right\}.$$

If one now assumes the amplitude R to be small compared with the cell radius r_1, one can develop the quantity in { } into a power series according to R/r_1, and finds

$$\{ \ \} = \frac{r_0{}^{12}}{5r_1{}^{10}} \left[20\frac{R}{r_1} + 484\left(\frac{R}{r_1}\right)^3 \right] - \frac{r_0{}^6}{2r_1{}^4} \left[8\frac{R}{r_1} + 40\left(\frac{R}{r_1}\right)^3 \right]. \tag{86–2}$$

One therefore gets

$$H' = \varepsilon\tilde{N} \left\{ \left(\frac{r_0}{r_1}\right)^{12} \left[4 + 96.8\left(\frac{R}{r_1}\right)^2 \right] - \left(\frac{r_0}{r_1}\right)^6 \left[4 + 20\left(\frac{R}{r_1}\right)^2 \right] \right\} \tag{86–3}$$

$$= 4\varepsilon\tilde{N} \left\{ \left(\frac{r_0}{r_1}\right)^{12} - \left(\frac{r_0}{r_1}\right)^6 \right\} + 20\varepsilon\tilde{N} \left(\frac{R}{r_1}\right)^2 \left[4.84\left(\frac{r_0}{r_1}\right)^{12} - \left(\frac{r_0}{r_1}\right)^6 \right].$$

[1] K. F. Herzfeld, *J. Chem. Phys.* 22, 288 (1952).

[2] J. O. Hirschfelder, C. F. Curtiss, and R. B. Bird, "Molecular Theory of Gases and Liquids." Wiley, New York, 1954.

The first term is the binding energy; the second, the potential energy of the restoring force.

If the molecule were vibrating around the center of the sphere, one would have

$$(2\pi\nu)^2 = \frac{1}{m}\frac{40\varepsilon\tilde{N}}{r_1^2}\left[4.84\left(\frac{r_0}{r_1}\right)^{12} - \left(\frac{r_0}{r_1}\right)^6\right] = \frac{R}{M}\,40\,\frac{\varepsilon}{k}\frac{\tilde{N}}{r_1^2}\left[4.84\left(\frac{r_0}{r_1}\right)^{12} - \left(\frac{r_0}{r_1}\right)^6\right]. \tag{86–4}$$

Since the molecules are vibrating against each other, one should substitute $\tilde{M}$ for M. Since for each period there are two "collisions" at the end of the swing, $\tau_c = 1/2\nu$. A method is now needed to calculate r_1. It seems simplest (although not in agreement with the usual assumptions of the cell theory) to assume all molecules to be arranged in spherical layers. Then the sphere containing n layers would contain $\sum_1^n s^2\tilde{N}$ molecules and have a volume $\Sigma 4\pi(sr_1)^2 \cdot r_1 = 4\pi r_1^3 \Sigma s^2$. One finds the average volume per molecule to be $4\pi r_1^3/\tilde{N}$, or

$$4\pi r_1^3 = \frac{M}{\rho}\frac{\tilde{N}}{N_A}$$

$$r_1^3 = \frac{3M}{\pi\rho N_A}\frac{\tilde{N}}{12} \tag{86–5}$$

$$\tau_c = \pi\left(\frac{\tilde{M}}{40}\right)^{1/2}\left(12\,R\frac{\varepsilon}{k}\frac{\tilde{N}}{12}\right)^{-1/2} r_0 \cdot$$

$$\left(\frac{3M}{\pi\rho N_A}\frac{\tilde{N}}{12}\frac{1}{r_0^3}\right)^{4/3}\left[4.84\left(\frac{\pi\rho N_A}{3M}r_0^3\frac{12}{\tilde{N}}\right)^2 - 1\right]^{-1/2} \tag{86–6}$$

or, writing $r_0' = r_0 \times 10^8$ and $\tilde{M} = \frac{1}{2}M$

$$\tau_c = 2.056 \times 10^{-13}\left(\frac{\varepsilon}{k}\right)^{-1/2}\frac{M^{11/6}}{\rho^{4/3}}\left(\frac{\tilde{N}}{12}\right)^{5/6}(r_0')^{-3}\cdot\left[1.921\left(\frac{12}{\tilde{N}}\frac{\rho}{M}r_0'^3\right)^2 - 1\right]^{-1/2}. \tag{86–7}$$

Numerical calculation gives the collision times τ_c as the times between maximum amplitudes of a simple harmonic motion as follows: CH_2Cl_2, 0.84×10^{-13} sec; $CHCl_3$, 1.78; CCl_4, 1.40; C_6H_6, 1.44; C_6H_{14}, 1.54; and CS_2, 5.22×10^{-13} sec.

Lord and Andrews[3] found, from the specific heat for crystallized benzene at low temperature, $\nu = 3.1 \times 10^{12}\ \mathrm{sec}^{-1}$ or $\tau_c = 1.6 \times 10^{-13}$ sec.

B. The Space Distribution Function and Its Relaxation Time

87. The Distribution Function; Calculation of η and η'

A much more fundamental approach to the theory of liquids—but applied, at present, to monatomic liquids only—has been taken by Kirkwood and his collaborators[1] on the one side, and by Born and Green[2] on the other. The fundamental quantities are successive distribution functions (x shall stand for all three coordinates).

The probability that one particular molecule is within the volume element dv located at x is

$$\rho^{(1)}(x)dv = \frac{1}{V}\,dv. \tag{87–1}$$

The probability that one molecule is in dv_1 located at x_1, and another molecule in dv_2 located at x_2, is

$$\rho^{(2)}(x_1,x_2)dv_1dv_2 = \frac{1}{V^2}\,g^{(2)}(x_1,x_2)dv_1dv_2. \tag{87–2}$$

In an isotropic medium, far from the walls, $g^{(2)}(x_1,x_2)$ depends only on the distance r_{12}; $g^{(2)}$ is closely related to X-ray scattering in liquids, with

$$\frac{N_A}{V}\,4\pi r_{12}{}^2 g^{(2)}(r_{12})dr_{12} \tag{87–3}$$

being the number of molecules in the spherical shell of thickness dr_{12}. The probability that three molecules are simultaneously in dv_1, dv_2, and dv_3, respectively, is

$$\rho^{(3)}(x_1,x_2,x_3)dv_1dv_2dv_3 = \frac{1}{V^3}\,g^{(3)}(x_1,x_2,x_3)dv_1dv_2dv_3. \tag{87–4}$$

---

[3] R. C. Lord, J. E. Ahlberg and D. H. Andrews, *J. Chem. Phys.* **5**, 649 (1937).

[1] J. G. Kirkwood and E. M. Boggs, *J. Chem. Phys.* **10**, 394 (1942); J. G. Kirkwood, E. K. Maun, and B. J. Alder, *J. Chem. Phys.* **18**, 1040 (1950); J. G. Kirkwood, V. A. Lewinson, and B. J. Alder, *J. Chem. Phys.* **20**, 929 (1952).

[2] M. Born and H. S. Green, "A General Kinetic Theory of Liquids." Cambridge Univ. Press, London and New York, 1949.

If one considers the transport of momentum one finds the following expressions[3]

$$p = \frac{N_A}{V} kT - 2\pi \left(\frac{N_A}{V}\right)^2 \int_0^\infty r^3 \frac{dH}{dr} g_0^{(2)} dr \tag{87–5}$$

$$\eta = \frac{MRT}{V\,2N_A\zeta} + \frac{\pi\zeta}{15\,kT}\left(\frac{N_A}{V}\right)^2 \int_0^\infty r^3 \frac{dH}{dr} g_0^{(2)} \cdot \psi_2(r) dr \tag{87–5′}$$

$$\eta' = \frac{\pi\zeta}{9kT}\left(\frac{N_A}{V}\right)^2 \int_0^\infty r^3 \frac{dH}{dr} g_0^{(2)} \psi_0(r) dr. \tag{87–5″}$$

In these equations, H is the interaction potential of a pair of molecules; $g_0^{(2)}$ is the undisturbed correlation function of a pair of molecules; ψ_2 and ψ_0, disturbances in $g_0^{(2)}$ due to the flow; and ζ, the "Brownian motion" friction constant, is defined as $\zeta = kT/D$, where D is the coefficient of self diffusion. The first terms in p and η are due to the same kind of transport of momentum as in an ideal gas; ψ_0 and ψ_2 are given by certain differential equations.[4] If one assumes an interaction energy containing two constants, ε and r_0, such that H/ε is a universal function of r/r_0—the Lennard-Jones function belongs here—one gets

$$\eta' = \frac{\zeta}{9r_0} I_0' \qquad \eta = \frac{\zeta}{15r_0} I_2'. \tag{87–6}$$

In η the first term of Eq. (87—5′) has been neglected. I_0' and I_2' are dimensionless integrals.[5]

$$I_0' = \frac{\varepsilon}{kT}\left(\frac{N_A r_0^3}{V}\right)^2 \int_0^\infty \left(\frac{r}{r_0}\right)^3 \left(\frac{d}{dr/r_0}\frac{H}{\varepsilon}\right) g_0^{(2)}\left(\frac{r}{r_0}\right) \psi_0\left(\frac{r}{r_0}\right) d\left(\frac{r}{r_0}\right). \tag{87–7}$$

In I_2', ψ_2 replaces ψ_0.

Unfortunately, the distribution function $g^{(2)}$ is not given with sufficient accuracy by X-ray diffraction experiments. An improved function was used[6] and the integrals then calculated for the Lennard-Jones potential.

[3] J. G. Kirkwood, F. P. Buff, and M. S. Green, *J. Chem. Phys.* **17**, 988 (1949).

[4] R. W. Zwanzig, J. G. Kirkwood, K. F. Stripp, and I. Oppenheim, *J. Chem. Phys.* **21**, 2050 (1953).

[5] These differ from Kirkwood's insofar as "9" and "15" have been taken out.

[6] R. W. Zwanzig, J. G. Kirkwood, K. F. Stripp, and I. Oppenheim, *J. Chem. Phys.* **21**, 1268 (1953).

At the boiling point of argon, $V/(N_A r_0^3) = 0.7454$ and $kT/\varepsilon = 1.223$. I_0' is very sensitive to $g^{(2)}$. If this is adjusted so as to give the right vapor pressure, one finds $I_0' = 0.342$. I_2' is not sensitive to $g^{(2)}$. One gets, under the same conditions, $I_2' = 1.176$.

For ζ, 9.87×10^{-10} g/sec is used.

One finds $\eta' = 0.00036$ and $\eta = 0.00073$ poise.

The experimental values are $\eta' \sim 0, \eta = .0024$.

88. The Relaxation Time of the Distribution. Green's Theory

Green[1] has developed a theory which connects both shear and bulk viscosity with the fluctuations of some molecular quantity and the time during which a particular fluctuation persists.

Consider a quantity q_j which has a particular value at a given moment for molecule number j; e.g., this might be the kinetic energy of molecule j. Then define another quantity A which is the sum of q_j over all the molecules contained in the volume considered (e.g., the total kinetic energy)

$$A = \sum q_j. \tag{88-1}$$

A will vary with time; if its average value is $\bar{A}$, $A(t) - \bar{A}$ is the momentary deviation of A from its average, or the fluctuation. Now take the value of $A(t) - \bar{A}$ and multiply it with the value of the same difference at a time t' later, i.e.

$$[A(t) - \bar{A}]\,[A(t + t') - \bar{A}]. \tag{88-2}$$

Then take the average of this quantity[2] (average over t). This is called the correlation function of $A - \bar{A}$ for the time difference t'. In irregular fluctuations, the behavior of the correlation function is usually such that, for short

[1] M. S. Green, *J. Chem. Phys.* **22**, 398 (1954).

[2] The meaning of these formulas may be illustrated by the following, although only approximately

t	1	2	3	4	5	6	7	8	9	10
$A(t) - \bar{A}$	−36	−31	−4	+16	−29	+28	−41	−34	+29	+27
t	11	12	13	14	15	16	17	18	19	20
$A(t) - \bar{A}$	−7	+13	−16	+14	+5	+36	−24	+6	+26	+14

One finds

$$\{[A(t) - \bar{A}]^2\}_{\text{av}} = 595$$

$$\{[A(t) - \bar{A}]\,[A(t+1) - \bar{A}]\}_{\text{av}} = \frac{1}{19}\{(-36)\cdot(-31) + (-31)(-4) + \ldots\} = -61.$$

The A's were taken from a table of random numbers and therefore have an equivalent correlation time zero.

time intervals t', the fluctuation has not changed much and therefore the quantity Eq. (88–2) is positive, $A - \bar{A}$ being positive at $t + t'$ when it was positive at t, and negative when it was negative at t. With increasing t', however, the fluctuation changes, and when t' is sufficiently large, the fluctuation at $t + t'$ has no apparent connection with that at t; if $A(t) - \bar{A}$ is positive, $A(t + t') - \bar{A}$ may equally probably be positive or negative, i.e., the product Eq. (88–2) will equally probably be positive or negative. Accordingly, if one forms

$$\{[A(t) - \bar{A}]\,[A(t + t') - \bar{A}]\}_{\text{av over } t} \tag{88–2'}$$

this quantity will be largest for small t' and decrease to zero for sufficiently large t'.

Next, Green forms the integral

$$\int_0^\infty dt'\,\{[A(t) - \bar{A}]\,[A(t + t') - \bar{A}]\}_{\text{av over } t}. \tag{88–3}$$

He assumes that[3] for this, one can substitute the largest value of the integrand, i.e., the value for $t' = 0$, multiplied by an average time τ, the correlation time, over which the fluctuation "remembers" previous values

$$\text{Eq. (88–3)} = \tau\,\{[A(t) - \bar{A}]^2\}_{\text{av over } t}. \tag{88–3'}$$

The time τ can be considered as the relaxation time during which a given molecular distribution (which determines A) persists.

The preceding considerations can be applied to any random molecular function q_j.

We next assume that the forces between molecules have a potential H, so that the x component of the force which molecule s exerts on molecule j is

$$-\frac{\partial H}{\partial(x_j - x_s)}.$$

Green now defines three quantities A_1, A_2, A_3

$$A_1 = \sum m\dot{x}_j^2 - \sum x_j \frac{\partial H}{\partial x_j} \tag{88–4}$$

$$A_2 = \sum m\dot{y}_j^2 - \sum y_j \frac{\partial H}{\partial y_j} \tag{88–4'}$$

$$A_3 = \sum m\dot{z}_j^2 - \sum z_j \frac{\partial H}{\partial z_j} \tag{88–4''}$$

---

[3] This amounts to replacing the area which the integral in Eq. (88–3) represents by a rectangle the height of which is the maximum height of the curve, and the width of which is a properly chosen mean value of the width.

To this, we add another definition

$$A = A_1 + A_2 + A_3 = \sum m(\dot{x}_j^2 + \dot{y}_j^2 + \dot{z}_j^2) - \sum \left(x_j \frac{\partial H}{\partial x_j} + y_j \frac{\partial H}{\partial y_j} + z_j \frac{\partial H}{\partial z_j} \right). \quad (88\text{–}4''')$$

This quantity is usually called the virial.

Green (his equations 45 A, 46 A) now defines certain stresses T, which, using the preceding discussion, we can write[4]

$$\frac{1}{v} \tau \{[A_1(t) - \bar{A}_1]^2\}_{\text{av}} = T^{(4)}_{1111} = kT \left(\eta' + \frac{4}{3}\eta\right) \quad (88\text{–}5)$$

$$\frac{1}{v} \tau \{[A_1(t) - \bar{A}_1]\,[A_2(t) - \bar{A}_2]\}_{\text{av}} = T^{(4)}_{1212} = kT \left(\eta' - \frac{2}{3}\eta\right). \quad (88\text{–}5')$$

Therefore

$$T^{(4)}_{1111} + 2T^{(4)}_{1212} = 3kT\eta'. \quad (88\text{–}6)$$

Equations (88–5), (88–5′), and (88–6) are the important physical results of Green's paper. To make further progress, one can[5] evaluate the A's in terms of the fluctuations of macroscopic quantities, following a procedure first introduced by Einstein.[6]

Accordingly, one has for the virial A at every moment[5]

$$A = 3 \int p\,dv. \quad (88\text{–}7)$$

One easily shows by actual squaring out that

$$\{[A(t) - \bar{A}]^2\}_{\text{av}} = 3\{[A_1(t) - \bar{A}_1]^2\}_{\text{av}} + 6\{[A_1(t) - \bar{A}_1]\,[A_2(t) - \bar{A}_2]\}_{\text{av}} \quad (88\text{–}8)$$

since, because of the average spatial isotropy

$$\{A_1^2\}_{\text{av}} = \{A_2^2\}_{\text{av}} = \dots \qquad \{A_1A_2\}_{\text{av}} = \{A_2A_3\}_{\text{av}} = \dots$$

Inserting Eqs. (88–5) and (88–5′) into Eq. (88–6) and using Eq. (88–8), one finds

$$\eta' = \frac{1}{9vkT} \tau \{[A(t) - \bar{A}]^2\}_{\text{av}} \quad (88\text{–}8')$$

---

[4] In Eq. (88–5) we use the definition of η' given in Eq. (6–7). Green calls a different quantity η' the bulk viscosity, namely, our $\eta' - 2/3\,\eta$.

[5] K. F. Herzfeld, *J. Chem. Phys.* **28**, 595 (1958).

[6] A. Einstein, *Ann. Physik* [4], **33**, 1275 (1910).

and, with Eq. (88–7)

$$\eta' = \frac{\tau}{vkT}\left\{\left[\int(p - \bar{p})dv\right]^2\right\}_{\text{av}}. \tag{88–9}$$

One now assumes that p is determined by the local density $\rho = \bar{\rho} + \Delta\rho$ and temperature $T = \bar{T} + \Delta T$ and develops $p - \bar{p}$

$$p - \bar{p} = \left(\frac{\partial p}{\partial \rho}\right)_T \Delta\rho + \left(\frac{\partial p}{\partial T}\right)_\rho \Delta T + \tag{88–10}$$
$$\frac{1}{2}\left(\frac{\partial^2 p}{\partial \rho^2}\right)_T [(\Delta\rho)^2 - \overline{(\Delta\rho)^2}] + \frac{\partial^2 p}{\partial\rho\partial T}\Delta\rho\Delta T + \frac{1}{2}\left(\frac{\partial^2 p}{\partial T^2}\right)_\rho [(\Delta T)^2 - \overline{(\Delta T)^2}].$$

According to Green, only those fluctuations are considered which keep the total mass and total energy in the volume unchanged.

We will now apply this theory in three different cases; case (a), monatomic fluids; case (b), Kneser liquids; case (c), fluids with two structural states.

a) When we next form $\int (p - \bar{p})dv$, the first and second term on the right contain factors

$$\int \Delta\rho dv = \text{variation of total mass}$$

and

$$\int \Delta T dv = 1/c_v \times \text{variation of total energy}$$

which equal zero. If we further assume that fluctuations of temperature and density are independent, the fourth term does not contribute anything.

The third term contains the factor

$$\int [(\Delta\rho)^2 - \overline{(\Delta\rho)^2}]dv. \tag{88–11}$$

We divide the volume v into volume elements v_j of size v', v' being small enough so that the fluctuations in neighboring elements are independent. Equations (88–11) then takes the form

$$\sum v_j [(\Delta\rho_j)^2 - \overline{(\Delta\rho)^2}] = v' \sum [(\Delta\rho_j)^2 - \overline{(\Delta\rho)^2}]. \tag{88–11$'$}$$

When this is squared and averaged, as is necessary to get Eq. (88–9), one has

$$(v')^2 \sum_j \{\Delta\rho_j)^4 - 2\,\overline{(\Delta\rho)^2}\,(\Delta\rho_j)^2 + [\overline{(\Delta\rho)^2}]^2\}_{\text{av}} \tag{88–11$''$}$$
$$= (v')^2 \left\{\sum_j [(\Delta\rho_j)^4 - \overline{(\Delta\rho)^2}\cdot\overline{(\Delta\rho)^2}]\right\}_{\text{av}}$$
$$= v'v\,\{(\Delta\rho)^4 - \overline{(\Delta\rho)^2}\,\overline{(\Delta\rho)^2}\}_{\text{av}}.$$

A similar expression with ΔT results from the last term. This then has to be averaged properly, and the end result is a follows.

Note: In the following, the methods for calculating the mean square fluctuations, etc., are indicated.

(a) The work necessary to produce the density variations $\Delta\rho_j$ by compression is

$$\frac{1}{2\kappa}\sum v_j(\Delta\rho_j)^2. \tag{88–12}$$

To calculate the probability of a certain distribution of density fluctuations, this work is used in the exponent of a Maxwell-Boltzmann distribution function as if it were a potential energy. If one has a distribution of a quantity x according to $\exp(-ax^2)$, one easily finds

$$\overline{x^4} - \overline{x^2}\,\overline{x^2} = \frac{3}{4a^2} - \left(\frac{1}{2a}\right)^2 = \frac{1}{2a^2}. \tag{88–12′}$$

In our case

$$a = \frac{1}{2\kappa kT}v'. \tag{88–12″}$$

(b) The probability of a state is proportional to $\exp(-S/k)$. If we have two systems in contact, with heat capacities c_1 and c_2, the entropy change due to the transfer of heat in the amount

$$c_1\Delta T_1 = -c_2\Delta T_2$$

from system (2) to system (1) is

$$\Delta S = c_1 \ln\frac{T_1}{T_0} + c_2\ln\frac{T_2}{T_0} = c_1\ln\frac{T_0+\Delta T_1}{T_0} + c_2\ln\frac{T_0+\Delta T_2}{T_0}. \tag{88–13}$$

Developing up to quadratic terms in the temperature change, one gets

$$\Delta S = -\frac{c_1}{2}\left(\frac{\Delta T_1}{T_0}\right)^2 - \frac{c_2}{2}\left(\frac{\Delta T_2}{T_0}\right)^2 = -\frac{1}{2}\,\frac{c_1(c_1+c_2)}{c_2}\left(\frac{\Delta T_1}{T_0}\right)^2.$$

It follows that the average valuc of $(\Delta T_1)^2$ is

$$\overline{(\Delta T_1)^2} = \frac{c_2 k}{c_1(c_1+c_2)}T_0^2. \tag{88–13′}$$

If c_2 is very large, this is

$$\overline{(\Delta T_1)^2} = \frac{k}{c_1}T_0^2.$$

(c) If a number of N particles is divided into two groups, N_1 and N_2, the probability of a certain division is given by

$$\exp\left\{N_1\ln\frac{N_1}{N} - \bar{N}_1\ln\frac{\bar{N}_1}{N} + N_2\ln\frac{N_2}{N} - \bar{N}_2\ln\frac{\bar{N}_2}{N}\right\}. \tag{88–14}$$

Again, developing the previous equation into a power series of the small quantity $(N_1 - \bar{N}_1)/N = -(N_2 - \bar{N}_2)/N$, one gets, for the quadratic term (the linear term drops out because $\bar{N}_1$, $\bar{N}_2$ is the most probable distribution)

$$\frac{1}{2}\frac{1}{N}\left(\frac{1}{\bar{N}_1} + \frac{1}{\bar{N}_2}\right)(N_1 - \bar{N}_1)^2.$$

As a result—similar to that found in (b)

$$\{(N_1 - \bar{N}_1)^2\}_{\text{av}} = N\left[\frac{N}{\bar{N}_1} + \frac{N}{\bar{N}_2}\right]^{-1} = \frac{\bar{N}_1\bar{N}_2}{N}. \tag{88–14′}$$

Inserting the calculations indicated in Eqs. (88–12′) and (88–12″) into Eqs. (88–9) and (88–11″), one has

$$\eta' = \frac{1}{2}\frac{kT}{v'}\tau\left\{\left[\rho\left(\frac{\partial^2 p}{\partial \rho^2}\right)_T \bigg/ \left(\frac{\partial p}{\partial \rho}\right)_T\right]^2 + \left(\frac{1}{C_v}V\frac{\partial C_v}{\partial V}\right)^2\right\} = \frac{1}{2}\frac{RT}{VN'}\tau\{\ldots\}. \tag{88–15}$$

Here N' is the number of molecules contained in v'. From Eq. (88–15), it follows that $\eta' = 0$ for ideal gases, as must be, since for ideal gases $\partial^2 p/\partial \rho^2$ and $\partial^2 p/\partial T^2$ are zero. The values for $\rho(\partial^2 p/\partial \rho^2)_T/(\partial p/\partial \rho)_T$ are[7] 7 and 11 for water and carbon tetrachloride; the second term is much smaller than the first. Equation (88–15) contains two unknowns[8], v' and τ.

We next discuss molecules with internal degrees of freedom, case (b); and fluids made up of two structural states, case (c). In both cases one gets contributions to the first order terms in Eq. (88–10) which were zero for monatomic liquids.

b) In the case of Kneser liquids, it is assumed that only the external degrees of freedom (temperature, T_{tr}; specific heat, $C_v - C'$) affect the equation of state, so that ΔT in Eq. (88–10) is ΔT_{tr} and we get a contribution to η' equal to

$$\frac{\tau''}{vkT}\left[\left(\frac{\partial p}{\partial T}\right)_\rho\right]^2 \sum v_j^2\, \overline{(\Delta T_{\text{tr}})^2}. \tag{88–16}$$

---

[7] F. E. Fox and W. A. Wallace, *J. Acoust. Soc. Am.* **26**, 999 (1954).

[8] If one writes

$$v' = \frac{4\pi}{3}l^3$$

l is a "correlation length." One may further assume that

$$\tau = 2l/\mathfrak{B}.$$

One finds, for $\eta' = 0.01$ poise, $\mathfrak{B} = 1.5 \times 10^5$ cm/sec, $\rho(\partial^2 p/\partial \rho^2)/(\partial p/\partial \rho) = 10$, $\tau = 3.3 \times 10^{-13}$ sec, and $2l = 5$ Å.

The latter fluctuation arises because the distribution of the total energy (the energy being constant) fluctuates between the two temperature reservoirs of heat capacities $(C_v - C')v'/V$ and $(C')v'/V$. It follows from Eq. (88–13′) that one gets for η'

$$\eta' = \frac{\tau''}{kTv} v' v \left[\left(\frac{\partial p}{\partial T}\right)_\rho\right]^2 \frac{C'k}{(C_v - C')C_v} \frac{V}{v'} T^2 = \rho \mathfrak{V}_0{}^2 \frac{C'\Delta}{(C_v - C')C_p} \tau''. \quad (88\text{–}16')$$

Here, Eqs. (4–1) and (4–9) have been used. In comparing the result in Eq. (88–16′) with Eqs. (8–2) and (15–8) one notes agreement if τ' is interpreted as the relaxation time at constant pressure or constant entropy (Sec. 31).

c) In the case of a two-state liquid, one should add another linear term

$$\left(\frac{\partial p}{\partial N_1}\right)_s (N_1 - \bar{N}_1) = \left(\frac{\partial p}{\partial V}\right)_s \frac{\partial V}{\partial N_1} (N_1 - \bar{N}_1) \quad (88\text{–}17)$$

to the linear terms in Eq. (88–10); N_1 and N_2 are the occupation numbers of the two states. One therefore gets a contribution to the bulk viscosity equal to

$$\frac{\tau'}{vkT} v^2 \left[\left(\frac{\partial p}{\partial V}\right)_s\right]^2 \left(\frac{V_2 - V_1}{N}\right)^2 \{(N_1 - \bar{N})^2\}_{\text{av}}. \quad (18\text{–}17)$$

Inserting the value of the last factor according to Eq. (88–14′), one has

$$\eta' = [\rho \mathfrak{V}_0{}^2]^2 \frac{(V')^2}{VRT} x_1 x_2 \tau' \quad (88\text{–}17')$$

in complete agreement with Eq. (29–10′).

Next, one tries to calculate the shear viscosity from these equations. This will require some assumptions. According to Eqs. (88–5) and (88–8′)

$$\frac{4}{3}\eta = \frac{\tau}{vkT}\left\{(A_1 - \bar{A}_1)^2 - \frac{1}{9}(A - \bar{A})^2\right\}_{\text{av}}. \quad (88\text{–}18)$$

To calculate A_3, we introduce two angles, ϑ_j and φ_j. The first is the angle between the molecular speed and the x axis; the second is defined by

$$x_j \frac{\partial H}{\partial x_j} = \cos^2 \varphi_j \left[x_j \frac{\partial H}{\partial x_j} + y_j \frac{\partial H}{\partial y_j} + z_j \frac{\partial H}{\partial z_j}\right].$$

A_1 [Eq. (88–4)] can then be rewritten in the following manner

$$A_1 = \sum m(\dot{x}_j{}^2 + \dot{y}_j{}^2 + \dot{z}_j{}^2)(\cos^2 \vartheta_j - \cos^2 \varphi_j) + \quad (88\text{–}19)$$

$$\sum \cos^2 \varphi_j \left[m(\dot{x}_j{}^2 + \dot{y}_j{}^2 + \dot{z}_j{}^2) - \left(x_j \frac{\partial H}{\partial x_j} + y_j \frac{\partial H}{\partial y_j} + z_j \frac{\partial H}{\partial z_j}\right)\right].$$

For Eq. (88–18), we need $A_1 - \bar{A}_1$. We are going to use the following approximation. We set [for q_j see Eq. (88–1)]

$$\sum (q_j \cos^2 \vartheta_j - \overline{q \cos^2 \vartheta}) = \sum (q_j - \bar{q})\, \overline{\cos^2 \vartheta_j} + \qquad (88\text{–}19')$$

$$\sum \bar{q}\, (\cos^2 \vartheta_j - \overline{\cos^2 \vartheta}) = \tfrac{1}{3} \sum (q_j - \bar{q}) + \bar{q} \sum (\cos^2 \vartheta_j - \tfrac{1}{3}).$$

In this, we have assumed

$$\overline{q_j \cos^2 \vartheta_j} = \tfrac{1}{3}\, \bar{q}$$

(independence of fluctuations of q and the angle) and have neglected

$$\sum (q_j - \bar{q})\, (\cos^2 \vartheta_j - \overline{\cos^2 \vartheta}).$$

Since $\Sigma m(\dot{x}_j{}^2 + \dot{y}_j{}^2 + \dot{z}_j{}^2)$ is twice the kinetic energy, and the mean value of $\cos^2 \vartheta_j - \cos^2 \varphi_j$ is zero, one gets

$$A_1 - \bar{A}_1 = 3kT \sum (\cos^2 \vartheta_j - \cos^2 \varphi_j) + (A - \bar{A})\, \overline{\cos^2 \varphi} +$$

$$\frac{\bar{A}}{N} \sum (\cos^2 \varphi_j - \tfrac{1}{3}). \qquad (88\text{–}19'')$$

Forming Eq. (88–18) and taking into account that all double products vanish on averaging, one has

$$\eta = \frac{3}{4} \frac{\tau}{vkT} \left\{ (3kT)^2 \left[\sum (\cos^2 \vartheta_j - \cos^2 \varphi_j) \right]^2 + \frac{1}{9} [A - \bar{A}]^2 + \right.$$

$$\left. \left(\frac{3pv}{N} \right)^2 \left[\sum \left(\cos^2 \varphi_j - \frac{1}{3} \right) \right]^2 - \frac{1}{9} [A - \bar{A}]^2 \right\}_{\text{av}} \qquad (88\text{–}20)$$

$$= \frac{27}{4} \tau \frac{kT}{v} \left\{ \left[\sum (\cos^2 \vartheta_j - \cos^2 \varphi_j) \right]^2 + \left(\frac{pv}{NkT} \right)^2 \left[\sum \left(\cos^2 \varphi_j - \frac{1}{3} \right) \right]^2 \right\}_{\text{av}}.$$

To evaluate the averages, some assumptions have to be made. The first bracket gives

$$\left[\sum (\cos^2 \vartheta_j - \cos^2 \varphi_j) \right]^2 = \sum (\cos^4 \vartheta_j - 2 \cos^2 \vartheta_j \cos^2 \varphi_j + \cos^4 \varphi_j)$$

$$+ \sum_s{}' \sum_j (\cos^2 \vartheta_s \cos^2 \vartheta_j - 2 \cos^2 \vartheta_s \cos^2 \varphi_j + \cos^2 \varphi_s \cos^2 \varphi_j). \qquad (88\text{–}21)$$

The prime on the sum means that $s = j$ is to be excluded, but otherwise the summation goes over s and j independently. One assumes now that ϑ

and φ for the same molecule, the ϑ for two different molecules, and the φ for two different molecules are not correlated.[9]

Then[10] the average value of Eq. (88–21) is

$$N\left(\frac{1}{5}-\frac{2}{9}+\frac{1}{5}\right)=\frac{8}{45}N. \tag{88–21'}$$

Similarly

$$\left\{\left[\sum\left(\cos^2\varphi_j-\frac{1}{3}\right)\right]^2\right\}_{\text{av}} \tag{88–21''}$$

$$=\left\{\sum\left(\cos^2\varphi_j-\frac{1}{3}\right)^2+\sum_s{}'\sum_j\left(\cos^2\varphi_j-\frac{1}{3}\right)\left(\cos^2\varphi_s-\frac{1}{3}\right)\right\}_{\text{av}}$$

$$=\left\{\sum\cos^4\varphi_j-\frac{2}{3}\sum\cos^2\varphi_j+\frac{N}{9}\right\}_{\text{av}}=N\left(\frac{1}{5}-\frac{2}{9}+\frac{1}{9}\right)=\frac{4}{45}N.$$

Therefore, taking one mole,

$$\eta=\frac{6}{5}\frac{RT}{V}\tau\left[1+\frac{1}{2}\left(\frac{pV}{RT}\right)^2\right].$$

For liquids, the second term is much smaller than the first; the latter agrees with Eyring's expression, Eq. (90–4), except for the factor 6/5.

C. Molecular "Jump" Theories

89. Brillouin's Theory of Viscosity

Brillouin[1] first applied a crystalline model of the liquid to considerations of viscosity. Consider two adjacent layers of a pure ideal crystal. Their relative potential energy will vary periodically with the displacement of one against the other. In equilibrium it will be a minimum, it will increase with displacement (at first quadratically, when we have shear according to Hookes' law), pass a maximum, and then decrease again to a minimum,

---

[9] The first assumption is much less doubtful than the second one, but if one does not make all three, one gets into difficulties.

[10] Average over the sphere

$$\int_0^\pi \cos^4\vartheta\,\sin\vartheta\,d\vartheta \Big/ \int_0^\pi \sin\vartheta\,d\vartheta=\frac{1}{5}$$

[1] L. Brillouin, *J. phys.* **3**, 326, 362 (1922).

when we get to the new equilibrium position, after a shift of one lattice distance (this considers the planes as infinite, and neglects edge effects). If the lattice planes were rigid, no work would have been done. However, as Brillouin points out, the planes are not rigid. Instead, the particles are bound by elastic forces. When the two planes move past each other to positions of higher energy, the particles in the plane will give, moving away from each other, and then will return to their old position when minimum energy has been reached again.

This "giving" and returning of the particles, however, sets up elastic waves, running away into the crystal. This amounts to a loss of energy, corresponding to a frictional force. If the speed of relative motion of the two planes is slow, the "giving" motion will be nearly static, having a constant amplitude b. The energy radiated per particle will then be proportional to b^2 times the square of frequency. The latter is determined by the rate at which the planes pass over a lattice point (a_0 being lattice distance) and is therefore w'/a_0. In shear flow (simple cubic lattice)

$$w' = \frac{\partial w}{\partial z} a_0$$

and the energy lost per second is

$$\sim b^2 \left(\frac{\partial w}{\partial z}\right)^2$$

and therefore represents a viscosity loss.[2]

[2] A numerical calculation leads to failure. A sphere of radius $r_0/2$ oscillating with amplitude b emits, per second, a sound intensity (ρ is the density of the liquid)

$$\frac{1}{6}\pi\rho \frac{\omega^2}{\mathfrak{B}^3}\left(\frac{r_0}{2}\right)^6 b^2.$$

Looking at Fig. 90–1 one sees that the amplitude may be put

$$b = r_0\left(1 - \frac{1}{\sqrt{2}}\right)$$

so that the intensity is

$$\frac{1}{6}\pi\rho \frac{\omega^2}{\mathfrak{B}^3}\left(\frac{r_0}{2}\right)^6 r_0^2\left(1 - \frac{1}{\sqrt{2}}\right)^2 = \frac{1}{6}\frac{\pi\rho}{\mathfrak{B}^3} 4\pi^2\left(\frac{\partial w_1}{\partial z}\right)^2 \frac{3r_0^8}{2^7}\left(1 - \frac{4}{3\sqrt{2}}\right).$$

One easily sees that the wave length is very large compared to the distance between molecules, but the waves are emitted with random phases, so that one multiplies with N to get the contribution from 1 cc to the loss per second. From Eq. (83–2) one gets

$$\eta = \frac{\pi^3}{64}\left(1 - \frac{4}{3\sqrt{2}}\right)\frac{\rho^2}{M\mathfrak{B}^3} N_A r_0^8.$$

For a liquid like benzene with $\rho = 0.88$, $M = 78$, $\mathfrak{B} = 1.5 \times 10^5$, and $r_0 = 5 \times 10^{-8}$, this turns out to be of the order 10^{-53}. Even some coherence between neighboring waves cannot save the result.

This effect is mainly temperature independent; the experimental decrease of η with T is ascribed mainly to the decrease of η with increasing volume and the thermal expansion. There is a small intrinsic decrease of η with T, due to the momentum transport by elastic waves.

Brillouin's description can also be put into different language. One can consider the energy maxima mentioned before as heats of activation, and the loss as due to energy changed into heat when the particles "fall back" into the energy valleys.

This approach has some connection with the theory of plasticity of crystals. This, in turn, is based on the existence and movements of "faults" and "dislocations,"[3] while in Brillouin's approach the crystal is considered ideal.

In Brillouin's consideration, a whole plane moves together, while in the theories discussed next, individual particles move independently.

90. Eyring's Theory of Viscosity

Eyring[1] has proposed a theory of viscosity which has been very successful in explaining experimental data and has had great influence on theoretical considerations. He considers a hole in the liquid. In the absence of shear stress, molecules from the left and from the right will have equal probability of filling the hole; let us assume that this occurs $\bar{k}$ times a second. In making this transition, it is assumed that a molecule has to overcome an activation energy E'. When a molecule from the left fills the hole, it means the hole has moved one position to the right. Eyring now argues as follows: If a stress P_{xy} per square centimeter acts on the liquid, a force $L_1L_2P_{xy}$ will act on a molecule, L_1 and L_2 being lengths characterizing the arrangement of the molecules. If the distance of the center of the molecule from the center of the hole is L_3, the distance of the center of the molecule from the peak of the potential hill providing the activation energy will be $L_3/2$, where L_3 is the molecular distance in the direction of the force. Then the probability of a molecule filling the hole will be increased by the factor

$$\exp\left(+ L_1L_2 \frac{L_3}{2kT} P_{xy}\right)$$

if it goes in the direction of the force, and decreased by the reciprocal if it goes in the opposite direction. Each molecule moves the distance L_3.

---

[3] A. Seeger, *in* "Encyclopedia of Physics" (S. Flügge, ed.), Vol. VII, Part 1. Springer, Berlin, 1955.

[1] H. Eyring, *J. Chem. Phys.* 4, 283 (1936).

Therefore, the resultant flow in the direction of the force, if there are N_h holes per cubic centimeter, is

$$N_h\bar{k}L_3\left\{\exp\left(\frac{+L_1L_2L_3}{2kT}P_{xy}\right)-\exp\left(-\frac{L_1L_2L_3}{2kT}P_{xy}\right)\right\}\sim N_h\bar{k}\frac{L_1L_2L_3{}^2}{kT}P_{xy} \tag{90–1}$$

or, with

$$P_{xy}=\eta\frac{\text{flow}}{L_1} \tag{90–2}$$

$$\eta=\frac{kT}{L_2L_3{}^2}(N_h\bar{k})^{-1}. \tag{90–3}$$

However, $(N_h\bar{k})^{-1}$ is equal to the average time between jumps, τ_j.

Furthermore, if we identify $L_2L_3{}^2$ with the average volume occupied by one molecule, we get

$$\eta=\frac{RT}{V}\tau_j. \tag{90–4}$$

Wirtz[2] has pointed out that, if τ_j measures all the jumps into the hole, while only those in the direction of the force matter, Eq. (90–4) should be replaced by

$$\eta=6\frac{RT}{V}\tau_j. \tag{90–4′}$$

Eyring has also pointed out that the coefficient of self diffusion is

$$D=\frac{L^2}{6\tau_j} \tag{90–5}$$

so that

$$\eta D=\frac{RT}{V}L^2. \tag{90–5′}$$

In case of increased external pressure P, the work to make a mole of cavities is increased by PV' (V' is the volume of a mole of cavities), their number therefore decreased by the factor $\exp(-PV'/RT)$ and τ_j correspondingly increased by the factor $\exp(PV'/RT)$; see Sec. 92, particularly Eq. (92–12).

The theory has the great advantage (among others) of explaining simply why the relaxation time is apparently the same for shear viscosity and bulk

---

[2] K. Wirtz, *Z. Naturforsch.* **A3**, 672 (1948).

viscosity in associated liquids (see Chap. XII), since it is in both cases the average time between jumps of a molecule into a hole.

It has two disadvantages.

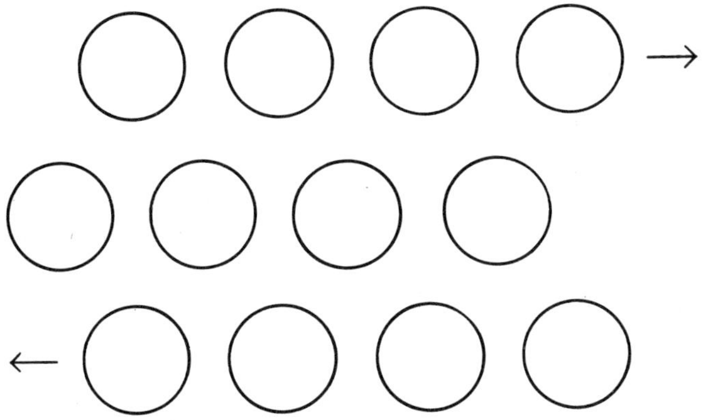

FIG. 90–1. Shear flow considered as the motion of layers past each other, according to Eyring.[1]

The meaning of the deduction is difficult to understand, since no (average) force acts on a molecule in simple shear flow, but only a shear stress (a force arises only from a nonuniform stress, see Sec. 16). If we have simple shear flow, we can always imagine a *uniform* velocity opposite to the direction of the flow superimposed, so that the layer we are considering is at rest. The layer above it then moves in one direction; the layer below, in opposite direction. (See Fig. 90–1.) These exert equal and opposite forces on the layer considered and, on the average, these forces cancel on each molecule in the layer. However, there is a resultant torque.

The second difficulty is a numerical one. One should expect the heat of formation of a cavity to be equal to the heat of evaporation, ΔH_{evap}. The heat of activation belonging to τ_j should be ΔH_{evap} plus an additional heat of activation corresponding to the jump of a molecule into the hole already formed, i.e., the heat of activation E' belonging to η should be the heat of activation for forming a hole plus the heat of activation for jump into the hole formed. Instead, E' turns out to be about[3] $(1/4)\, \Delta H_{evap}$ to $(1/3)\, \Delta H_{evap}$.

Both difficulties are removed in a slightly modified theory by Hirschfelder *et al.*[4] They consider a pair of molecules close together, lying obliquely to the direction of flow. There will be a torque trying to align the pair with

---

[3] R. H. Ewell, *J. Appl. Phys.* **9**, 252 (1938).

[4] J. O. Hirschfelder, D. Stevenson, and H. Eyring, *J. Chem. Phys.* **5**, 896 (1937).

the flow, moving the upper molecule forward, which represents a flow in the direction of the corresponding shear stress, Fig. 90–2. However, this rolling of one molecule over the other can only take place if there is a free space (cavity) available, though this cavity may be appreciably smaller than the space occupied by one molecule and may need a smaller heat of activation for its formation than if it were large enough to accomodate a whole molecule.

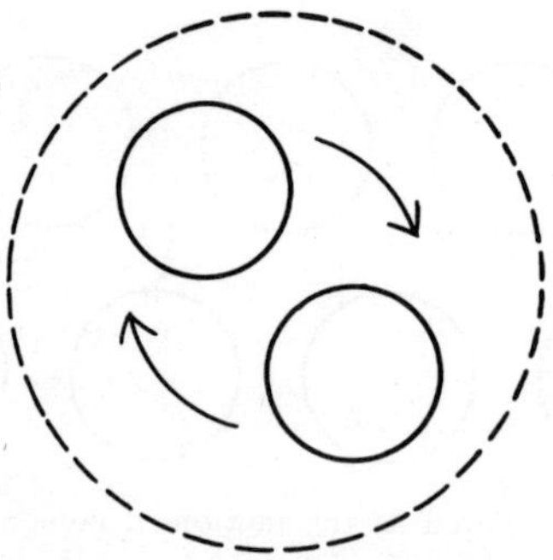

FIG. 90–2. Shear flow, considered as the rolling of molecules over each other, according to Hirschfelder, Stevenson, and Eyring.[4]

Of course, if this torque were acting by itself, the molecules would all arrange themselves in layers exactly parallel to the flow direction. However, the temperature motion (Brownian motion) would immediately spoil this and again form oblique pairs.

One may preserve the explanation of equality of relaxation time for bulk and shear viscosity by assuming that the activation energy is determined by a breaking of a hydrogen bond.

91. The Theory of Bulk Viscosity by Gierer and Wirtz[1]

Assume that the compressibility consists of two parts. One, κ_∞, describes a volume change occurring immediately with pressure change; the other, κ', describes a volume change which needs a relaxation time τ. Then, for an infinitely slow pressure change

$$\frac{V - V_0}{V_0} = \kappa(p - p_0) = (\kappa_\infty + \kappa')\,(p - p_0) = [(V'' - V_0'') + (V' - V_0')]/V_0 \tag{91–1}$$

$$\frac{V'' - V_0''}{V_0} = \kappa_\infty(p - p_0). \tag{91–1'}$$

[1] A. Gierer and K. Wirtz, *Z. Naturforsch.* **A 5**, 270 (1950).

The relaxation equation is

$$\frac{dV'}{dt} = -\frac{1}{\tau}(V' - V_0') + \frac{V_0}{\tau}\kappa'(p - p_0). \tag{91–2}$$

If everything is proportional to $e^{i\omega t}$

$$(1 + i\omega\tau)\frac{V' - V_0'}{V_0} = \kappa'(p - p_0) \tag{91–3}$$

and

$$\frac{V - V_0}{V_0} = \frac{V'' - V_0''}{V_0} + \frac{V' - V_0'}{V_0} = \kappa_\infty (p - p_0) + \frac{\kappa'}{1 + i\omega\tau}(p - p_0)$$

$$= \left(\kappa_\infty + \frac{\kappa'}{1 + i\omega\tau}\right)(p - p_0). \tag{91–4}$$

Proceeding as before (e.g., Sec. **31**) one gets

$$p - p_0 \doteq \frac{V - V_0}{V_0}\left[\frac{1}{\kappa} + \frac{\kappa'}{\kappa(\kappa - \kappa')}\frac{i\omega\tau'}{1 + i\omega\tau'}\right] \tag{91–4′}$$

$$\tau' = \frac{\kappa - \kappa'}{\kappa}\tau. \tag{91–4″}$$

The low frequency bulk viscosity follows, if one proceeds as in Sec. **29**, as

$$\eta' = \frac{\kappa'}{\kappa(\kappa - \kappa')}\tau' = \frac{\kappa'}{\kappa^2}\tau. \tag{91–5}$$

Next, it is assumed that the process responsible for the delayed compression is due to the existence and closure of the same kind of holes as discussed in the first theory of Eyring (Gierer and Wirtz talk about the recombination of a hole and complementary fault, but this would probably be independent of pressure).

Therefore, with n_h moles of holes per cubic centimeter and with V' the volume of 1 mole of holes[2]

$$\kappa' = \frac{V'}{V}\frac{\partial n_h}{\partial p} = \frac{V'}{V}\frac{V'}{RT}n_h = \frac{RT}{V}\left(\frac{\partial \ln \eta}{\partial p}\right)_T^2 n_h. \tag{91–6}$$

See the discussion following Eq. (90–5′).

Furthermore, it is assumed for geometrical reasons that

$$\tau = 3\tau_s = \frac{V}{2RT}\eta \tag{91–7}$$

---

[2] This differs from Eq. (29–10′) by having n_h instead of x_1x_2/x_0.

so that, with $\kappa^{-1} = \rho \mathfrak{V}_0^2$

$$\eta' = \frac{\kappa'}{\kappa^2}\tau = \rho^2 \mathfrak{V}_0^4 \frac{RT}{V}\left(\frac{\partial \ln \eta}{\partial p}\right)_T^2 n_h \frac{V}{2RT}\eta = \frac{1}{2}\rho^2 \mathfrak{V}_0^4 \eta \left(\frac{\partial \ln \eta}{\partial p}\right)_T^2 n_h. \tag{91–8}$$

Finally, it is assumed that

$$n_h = \exp\left(-\frac{E'}{2RT}\right) \tag{91–9}$$

where

$$\frac{E'}{RT} = 1 - T\frac{\partial \ln \eta}{\partial T} \tag{91–9'}$$

so that

$$n_h = 0.606 \exp\left(\frac{T}{2}\frac{\partial \ln \eta}{\partial T}\right). \tag{91–9''}$$

The authors apply their formula to the absorption measurements of a large number of liquids including associated liquids (alcohols, glycerine, acetic acid); Kneser liquids, such as hexane, ethyl bromide and iodide, benzene, toluene, and xylene; and even "monatomic" liquids like liquid A, O_2, N_2, and Hg. From viscosity values they find, except for the last group, values for the ratio $E'/\Delta H_{\text{evap}}$ of between 0.14 (hexane) and 0.40 (propyl alcohol and ethyl iodide) and values for the ratio V'/V of between 0.14 and 0.27.

92. Theory of Relaxation Time. Theory of Absolute Reaction Rates

The "theory of absolute reaction rates" has been developed mainly by Eyring.[1,2] It has been applied to structural relaxation by Hall.[3]

The assumption is made that two different states, (1) and (2), exist which are present in the mole fractions x and $(1 - x)$. Their free energies per mole when present alone, $x = 1$ or 0, shall be called F_1 and F_2, and their energies E_1 and E_2, all these counted from a common, but otherwise arbitrary, level. It is assumed that the two states are separated by a "potential hill" which characterizes an "activated" state; to this belongs a free energy (if this state could exist in mole concentration unity) F^*, its average energy E^*.

---

[1] H. Eyring, *J. Chem. Phys.* **3**, 107 (1935).

[2] S. Glasstone, H. Eyring, and K. Laidler, "Theory of Rate Processes." McGraw-Hill, New York, 1941.

[3] L. Hall, *Phys. Rev.* **73**, 775 (1948).

A molecule in state (1) can go to state (2) only by passing through the activated state, and vice versa. $E^* - E_1$ is the heat of activation for the passage from state (1) to state (2); $E^* - E_2$, for the passage from state (2) to state (1).

In equilibrium

$$\ln \frac{x^*}{x_1} = -\frac{F^* - F_1}{RT} \tag{92–1}$$

$$\ln \frac{x^*}{x_2} = -\frac{F^* - F_2}{RT} \tag{92–1$'$}$$

and, of course

$$\ln \frac{x_2}{x_1} = -\frac{F_2 - F_1}{RT}. \tag{92–1$''$}$$

See, for example, Eqs. (27–2) and (27–3). The mole fraction of the excited state, x^*, is so small that it does not appreciably change $x_1 = x$, $x_2 = 1 - x$.

For the sake of simpler printing, we will introduce, instead of the free energies F, the partition functions[4] Q. In Sec. 62 the letter Q was used as scattering cross section. The present Q has no connection with the former use.

Q is defined as

$$\ln Q = -\frac{F}{RT} \tag{92–2}$$

so that Eqs. (92–1), (92–1$'$), and (92–1$''$) can be written in equilibrium

$$\frac{x^*}{x_1} = \frac{Q^*}{Q_1} \tag{92–3}$$

$$\frac{x^*}{x_2} = \frac{Q^*}{Q_2} \tag{92–3$'$}$$

$$\frac{x_2}{x_1} = \frac{Q_2}{Q_1}. \tag{92–3$''$}$$

The theory of absolute reaction rate is now based on the following assumption: Consider a case in which there is no equilibrium between x_1 and x_2, e.g., there is too much x_1 and too little x_2.

Then, it is assumed, the activated state sets itself very quickly in equilibrium with the state that is present in excess—in the assumed case, state (1)—but not with the underpopulated state—in our case, state (2). That is Eq. (92–3) is valid but Eq. (92–3$'$) is not. A certain fraction f of the particles

---

[4] J. E. Mayer and M. G. Mayer, "Introduction to Statistical Mechanics." Wiley, New York, 1940.

in the excited state now goes over into state (2) per second, and is immediately replaced from state (1). This number is

$$fx^* = f\frac{Q^*}{Q_1}x_1 = k_{1\to 2}\,x_1. \tag{92–4}$$

Conversely, the number of particles from state (2) which is supplied to the activated state and lost by it to (1) is

$$f\frac{Q^*}{Q_2}x_2 = k_{2\to 1}\,x_2 \tag{92–4$'$}$$

with a resultant flow from (1) to (2) equal to

$$k_{1\to 2}\,x_1 - k_{2\to 1}\,x_2 = fQ^*\left(\frac{x_1}{Q_1} - \frac{x_2}{Q_2}\right).$$

In equilibrium, this is zero.

$$f\frac{Q^*}{Q_1}x_{1\text{ equil}} = f\frac{Q^*}{Q_2}x_{2\text{ equil}}. \tag{92–5}$$

Crossing fQ^* out, this leaves the correct equilibrium equation, Eq. (92–3″); this proves that f must have the same value in the forward and backward reaction.

The absolute theory of reaction rates assigns to f a definite value

$$f = \frac{kT}{h} \tag{92–6}$$

but even if this is not correct, it will not affect our argument, provided f is not strongly temperature or pressure dependent.

Using the results of Sec. 19 for the two-state systems, we have

$$\frac{1}{\tau} = k_{1\to 2} + k_{2\to 1} = f\left(\frac{Q^*}{Q_1} + \frac{Q^*}{Q_2}\right) \tag{92–7}$$

$$\tau = \frac{Q_1Q_2}{fQ^*(Q_1+Q_2)}. \tag{92–7$'$}$$

We can investigate the dependence of τ on a change of hydrostatic pressure P or temperature.

One has[4]

$$\frac{\partial \ln Q}{\partial P} = -\frac{V}{RT} \tag{92–8}$$

$$\frac{\partial \ln Q}{\partial T} = \frac{H}{RT^2}. \tag{92–9}$$

Therefore

$$\frac{\partial \ln \tau}{\partial P} = -\frac{\partial \ln f}{\partial P} + \frac{\partial \ln Q_1}{\partial P} + \frac{\partial \ln Q_2}{\partial P} - \frac{\partial \ln Q^*}{\partial P} - \frac{\partial \ln (Q_1 + Q_2)}{\partial P} = -\frac{\partial \ln f}{\partial P} +$$
$$\frac{\partial \ln Q_1}{\partial P} + \frac{\partial \ln Q_2}{\partial P} - \frac{\partial \ln Q^*}{\partial P} - \left(\frac{Q_1}{Q_1 + Q_2}\right)\frac{\partial \ln Q_1}{\partial P} - \frac{Q_2}{Q_1 + Q_2}\frac{\partial \ln Q_2}{\partial P}$$
$$= +\frac{1}{RT}\left\{- V_1 - V_2 + V^* + \frac{Q_1}{Q_1 + Q_2} V_1 + \frac{Q_2}{Q_1 + Q_2} V_2\right\} \qquad (92\text{–}10)$$

neglecting $\partial \ln f/\partial P$.

However, from Eq. (92–3″)

$$\frac{Q_1}{Q_1 + Q_2} = \frac{x_1}{x_1 + x_2} = x_1, \qquad x_1 V_1 + x_2 V_2 = V \qquad (92\text{–}11)$$

so that

$$\frac{\partial \ln \tau}{\partial P} = \frac{1}{RT}[V^* - (1-x)V_1 - xV_2] = \frac{1}{RT}(V + V^* - V_1 - V_2). \qquad (92\text{–}12)$$

Similarly

$$\frac{\partial \ln \tau}{\partial T} = \frac{1}{RT^2}[(1-x)H_1 + xH_2 - H^*]. \qquad (92\text{–}13)$$

Furthermore, differentiating Eq. (92–12) with respect to T or Eq. (92–13) with respect to P

$$\frac{\partial}{\partial T}\frac{\partial \ln \tau}{\partial P} = \frac{\partial}{\partial P}\frac{\partial \ln \tau}{\partial T} = \frac{\partial}{\partial T}\left[\frac{V + V^* - V_1 - V_2}{RT}\right]. \qquad (92\text{–}14)$$

Accordingly, the only general conclusion one can draw if τ decreases with increasing P is that

$$V + V^* < V_1 + V_2$$

or

$$V^* < (1-x)V_1 + xV_2. \qquad (92\text{–}15)$$

Since H^* must be larger than either H_1 or H_2 to provide a potential hill, we see from Eq. (92–13) that

$$\frac{\partial \ln \tau}{\partial T} < 0 \qquad (92\text{–}16)$$

if we neglect $\partial \ln f/\partial T$.

This means that we always expect τ to decrease with increasing temperature, which is in accordance with all our experience.

XI. Kneser Liquids

93. Discussion of Specific Heats in Nonassociated Organic Liquids with Molecules of Moderate Size

As mentioned in Sec. 73, Pinkerton[1] assumes that in those polyatomic liquids which have a positive temperature coefficient of the absorption, the

TABLE 93–1
SPECIFIC MOLAR HEATS OF LIQUIDS

Substance	T (°C)	Δ/R*	γ*	C_p/R†	$\Sigma C_i'/R$‡	$(C_p - \Sigma C_i')/R$
C_5H_{12}	0	3.7	1.25			
C_6H_{14}	23	5.2		26.1	16.7	9.4
CH_2Cl_2				12.3	2.21	10.1
$CHCl_3$	15	4.8	(1.36)	14.1	3.97	10.1
CCl_4	20	5.05	1.46	15.5	6.12	9.4
C_2H_5Cl	0	6.4	1.83			
$C_2H_4Cl_2$	10	5.2	1.50	15.2	6.2 or 6.4	9.0 or 8.8
C_6H_6	6	5.0	1.44		6.45	9.75
C_6H_6	30			16.2		
C_6H_6	50	5.5	1.45			
C_6H_6	79	5.6	1.43			
$C_6H_5CH_3$	0	5.25	1.45	17.9		
$C_6H_5CH_3$	66	5.35	1.31	17.9		
$C_6H_5CH_3$	100	5.4	1.27			
CH_3COOH	25	5.17	1.22	9.7	2.27	7.43
CH_3COOCH_3	14	5.1				
CH_3COOCH_3	100	5.45				
C_3H_7OH	0	1.70	1.12	15.9		
C_3H_7OH	50	3.73	1.21			
Glycerine	20	2.60	1.21			
CS_2**	25	3.25	1.55	9.15	1.98	7.17

* See Ref. 2.
† See Ref. 3.
‡ See Ref. 4.
** See Sec. 97.

[1] J. M. M. Pinkerton, *Proc. Phys. Soc. London* **B62**, 129 (1949).

excess absorption is caused by thermal relaxation, as in gases. However, this opinion is not universally accepted, and this and the next section will be devoted to a discussion of it.

Since Δ and C_p are not always available in the literature, a few regularities for simple, unassociated organic (and a few inorganic) liquids are shown in Table 93–1.

CS_2 would be called an inorganic liquid. The four preceeding ones are associated and have only been included for comparison. Those γ values from Ref. 2 which give a C_p widely different from that listed from Ref. 3 have been put in brackets. One sees that for the simple nonassociated organic liquids Δ/R is near 5 (pentane is an exception) and $(C_p - \Sigma C'_i)/R$ is between 9 and 10. Therefore, if one wants to get an approximate estimate for a liquid in which these quantities have not been measured, using the above average values will not lead to an error larger than 10 to 20%. The situation is quite different for the associated liquids.

94. A Cooperative Theory of Relaxation Time for Kneser Liquids

An attempt had been made by Herzfeld[1] to develop a theory of relaxation time for Kneser liquids on the basis of the cell model, developing the ideas discussed in Sec. 86, after a first attempt by Bauer.[2] The molecule in question is considered as vibrating in the center of a spherical cell, the walls of which are made up of other molecules in a number equal to the coordination number. The interaction between molecules is supposed to be given by the Lennard-Jones potential. The field in the cell produced by the wall molecules (and those in outer layers) is then developed into a power series around the center[3]

$$H = H_0 + b_1 R^2 + b_2 R^4 \tag{94–1}$$

with b_1 and b_2 determined by the constants of the potential and the radius of the cell. The constant b_1 determines the frequency of vibration of the molecule in question (see Sec. 86), while the next term determines the coupling between the intermolecular and the intramolecular vibration, i.e., produces a transfer of energy from an intramolecular vibration to the Debye (heat)

---

[2] F. A. Schulze, *Physik. Z.* **26**, 153 (1925).
[3] "International Critical Tables," Vol. V. McGraw-Hill, New York, 1929.
[4] Data from Tables 54–1 and 54–2.
[1] K. F. Herzfeld, *J. Chem. Phys.* **20**, 288 (1952).
[2] E. Bauer, *Proc. Phys. Soc. London* **A62**, 141 (1949).
[3] In this section, R is the distance of an atom of the molecule from the center of the cell.

waves. Since the amplitude of the intermolecular vibration enters R, just as in the gas case (see Sec. 57), one has

$$R^4 = r^4 + 3r^3X \ldots \tag{94–2}$$

The second term is the important one, producing a transfer of an internal quantum to three Debye waves.

The numerical calculation for benzene gives a relaxation time one hundredfold too long, i.e., a probability a hundred times too small. This is not changed materially if one assumes that the cell wall is not spherical or that some molecules are missing from it (holes).

On the other hand, the results of Sec. 95 will show a relative success for the type of calculation made for a gas. The meaning of these two calculations is this. The first calculation shown is the probability of energy transfer by the cooperative interaction of molecules with average kinetic energy. Although this goes on all the time, the probability of transfer during one period is so small that it does not play a role in the over-all effect.[4] The main contribution to the energy transfer comes from a very few collisions with exceptionally high energy, just as in gases. In these collisions the molecule in question comes particularly close to and interacts almost exclusively with a single molecule of the surrounding, not with the cell wall as a whole.

In fact, the results on the absorption in liquid mixtures confirm the idea that the significant interactions are between pairs of molecules, not larger complexes.

95. Comparison of Relaxation Time in the Gaseous and Liquid States. Thermal Relaxation as due to Interaction between a Pair of Molecules

We will now use the equation

$$\frac{\alpha'}{f^2} = \frac{2\pi^2}{\mathfrak{V}_0}\frac{\Delta\Sigma(C_i')}{C_v C_p}\bar{\tau} \tag{95–1}$$

which presupposes thermal relaxation, to calculate[1,2] $\bar{\tau}$

$$\bar{\tau} = \frac{\alpha'}{f^2}\frac{\mathfrak{V}_0}{2\pi^2}\frac{C_v C_p}{\Delta(\Sigma C_i')} \simeq \frac{\alpha'}{f^2}\frac{\mathfrak{V}_0}{2\pi^2}\left(5 + \Sigma\frac{C_i'}{R}\right)\left(10 + \Sigma\,\frac{C_i'}{R}\right)\left(5\Sigma\,\frac{C_i'}{R}\right)^{-1} \tag{95–2}$$

---

[4] In the original paper, it was concluded that the theory gave correct results. This was due to a numerical error.

[1] K. F. Herzfeld, *J. Acoust. Soc. Am.* **13**, 33 (1941).

[2] H. O. Kneser, *Naturwissenschaften* **34**, 53, 54 (1947).

and compare[3a] $\bar{\tau}$ with the measured relaxation time of the same substance in the vapor state, Tables 54–1, 54–2, and 54–3.

TABLE 95–1

COMPARISON OF AVERAGE RELAXATION TIME, $\bar{\tau}$, CALCULATED FROM ABSORPTION IN LIQUID, WITH τ MEASURED IN VAPOR (1 ATM, ROOM TEMPERATURE)

Substance	$\mathfrak{B}_0$ in 10^5 cm/sec	$\alpha'/f^2 \times 10^{17}$*	$\bar{\tau} \times 10^{10}$ sec	$\tau \times 10^8$ sec	$\tau/\bar{\tau}$	$\rho_{\text{liquid}}/\rho_{\text{gas}}$
CH_3Br	0.905	304	1.26	7.5	600	460
CH_2Cl_2	1.10	1185	5.3	5.8†	110	
CH_2Cl_2			10.85‡	9.46	87	
$CHCl_3$	0.995	380	1.30	1.35	105	320
CCl_4	0.930	510	1.26	2.1	170	260
$(CH_2Cl)_2$	1.23	136	0.495	0.5	100	320
$(CHCl)_2$	1.2(?)	577	2.1	0.6(?)	350	325
C_6H_6	1.31	800	2.7	5.0	180	280
C_6H_{14}	1.250	36	0.152	0.65**	420	190
CS_2	1.14	5813††	28.3††	72.7	260	420
CH_3OH***	1.123	22	0.13	2.2	1700	630

* Most of the data are from Ref. 3b; data for CH_2Cl_2, $(CHCl)_2$, and $(CH_2Cl)_2$ are from Ref. 4.

† τ has been calculated as $\tau = (C_1'\tau_1 + C_2'\tau_2)/(C_1' + C_2')$.

‡ See Ref. 5. This is the longer of the two relaxation times in CH_2Cl_2.

** See Ref. 6.

†† See Sec. 97.

*** Methyl alcohol, an associated liquid, has been included for comparison purposes.

Inspection of Table 95–1 shows that while τ and $\bar{\tau}$ vary over a wide range (by a factor of more than 100), the ratio $\tau/\bar{\tau}$ varies in a much narrower range (if CH_3OH is excluded, over a factor 6) and are of the order of magnitude of the ratio of the densities of the liquid to that of the gas (1 atm, 30° C), although there is no exact parallelism.

To test this theory, Henderson and Peselnick[7] have followed the dispersion and absorption curves of CO_2 to high densities. At present, this has only been done above the critical point, at 51° C, and about 0.9 of the normal

[3a] K. F. Herzfeld, *J. Acoust. Soc. Am.* **29**, 1180 (1957.)

[3b] J. R. Pellam and J. K. Galt, *J. Chem. Phys.* **14**, 608 (1946).

[4] D. Sette, *J. Chem. Phys.* **19**, 1337 (1951).

[5] J. H. Andreae, *Proc. Phys. Soc. London* **B70**, 71 (1957).

[6] J. Klose, *J. Acoust. Soc. Am.* **30**, 605 (1958).

[7] M. C. Henderson and L. Peselnick, *J. Acoust. Soc. Am.* **29**, 1074 (1957).

liquid density has been reached. The measurements were made in an interferometer, and the results are shown in Table 95–2.

TABLE 95–2
DISPERSION FREQUENCY f'' IN CO_2 AT 51° C AND HIGH DENSITY

Pressure (atm)	Density (amagat)	Frequency (Mc)	f''/p	f''/ρ
1	—	—	—	—
7.5	6.4	0.3	38	47
26.5	24.5	2	36	41
47	50	3	40	40
70.5	91	6	39	33

Recent still unpublished work of Henderson and Klose[8] extends the measurements up to 500 atm and about 500 amagat. It turns out that in the high pressure region, f''/ρ is more nearly constant than f''/p. Below the critical point, there is, of course, a gap in the measurements between the density of the saturated vapor and that of the liquid. A fairly smooth curve for the absorption coefficient can be drawn, joining the two sides of the gap.

This suggests the idea that the thermal relaxation in Kneser liquids is due to the same mechanism as in a gas, namely, that it occurs during particularly violent interactions ("collisions") between a *pair* of molecules. One assumes then that the transition probability and its reciprocal, the number Z, are the same in both cases, i.e.

$$\bar{\tau} = Z(\tau_c)_{\text{liquid}} = [\tau_{\text{gas}}/(\tau_c)_{\text{gas}}]\,(\tau_c)_{\text{liquid}} \tag{95–4}$$

or

$$(\tau_c)_{\text{liquid}} = \frac{\bar{\tau}}{\tau}\,(\tau_c)_{\text{gas}}. \tag{95–4'}$$

Another assumption also seems possible. In Sec. 59 a factor $\exp(-\varepsilon/RT)$ was introduced in the calculation of Z and explained as due either to the increase of effective collision velocity or to the increase in density of the colliding molecules due to the attractive forces. However, in the liquid, the molecules *start* from the potential minimum. Therefore, this factor should probably be omitted, giving

$$(\tau_c)_{\text{liquid}} = \frac{\bar{\tau}}{\tau}\,(\tau_c)_{\text{gas}} \exp\left(-\frac{\varepsilon}{RT}\right). \tag{95–5}$$

Table (95–3) compares the values of $(\tau_c)_{\text{liquid}}$ calculated in this manner with those from various theories of the liquid state, Secs. 82–86.

[8] M. C. Henderson and J. Klose, *J. Acoust. Soc. Am.* **31** 29 (1959).

TABLE 95–3

"COLLISION TIMES," τ_c, IN LIQUIDS, CALCULATED FROM ULTRASONIC ABSORPTION, EQ. (95.4′) OR (95.5), COMPARED WITH THOSE CALCULATED FROM VARIOUS LIQUID THEORIES; τ_c IN 10^{-13} SEC

		τ_c liquid								
Substance	$(\tau_c)_{gas}$	From ultrasonics		From theories of liquid state						
		Eq. (95–4′)	Eq. (95–5)	Eq. (82–9)	Eq. (83–6′)	Eq. (84–2)	Eq. (84–2′)	Eq. (84–5)	Eq. (85–5)	Eq. (86–7)
CH_3Br	900,* 1080†	1.5, 1.8	—	—	—	—	—	—	4.4	—
CH_2Cl_2	802	7.3	1.9	—	1.37	—	16.6	—	2.84	0.84
$CHCl_3$	822	7.8	2.6	1.37	1.27	—	22.0	11.3	3.17	1.78
CCl_4	786	4.6	0.95	0.86	0.96	—	26.2	11.0	3.56	1.47
C_6H_{14}	522	1.2	0.3	—	1.34	0.7	22.5	9.9	—	1.54
C_6H_6	620	3.45	0.79	0.72	0.72	0.09	18.6	8.1	—	—
CS_2	797	3.06	0.60	0.86	1.20	4	22.2	8.0	3.27	5.22

* The 900 (and most of the other numbers in this column) is calculated from the data used in Eq. (59–2).

† This number is calculated from η, in accord with "Landolt-Börnstein, Zahlenwerte und Funktionen," 6th ed. of "Physikalisch-Chemischen Tabellen," Vol. 4, Part 1. Springer, Berlin, 1955.

To see which liquid theory gives the most consistent data, Table 95–4 gives the ratio of the acoustically calculated collision time to that calculated from a specific liquid theory.

TABLE 95–4

RATIO OF ULTRASONICALLY DETERMINED COLLISION TIME TO THAT CALCULATED FROM A THEORY OF THE LIQUID STATE

Substance	Eq. (82–9)	Eq. (83–6′)	Eq. (84–2)	Eq. (84–2′)	Eq. (84–5)	Eq. (85–5)	Eq. (86–7)
(*τ*) *Ultrasonically determined collision time found from Eq.* (95–4′)							
CH_3Br	—	—	—	—	—	0.34, 0.41	—
CH_2Cl_2	—	5.3	—	0.44	—	2.6	0.87
$CHCl_3$	5.7	6.1	—	0.35	0.69	2.5	4.4
CCl_4	5.3	4.8	—	0.18	0.42	1.3	3.2
C_6H_{14}	—	0.9	1.7	0.05	0.12	—	0.8
C_6H_6	4.8	4.8	38	0.19	0.43	—	2.4
CS_2	4.6	2.5	0.76	0.14	0.38	0.94	0.59
(*b*) *Ultrasonically determined collision time found from Eq.* (95–5)							
CH_3Br	—	—	—	—	—	—	—
CH_2Cl_2	—	1.4	—	0.11	—	0.67	2.3
$CHCl_3$	1.9	2.0	—	0.12	0.23	0.82	1.5
CCl_4	1.1	0.99	—	0.036	0.86	0.37	0.64
C_6H_{14}	—	0.22	0.42	0.012	0.03	—	0.2
C_6H_6	1.1	1.1	8.8	0.04	0.098	—	0.55
CS_2	0.70	0.50	0.15	0.027	0.075	0.18	0.11

We are now looking for those expressions which produce ratios in Table 95–4 which are (a) independent of the substance and (b) nearly unity. Unfortunately, we do not have a sufficient number of substances, because of lack of experimental data. It becomes clear from Tables 95–2 and 95–3 that hexane behaves anomalously[9], and must be left out of any comparison.

From the standpoint of constancy of ratio, the combination of Eqs. (95–4′) and (82–9) is best, since among four substances the ratio varies by less than 25%. On the other hand, the times given by Eq. (82–9) are too short by an

[9] This is due to the fact that $\tau/\bar{\tau}$ is 420 compared to 100–180, while the theories of the liquid state do not give an appreciably smaller τ_c for hexane.

average factor 5.1. Next as to constancy is the combination of Eqs. (95–4′) and (84–5)—variation by a factor 1.8—then Eqs. (95–4′) and (83–6′)—variation by a factor 2.5—then Eqs. (95–5) and (82–9)—variation by a factor 2.7—then Eqs. (95–4′) and (84–2′)—variation by a factor 3—and, if one omits CH_3Br, Eqs. (94–4′) and (85–3)—variation by a factor 2.8. If CH_3Br is included, Eqs. (94–4′) and (85–3) variation by a factor 6.5 and, finally, with five substances, Eqs. (95–5), (83–6′), and (84–2′) follow—factors 4 and 4.5. If one also considers the absolute values, the two combinations, Eqs. (95–5) and (82–9) and Eqs. (95–5) and (83–6′), are probably best. Of course, the theory represented by Eq. (84–2) may give much better results if one adjusts r_0 (see Sec. 97).

96. Temperature Dependence of the Absorption in Kneser Liquids

Next, we will discuss the positive temperature coefficient, which Pinkerton considers a characteristic of Kneser liquids, and which up to now is theoretically unexplained. Let us see how $\bar{\tau}$ varies with temperature. This needs good data on the static properties of the liquid, which fortunately exist for benzene.

We can rewrite Eq. (4–9) in the form

$$\Delta = MT\beta^2\left(\frac{\partial p}{\partial \rho}\right)_T \tag{96–1}$$

with M representing molecular weight.

Since static measurements give C_p, one can set down the following expression

$$\frac{\Delta}{C_v C_p} = \frac{\Delta\gamma}{C_p^2} = MT\left(\frac{\beta}{C_p}\right)^2 \gamma\left(\frac{\partial p}{\partial \rho}\right)_T.$$

However

$$\gamma\left(\frac{\partial p}{\partial \rho}\right)_T = \mathfrak{V}_0^2.$$

Therefore

$$\frac{\alpha'}{f^2} = \frac{2\pi^2}{\mathfrak{V}_0}\frac{\Delta C'}{C_v C_p}\bar{\tau} = \frac{2\pi^2}{\mathfrak{V}_0} MT\left(\frac{\beta}{C_p}\right)^2 \mathfrak{V}_0^2 C'\bar{\tau} = 2\pi^2 MT\left(\frac{\beta}{C_p}\right)^2 \mathfrak{V}_0 C'\bar{\tau} \tag{96–2}$$

$$\bar{\tau} = \frac{1}{2\pi^2 M}\left(\frac{C_p}{\beta}\right)^2 \frac{1}{\mathfrak{V}_0 C' T}\frac{\alpha'}{f^2} \tag{96–2′}$$

(C' and C_p are in absolute units).

TABLE 96–1

TEMPERATURE DEPENDENCE OF (CALCULATED) $\bar{\tau}$ FOR BENZENE

T (°C)	$1000\frac{1}{V}\left(\frac{\partial V}{\partial T}\right)_p^*$	C_p/M (cal/g degree)*	$\frac{1}{R}\sum C_i'$†	$\mathfrak{V}_0$ (m/sec)‡	$\frac{\alpha'}{f^2} \times 10^{17}$ ‡	$\bar{\tau} \times 10^{10}$ sec
10	1.186	0.4040	5.695	1360	670	2.953
20	1.208	0.4107	6.076	1315	700	2.877
30	1.232	0.4182	6.450	1270	730	2.824
40	1.257	0.4263	6.825	1225	760	2.782
50	1.284	0.4345	7.205	1180	790	2.725
60	1.315	0.4427	7.555	1135	820	2.711

* See Ref. 1.

† See Ref. 2.

‡ Ref. 3, interpolated linearly.

It is seen in Table 96–1 that there is a decrease in $\bar{\tau}$ with increasing temperatures, as expected, although this decrease is very small (less than 10% for an increase of 50°).

The increase in α' comes about in a complicated manner, Δ (or β) and C' in the numerator increasing, $C_p{}^2$ in the denominator increasing, $\mathfrak{V}_0$ decreasing, and $\bar{\tau}$ decreasing, with considerable compensation. Quinn[3] has pointed out that $\alpha'\mathfrak{V}_0$ is nearly constant.

97. Carbon Disulfide CS_2

The ultrasonic absorption of carbon disulfide had been measured by Bazulin[1] at 1.9 Mc and in the range from 3 to 6 Mc; α/f^2 was found very large, from 6500 to 5100×10^{-17} cm^{-1}. This was confirmed by Ouang[2] at 1.6 Mc and by Bär[3] at 50 Mc, while Rapuano[4] found a decrease to 1400×10^{-17} at 105 Mc.

---

[1] J. S. Burlew, *J. Am. Chem. Soc.* **62**, 690, 696 (1940).

[2] L. Cheng, *J. Chem. Phys.* **19**, 693 (1951).

[3] J. Quinn, *J. Acoust. Soc. Am.* **18**, 185 (1946).

[1] P. Bazulin, *Zhur. Eksptl. i Teoret. Fiz.* **8**, 457 (1938).

[2] Te-Tchao Ouang, *Compt. rend.* **222**, 1165 (1946).

[3] R. Bär, *Helv. Phys. Acta* **10**, 332 (1937).

[4] R. A. Rapuano, *Phys. Rev.* **72**, 78 (1947).

Andreae and Lamb[5] combined some of their own measurements with those of Rapuano and expressed the result by

$$10^{17}\,\alpha/f^2 = 5385\,[1 + (2\pi\tau^* f)^2]^{-1} + 428$$

$$\frac{1}{2\pi\tau^*} = f^* = 72.1 \text{ Mc.} \qquad (97\text{–}1)$$

In this expression the first, relaxation, term could be explained as thermal relaxation of nearly all of the internal specific heat. However this leaves the very large constant term $(\alpha/f^2)_\infty = 428 \times 10^{-17}$, for which no sufficient internal specific heat is available, and which therefore would have to be explained by structural relaxation. Still, it is exceedingly large, even for this explanation.

Heasell and Lamb[6] recently measured the absorption in the range from 10 to 190 Mc themselves, and also redetermined the other significant constants. The new results can be explained completely by the theory, the additional constant having disappeared. The classical value $(\alpha/f^2)_{\text{class}} = 6.6 \times 10^{-17}$ is too small to show up in the measurements.

One has,[6] at 25° C, $C_p = 9.147\,R$; $C_v = 5.895\,R$; $C' = 1.980\,R$; $\Delta = 3.252\,R$; $\gamma = 1.551$; and $\mathfrak{B}_0 = 1.142 \times 10^5$ cm/sec.

If one assumes that the whole internal specific heat C' is involved with a single relaxation time, one can represent the results by[7]

$$10^{17}\,(\alpha/f^2)\,\frac{\mathfrak{B}}{\mathfrak{B}_0} = 5867\,[1 + (2\pi\tau' f)^2]^{-1} \qquad (97\text{–}2)$$

with[8a, 8b]

$$\tau' = \tau^* \left[1 - \frac{C'\Delta}{C_v(C_p - C')}\right]^{-1/4} = 1.04\,\tau^*,$$

$$f' = 78 \text{ Mc}, \qquad \tau' = 2.04 \times 10^{-9} \text{ sec}, \qquad \tau = 2.60 \times 10^{-9} \text{ sec}. \qquad (97\text{–}3)$$

This equation is found by trial and error. The agreement between experiment and the assumption of a single relaxation time for the whole C' is shown in Table 97–1. At $-63°$ C, f' is found as 31 Mc.

Sette[9] has measured the absorption as a function of temperature. Litovitz *et al.*[10] have measured the effect of pressure on sound absorption and velocity

---

[5] J. H. Andreae and J. Lamb, *Proc. Phys. Soc. London* **B64**, 1021 (1951).

[6] E. L. Heasell and J. Lamb, *Proc. Phys. Soc. London* **B69**, 869 (1956).

[7] It ought to be mentioned that C. J. Moen [*J. Acoust. Soc. Am.* **23**, 62 (1951)] finds that for very low frequency Å = 4545. The value is probably too low.

[8a] R. Bass and J. Lamb, *Proc. Roy. Soc.* **A 243**, 94 (1957).

[8b] At $-63°$ C, Heasell and Lamb find a B which is about 0.008 A.

[9] D. Sette, *J. Chem. Phys.* **19**, 1342 (1951).

[10] T. A. Litovitz, E. H. Carnevale, and P. Kendall, *J. Chem. Phys.* **26**, 465 (1957).

in CS_2 at $-29°$ C over a frequency range from 5 to 75 Mc and up to pressures of almost 1000 kg/cm². The data at each pressure can be represented by the expression

$$10^{17}\,\alpha/f^2 = A\,[1 + (2\pi\tau^* f)^2]^{-1} + B. \tag{97–4}$$

TABLE 97–1

COMPARISON BETWEEN EXPERIMENTAL ABSORPTION IN CS_2 AND THE THEORETICAL VALUE FOR COMPLETE THERMAL RELAXATION OF THE VIBRATIONAL SPECIFIC HEAT

f (Mc)	$10^{17}\,(\alpha/f^2)_{exp}$	$10^{17}\,(\alpha/f^2)_{calc}$
<6	5870	5829
10	5650	5763
23	5390	5359
29.6	5100	5071
37.4	4650	4692
48.5	4120	4129
66.7	3240	3267
81.2	2800	2692
103.5	2060	2013
111	1955	1832
148.2	1200	1191
168.0	970	971
189.2	776	793

TABLE 97–2

PRESSURE DEPENDENCE OF THE RELAXATION PARAMETERS FOR CS_2 AT $-29°$ C

p (kg/cm²)	$A \times 10^{17}$ (cm^{-1} sec^{-2})	τ^* ($\times$ 10⁹ sec)	$\mathfrak{V}_0$ (m/sec)
1	5880	3.44	1314
443	4350	3.05	1449
720	3450	2.73	1495
978	2940	2.30	1534

It was found that both quantities A and τ^* varied with pressure. These values are tabulated in Table 97–2, along with the measured velocities. It can be seen that α/f^2 decreases with increasing pressure. This is partly due to the increase in $\mathfrak{V}_0$. However, the main effect of the increase in pressure is to reduce the relaxation time.

The data on the pressure dependence of τ have been used to determine which theory of liquids is best for the calculation of collision times. It can be seen from Eq. (95–4) that Z^{-1}, the probability of transfer of energy per collision, should be pressure independent. It is possible that ν, the frequency of the excited vibrational state, might vary slightly, but a significant change in this quantity is highly unlikely, as one can see by comparison of infra-red absorption spectra. Therefore, the decrease in τ with increasing pressure (or density) must be attributed to a decrease in the collision times in the liquid.

Litovitz[11] has shown that the pressure and temperature dependence of τ and the magnitude of Z can be accounted for by using the cubic cell model for the liquid (see Sec. 84). To give the pressure dependance of τ, Eq. (84–2) can be used if one assumes that the change in τ is due only to a change in collision times. Thus

$$\frac{\tau_p}{\tau_0} = \frac{(V_p/N_A)^{1/3} - r_0}{(V_0/N_A)^{1/3} - r_0} \tag{97–5}$$

where the subscripts 0 and p refer to the value of the quantity at atmospheric pressure and at some higher pressure, respectively.

Hirschfelder *et al.*[12] list the value of r_0 for CS_2 as 4.44 Å. It should be noted that the values obtained for r_0 vary by as much as 5%, depending on the type of experiment used to calculate it. Furthermore, since CS_2 is not a spherical molecule it is conceivable that the "effective" value of r_0 may depart by a few per cent from Hirschfelder's value, which was based on the assumption of a spherical molecule. In Table 97–3, the values τ_p/τ_0 calculated from Eq. (97–5) for two different values of r_0 are compared with the experimental results.

It can be seen that the results are highly dependent on the value of r_0 chosen. A 2% change in r_0 causes a change by a factor of 2 in the pressure dependence of τ. With a value of $r_0 = 4.32$ Å, one finds good agreement between theory and experiment. This result indicates that the cubic cell model is adequate for calculating the collision times in this liquid if the correct "effective" value of r_0 (4.32 Å) is assumed.

Using Eq. (84–2) to calculate τ_c one can then calculate $Z = \tau/\tau_c$ with the experimental values for τ. One finds in CS_2 at 298 °K that the value of Z is 8120. The most reliable value of Z obtained for the gaseous CS_2 is 9200 (see Table 52–4).

---

[11] T. A. Litovitz, *J. Chem. Phys.* **26**, 469 (1957).

[12] J. O. Hirschfelder, C. F. Curtiss, and R. B. Bird, "Molecular Theory of Gases and Liquids," Wiley, New York, 1954.

TABLE 97–3

PRESSURE DEPENDENCE OF THE THERMAL RELAXATION TIMES IN CS_2 AT − 29° C*

p (kg/cm²)	τ_p/τ_0 cubic cell model		$(\tau_p/\tau_0)_{\text{exp}}$
	$r_0 = 4.44$ Å	$r_0 = 4.32$ Å	
1	1.0	1.0	1.0
500	0.67	0.83	0.87
1000	0.33	0.67	0.65

* Theoretical values are calculated using the cubic cell model theory; observed values are taken from absorption data. It is assumed that $\tau_p^*/\tau_0^* = \tau_p/\tau_0$.

The excellent agreement between gas and liquid values of Z is consistent with the view that the mechanism of thermal energy transfer is the same in the liquid state as in the gas. If this is so then the theory for Z developed in Secs. 62 and 64 for gases should also be applicable to liquids. Litovitz has applied this theory to the calculation of the temperature dependence of Z in liquid CS_2.

Using the value of l in Eq. (62–16) which best fits the gas data and assuming that the $(1 + C/T)^{-1}$ term is unimportant in liquids, the value of Z in liquid CS_2 has been calculated. The absolute values of Z are too high, as in the gas, but are much more sensitive to l than is the temperature dependence.

TABLE 97–4

COMPARISON OF THEORETICAL AND EXPERIMENTAL TEMPERATURE DEPENDENCE OF Z IN LIQUID CS_2

T (°K)	Z_T/Z_{298}	
	Theory*	Acoustic data
298	1.0	1.0
244	2.1	2.1
210	3.6	3.4

* The results in this column are from the theory of Sec. 62.

In Table 97–4 the values of the ratio Z_T/Z_{298} are calculated, using the above assumptions. The experimental values are obtained from the ultrasonic data in conjunction with the cubic cell model theory.

It can be seen from Table 97–4 that the agreement between theory and experiment is quite good. Thus, it appears that not only is the mechanism for thermal energy transfer the same in liquids and gases but also the Schwartz-Herzfeld theory is just as applicable to liquids as it is to the gas state.

98. Relaxation due to Rotational Isomerism

Within the past ten years a series of liquids exhibiting relatively long relaxation times have been discovered. The measurements of Liebermann,[1] Pinkerton,[2] Biquard,[3] and Andreae,[4] who reported relaxation effects in the esters methyl and ethyl formate and methyl and ethyl acetate, respectively, are summarized in Table 98–1.

TABLE 98–1
COMPARISON OF RELAXATION PARAMETERS FOR SEVERAL ESTERS

Ester	T (°C)	f' (Mc/sec)	$10^2 (\alpha\lambda)_{max}$	Reference
Methyl formate	25	0.35	3.1	4
Ethyl formate	25	0.40	4.8	1
Methyl acetate	20	6.8	0.072	3
Ethyl acetate	20	11.8	0.020	2

It has been mainly as a result of the extensive investigations of Lamb and his students that the origin of the loss in these esters is now understood.

The explanation of these relaxations was first published by Karpovich.[5] The acetates and formates listed in Table 98–1 can exist in two isomeric

[1] L. Liebermann, *Phys. Rev.* **76**, 440 (1949).
[2] J. M. M. Pinkerton, *Koninkl. Vlaam. Acad. Wetenschap., Letter. en Schone Kunsten, Belgie, Colloq. Conf. Ultrasonore Trillingen, Brussels,* 1951 p. 117.
[3] P. Biquard, *Ann. phys.* [11] **6**, 195 (1936).
[4] J. H. Andreae, unpublished, mentioned in Ref. 5.
[5] J. Karpovich, *J. Chem. Phys.* **22**, 1767 (1954).

forms. These two forms have negligible volume differences but a significant energy difference. The temperature rise in the sound wave perturbs the following isomeric equilibrium:

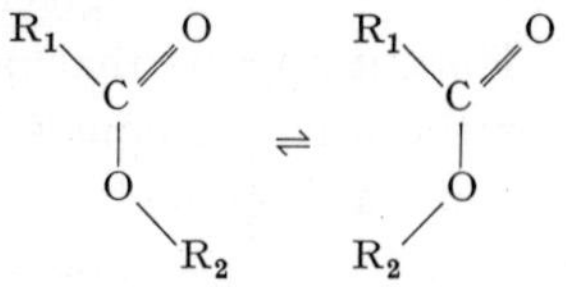

For the formates R_1 is H and for the acetates R_1 is CH_3.

De Groot and Lamb[6,7] have found relaxation effects in aldehydes, ketones, and vinyl ethers. The data on certain aldehydes are listed in Table 98–2. A and B in this table are the constants in the absorption formula

$$\frac{\alpha'}{f^2} = \frac{A}{1 + (f/f')^2} + B.$$

TABLE 98–2

ULTRASONIC ABSORPTION DATA FOR CERTAIN ALDEHYDES

Aldehyde	T (°C)	$10^{17} A$ (sec^2 cm^{-1})	$10^{17} B$ (sec^2 cm^{-1})	f' (Mc/sec)	10^{-5} $\mathfrak{V}$ (cm/sec)	$10^2(\alpha\lambda)_{max}$
Crotonaldehyde	25	674	29	30.3	1.268	1.29
	50	355	34	70.0	1.165	1.45
Cinnamaldehyde	25	722	78	15.7	1.563	0.885
Acraldehyde	25	250	—	250	—	—

In acraldehyde ($CH_2 = CH - CHO$), for example, the following equilibrium is perturbed by the sound wave:

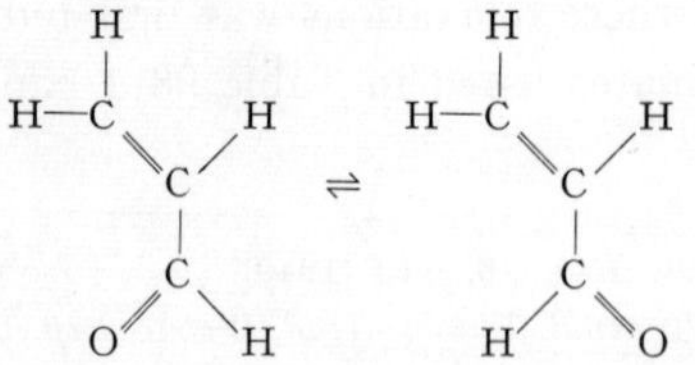

[6] M. S. de Groot and J. Lamb, *Nature* **177**, 1231 (1956).
[7] M. S. de Groot and J. Lamb, *Proc. Roy. Soc.* **A242**, 36 (1957).

The stability of these planar configurations is due to conjugation of the bond between the central carbon atoms, which is pictured as a resonance between two structures:

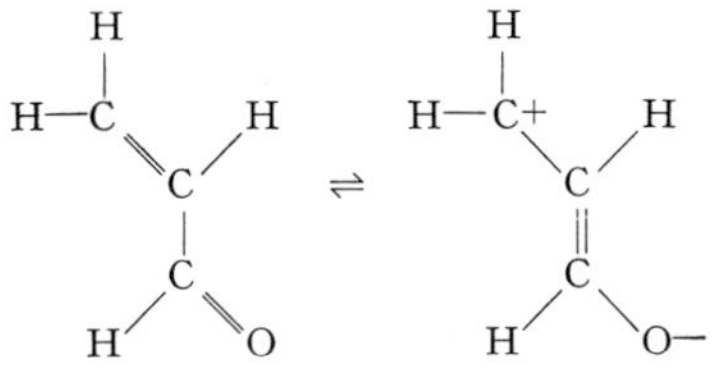

Measurements by Karpovich[5] and Lamb and Sherwood[8] in cyclohexane derivatives have demonstrated the existence of isomeric relaxation effects in some of these liquids with relaxation frequencies below 200 kc/sec. These data are summarized in Table 98–3.

TABLE 98–3

COMPARISON OF RELAXATION PARAMETERS FOUND IN CYCLOHEXANE AND DERIVATIVES

Cyclohexane and Derivatives	T (°C)	f' (kc/sec)	$10^{17} A$ (sec^2 cm^{-1})	$10^{17}\, \alpha/f^2$ (sec^{2}cm^{-1} at 25° C)	Reference
Cyclohexane	No relaxation observed			192	5
Methyl	16	140	200,000	118	8
	25	220	260,000	—	8
Ethyl	16	60	500,000	—	8
Cis-1,2-dimethyl	No relaxation observed			—	8
Trans-1,2-dimethyl	16	120	55,000	78	8
Trans-1,3-dimethyl	No relaxation observed			84.6	5
Cis-1,4-dimethyl	No relaxation observed			87.6	8
Trans-1,4-dimethyl	16	150	26,000	112	8

These molecules are puckered rings of six carbon atoms. Karpovich[5] and Lamb and Sherwood[8] suggest that the relaxation process involves the

[8] J. Lamb and J. Sherwood, *Trans. Faraday Soc.* **51**, 1674 (1955).

perturbation of equilibrium between the equatorial and polar form of the molecule, as pictured in Fig. 98–1 for methylcyclohexane.

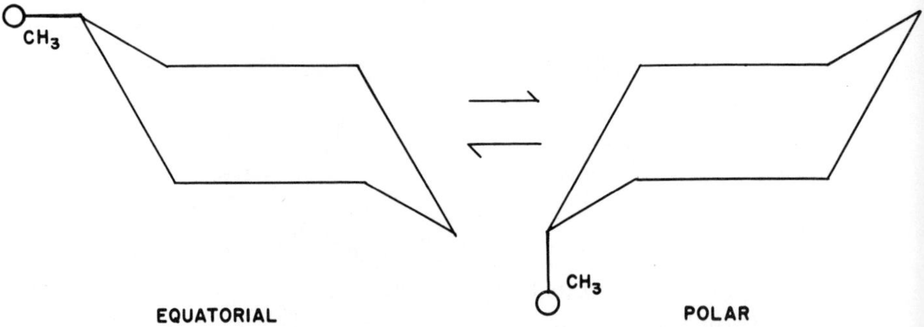

FIG. 98–1. The polar-equatorial type of rotational isomers of methylcyclohexane.

In cyclohexane the polar and equatorial forms have the same energy, and no relaxation is observed. However, upon substitution of methyl or other groups these two forms do have a different energy. For example, in methylcyclohexane the energy difference is found to be 1.6 kcal/mole.

Lamb and Sherwood's measurements on a series of dimethylcyclohexanes indicate that relaxation effects do not occur in all of these liquids at low frequencies. No relaxation is observed in *cis*-1,2-dimethyl; *trans*-1,3-dimethyl; and *cis*-1,4-dimethylcyclohexane; because in each of these cases when a rotation of a methyl group from an axial to an equatorial position occurs, it is accompanied by a reverse rotation of a second methyl group.

Karpovich[5] has noted a relaxation frequency in cyclohexene of about 80 kc/sec. The loss here is attributed to a perturbation of equilibrium between the "chair" and "boat" forms of this molecule.

Young and Petrauskas[9] have investigated isomeric relaxation in saturated hydrocarbons at low temperatures. Their results in 2-methylbutane shown in Fig. 98–2 are of interest. The rotational isomerism here is due to different possible orientations of methyl groups around the C-C bond. There are four possible orientations, one of which differs in energy from the other three. The data cover a temperature range from 180° to 220 °K. As can be seen in Fig. 98–2, the values of $(\alpha\lambda)_{max}$ vary with temperature, exhibiting a maximum near 190 °K. This maximum is significant in demonstrating the

---

[9] J. M. Young and A. A. Petrauskas, *J. Chem. Phys.* **25**, 943 (1956).

existence of a two-state type of specific heat (in contradistinction to the internal vibrational type of specific heat). This is the only ultrasonic relaxation measurement of any type in which this peak in $(\alpha\lambda)_{max}$ has been noted.

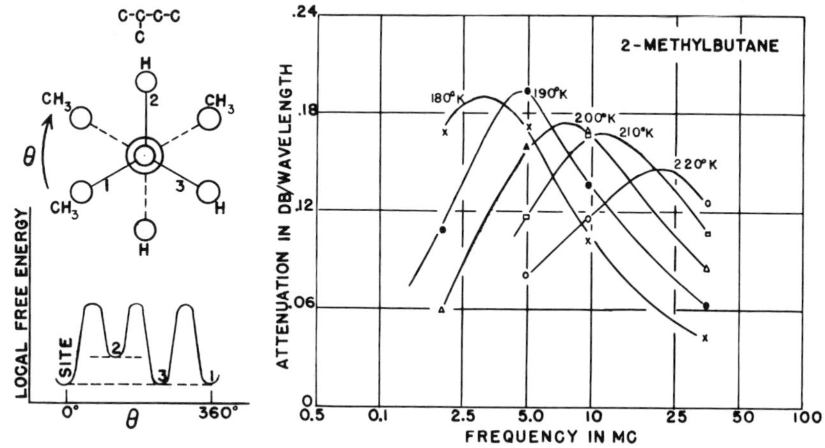

FIG. 98–2. Sound absorption in 2-methylbutane as a function of frequency at 5 different temperatures. Diagram at left shows different orientations of methyl groups about the C-C bonds.

Moen[10] and Beyer[11] have detected ultrasonic relaxation in toluene ($C_6H_5CH_3$) at frequencies below 400 kc. The data of Beyer are listed in Table 98–4.

TABLE 98–4

ULTRASONIC ABSORPTION IN TOLUENE[11]

T (°C)	6	12	17	24
f' (kc/sec)	55	76	98	165
$(\alpha\lambda)_{max}$ 10^5	2.3	2.75	3.1	3.6

After the publication of Moen's paper, Andreae and Lamb[12] suggested that this relaxation process was one involving excitation of a stretching

[10] C. J. Moen, *J. Acoust. Soc. Am.* **23**, 62 (1951).

[11] R. Beyer, *J. Acoust. Soc. Am.* **27**, 1 (1955).

[12] J. H. Andreae and J. Lamb, *Proc. Phys. Soc. London* **B64**, 1021 (1951).

mode of a C-H bond in the methyl group. This vibration has a wave number of 2960 cm^{-1}. Assuming a degeneracy of 3, one obtains the value 1.28×10^{-5} from Eq. (16–6) for $(\alpha\lambda)_{max}$, as compared with the experimental value 3.8×10^{-5}, an unsatisfactory agreement. In addition, Beyer has shown that the temperature dependence of $(\alpha\lambda)_{max}$, calculated assuming a vibrational relaxation, does not agree with experiment.

TABLE 98–5
RELAXATION OF TRIETHYLAMINE

T (°C)	$10^{17} A$ (sec^2cm^{-1})	$10^{17} B$ (sec^2cm^{-1})	f' (Mc/sec)	$10^2 (\alpha\lambda)_{max}$
25	413	31	89.3	2.07
35	293	22	137	2.16
45	230	15	197	2.34
55	186	7	320	2.94

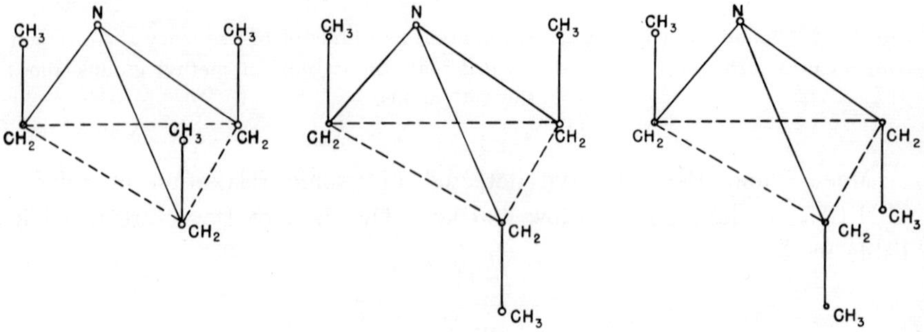

FIG. 98–3. Rotational isomers of triethylamine.

Beyer quotes a suggestion of Karpovich and Freedman that a hindered rotation of the methyl group around the C-C bond joining it to the benzene ring is responsible for the relaxation in toluene.

At the moment, the origin of this effect is not clear; it seems improbable that it is a vibrational relaxation.

Relaxation processes in liquid triethylamine have been studied by Heasell and Lamb[13] over a temperature range from 25° to 70° C. These data appear in Table 98–5. There are three rotational isomers of triethylamine

[13] E. L. Heasell and J. Lamb, *Proc. Roy. Soc.* **A237**, 233 (1956).

(see Fig. 98–3); from the results it is not possible to determine whether all three states play a role in the measured absorption.

De Groot and Lamb[7] have measured f' for solutions of crotonaldehyde in the nonpolar liquid, n-hexane; and in the polar liquid, acetone. In n-hexane f' was independent of concentration. In the polar solvent a slight change in f' was noted. For a 2.88 M solution $f' = 33.3$ Mc/sec, whereas in the pure crotonaldehyde $f' = 30.3$ Mc/sec. These results are in striking contrast to those found in cases in which vibrational relaxation is the cause of absorption. The lack of dependence on "impurities" found here for f' is in agreement with the pressure data (see Sec. 118) in showing that the mechanism of energy transfer in rotational isomers is an intramolecular process and is relatively insensitive to the environment of the molecule.

The internal specific heat associated with the isomeric process is given by Eq. (28–1) with

$$C' = R\left[\frac{H'}{RT}\frac{1}{2\cosh F'/RT}\right]^2 = R\left[\frac{H'}{RT}\right]^2 x_1(1 - x_1). \qquad (98\text{–}1)$$

The relaxation frequency f' is given by Eq. (28–2)

$$f' = \frac{k_{12} + k_{21}}{2\pi} = \frac{1}{2\pi}\frac{kT}{h}\left[\exp -\left(\frac{F^* - F_1}{RT}\right) + \exp -\left(\frac{F^* - F_2}{RT}\right)\right] \qquad (98\text{–}2)$$

where k_{12} and k_{21} are the forward and reverse rate constants, respectively.

Under certain conditions the available ultrasonic data can be used to evaluate $F^* - F_2$, and other parameters. If F'/RT is several times greater than unity $(F^* - F_2 < F^* - F_1)$ then k_{21} is larger than k_{12} and Eq. (98–2) can be approximated by

$$f' = \frac{k_{21}}{2\pi} = \frac{1}{2\pi}\frac{kT}{h}\exp -\left[\frac{F^* - F_2}{RT}\right]$$

or

$$f' = \frac{1}{2\pi}\frac{kT}{h}\exp\left[\frac{S^* - S_2}{R}\right]\exp -\left[\frac{H^* - H_2}{RT}\right].$$

Under these conditions one can use the temperature dependence of f' to determine $H^* - H_2$ and $S^* - S_2$. These values have been tabulated for several liquids by Davies and Lamb[14] and are listed in Table 98–6.

[14] R. O. Davies and J. Lamb, *Quart. Revs.* **11**, 134 (1957).

Toluene has been included in this list to show that the values obtained are comparable to those for liquids known to exhibit rotational isomeric processes.

TABLE 98–6

$H^* - H_2$, $S^* - S_2$, AND H' FOR SEVERAL LIQUIDS EXHIBITING ROTATIONAL ISOMERIC RELAXATION*

Liquid	$H^* - H_2$ (kcal/mole)	H' (kcal/mole)	$S^* - S_2$ (kcal/mole-degrees)
Crotonaldehyde	5.5	1.93	−2.1
Cinnamaldehyde	5.6	1.5	−3.0
Ethylacetate	5.7	—	−3.2
Triethylamine	6.8	3.4	4.5
2-Methylbutane	4.7	0.9	0.9
Toluene	8.5	—	−2.3

* H' is calculated assuming $S' = 0$ and thus $F' = H'$.

It can be seen in Tables 98–1 and 98–2 that in a homologous series of molecules the relaxation frequency changes systematically. For example, increasing the size of the R_1 or R_2 groups in the esters (going from formates to acetates) causes a considerable increase in f'. On the other hand, a decrease in f' is observed in the aldehydes when hydrogen is replaced by a methyl group in the trans-position on the top carbon atom.

The variation in f' in the esters can be accounted for by steric hindrance. The larger R_1 or R_2 groups have a greater mutual steric hindrance, causing an increase in the energy of state 2. Assuming no increase in F^*, $F^* - F_2$ will be smaller, and k_{21} and thus f' will be larger.

The explanation is in agreement with the fact that $(\alpha\lambda)_{max}$ and thus C' is smaller for the acetates. However, the assumption that F^* does not change has not been checked experimentally.

In the aldehydes de Groot and Lamb suggest that F_2 and F_1 are determined by the resonance energy or amount of conjugation. Replacing hydrogen by a methyl group (going from acraldehyde to crotonaldehyde) strengthens conjugation, decreases F_1 and F_2, increases $F^* - F_2$ and $F^* - F_1$, and thus decreases f'.

The use of ultrasonic absorption and dispersion to investigate the phenomena of rotational isomerism should prove quite fruitful. Infra-red studies have long been used to study rotational isomers but the ultrasonic technique offers certain advantages, especially in conjunction with infra-red.

The strength of the ultrasonic absorption is particularly sensitive to the number of molecules in the excited state; see Eq. (98–1). As Lamb has shown, prominent relaxations can be observed when there are less than 1% of the molecules in the excited state. One is not always able to do this using infra-red techniques.

99. Liquid Mixtures

Bauer[1] was the first to give a theory of absorption in a mixture of two Kneser liquids. This was developed in analogy to the theory of Sec. 26, which is based on the assumption that only pairs of molecules interact, an assumption which is obviously valid for gases.

Just as in the case of gases, if a small amount of impurity B is mixed with a heavily absorbing liquid A, the effect of the impurity may be unexpectedly large. The pure liquid A absorbs so strongly because collisions between molecules A are ineffective in transferring internal vibrational energy to translation. The assumption is made by Bauer that *any* foreign molecule B—which by itself forms a liquid with small absorption—should be more effective in producing this transfer. For the liquids with which we are dealing, which are made up of fairly large organic molecules, this is probably true due to complex collision (see Secs. 65 and 67). If the liquid A is not strongly absorbing, the addition of a small amount of B is not very effective (just as, in gases, water strongly affects the τ of CO_2, but probably does not strongly affect the τ of C_6H_{14}).

Examples of the effect of impurities in highly absorbing liquids were found for the pairs CCl_4 (A) with ethyl ether (B), by Bazulin;[2] for CS_2 (A) with either CCl_4 or C_6H_6 (B), by Claeys *et al.*,[3] for C_6H_6 (A) with $C_6H_5CH_3$ (B), by Grobe;[4] and for C_6H_6 (A) with acetone (B), by Willard.[5] Willard's curve is shown in Fig. 99–1. Many other examples are given by Sette.[6] He showed later that B may just as well form an associated liquid or be polar; for example, nitrobenzene and ethyl alcohol in benzene behave similarly to acetone in C_6H_6. This can be understood, since the "associated" character

---

[1] E. Bauer, *Proc. Phys. Soc. London* **A62**, 141 (1949).

[2] P. Bazulin, *Zhur. Eksptl. i Teoret. Fiz.* **8**, 457 (1939).

[3] J. Claeys, E. Errera, and H. Sack, *Trans. Faraday Soc.* **33**, 136 (1937).

[4] H. Grobe, *Physik. Z.* **39**, 333 (1938).

[5] G. W. Willard, *J. Acoust. Soc. Am.* **12**, 438 (1941).

[6] D. Sette, *Nuovo cimento* [9] **7** Suppl. 2, 318 (1950); *J. Acoust. Soc. Am.* **23**, 359 (1951).

of B is dependent upon the existence of a group of molecules B being together, while in dilute solution the B's are surrounded by molecules A and are isolated from each other.

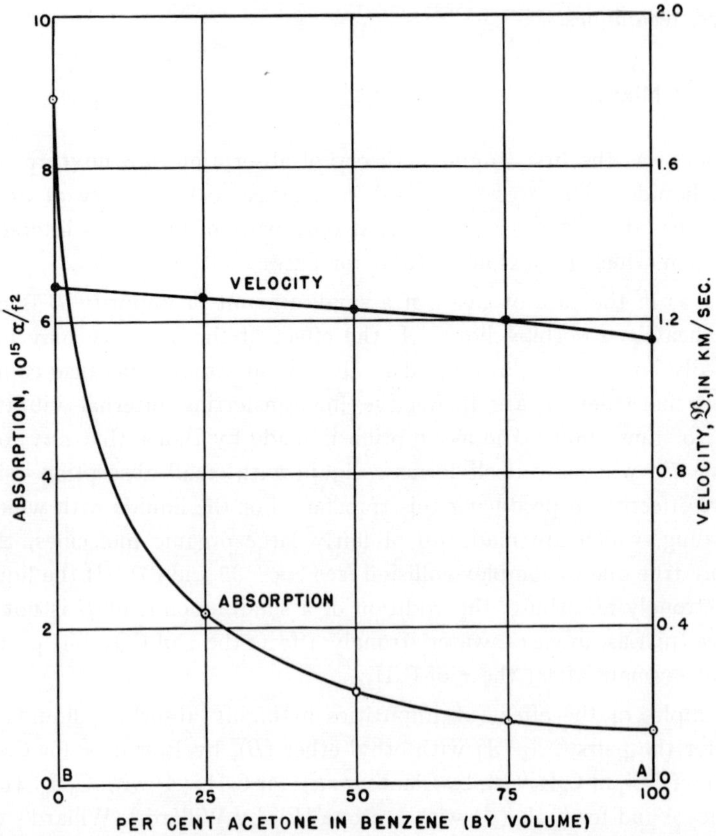

FIG. 99–1. Absorption and velocity in benzene-acetone mixtures, according to Willard.[5]

Sette[6,7] has generalized the expression which Bauer developed. Let τ_{AA} be the relaxation time in pure A, τ_{BB} that in pure B, τ_{AB} the relaxation time for the deactivation of an excited molecule A by a molecule B, and τ_{BA} the time with the roles of B and A exchanged. Then

$$\frac{\Delta}{\mathfrak{B}C_vC_p} \approx \left(\frac{\Delta}{\mathfrak{B}C_vC_p}\right)_B \left\{1 - \left[1 - \left(\frac{\mathfrak{B}C_vC_p}{\Delta}\right)_B \left(\frac{\Delta}{\mathfrak{B}C_vC_p}\right)_A\right] x\right\} \qquad (99\text{–}1)$$

[7] D. Sette, *J. Chem. Phys.* **18**, 1592 (1950).

where x is the mole fraction of A. Then[8]

$$\alpha/f^2 = (\alpha/f^2)_B \left\{1 - \left[1 - \left(\frac{\mathfrak{B}C_v C_p}{\Delta}\right)_B \left(\frac{\Delta}{\mathfrak{B}C_v C_p}\right)_A\right] x\right\}$$

$$\left\{x \frac{\tau_{AA}}{\tau_{BB}} \frac{C_A'}{C_B'} \left[x + (1 - x) \frac{\tau_{AA}}{\tau_{AB}}\right]^{-1} + (1 - x) \left[1 - x + x \frac{\tau_{BB}}{\tau_{BA}}\right]^{-1}\right\}. \qquad (99\text{–}2)$$

Bauer had put $\tau_{AB} = \tau_{BA} = \tau_{BB}$.

The agreement between Eq. (99–2) and the experiments is good; e.g., the curve of α/f^2 against x for a mixture C_6H_6-CCl_4 (both highly absorbing liquids) has a flat minimum; the curve for the mixture C_6H_6-$CHCl_3$ is a straight line.

Mez and Maier[9] measured the absorption of 20 Mc waves in solutions of toluene in CCl_4 and in chlorobenzene as function of the temperature. The authors find a decrease in absorption of the solvent by addition of toluene, but this decrease is temperature independent, i.e., the curves α against T are all parallel to that of the pure solvent, for which α increases with T.

[8] Sette writes a instead of x, z instead of τ_{AA}/τ_{BB}, t instead of τ_{AA}/τ_{AB}, and u instead of τ_{BB}/τ_{BA}.

[9] A. Mez and W. Maier, *Z. Naturforsch.* **10a**, 997 (1955).

XII. Associated Liquids and Liquids with High Viscosity

100. The Theory of Hall

Water is an exceptional liquid, insofar as it has a density maximum. As has been pointed out in Sec. 72, if follows that in water at 4° C sound propagation is an isothermal process (and below 4° C and somewhat above it, nearly isothermal) and therefore thermal relaxation can play no role in the excess sound absorption. (It *need* not play an important role, even if sound propagation is not isothermal; this is probably the case for the liquids discussed in Sec. 113.)

The experimental absorption data and their dependence on temperature have been discussed in Sec. 73. No velocity dispersion has been found.

Hall[1] was the first to give a theory of the molecular absorption in water. He based it on the assumptions of Bernal and Fowler[2] on the constitution of liquid water. According to these authors, the peculiar properties of water can be explained as follows: The water molecule can be considered as a sphere, with a negative charge and two positive charges arranged as a triangle of angle 109° inside the sphere. In ice, these molecules form a regular structure with rather large holes. This is tridymite-like and has coordination number four. Each molecule is surrounded by a tetrahedron of others so that the hydrogens always point at an oxygen of the neighbor. As is well known, a mole of ice has a volume of 19.62 cc. If one takes the nearest approach of the two molecules in ice as 2.76 Å, the "true volume" of the molecules is then 6.63 cc.

In liquid water at low temperature, this structure is always present. In addition, however, a "quartzlike" structure, also of coordination number four, is present. This is more closely packed than the tridymite structures. While the distance to the immediate neighbors is 2.76 Å in both, the distance to the next nearest neighbors is 4.2 Å in the quartz structure and 4.5 Å in the tridymite structure. The volume of a mole of pure quartz structure at 0° C would be 16.67 cc.

---

[1] L. Hall, *Phys. Rev.* **73**, 772 (1948).

[2] J. D. Bernal and R. H. Fowler, *J. Chem. Phys.* **1**, 515 (1933).

The density minimum at 4° C is then explained by a gradual change of the tridymite structure to the quartz structure when the temperature is raised, which results in an increase in density, on which process is superposed the usual thermal expansion of both structures. At 0° C, there would be 45% tridymite structure present.

Hall modifies the ideas of Bernal and Fowler. He uses[3] the equivalent of our Eq. (29–5) to write

$$\kappa' = \frac{(V_2 - V_1)^2}{VRT} x_1 x_2 = \frac{(V_2 - V_1)^2}{VRT} \frac{Q_1 Q_2}{(Q_1 + Q_2)^2}$$

$$= \frac{(V_2 - V_1)^2}{2VRT}\left[1 + \cosh\frac{F_2 - F_1}{RT}\right]^{-1}$$

$$\kappa^{-1} = \rho\, \mathfrak{V}_0^{\,2}. \tag{100–1}$$

Equations (29–8) and (92–7) combined give

$$\tau^{-1} = \frac{kT}{h}\left(\frac{Q^*}{Q_1} + \frac{Q^*}{Q_2}\right) = \frac{kT}{h}\left[\exp\left(-\frac{F^* - F_1}{RT}\right) + \exp\left(-\frac{F^* - F_2}{RT}\right)\right]. \tag{100–2}$$

Hall now identifies the relaxation time τ_η occurring in viscous flow with the time for reaction from state (1) over the potential hump[4]

$$\tau_\eta^{-1} = \frac{kT}{h}\frac{Q^*}{Q_1} \tag{100–3}$$

or

$$\tau^{-1} = \tau_\eta^{-1}\left(1 + \frac{Q_1}{Q_2}\right). \tag{100–3'}$$

Then, with Eq. (90–4), one has

$$\tau = \frac{V}{RT}\eta \frac{Q_2}{Q_1 + Q_2} = \frac{V}{RT}\eta\left[1 + \exp\frac{F_2 - F_1}{RT}\right]^{-1} \tag{100–4}$$

---

[3] Hall did not have the general formulas of Sec. 29 available, but developed expressions for his case. Hall's β_0 is our κ, his β_r our κ'.

[4] For reasons explained in Sec. 102, we assume that the less populated structure x_2 is the open structure, in contradiction to Hall. In the following, the index 2 refers to the open structure.

and, finally

$$\alpha'/f^2 = 2\pi^2\rho\, \mathfrak{B}_0\, \eta \left(\frac{V_2 - V_1}{RT}\right)^2 \frac{Q_1 Q_2^2}{(Q_1 + Q_2)^3} = 2\pi^2\rho\, \mathfrak{B}_0\, \eta \left(\frac{V_2 - V_1}{RT}\right)^2 (1 - x_2)x_2^2 \tag{100–5}$$

or, using Eq. (7–8)

$$\begin{aligned} \alpha'/\alpha_{\text{class}} &= \frac{3}{4}(\rho\, \mathfrak{B}_0^2)^2 \left(\frac{V_2 - V_1}{RT}\right)^2 (1 - x_2)x_2^2 \\ &= \frac{3}{4}\left(\frac{M}{RT}\mathfrak{B}_0^2\right)^2 \left(\frac{V_2 - V_1}{V}\right)^2 (1 - x_2)x_2^2 \\ &= \frac{3}{4}\left(\frac{M}{RT}\mathfrak{B}_0^2\right)^2 \left(\frac{V - V_1}{V}\right)^2 (1 - x_2). \end{aligned} \tag{100–6}$$

These equations follow from, but are not shown in, Hall's paper.

If τ and τ_η had been identified, instead of being connected by Eq. (100–3′), x_2 instead of x_2^2 would appear in Eqs. (100–5) and (100–6). Since the left side of Eq. (100–6) is about 2 for water, $|(V_2 - V_1)/V|$ must be larger than 0.25; otherwise, one gets a negative x_2.

Hall assumes that the denser phase in water is not the one with the quartzlike structure, but a nearly close packed one which, according to Bernal and Fowler, mainly appears at higher temperatures. This phase would have a mole volume of 8.98 cc. Hall takes the closest distance of two water molecules as 2.90 Å (as suggested by X-ray data on water) instead of 2.76 Å, so that $V_1 = 10.4$ cc. He assumes that

$$\frac{V_2 - V_1}{V} = +0.47$$

and takes it as temperature independent.

This leaves one more constant to be determined for each temperature, x_2, Q_2/Q_1, or $F_2 - F_1$.

Hall proceeds by assuming a value for $\kappa - \kappa'$. The compressibility of ice is 10×10^{-12} cm^2 (dyne)$^{-1}$. He takes $\kappa - \kappa' = 18 \times 10^{-12}$. Since κ at 4° C is 50×10^{-12}, this gives $\kappa' = 32 \times 10^{-12}$ and, from Eq. (100–1), $x_2 = 0.25$. At 60° C, x_2 would be 0.24.

Accepting $(V_2 - V_1)/V = 0.47$ and $x_2 = 0.26$ (see Table 100–1), one gets

$$0.74\, V_1 + 0.26\, V_2 = 18 \tag{100–7}$$

$$V_2 - V_1 = 0.47 \times 18 = 8.5$$

or $$V_1 = 15.8 \text{ cm}^3, \quad V_2 = 24.1 \text{ cm}^3.$$

One can use Eq. (100–6) to calculate x_2 from the measured absorption. The results are given in Table 100–1, which show that x_2 is almost independent of temperature. Therefore

$$\ln \frac{x_2}{1 - x_2} = - \frac{F_2 - F_1}{RT} = -1.05 \tag{100–8}$$

is independent of the temperature, and

$$H_1 = H_2 \tag{100–8'}$$

$$S_1 - S_2 = 1.05\,R = 2.1 \text{ cal/mole degree.}^5 \tag{100–8''}$$

Equation (100–8) agrees with Hall's estimate. From Eq. (100–4), Hall estimates τ as 1.6×10^{-12} sec at 30° C.

TABLE 100–1

MOLE FRACTION x_2 OF OPEN-PACKED PHASE OF WATER, CALCULATED FROM THE MEASURED ABSORPTION*

T (°C)	0	4	10	30	60
$((V_2 - V_1)/V)^2 (1 - x_2)x_2{}^2$	0.0126	0.0121	0.0113	0.0107	0.0112
x_2	0.281	0.275	0.263	0.255	0.263

* If one had written $\tau = \tau_\eta$, x_2 would follow as ~ 0.06.

One more calculation may be made. As mentioned before, the exceptionally low coefficient of thermal expansion of water, β, is explained by Bernal and Fowler by assuming that the normal expansion coefficient, $\tilde{\beta} \sim 0.001$, which occurs in other liquids is nearly compensated by the derease of mole fraction x_2 of the open phase with temperature, i.e.

$$\beta = \tilde{\beta} + \frac{V_2 - V_1}{V} \frac{dx_2}{dT}. \tag{100–9}$$

This would give

$$\frac{dx_2}{dT} \sim -\tilde{\beta}\left(\frac{V_2 - V_1}{V}\right)^{-1} \sim -0.002$$

---

[5] This looks almost as if the only thermodynamical difference between the two structures is that the dense structure has the full communal entropy, while the open structure has none.

This is in moderately good agreement with the temperature variation of x_2 between 0 and 10° C, as can be seen from Table 100–1. On the other hand, between 10° C and 60° C, x_2 is practically constant, leading to a normal value of the coefficient of thermal expansion, in agreement with experiment.

101. Eucken's Theory of the Constitution of Water

In several papers, Eucken[1] has developed a more chemical theory of the constitution of water. He assumes that it is a mixture of single molecules H_2O, of double molecules $(H_2O)_2$, quadruple molecules $(H_2O)_4$, and eightfold

TABLE 101–1
CONSTITUTION OF WATER ACCORDING TO EUCKEN

T (°C)	Monomer H_2O	Dimer $(H_2O)_2$	Tetramer $(H_2O)_4$	Octamer $(H_2O)_8$
		Dissociation Energies in cal/mole H_2O		
		2350	2750	3200
		Mole Fraction $\bar{x}$ *in Mole* H_2O		
0	0.050	0.350	0.300	0.300
20	0.081	0.434	0.308	0.178
40	0.119	0.492	0.293	0.096
60	0.162	0.529	0.261	0.048
		Mole Fraction x		
0	0.148	0.519	0.222	0.111
20	0.193	0.518	0.184	0.106
40	0.264	0.547	0.163	0.027
60	0.326	0.531	0.131	0.012

molecules $(H_2O)_8$. It is assumed that the first three kinds have the same volume per molecule H_2O, but that the eightfold molecule (octamer) has a tridymite structure, with a considerable unoccupied space in the center and that, accordingly, an octamer molecule occupies more space than eight H_2O molecules, four $(H_2O)_2$ molecules, or two $(H_2O)_4$ molecules. It is, in fact,

[1] A. Eucken, *Nachr. Ges. Wiss. Göttingen Math. physik. Kl.* 38 (1946); 1 (1949); *Z. Elektrochem.* **52**, 255 (1948).

assumed that the space occupied by 1/8 mole of octamer (which contains 1 mole of H_2O) is 1.8 cc larger than the volume of 1 mole of H_2O.

Eucken's principal conclusions come from a consideration of the specific heat of water, which is exceptionally high because it contains contributions from the heat of dissociation of the higher complexes.

However, Eucken also tries to represent the compressibility and heat expansion, assuming, besides the shifting chemical equilibrium, a "normal" equation of state, which becomes dominating at high temperatures where practically no octamer is present. Eucken also considers the variation of sound velocity with temperature and of viscosity with pressure. His results for the mole fraction and heats of dissociation are given in Table 101–1.

The quantity $\bar{x}_s$ (which Eucken calls γ_s') is the fraction of H_2O molecules in the form $(H_2O)_s$. The mole fraction x_s, according to our definition, follows through

$$x_s = \frac{1}{s} \bar{x}_s \left[\bar{x}_1 + \frac{1}{2} \bar{x}_2 + \frac{1}{4} \bar{x}_4 + \frac{1}{8} \bar{x}_8 \right]^{-1} \tag{101–1}$$

$$\bar{x}_s = s x_s \left[x_1 + 2x_2 + 4x_4 + 8x_8 \right]^{-1}. \tag{101–1'}$$

Gierer and Wirtz[2] have compared Eucken's theory with that of Bernal and Fowler, discussed in the preceding section. They emphasize the idea of the hydrogen bridge, describe the octamer as a stretched, closed bridge structure, and identify it with Bernal and Fowler's tridymite structure. In Eucken's theory there is no quartzlike structure, but the dimers and tetramers are linear systems with puckered hydrogen bridges. Finally, the single H_2O molecules correspond to densest packing, with no hydrogen bridges, but probably with increased distance (3.2 Å) between water molecules. The authors give tables for the average number of hydrogen bridges as function of the temperature.

It may be mentioned here that Pople[3] has assumed that in water the hydrogen bridges are bent, not broken, with increasing temperature, but the theory does not lend itself at present to a calculation of sound absorption.

We next apply Eucken's theory to a calculation of sound absorption at 4° C (which he has not done). It is easier to use, not with our mole fraction x, but with Eucken's quantities $\bar{x}_s$, which, as said before, measure the

---

[2] A. Gierer and K. Wirtz, *Z. Naturforsch.* **5a**, 577 (1950).

[3] J. A. Pople, *Proc. Roy. Soc.* **A205**, **163** (1951).

number of moles of H_2O contained in $(H_2O)_s$ for 18 g of water. Then Eq. (100–7) takes the form (the bar referring to 18 g of water)

$$\bar{V} = \bar{V}_1(1 - \bar{x}_8) + \bar{V}_2\,\bar{x}_8 = \bar{V}_1 + (\bar{V}_2 - \bar{V}_1)\,\bar{x}_8 = \bar{V}_1 + 1.8\,\bar{x}_8 \quad (101\text{–}2)$$

and the compressibility is

$$\kappa = \tilde{\kappa} + \kappa' = -\frac{1}{V}\left\{\frac{\partial \bar{V}_1}{\partial p} + \bar{x}_8 \frac{\partial}{\partial p}(\bar{V}_2 - \bar{V}_1) + (\bar{V}_2 - \bar{V}_1)\frac{\partial \bar{x}_8}{\partial p}\right\} \quad (101\text{–}3)$$

$$\kappa' = -\frac{\bar{V}_2 - \bar{V}_1}{V}\frac{\partial \bar{x}_8}{\partial p} = -\frac{1.8}{18}\frac{\partial \bar{x}_8}{\partial p} = -\,0.1\,\frac{\partial \bar{x}_8}{\partial p}, \quad (101\text{–}3')$$

We have the equilibrium equations

$$\frac{x_2}{x_1{}^2} = K_2 \qquad \frac{x_4}{x_1{}^4} = K_4 \qquad \frac{x_8}{x_1{}^8} = K_8. \quad (101\text{–}4)$$

We make the assumption that the equilibrium is established very rapidly between monomers, dimers, and tetramers, and that the formation of the octamer from another form has the relaxation time τ, whatever that form. Then, by definition—the variation δ will be used in the sense $(\partial/\partial p)\delta p$—

$$\delta x_1 + \delta x_2 + \delta x_4 + \delta x_8 = 0 \quad (101\text{–}5)$$

$$\delta \bar{x}_8/\bar{x}_8 = \delta x_8/x_8 - (\delta x_1 + 2\delta x_2 + 4\delta x_4 + 8\delta x_8)\,[x_1 + 2x_2 + 4x_4 + 8x_8]^{-1} \quad (101\text{–}5')$$

and from the equilibrium equations, remembering that K_2 and K_4 are independent of pressure

$$\delta x_2/x_2 - 2\delta x_1/x_1 = 0$$

$$\delta x_4/x_4 - 4\delta x_1/x_1 = 0$$

$$\delta x_8/x_8 - 8\delta x_1/x_1 = \delta \ln K_8. \quad (101\text{–}6)$$

These five equations permit the elimination of all the δx from Eq. (100–5'). One finds

$$\frac{\partial \bar{x}_8}{\partial p} = \frac{\partial \ln K_8}{\partial p}\,\bar{x}_8\left[1 - \frac{7}{8}\,\bar{x}_8\right]. \quad (101\text{–}7)$$

Since

$$\frac{\partial \ln K_8}{\partial p} = -8 \frac{\bar{V}_2 - \bar{V}_1}{RT} \tag{101–8}$$

one has, from Eq. (101—3′)

$$\kappa' = 8\left(\frac{\bar{V}_2 - \bar{V}_1}{V}\right)^2 \frac{V}{RT} \bar{x}_8 \left(1 - \frac{7}{8} \bar{x}_8\right) \tag{101–9}$$

or, at 4° C with the numbers from Table 101–1 at 0° C

$$\kappa' = 1.73 \times 10^{-12} \, \mathrm{cm}^2 (\mathrm{dyne})^{-1}. \tag{101–9′}$$

This differs from Hall's Eq. (100–1) formula by the substitution of $\bar{x}_8(1-7/8\,\bar{x}_8)$ for $x_2(1 - x_2)$, but the values of $\bar{x}_8$ (0.300) and x_2 (0.27) are nearly equal. In addition, Eucken's $|(V_2 - V_1)/V|$ is 0.1 compared to Hall's 0.47, so that Eucken's value of κ' is 20 times smaller than Hall's value, 34×10^{-12}. Accordingly, to get the correct sound absorption, Eucken's τ must be taken 20 times larger than Hall's, 7×10^{-11} sec instead of 3.5×10^{-12} sec. At 100 Mc, $\omega\tau$ would still be only 0.044, so that a direct experimental decision is not possible at present.

There is however indirect evidence that the Eucken theory gives a value of κ'/κ which is too small by an order of magnitude. Considering the values of κ'/κ in Table 111–3 below, one finds that they range from about 0.20 to 0.60 for those liquids in which the dispersion has been measured. Furthermore Table 111–4 shows that the isothermal values of κ'/κ as obtained by glass transition measurements indicate a range of values from 0.19 to 0.76. Using Hall's and Eucken's theories one gets 0.61 and 0.038, respectively. In the light of the above data Eucken's value appears too small, whereas Hall's value is quite reasonable. Furthermore the success of Hall's theory in explaining the pressure dependence of ultrasonic absorption in water tends to lend greater credence to his approach.

102. The Effect of Pressure on Sound Absorption in Water

A criticism of Hall's theory, pointed out by Markham, Beyer, and Lindsay,[1] lies in the fact that fitting the expressions to the temperature dependence of the excess sound absorption in water is not a conclusive test. The evaluation of $F_2 - F_1$ and $V_2 - V_1$ in Eq. (100–5) is only approximate.

---

[1] J. J. Markham, R. T. Beyer, and R. B. Lindsay, *Revs. Modern. Phys.* **23**, 353 (1951).

It can be seen from Table 100–1 that x_2 must remain constant to within about 10% to fit the data. (This is accomplished by assuming that $(F_2 - F_1)/T$ is temperature independent.) Under these conditions Eq. (100–5) reduces essentially to the statement that α'/f^2 is proportional to η, where the constants are obtained by fitting theory to data at 0° C. Since the ratio of η'/η has been experimentally found to be nearly independent of temperature, any theory which deduces a compressional loss proportional to the shear viscosity would naturally give the correct temperature dependence.

A further test of the two-state theory is obtained if one considers the data on pressure dependence of sound absorption in water as measured by Litovitz and Carnevale.[2] The pressure dependence of α'/f^2 is very sensitive to the value of $V_2 - V_1$ chosen to fit the data at atmospheric pressure. This fact allows a more definite evaluation of $V_2 - V_1$ and x_2.

From thermodynamic considerations the variation of K_{equil}, the equilibrium constant, with pressure is given by the following (see Eq. 27–8′)

$$\frac{\partial \ln K_{\text{equil}}}{\partial p} = -\frac{V_2 - V_1}{RT} \tag{102–1}$$

where

$$K_{\text{equil}} = \frac{x_2}{1 - x_2}. \tag{102–2}$$

From Eq. (102–1) one finds that the ratio of the equilibrium constants at the pressures 0 and p is given by the following

$$\frac{(K_{\text{equil}})_p}{(K_{\text{equil}})_0} = \exp\left[-\frac{p(V_2 - V_1)}{RT}\right] \tag{102–3}$$

where $V_2 - V_1$ is assumed to be constant with pressure. Using the measured ultrasonic absorption data and Eq. (100–6), x_2 can be calculated as a function of pressure.

The application of Eq. (100–5) to the data on sound absorption at atmospheric pressure evaluates only the magnitude of $V_2 - V_1$, not the sign of the difference. This is so because this quantity appears only as $(V_2 - V_1)^2$. Since x_2 is less than 0.5 at atmospheric pressure, it is the mole fraction of the higher free energy state. From the fact that x_2 decreases with pressure one must conclude that the higher energy state also has the higher volume.

---

[2] T. A. Litovitz and E. H. Carnevale, *J. Appl. Phys.* **26**, 816 (1955).

Using Eq. (102–3) one can calculate the value of x_2 at any higher pressure if the value at atmospheric pressure is known. Starting with the value obtained for x_2 from Eq. (100–6) for atmospheric pressure, and letting $V_2 - V_1 = 0.47\ V$, the value of x_2 at 1000 and 2000 kg/cm² is calculated with the help of Eqs. (102–2) and (102–3). Table 102–1 shows that the values of x_2 obtained from Eq. (102–3) and from absorption data are in good agreement up to the highest pressure measured. This result lends support to the two-state theory of sound absorption in water and to the value of $V_2 - V_1$.

TABLE 102–1

COMPARISON OF MOLE FRACTION OF OPEN PHASE WATER VS PRESSURE AT 0° C AS CALCULATED FROM SOUND ABSORPTION USING EQ. (100–6) WITH THE VALUES PREDICTED BY USE OF EQ. (102–3)

p (kg/cm²)	$\left(\frac{V_2 - V_1}{V}\right)^2 (1 - x_2)x_2{}^2$	$(1 - x_2)x_2{}^2$	x_2	
			Experimental*	Theoretical†
1	0.0132	0.060	0.29	0.29
1000	0.0089	0.037	0.22	0.223
2000	0.0049	0.020	0.155	0.165

* From Eq. (100–6).
† From Eq. (102–3).

Liebermann[3] has made an interesting calculation showing that the pressure dependence of the molar volume of water can be accounted for on the basis of a two-state theory. The molar volume of water can be written

$$V = V_1 + x_2(V_2 - V_1) \tag{102–4}$$

where x_2 is the mole fraction in the open packing.

Rewriting this one finds

$$x_2 = \frac{V - V_1}{V_2 - V_1}. \tag{102–5}$$

[3] L. N. Liebermann, *J. Acoust. Soc. Am.* 28, 1253 (1956).

The equilibrium constant, K_{equil}, can now be expressed in terms of the volume by combining Eqs. (102–2) and (102–5)

$$K_{\text{equil}} = \frac{V - V_1}{V_2 - V}. \tag{102–6}$$

On inserting this result in Eq. (102–3) an equation of state is obtained

$$\left[\frac{V_2 - V_p}{V_p - V_1}\right]\left[\frac{V_0 - V_1}{V_2 - V_0}\right] = \exp\left[\frac{p(V_2 - V_1)}{RT}\right]$$

where V_0 is the molar volume at zero pressure, which is for practical purposes the volume at atmospheric pressure, and V_p is the volume at some elevated pressure, p.

Liebermann obtains a good fit with the compressibility data for water at 0° C, by empirically letting $V_2 = 1.38\ V$ and $V_2 - V_1 = 0.54\ V$. This result for $V_2 - V_1$ is in reasonably good agreement with Hall's assumption of $0.47\ V$. Using these empirical values for V_2 and V_1 in Eq. (102–5), a value of 0.297 is found for x_2 at 0° C and atmospheric pressure. This should be compared with the value of 0.29 which is obtained by applying the two-state theory to the ultrasonic absorption data.

Substituting the values Liebermann obtains from pV data into Eq. (100–5) yields a value of 57.4×10^{-17} for α'/f^2 at 0° C. This is about 40% higher than the measured amount. The disagreement found here is due to the value of $(V_2 - V_1)/V$ chosen by Liebermann, which is about 15% higher than that chosen by Hall.

These results all indicate the usefulness of the two-state concept. However, there is some difficulty in correlating the concept that the open packing is the higher free energy state with other physical data available on the structure of water.

Bernal and Fowler[4] have assumed that as much as 70% of the ice-type or open packing exists near the freezing point. Ultrasonic data indicate that less than 30% of the open packing exists in this region. It must be mentioned that later X-ray data by Morgan and Warren[5] also dispute the hypothesis of Bernal and Fowler.

Eucken's theory[6] states that water consists of a distribution of polymers, mainly $(H_2O)_2$, $(H_2O)_4$, and $(H_2O)_8$. The $(H_2O)_8$ molecules would correspond

---

[4] J. D. Bernal and R. H. Fowler, *J. Chem. Phys.* **1**, 515 (1933).

[5] J. Morgan and B. F. Warren, *J. Chem. Phys.* **6**, 666 (1938).

[6] A. Eucken, *Nachr. Ges. Wiss. Göttingen, Math.-physik. Kl. I* p. 38 (1946).

to the open type of packing. Eucken has calculated that about 30% of the water molecules are in this form. This is in numerical agreement with the 28.5% found above.

103. The Associated Liquids (Other than Water) and the Glassy State

(a) *General*

As mentioned in Sec. 73 the associated liquids behave acoustically very much like water. In all of these liquids $\alpha/\alpha_{\text{classical}}$ lies between unity and three and is nearly independent of temperature; therefore α has a negative temperature coefficient of absorption. Furthermore, many of the physical properties of the associated liquids (including water) are quite similar. An example of this is the fact that the relationship between $\ln \eta$ and $1/T$ is not linear, as is the case in the nonassociated liquids. These similarities suggest that if a structural relaxation mechanism is the cause of the excess absorption in water, it is probably the cause in all associated liquids.

Unfortunately, none of these associated liquids (other than water) have a temperature of maximum density where one can prove directly that internal vibrational degrees of freedom are not responsible for the loss. Furthermore, because of the more complicated molecular structures involved, it is difficult to obtain from X-ray data the clear cut type of structural distributions found in water, which proved so useful as a basis for a two-state theory.

There is, however, a property characteristic of many of the associated liquids which is useful from an experimental standpoint. This is the fact that these liquids become highly viscous at low temperatures.

From the theories discussed in Secs. 84–86 one can conclude that the increase in viscosity indicates an increase in structural relaxation time. One can therefore hope that, by lowering the temperature, the relaxation time which, at room temperature, is often less than 10^{-9} sec, may be shifted into a region where it can be measured more easily.

(b) *The Distribution Function*

The radial distribution function describes the distribution of atoms as a function of distance from an arbitrary central atom. The distribution functions obtained from X-ray data for liquids are similar to those found for the crystalline phase and can be broadly interpreted by assuming that a liquid is made up of a large number of submicroscopic crystals which contain perhaps five to 50 or more molecules. These crystalline groups can be thought of as continually breaking up and reforming.

As the temperature or pressure of a liquid is changed, the degree of order changes. For example, the short range order in a liquid near the boiling point may extend for no more than three or four molecular diameters.[1] Also, atoms which should be in the immediate neighborhood may be missing. However, near the melting point this order may extend for a distance of tens of molecular diameters. Not only will the range of the order increase upon lowering the temperature, but the completeness of the short range order will also increase. That is to say, the number of "holes" in the short range order will decrease. Thus, at every pressure and temperature a degree of order which describes the geometric state is associated with a liquid.

Any variation of this degree of order requires energy to be added to or taken from the substance because of the change in potential energy associated with a change of structure. Thus, the specific heat of a liquid contains a structural contribution.[2]

An increase in temperature causes more "holes" to appear in the liquid; this effect contributes to the thermal expansion coefficient of a liquid. An increase in pressure causes a decrease in the number of "holes" in the liquid and increases the short range order which leads to a structural contribution to the compressibility.[2] (See Secs. 30 and 31.)

---

[1] In an ideal crystal, short range order and long range order exist. Consider an ideal crystal with a space-centered cubic lattice of lattice constant 3.5 Å. Then we know that in the neighborhood of each of the central atoms there will be eight atoms at distances $\sqrt{3}/2 \times 3.5$ Å and six atoms at distances 3.5 Å. This is what is meant by short range order. There will also be six atoms at distances of exactly 3500 Å. This would be called long range order. If, instead, one has a microcrystalline aggregate, made up of perfect crystal grains of size 1000 Å, but arbitrarily oriented, one would still find (except at the grain surfaces) the eight neighbors at $\sqrt{3}/2 \times 3.5$ Å and six at 3.5 Å, but one would *not* find six atoms at 3500 Å. If the size of the grains is much smaller, short range, but not long range order, would exist.

To take another example, in SiO_2 each silicon atom lies at the center of a tetrahedron formed by four oxygen atoms, and each silicon lies between two oxygen atoms. The tetrahedra have the same shape in crystalline quartz and quartz glass (short range order). In crystalline quartz, however, the orientation of subsequent tetrahedra is in a certain order (long range order) while in quartz glass irregularities occur in this respect, subsequent tetrahedra having orientations deviating from the expected ones.

[2] I. Prigogine and R. Defay, "Chemical Thermodynamics," Chapter 29. Longmans, Green, New York, 1954.

It is possible to supercool many liquids. This can be understood if one considers the two steps involved in the process of crystallization.[3–5] First nuclei must form, and then these nuclei must grow. Depending on the temperature, either of these steps may determine the rate of crystallization. A free energy barrier to crystallization exists, owing to the fact that the melting point of very small crystals is lower than that of large ones. Thus, in a supercooled liquid, crystals smaller than a certain size are unstable. To form a stable nucleus one must first form nuclei having a higher free energy than the same amount of liquid. The free energy barrier to crystal growth[6] is simply that which prevents the motion of a molecule from one lattice site to another, and is therefore similar to the barrier involved in viscous flow. Thus, as the viscosity in a liquid increases the rate of growth of nuclei decreases. As the temperature of a liquid is lowered the rate of formation of nuclei rises to a maximum. However, the rate of crystal growth diminishes, because of the increased time involved in the molecular motions necessary for growth. In many liquids the latter effect is predominant, and temperatures well below melting can be reached. In this case one may reach the so-called glassy state.

(c) *The Glassy State*

Tammann[7] and Simon[8] have pointed out that, as a liquid is cooled, the rate of any molecular diffusion process necessary to accomplish structural rearrangements becomes increasingly smaller.

It is essential in all that follows for τ to increase strongly with decreasing temperature, in first approximation like a reciprocal reaction rate.

We assume that, roughly, τ varies proportionally with η when the temperature is changed; for example, in Eq. (104–7‴), that K_2 varies much less with T. Therefore, there will be a temperature below which the relaxation

---

[3] J. Frenkel, "Kinetic Theory of Liquids." Oxford Univ. Press, London and New York, 1946.

[4] G. Tammann, "Kristallisieren und Schmelzen." Barth, Leipzig, 1903.

[5] M. Volmer, "Kinetik der Phasenbildung." Steinkopf, Leipzig, 1939.

[6] Whether there is a free energy barrier to crystal growth in monatomic liquids like silver or NaCl is very doubtful, although there is a time delay needed for removing the heat of crystallization by conduction. On the other hand, nonspherical molecules fit into the crystal lattice only in special orientations; accordingly, for these such a barrier exists.

[7] G. Tammann, "Der Glaszustand." Voss, Leipzig, 1933.

[8] F. Simon, *Ergeb. exakt. Naturw.* **9**, 222 (1930).

time necessary for any structural changes to occur will be much larger than the time scale of any normal experiment (of the order of 30 min). In this region the liquid is said to become a glass. Below these temperatures the degree of order will appear fixed and will not vary with either temperature or pressure during any reasonable length of time.

The supercooled liquid below this "glass transition" region is no longer in thermodynamic equilibrium.[9] The degree of order at a given temperature is representative of some higher liquid temperature. If the cooling could have been infinitely rapid, the structure at the beginning of cooling would have been frozen in. Actually, since the rate of adjustment is much more dependent on temperature than the structure itself, in most cases the structure frozen in for the glass state corresponds to the temperature at which the relaxation time is of the order of several minutes. However, by cooling more slowly, one can freeze in the structure belonging to a lower temperature, with longer relaxation time. Thus, the "effective" temperature of the structural degrees of freedom is fixed and higher than the temperature of the other degrees of freedom. Given a sufficient time this "effective" temperature will approach the actual temperature of the glass, but far below the glass transition temperature the relaxation times for structural rearrangement can rise to the order of magnitude of thousands of years.

Because of this inability of the structure to change (in a reasonable length of time) with either pressure or temperature at temperatures below the glass transition, the structural degrees of freedom are said to be "frozen out." Thus, the structural contributions to the specific heat, thermal expansion coefficient, and compressibility are absent in the glassy state. Instead, these quantities have magnitudes characteristic for a crystal. In fact, it is this decrease in C_p, β, and κ which allows one to determine the temperatures of the glass transition.

The differences in the values of C_p, β, and κ found in the liquid and the glass are that part of the specific heat, C_p'; that contribution to the expansion coefficient, β'; and that part of the compressibility, κ'; which have been frozen out. These relationships may be expressed as

$$C_{p\,\mathrm{liq}} = C_p' + C_{p\,\mathrm{glass}} \tag{103–1}$$

$$\beta_{\mathrm{liq}} = \beta' + \beta_{\mathrm{glass}} \tag{103–2}$$

$$\kappa_{\mathrm{liq}} = \kappa' + \kappa_{\mathrm{glass}} \tag{103–3}$$

---

[9] It follows that the liquid-glass transition is not a transition between two phases in a thermodynamic sense.

These equations demonstrate that by measuring these quantities in both the liquid and glass states, the structural contributions to the thermodynamic properties of a liquid can be obtained.

It might appear at first that the procedures and results of Secs. 28 and 29 would be useful in calculating the values of C', β', and κ' frozen out in a glass transition. This is generally not so, due to the fact that in all glasses thus far measured a distribution of relaxation times appears to exist. The results of Secs. 28 and 29 are specifically based on a two-state theory which implies a single relaxation time.

The kinetics of the stabilization of the structure of liquids at temperatures near the glass transition offer possibilities for the direct study of structural relaxation times. The experiments of Davies and Jones[10] are of interest in this regard.

In this work glycerol and glucose were studied. Glucose has a transition temperature at 30° C. Relaxation experiments were conducted, using the changes in volume following a rapid change in temperature as a measure of the approach to equilibrium. The changes in volume were observed by surrounding a cylindrical glucose specimen with kerosene within a glass dilatometer connected to a capillary. The temperature of the sample was changed in a time which was small compared with the relaxation time of the sample.

The resulting change in volume is made up of two parts. First, an instantaneous change in volume is noted which is due to a change in the intermolecular spacings. Secondly, a much slower, time-dependent change in volume can be observed which is due to a change in structure or degree of order in the liquid. This structural change needs time, since it involves the motion of molecules from one lattice site to another. The time involved here is the structural relaxation time at constant pressure and temperature.

From considerations of the thermodynamic theory of relaxation the relations between volume and time after a step function of temperature is expressed can be obtained. The derivation here is similar to that used in obtaining Eq. (31–20″) from Eq. (31–11). The result is

$$s = (T - T_0)\,[\tilde{\beta} + (\beta - \tilde{\beta})(1 - e^{-t/\tau_{T,p}})]. \tag{103–4}$$

Relaxation experiments of a type similar to the one above were carried out in glycerol by Davies and Jones. The glass transition temperature in glycerol lies at 180 °K, so that low-temperature calorimetric techniques were

[10] R. O. Davies and G. O. Jones, *Proc. Roy. Soc.* **A217**, 26 (1953).

used to study the thermal properties. Using a modified Nernst calorimeter it was possible to cool or heat the specimen rapidly from an equilibrium state and then, after isolating the calorimeter, to observe the change in temperature as the new equilibrium structure was obtained. The temperature changes are due to the energy given up or taken in by the structural degrees of freedom as they approach equilibrium. The relaxation time involved in this experiment is $\tau_{S,p}$.[11]

---

[11] In this experiment the enthalpy is constant. Thus

$$dH = \left(\frac{\partial H}{\partial T}\right)_{p,\xi} dT + \left(\frac{\partial H}{\partial \xi}\right)_{T,p} d\xi = \tilde{C}_p dT + d\xi \left(\frac{\partial H}{\partial \xi}\right)_{T,p} = 0.$$

Integrating this equation and combining with the rate equation

$$\frac{1}{\bar{\bar{k}}}\frac{d\xi}{dt} = \left(\frac{\partial A}{\partial T}\right)_{p,\xi}(T - T_1) + \left(\frac{\partial A}{\partial \xi}\right)_{p,T}(\xi - \xi_1)$$

where T_1 is the initial temperature and ξ_1 is the internal state of the system at T_1, one obtains

$$\frac{dT}{dt} = \bar{\bar{k}}\left\{\left(\frac{\partial A}{\partial \xi}\right)_{p,T} - \frac{1}{\tilde{C}_p}\left[\left(\frac{\partial H}{\partial \xi}\right)_{T,p}\left(\frac{\partial A}{\partial T}\right)_{\xi,p}\right]\right\}(T - T_2)$$

where T_2 is the final temperature. From Eq. (31–7) one finds that

$$\left(\frac{\partial H}{\partial \xi}\right)_{T,p} = T\left(\frac{\partial S}{\partial \xi}\right)_{T,p} - A$$

and from Eq. (31–25) that

$$\left(\frac{\partial A}{\partial T}\right)_{p,\xi} = \left(\frac{\partial S}{\partial \xi}\right)_{T,p}.$$

Therefore

$$\frac{1}{\tau_{p,H}} = -\bar{\bar{k}}\left\{\left(\frac{\partial A}{\partial \xi}\right)_{T,p} - \frac{1}{\tilde{C}_p}\left(\frac{\partial S}{\partial \xi}\right)_{T,p}\left[T\left(\frac{\partial S}{\partial \xi}\right)_{T,p} - A\right]\right\}.$$

Combining this with Eq. (31–10‴) one gets

$$\frac{1}{\tau_{p,H}} = -\bar{\bar{k}}\left\{\left(\frac{\partial A}{\partial \xi}\right)_{S,p} + \frac{A}{C_p}\left(\frac{\partial S}{\partial \xi}\right)_{T,p}\right\}.$$

Near equilibrium the second term can be neglected ($A \approx 0$) and

$$\frac{1}{\tau_{p,H}} \cong \frac{1}{\tau_{S,p}}.$$

Either of the above two experiments allows one to measure the structural relaxation time in a liquid by other than ultrasonic means. The volume viscosity η' can be calculated using Eq. (31–23), where

$$\eta' = \frac{\kappa_S - \tilde{\kappa}_S}{\kappa_S^2} \tau_{S,p}. \tag{31–23}$$

Values of κ_S can be obtained either from compressibility studies near the glass transition temperatures or from ultrasonic velocity measurements.

It must be repeated that the glass transition temperature depends on the time scale of the experiment. A normal static specific heat or compressibility experiment takes about 10 to 30 min to perform. Ultrasonic measurements allow one to shift the time scale of experimentation down to the microsecond region. In this way the ultrasonic measurement can, in a sense, cause a "pseudo-glass" transition at temperatures which are well above the normal glass transition. Thus, by using ultrasonics, one can study the glass or solidlike properties of a liquid, i.e., the properties of a liquid when the structural contributions to C_p and κ have been removed.

It has been mentioned previously that a glass behaves like a solid insofar as the values of C_p, β, and κ are concerned. It also does so in another sense: it exhibits shear rigidity;[12] i.e., it can support a shear stress without flowing. This, however, is true only insofar as the application of the stress lasts for a duration shorter than a "shear relaxation time" which is, as will be shown in Sec. 109, of the same order of magnitude as the structural relaxation time mentioned before. If the stress is applied for a much longer time, shear flow will occur with high viscosity.

Since there is no sharp transition between the glassy state and a highly viscous liquid state, one might expect glasses and liquids to behave in a similar fashion; that is, a liquid sheared at a high rate might be expected to exhibit a shear rigidity. The only difference between the glass and the liquid experiment is the time scale of the shearing process necessary to detect shear elasticity. Ultrasonic shear measurement serves as a tool for experimenting at high rates of shear in the liquid state, and should allow one to measure the shear modulus of liquids.

In one more respect a glass behaves like a solid: the ultrasonic absorption is low,[13] as in a crystal. If one takes an associated liquid of fairly high viscosity and cools it down, the viscosity increases. Since for such liquids

---

[12] W. P. Mason and H. J. McSkimin, *J. Acoust. Soc. Am.* **19**, 464 (1947).
[13] T. A. Litovitz, *J. Acoust Soc. Am.* **23**, 75 (1951).

α is, at constant frequency, proportional to η, α must also increase. If one has made the temperature so low—the viscosity so high— that the liquid has become glassy, the ultrasonic absorption is low, much lower than would correspond to the classical absorption belonging to this high viscosity. Therefore, the proportionality to η must break down and the absorption per centimeter or, since the frequency has been kept constant, the absorption per wave length must have a peak.

Such a peak can be explained if we assume that, as the temperature is lowered, the relaxation time τ increases, roughly proportional to the viscosity. At high temperatures, τ is much smaller than $1/\omega$ (ω being 2π times the frequency used). When the temperature decreases, τ approaches $1/\omega$ and the absorption increases with η; the peak is reached when $\tau \sim 1/\omega$; when the temperature decreases further, τ moves away from $1/\omega$ to still larger values, and the absorption decreases again.

104. Elastic Moduli of Liquids

It is often useful to express the results of ultrasonic propagation measurements in terms of the elastic moduli or impedances instead of compressibilities or compliances. This is the case, for example, in the study of longitudinal waves in viscous liquids, where both shear and compressional relaxation effects appear simultaneously and can be expressed in terms of moduli as a simple sum of effects. The relation between the moduli and the compliances is analogous to the relation between impedance and admittance concepts in electrical circuit theory. Depending on the type of problem one or the other may give the simplest mathematical expression.

In this section the stress-strain relationships and expressions for absorption and velocity which have been derived earlier in terms of compliances will be rewritten in terms of the elastic moduli.

As discussed in Sec. 1, the stress tensor P_{ij} is transformed into another stress tensor if the (Cartesian) coordinate system is rotated.

It is useful to separate the stress tensor into two parts, a compressional part

$$P = -p = \tfrac{1}{3}(P_{11} + P_{22} + P_{33}) \tag{104–1}$$

and a deviatory part

$$P_{jj}' = P_{jj} - P$$
$$P_{ij}' = P_{ij} \qquad i \neq j. \tag{104–1'}$$

If the coordinate system is rotated, the compressional part remains unchanged; by proper choice of axes, P' may be transformed into a pure shear stress, i.e., $P_{jj}' = 0$.

The strain tensor s_{ij} can be expressed by the components X_i of the displacement of a point in the elastic medium

$$s_{ij} = \tfrac{1}{2}\left(\frac{\partial X_i}{\partial x_j} + \frac{\partial X_j}{\partial x_i}\right). \tag{104–2}$$

The strain also may be divided into a compressional part, s (which is scalar and therefore independent of the coordinate system)

$$- s = s_{11} + s_{22} + s_{33} = \frac{\partial X_1}{\partial x} + \frac{\partial X_2}{\partial y} + \frac{\partial X_3}{\partial z} \tag{104–2′}$$

(s is the condensation introduced earlier) and a deviatory strain

$$s_{jj}' = s_{jj} + \tfrac{1}{3} s \qquad s_{ij}' = s_{ij} \qquad i \neq j \tag{104–3}$$

which, by the same rotation of the coordinate system as above, can be reduced to a pure shear strain, $s_{jj}' = 0$.

In a viscoelastic medium, one now relates the compressional part of stress and strain by the compressional modulus and the deviatoric part of stress and strain by the shear modulus. For the former one has

$$P - P_0 = - Ks \tag{104–4}$$

and for the latter

$$P_{ij}' = 2Gs_{ij}'. \tag{104–4′}$$

If the applied stress varies with the time one should turn to the general thermodynamic theory of relaxation (see Sec. 31) where the general stress-strain relationship for fluids has been derived and expressed in Eq. (31–19). This equation gives, as a generalization of Eq. (104–4) for pure compressional deformation, in terms of the elastic moduli

$$P - P_0 + \tau_v \frac{\partial P}{\partial t} = - \left(K_0 s + K_\infty \tau_v \frac{\partial s}{\partial t}\right) \tag{104–5}$$

where $P - P_0$, the mean normal stress, is equal to $\frac{1}{3}\sum_j P_{jj}$; and $-s$, the mean normal strain, is equal to $\sum_j s_{jj}$. Here, K_0 is the static compressional modulus; K_∞, the high frequency value of the compressional modulus; and τ_v, the structural relaxation time at constant volume. This is related to the constant pressure relaxation time, τ_p, by

$$\tau_p = \frac{K_\infty}{K_0}\,\tau_v. \tag{104–6}$$

Just as for compressibilities, K_0, K_∞, and τ_v have one set of values if the process is isothermal and another if it is adiabatic. The latter is, of course, pertinent when considering acoustic phenomena. The moduli are related to the compressibilities by the following equations

$$\kappa_0 = \frac{1}{K_0} \qquad \kappa_\infty = \frac{1}{K_\infty} \qquad \kappa' = \frac{K_\infty - K_0}{K_\infty K_0}. \tag{104–6'}$$

If one applies a sinusoidal pressure to the liquid, one obtains a complex modulus of compression

$$K = \frac{P}{-s} = K_0 + \frac{K_2\omega^2\tau_v^2}{1+\omega^2\tau_v^2} + i\,\frac{K_2\omega\tau_v}{1+\omega^2\tau_v^2} \tag{104–7}$$

where $K_2 = K_\infty - K_0$, and K_2 is the relaxational modulus.

This can be compared with the expression for the complex compressibility which, from Eqs. (31–21') and (104–6), can be written

$$\kappa = \kappa_0 - \kappa'\,\frac{\omega^2\tau_p^2}{1+\omega^2\tau_p^2} + i\kappa'\,\frac{\omega\tau_p}{1+\omega^2\tau_p^2}. \tag{104–7'}$$

Note that the expression for compressibility contains τ_p, not τ_v, as the relaxation time. This difference between the expressions for K and κ is analogous to that between the expressions for $\mathfrak{B}^2$ and $\mathfrak{B}^{-2}$, see Eqs. (13–5) and (12–4).

Rewriting Eq. (104–7) one gets

$$P = K(-s) = [\operatorname{Re} K + i\omega\eta'(\omega)](-s). \tag{104–7''}$$

Re K is the real part of the modulus K, and $\eta'(\omega) = K_2\tau_v/(1+\omega^2\tau_v^2)$. This expression for $\eta'(\omega)$ is equivalent to that given in Eq. (31–22'), where $\eta' = \rho\mathfrak{B}_0^2\,((\tau_p - \tau_v)/\tau_v)\cdot\tau_v/(1+\omega^2\tau_v^2)$. At low frequencies the volume viscosity, from Eq. (104–7), is

$$\eta' = K_2\tau_v. \tag{104–7'''}$$

Similar to (104–5), one has, for the deviatory stress, assuming the nonexistence of a static shear modulus

$$P_{ij}' + \tau_s \frac{\partial P_{ij}'}{\partial t} = 2G_\infty \tau_s \frac{\partial s_{ij}'}{\partial t} \tag{104–8}$$

where τ_s is the shear relaxation time and G_∞ is the high frequency shear rigidity. When considering a sinusoidal applied stress

$$\begin{aligned} P_{ij}' &= \frac{2G_\infty \tau_s i\omega}{1 + i\omega\tau_s} s_{ij}' \\ &= \frac{2G_\infty \tau_s i\omega}{1 + \omega^2\tau_s^2} s_{ij}' + \frac{2G_\infty \omega^2 \tau_s^2}{1 + \omega^2\tau_s^2} s_{ij}'. \end{aligned} \tag{104–9}$$

The last term is in phase with the deformation s', so that the liquid has a rigidity which in the limit $\omega\tau_s > 1$ is equal to G_∞.

The complex shear modulus can be written

$$G = \frac{P_{ij}'}{2s_{ij}'} = \frac{G_\infty \omega^2 \tau_s^2}{1 + \omega^2\tau_s^2} + i\omega \frac{G_\infty \tau_s}{1 + \omega^2\tau_s^2} \tag{104–9′}$$

with $G_\infty \tau_s/(1 + \omega^2\tau_s^2)$ the frequency dependent shear viscosity which at low frequencies reduces to $\eta_s = G_\infty \tau_s$.

The propagation of an acoustic wave in a viscoelastic medium where both K and G are different from zero must now be considered. We first assume a nonviscous medium with a real compressional modulus K and shear modulus G. Equation (2–3), which is based on Newton's second law and expresses the relationship between the stress components, P_{ij}, and the velocity components of a volume element, can be rewritten in terms of X_i, the coordinates of the displacement of a point in the elastic medium

$$\rho \frac{\partial^2 X_i}{\partial t^2} = \sum_{j=1}^{j=3} \frac{\partial P_{ij}}{\partial x_j} = \frac{\partial (P - P_0)}{\partial x_i} + \sum_{j=1}^{j=3} \frac{\partial P_{ij}'}{\partial x_j}. \tag{104–10}$$

Substituting into Eq. (104–10) the expressions (104–1), (104–2), and (104–4), one finds

$$\rho \frac{\partial^2 X_i}{\partial t^2} = \left(K - \frac{2}{3} G\right) \sum_{j=1}^{j=3} \frac{\partial^2 X_j}{\partial x_i \partial x_j} + G \sum_{j=1}^{j=1} \left(\frac{\partial^2 X_i}{\partial x_j^2} + \frac{\partial^2 X_j}{\partial x_i \partial x_j}\right). \tag{104–11}$$

This is the differential equation governing the propagation of waves in an elastic medium. For an acoustic (irrotational) wave propagated along the x_1 axis, Eq. (104–11) reduces to the familiar form

$$\rho \frac{\partial^2 X_1}{\partial t^2} = (K + 4/3\,G) \frac{\partial^2 X_1}{\partial {x_1}^2}\,. \tag{104–12}$$

Assuming that X_1 is proportional to $\exp\{i\omega(t - x/\mathfrak{B})\}$, one gets the result

$$\mathfrak{B}^2 = \frac{K + 4/3\,G}{\rho}\,. \tag{104–13}$$

Thus, an acoustic wave traveling in an elastic medium has a velocity which is determined by a linear combination of the compressional and shear moduli.

If viscous loss processes are present then the compressional and shear moduli are frequency dependent and complex. One can easily obtain an expression relating the moduli and α and $\mathfrak{B}$ for the case of a steady-state sinusoidal wave.[1–3] Assuming a sinusoidal wave, K and G as defined by Eqs. (104–7′) and (104–9′) can be inserted into Eq. (104–10) to give

$$-\rho\omega^2 X_i = (K - 2/3\,G) \sum_{j=1}^{3} \frac{\partial^2 X_j}{\partial x_i \partial x_j} + G \sum_{j=1}^{3} \left(\frac{\partial^2 X_i}{\partial {x_j}^2} + \frac{\partial^2 X_j}{\partial x_i \partial x_j} \right). \tag{104–14}$$

This is the differential equation governing the propagation of a sinusoidal wave through a viscoelastic medium. For the case of a longitudinal wave in the x_1-direction this reduces to

$$-\rho\omega^2 X_1 = (K + 4/3\,G) \frac{\partial^2 X_1}{\partial {x_1}^2}\,. \tag{104–15}$$

It is convenient here to define[4] a complex "longitudinal" modulus, M

$$M = M' + iM'' = K + 4/3\,G. \tag{104–16}$$

---

[1] T. Alfrey, Jr., "Mechanical Behavior of High Polymers," p. 540. Interscience, New York, 1948.

[2] R. S. Marvin, R. Aldrich, and H. S. Sack, *J. Appl. Phys.* **25**, 1213 (1954).

[3] For more general motions, the problem is much more complicated. See, for example, W. Noll, *J. Rational Mech. Anal.* **4**, 5 (1955).

[4] The notation $M = M' + iM''$ is customary, analogous to that for the similar expression for the dielectric constant, $\varepsilon = \varepsilon' + i\varepsilon''$. This use of primes is unfortunately quite different from, and has no direct connection with, our previous notation $C = \tilde{C} + C'$; $\kappa = \tilde{\kappa} + \kappa' = \kappa_\infty + \kappa'$.

Assuming that X_1 is proportional to $\exp\{i\omega t - (\alpha + i\omega/\mathfrak{B})x_1\}$, one obtains

$$-\omega^2\rho = M(\alpha + i\omega/\mathfrak{B})^2 \tag{104–17}$$

or

$$\rho = M\left(\frac{1}{\mathfrak{B}} - \frac{i\alpha}{\omega}\right)^2. \tag{104–17'}$$

This equation relates the experimental quantities α and $\mathfrak{B}$ with the frequency dependent moduli M' and M''. Separating Eq. (104–17′) into real and imaginary parts a pair of equations results, from which one can solve for M' and M'' in terms of α and $\mathfrak{B}$

$$M' = \rho\mathfrak{B}^2\left[\frac{1 - \left(\frac{\alpha\mathfrak{B}}{\omega}\right)^2}{\left[1 + \left(\frac{\alpha\mathfrak{B}}{\omega}\right)^2\right]^2}\right] \tag{104–18}$$

$$M'' = \frac{2\rho\mathfrak{B}^2\left(\frac{\alpha\mathfrak{B}}{\omega}\right)}{\left[1 + \left(\frac{\alpha\mathfrak{B}}{\omega}\right)^2\right]^2}. \tag{104–19}$$

When $(\alpha\mathfrak{B}/\omega)^2$ is small compared with 1 these equations can be simplified to

$$M' = \rho\mathfrak{B}^2 \tag{104–20}$$

$$M'' = \frac{2\rho\mathfrak{B}^3\alpha}{\omega}. \tag{104–21}$$

The approximation that $(\alpha\mathfrak{B}/\omega)^2 \ll 1$ is often made for acoustic propagation in nonviscous liquids. In the associated liquids, which can become quite viscous and exhibit high values for $(\alpha\mathfrak{B}/\omega)$, one might inquire whether, as Truesdell (Sec. 7) supposes, it is possible that this assumption is no longer reasonable. The maximum values of $(\alpha\mathfrak{B}/\omega)^2$ for those associated liquids where the maximum in $(\alpha\mathfrak{B}/\omega)$ has been measured, with a viscous polymer included for comparison, are as follows: glycerol, 0.017; hexanetriol, 0.012; n-propyl alcohol, 0.003, diphenyl pentachloride, 0.005; and polyisobutylene, 0.02. It can be seen that the maximum values of $(\alpha\mathfrak{B}/\omega)^2$ are of the order of 0.02 or less. Thus, for example, in glycerol use of the approximate equations above to calculate M' and M'' from the measured $\mathfrak{B}$ and α lead to a maximum error of less than 6% in M' and less than 4% in M''. These errors are of the order of magnitude of the experimental uncertainties in the measurement in this highly absorbing region. It therefore appears that the approximate equations, Eqs. (104–20) and (104–21), can be used for the calculation of sound propagation even in highly viscous liquids. This approximation is not valid for propagation of shear waves where $(\alpha\mathfrak{V}/\omega)^2$ is not small compared with unity.

Combining Eqs. (104–7), (104–9′), (104–16) and (104–21) yields an expression for the absorption per wave length

$$\alpha\lambda = \pi \left[\frac{\dfrac{K_2\omega\tau_v}{1+\omega^2\tau_v^2} + \dfrac{\frac{4}{3}G_\infty\omega\tau_s}{1+\omega^2\tau_s^2}}{K_0 + \dfrac{K_2\omega^2\tau_v^2}{1+\omega^2\tau_v^2} + \dfrac{\frac{4}{3}G_\infty\omega^2\tau_s^2}{1+\omega^2\tau_s^2}} \right]. \tag{104–22}$$

Inserting Eqs. (104–7), (104–9′) and (104–16) into Eq. (104–20), the velocity squared of a liquid may be written as

$$\mathfrak{V}^2 = \frac{1}{\rho}\left(K_0 + \frac{K_2\omega^2\tau_v^2}{1+\omega^2\tau_v^2} + \frac{\frac{4}{3}G_\infty\omega^2\tau_s^2}{1+\omega^2\tau_s^2} \right). \tag{104–23}$$

At low frequencies this expression becomes

$$\mathfrak{V}_0^2 = \frac{K_0}{\rho} \tag{104–24}$$

and at high frequencies it takes the form

$$\mathfrak{V}_\infty^2 = \frac{1}{\rho}\left(K_0 + K_2 + \tfrac{4}{3}G_\infty \right). \tag{104–25}$$

At low frequencies $\alpha\lambda$ has the form

$$\alpha\lambda = \frac{\pi\omega}{K_0}\left(K_2\tau_v + \tfrac{4}{3}G_\infty\tau_s \right) = \frac{\pi\omega}{K_0}\left(\eta' + \tfrac{4}{3}\eta \right) \tag{104–26}$$

which is equivalent to the result derived from the classical hydrodynamic equations when generalized to include a volume viscosity.

It is often convenient to characterize liquids according to the ratio of the total measured absorption to that calculated on the basis of shear viscosity considerations alone. From Eq. (104–26) one finds at low frequencies

$$\left(\frac{\alpha}{\alpha_{\text{class}}} \right)_0 = 1 + \tfrac{3}{4}\frac{K_2\tau_v}{G_\infty\tau_s}. \tag{104–27}$$

There are many indications when considering viscous flow processes that τ_v is close to being equal to τ_s, at least in some associated liquids. If this is the case, then the above equations can be simplified, and $\alpha\lambda$ can be written

$$\alpha\lambda = \pi \frac{(K_2 + \frac{4}{3} G_\infty)}{K_0} \sqrt{\frac{K_0}{K_0 + K_2 + \frac{4}{3} G_\infty}} \frac{\omega \tau_s'}{1 + \omega^2 \tau_s'^2} \tag{104–28}$$

where

$$\tau_s' = \sqrt{\frac{K_0 + K_2 + \frac{4}{3} G_\infty}{K_0}} \tau_s. \tag{104–28'}$$

The velocity squared becomes

$$\mathfrak{V}^2 = \frac{1}{\rho}\left(K_0 + \frac{(K_2 + \frac{4}{3} G_\infty)\omega^2 \tau_s^2}{1 + \omega^2 \tau_s^2}\right). \tag{104–29}$$

The ratio $\alpha/\alpha_{\text{class}}$ can be written as

$$\left(\frac{\alpha}{\alpha_{\text{class}}}\right)_0 = 1 + \frac{3K_2}{4G_\infty}. \tag{104–30}$$

In viscous liquids it is at times experimentally difficult to measure $\mathfrak{V}$ and α directly. In this case one can use reflection techniques to measure the impedance of the liquid. It is therefore useful to develop equations relating the elastic moduli and the impedance.

The complex longitudinal impedance, Z, of a liquid is defined by

$$Z = R + iX = \rho\left(\frac{1}{\mathfrak{V}} + \frac{\alpha}{i\omega}\right)^{-1} \tag{104–31}$$

where R is the real part of the impedance, or radiation resistance, while X is the imaginary part. Writing out Eq. (104–31) and multiplying numerator and denominator by the conjugate complex of the numerator, one has

$$R + iX = \rho\left[\frac{1}{\mathfrak{V}} - \frac{\alpha}{i\omega}\right]\left[\frac{1}{\mathfrak{V}^2} + \frac{\alpha^2}{\omega^2}\right]^{-1}$$

$$= \frac{\rho}{1 + (\alpha\mathfrak{V}/\omega)^2}\left[\mathfrak{V} + i\frac{\alpha\mathfrak{V}^2}{\omega}\right] \tag{104–32}$$

or

$$R = \rho \mathfrak{B} \left[1 + \left(\frac{\alpha\lambda}{2\pi} \right)^2 \right]^{-1} \tag{104–33}$$

$$X = \rho \frac{\alpha \mathfrak{B}^2}{\omega} \left[1 + \left(\frac{\alpha\lambda}{2\pi} \right)^2 \right]^{-1} = R \frac{\alpha\lambda}{2\pi}. \tag{104–34}$$

Combining Eqs. (104–17′) and (104–31), one has

$$Z^2 = \rho M = \rho(M' + iM''). \tag{104–35}$$

By equating the real and imaginary parts on both sides separately, one finds

$$R^2 = \frac{\rho M'}{2} \left\{ \left[1 + \left(\frac{M''}{M'} \right)^2 \right]^{1/2} + 1 \right\} \tag{104–36}$$

$$X^2 = \frac{\rho M'}{2} \left\{ \left[1 + \left(\frac{M''}{M'} \right)^2 \right]^{1/2} - 1 \right\}. \tag{104–37}$$

It should be noted that the discussion of the complex longitudinal modulus from Eq. (104–31) on is applicable to the complex shear modulus if one replaces α, $\mathfrak{B}$, M', and M'' by α_s, the absorption coefficient of a shear wave; $\mathfrak{B}_s$, the velocity of a shear wave; G'; and G'', respectively. (See Sec. 108.)

105. Distribution of Relaxation Times

The relaxation process occurring in viscous liquids may be pictured in the following way. After an applied stress the liquid will tend to rearrange its structure in such a manner as to relieve the stress. To accomplish this, molecular flow must occur. That is to say, a molecule must jump from one lattice site to another of lower free energy. These molecules must wait until they accumulate sufficient thermal energy to overcome the potential barriers restraining them. This wait or "time between jumps" leads to a relaxation time. The relaxation time for a given transition is related to the activation free energy or potential barrier ΔF, by the relation

$$\tau = \tau_0 e^{\Delta F/RT} \tag{105–1}$$

where τ_0 is the period of oscillation of the molecule in the potential well.

One can understand the existence of a distribution of relaxation times by the following. All molecules in the liquid do not have the same activation energy, since not all are in the same configuration. The potential energy of the individual molecule depends on the number of nearest neighbors and on its orientation with respect to neighboring molecules. The fact that the number of nearest neighbors is not the same for all molecules is in agreement with the generally accepted Kirkwood, Born, and Green theory of liquid structure, which is supported by X-ray data. (See Sec. 92.) Since a distribution of activation energies exists, it follows from Eq. (105–1) that a distribution of relaxation times exists. It is of interest that in all ultrasonic relaxation effects studied which do not involve structure a single relaxation time is sufficient to account for the data. It appears that relaxation effects which involve intramolecular vibrations have a single time or a discrete spectrum, and those involving structural effects involve a distribution of times. This distribution of structural relaxation times seems to be inherently related to the type of structure existing in liquids. The fundamental concept that the short-range order in a liquid is not complete, and that there is a statistical randomness in the "incompleteness" of this order, necessarily leads to the conclusion that the environment of a molecule in a liquid is not the same for all molecules and this, as mentioned above, leads to a distribution of times. This same randomness should therefore lead to a distribution of relaxation times whenever molecular environments in the liquid come into play. That this is so is borne out by the fact that dielectric relaxation effects in many liquids measured and nuclear magnetic relaxation effects in liquids also require a distribution of relaxation times.

It should be noted that when a distribution of times exists one cannot use a single "average" relaxation time but rather must sum up the contributions of the molecules, each having an individual relaxation time.

The complex modulus of elasticity, M, for a longitudinal wave can be related to a distribution of times as follows.

If a distribution of relaxation times exists for either the compressional or shear relaxation processes or for both, then Eq. (104–3) can be written

$$K(\omega) = K_0 + K_2 \int_0^\infty \frac{k(\tau_v) i\omega\tau_v}{1 + i\omega\tau_v} d\tau_v \qquad (105\text{–}2)$$

and

$$K_\infty - K_0 = K_2 \int_0^\infty k(\tau_v) d\tau_v \qquad (105\text{–}3)$$

where $K_2 k(\tau_v) d\tau_v$ is the contribution to the high frequency compressional modulus, K_∞, of those molecules having individual relaxation times in a range $d\tau$ near τ; $K(\omega)$ is the value of K at any frequency ω.

Separating into real and imaginary parts one has

$$K' = K_0 + K_2 \int_0^\infty \frac{k(\tau_v)\omega^2\tau_v^2 d\tau_v}{1+\omega^2\tau_v^2} \tag{105–4}$$

and

$$K'' = K_2 \int_0^\infty \frac{k(\tau_v)\omega\tau_v}{1+\omega^2\tau_v^2} d\tau_v. \tag{105–5}$$

For a distribution of relaxation times the volume viscosity, η', is given by the following expression

$$\eta' = K_2 \int_0^\infty \tau_v k(\tau_v) d\tau_v. \tag{105–6}$$

Equation (104–9) for the real and imaginary part of the shear modulus can be written in a like manner when a distribution of times exist

$$G' = G_\infty \int_0^\infty \frac{\omega^2\tau_s^2 g(\tau_s) d\tau_s}{1+\omega^2\tau_s^2} \tag{105–7}$$

$$G'' = G_\infty \int_0^\infty \frac{\omega\tau_s g(\tau_s) d\tau_s}{1+\omega^2\tau_s^2}. \tag{105–8}$$

$G_\infty g(\tau_s) d\tau_s$ is the contribution to the shear modulus by those molecules which have relaxation times in a range $d\tau_s$ near τ_s.

The shear viscosity under these conditions is given by the relation

$$\eta = G_\infty \int_0^\infty \tau_s g(\tau_s) d\tau_s. \tag{105–9}$$

Equations (105–6) and (105–9) are of interest since they allow one to relate dynamic measurements in the dispersion region to the "static" viscosities involved. Equation (105–9) shows that η/G_∞ gives the average value of the shear relaxation times. A similar statement holds for Eq. (105–6).

The selection of a distribution function is to some extent an arbitrary procedure, since more than one function will often fit experimental data equally well. However, the description of the data by means of these empirical functions does serve a useful purpose, since it allows one to relate different types of measurements on the same liquid, as pointed out above.[1]

106. Absorption and Dispersion Measurements in Glycerol

Fox, Litovitz, and their students,[1-3] motivated by the arguments at the end of Sec. **103**, have investigated the ultrasonic properties of glycerol, $C_3H_5(OH)_3$, a liquid highly viscous even at room temperature. Glycerol is extremely hygroscopic and its viscosity is very dependent upon the water content. For example, addition of 1% water reduces the viscosity by almost 20%. The glycerol measured by Fox and Litovitz contained 5% water. The sample measured by Piccirelli contained about 0.5% water. It can be seen from Table 106–1 that the viscosity of glycerol is strongly temperature dependent.

TABLE 106–1

Viscosity of glycerol (5% H_2O)[4] as a function of temperature

T (°C)	20	10	0	−10	−20	−30
η (poise)	5.5	12.5	34	120	480	2400

The absorption was measured by the pulse technique at 30 Mc. Some of the velocity data were measured by this method and others with the interferometer. Above 13° C the absorption of ultrasonic waves in the sample containing 5% water was found to exceed the classical value by a constant factor of about 2.07. For glycerol with only 0.5% water content $\alpha/\alpha_{\text{class}}$ was found to be 1.78. This result is in agreement with data on water and other associated liquids where $\alpha/\alpha_{\text{class}}$ was found to be independent of temperature. The results of Hunter[5] using an interferometer method to measure

---

[1] B. Gross, "Mathematical Structure of the Theories of Viscoelasticity." Hermann, Paris, 1953.

[1] T. A. Litovitz, *J. Acoust. Soc. Am.* **23**, 75 (1951).

[2] F. E. Fox and T. A. Litovitz, *Koninkl. Vlaam. Acad. Wetenschap., Letter. en Schone Kunsten Belgie, Colloq. Ultrasonore Trillingen, Brussels*, 1951, p. 38.

[3] R. Piccirelli and T. A. Litovitz, *J. Acoust. Soc. Am.* **29**, 1009 (1957).

[4] D. Sette and T. A. Litovitz, *J. Chem. Phys.* **21**, 17 (1953).

[5] J. L. Hunter, *J. Acoust. Soc. Am.* **13**, 33 (1941).

absorption and of Moen[6] using a reverberation technique indicated that α/α_{class} is less than 2.07. However, both of these investigators used less accurate methods of measurement and neglected to measure the viscosity of their samples. Considering the dependence of η on water content as discussed above, the conclusions of Hunter and Moen as to the value of α/α_{class} are in doubt.

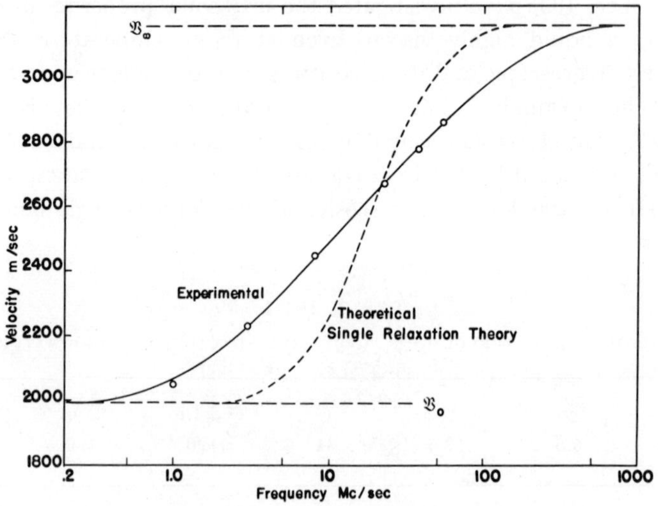

FIG. 106–1. Plot of ultrasonic velocity vs frequency in glycerol at a temperature of − 14° C and a viscosity of 616 poise. The dashed line is calculated using Eq. (104–29).

The fact that the observed absorption exceeds the classical value indicates that both shear and compressional viscous processes are important in glycerol. In Fig. 106–1 the velocity vs frequency in a sample of 99.5% pure glycerol[3] is plotted at a temperature of − 14° C and a viscosity of 616 poise. Over the frequency range up to 55 Mc the velocity has increased from a value of $\mathfrak{V}_0 = 2000$ m/sec to a value of 2860 m/sec at 55 Mc. The values of $\mathfrak{V}_0$ and $\mathfrak{V}_\infty$ shown in Fig. 106–1 are estimated by extrapolating velocity data down from high temperatures and up from lower temperatures, respectively.

In Fig. 106–2 the results of absorption measurements at 31 Mc made over a large temperature range[1] on a sample of glycerol containing 5% water are shown. The ordinate in Fig. 106–2 is $\alpha\lambda_0$ (which is equal to $\alpha\mathfrak{V}_0/f$)

---

[6] C. J. Moen, *J. Acoust. Soc. Am.* **23**, 62 (1951).

and the abscissa is $\omega\tau_L$ (ω here is equal to $2\pi \times 31$ Mc). The τ_L is defined by Eq. (7—9′) and equals $(\frac{4}{3}\eta + \eta')/\rho\mathfrak{B}_0^2$, which for glycerol is calculated using the fact that $\alpha/\alpha_{\text{class}} = (\frac{4}{3}\eta + \eta')/\frac{4}{3}\eta = 2.07$. When glycerol is cooled down to a region where the viscosity becomes of the order of 100 poise ($\omega\tau_L = 1.0$) a peak is noted in $\alpha\lambda_0$. At still lower temperatures the absorption falls to considerably lower than classical values.

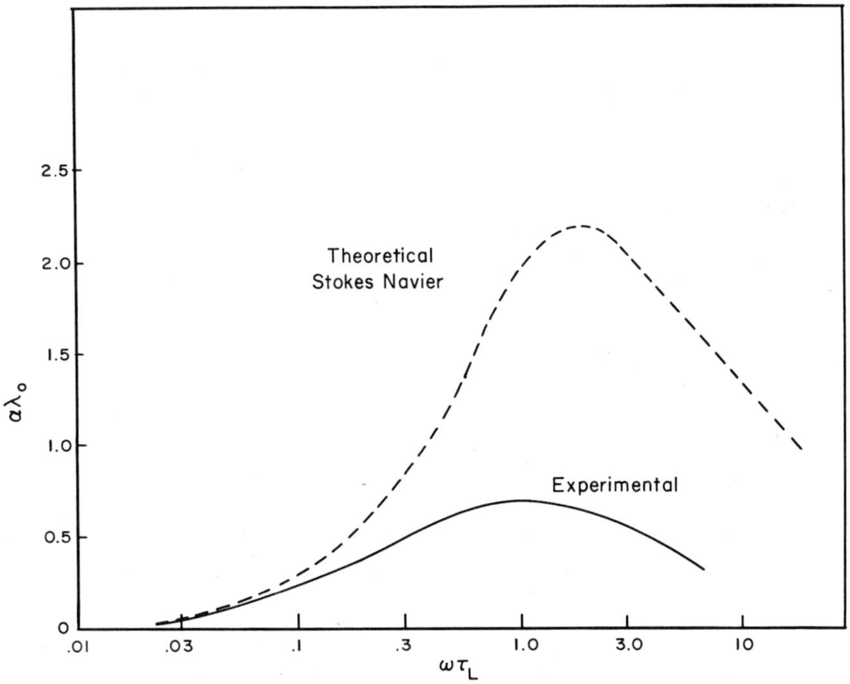

FIG. 106–2. Absorption at 31 Mc in glycerol as a function of $\omega\tau_L$. Sample contains 5% water. τ_L is defined by Eq. (7–9′).

The results of the velocity measurements at 30 Mc on glycerol of the same purity as above are plotted in Fig. 106–3 against the same abscissa as in Fig. 106–2. They show, at − 60° C, an increase in velocity of 75% over the 20° C value.

There are two theories one may apply in explaining these results: (1) the exact solution of the Stokes-Navier relations using frequency independent values of η and η' may be considered, see Sec. 7; or (2) the relaxation theory discussed in Sec. 104 can be applied.

In Figs. 106–2 and 106–3 the predictions of the Stokes-Navier equation are compared with the results (heat conduction has been neglected here). It can be seen that the velocity data are in complete disagreement with the assumption of a frequency-independent viscosity. The experimental absorption data exhibit a peak in $\alpha\lambda_0$ at $\omega\tau_L = 1.0$, not too great a disagreement with the Stokes-Navier theory, which predicts that $(\alpha\lambda_0)_{\max}$ occurs at $\omega\tau_L = \sqrt{3}$. On the other hand, the height of the peak is too small by a marked amount.

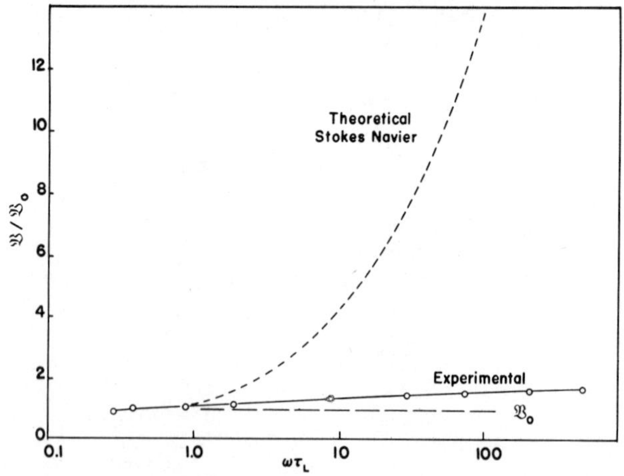

FIG. 106–3. Velocity measurements in glycerol (5% water) plotted as a function of $\omega\tau_L$.

To explain these results it must be assumed that a relaxation process is occurring; that is to say, a frequency-dependent viscosity must be assumed. From the absorption and velocity data it can be seen that both the shear and compressional viscosity have relaxed at the lowest temperatures measured. If, for example, the shear viscosity had not relaxed, the value of α could not have fallen at any temperature below $\alpha_{class} = 8\pi^2 f^2 \eta/(3\rho\mathfrak{V}^3)$. At $-20°$ C η equals 480 poise, ρ is 1.26 g/cm^3, and $\mathfrak{V}$ at 30 Mc equals 2650 m/sec; α_{class} at this temperature and frequency is about 450 cm^{-1}. The measured value is about 60 cm^{-1}. Thus, the shear viscosity must have relaxed also.

Comparison of Eqs. (104–22) and (104–23) with the data on glycerol shows that the data are not completely fitted by the assumption that $\tau_s = \tau_v$ or even by the more general assumption of a single relaxation time for the shear process and some other single time for the compressional viscous processes. That the data do not follow a single relaxation theory is best shown by the measurement of velocity vs frequency at a constant temperature. These data are plotted in Fig. 106–1. It can be seen that the experimental dispersion covers over two frequency decades, compared with about one decade for the single relaxation process.

It appears that a distribution of relaxation times is necessary to fit the results. The data on the shear modulus of glycerol discussed in Sec. 108 below demonstrate further that both the compressional and shear viscosity must have a distribution of relaxation times in order to account for the results.

107. Absorption and Dispersion in n-Propyl Alcohol

Data on absorption and velocity in *n*-propyl alcohol, C_3H_7OH, are of interest, owing to the large frequency and viscosity range covered. Measurements were made by Lyon and Litovitz[1] over a temperature range from 2° C to − 155° C. As can be seen in Table 107–1, the viscosity varies by a factor of about 10^8 over this temperature range.

TABLE 107–1

VISCOSITY AS A FUNCTION OF TEMPERATURE IN *n*-PROPYL ALCOHOL

T (°C)	2	−30	−90	−120	−140	−155
η (poise)	3.52×10^{-2}	9.7×10^{-2}	2.07	68.2	5.5×10^{3}	2.3×10^{6}

The absorption and velocity were measured, using pulse techniques over a frequency range of from 3.0 to 82.5 Mc. The experimental value of α at these frequencies is plotted in Fig. 107–1, as a function of the shear viscosity. It is often convenient to plot data in viscous liquids as functions of shear viscosity, since the relaxation times in these liquids are roughly proportional to η. It can be seen that there is a maximum in α which shifts to higher viscosities as the frequency decreases. Measurements of absorption in the nondispersion region proved that the ratio of $\alpha/\alpha_{\text{class}}$ is independent of temperature and has a value of 1.77. This is shown in Table 107–2.

There is a measurable dispersion in the region from − 70° C to − 155° C (above about 1.0 poise). The percentage dispersion defined as $(\mathfrak{V}_\infty - \mathfrak{V}_0)/\mathfrak{V}_0$ is about 16%, as compared with 60% for glycerol at comparable viscosities.

[1] T. Lyon and T. A. Litovitz, *J. Appl. Phys.* **27**, 179 (1956).

The absorption and dispersion data can not be represented by the exact solution of the Stokes-Navier equation with frequency-independent η and η', just as this proved impossible in glycerol.

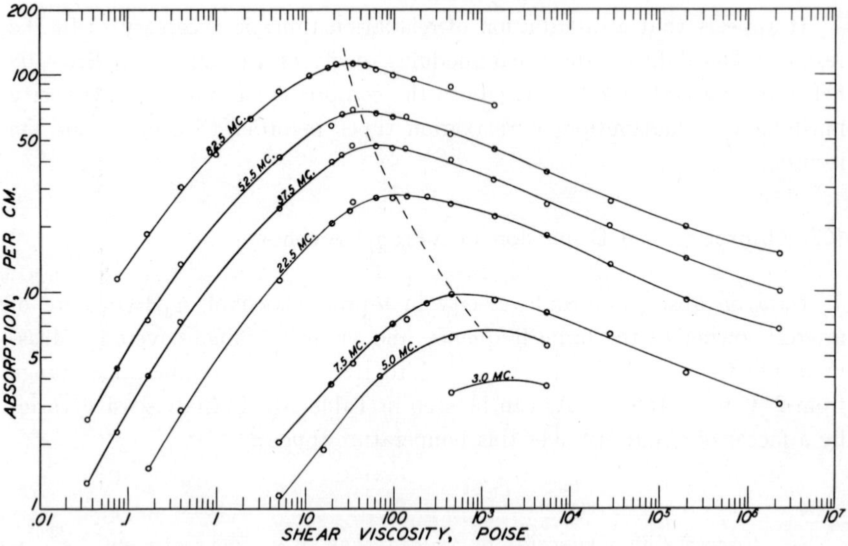

FIG. 107–1. Absorption coefficient plotted as a function of the shear viscosity in n-propyl alcohol.

TABLE 107–2

ABSORPTION IN n-PROPYL ALCOHOL AS A FUNCTION OF TEMPERATURE IN THE NONDISPERSION REGION (MEASUREMENTS AT 37.5 Mc)

T (°C)	η (poise)	$\mathfrak{B}$ (m/sec)	$(\alpha/f^2)_{class}$ ($\times 10^{17}$ cm^{-1} sec^2)	$(\alpha/f^2)_{obs}$ ($\times 10^{17}$ cm^{-1} sec^2)	α/α_{class}
2.0	3.5×10^{-2}	1285	53.4	94	1.77
−23.0	7.69×10^{-2}	1380	91.7	162	1.77

While the general character of the curves is that predicted by relaxation theory, the exact shape cannot be reproduced with a single relaxation time. Instead, a distribution must be used. The particular distribution which gives a fairly good representation is one which assumes that the free energies of activation $F^* - F_1$ are spread over a range from $(F^* - F_1) = (F^* - F_1)_0$ to $(F^* - F_1)_0 + 5kT$. A relaxation time $\tau_1' = A \exp (F^* - F_1)_0/kT$ corresponds to the lower value; the relaxation time $\tau_2' = \tau_1' e^5 = 150\tau_1'$ to the other limit. A relaxation time

$$\tau' = \tau_1' \exp \frac{\delta F}{kT}. \tag{107-1}$$

corresponds to the intermediate value, $(F^* - F_1)_0 + \delta F_1$.

It is then assumed that the fraction of systems having a free energy of activation $(F^* - F_1)_0 + \delta F$ is given by

$$\frac{1}{5kT}\, d\delta F^* = \frac{1}{5}\frac{d\tau'}{\tau'} \tag{107-2}$$

from τ_1' to $e^5\tau_1'$.

Lyon and Litovitz first assumed that the same distribution function applied to both the shear and compressional relaxation processes. However, it was evident from the results that two distinct relaxation processes were occurring. For lack of better knowledge the relaxation occurring at the lower frequencies and viscosities was assumed to be the shear process and to have a single relaxation time τ_s.

Under this assumption

$$M = K_0 + \frac{K_2}{5}\int_{\tau_1'}^{\tau_2'} \frac{i\omega\tau'}{1 + i\omega\tau'}\frac{d\tau'}{\tau'} + \frac{4}{3}\frac{G_\infty i\omega\tau_s}{1 + i\omega\tau_s} \tag{107-3}$$

$$M' = K_0 + \frac{K_2}{5}\int_{\tau_1'}^{\tau_2'} \frac{\omega^2\tau'^2}{1 + \omega^2\tau'^2}\frac{d\tau'}{\tau'} + \frac{4}{3}\frac{G_\infty\omega^2\tau_s}{1 + \omega^2\tau_s^2} \tag{107-4}$$

$$M'' = \frac{K_2}{5}\int_{\tau_1'}^{\tau_2'} \frac{\omega\tau'}{1 + \omega^2\tau'^2}\frac{d\tau'}{\tau'} + \frac{4}{3}\frac{G_\infty\omega\tau_s}{1 + \omega^2\tau_s^2}. \tag{107-4'}$$

The value of τ_s at one temperature was obtained from the "hook" in the curve of $(M'')_{\text{exp}}$ vs $\omega\tau_1'$. At this hook, occurring at values of $\omega\tau_1'$ below the maximum in M'', it was assumed that $\omega\tau_s = 1$. G_∞ is then calculated, using the relation $G_\infty = \eta/\tau_s$. In this manner a value of $G_\infty = 2 \times 10^8$ dynes/cm^2 is obtained. The value of τ_s found is 8.4 times larger than τ_2'.

Equations (107–4) and (107–4′) can be integrated, giving

$$M' - K_0 = \frac{K_2}{10} \ln \frac{1 + \omega^2\tau_1'^2 e^{10}}{1 + \omega^2\tau_1'^2} + \frac{4}{3} \frac{G_\infty \omega^2 \tau_s^2}{1 + \omega^2\tau_s^2} \tag{107–5}$$

$$M'' = \frac{K_2}{5} (\tan^{-1} \omega\tau_1' e^5 - \tan^{-1} \omega\tau_1') + \frac{4}{3} \frac{G_\infty \omega\tau_s}{1 + \omega^2\tau_s^2}. \tag{107–6}$$

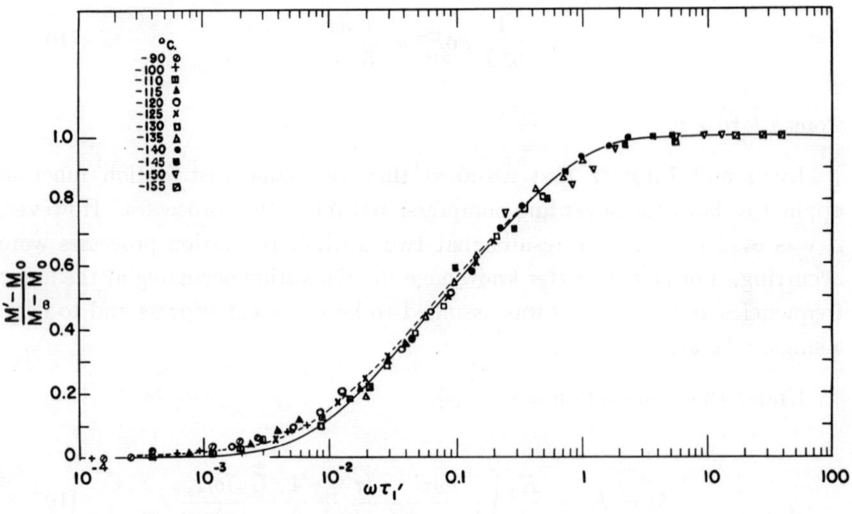

FIG. 107–2. Reduced plot of the real part of the relaxational longitudinal modulus plotted as a function $\omega\tau_1'$. The different temperatures are indicated by different symbols. The dashed line is calculated using Eq. (107–5). The solid line shows the effect of assuming for τ_s the same distribution as for τ'.

In Fig. 107–2 the ordinate is

$$\frac{M' - M_0}{M_\infty - M_0} = \frac{K' - K_0 + \frac{4}{3} G'}{M_\infty - M_0} = \frac{\mathfrak{V}^2 - \mathfrak{V}_0^2}{\mathfrak{V}_\infty^2 - \mathfrak{V}_0^2}$$

These quantities are functions of the temperatures only through $\omega\tau_1'$.

The dashed line represents Eq. (107–5), while the solid line shows the effect of assuming for τ_s the same distribution as for τ'. Similarly, Fig. 107–3 has as ordinate

$$\frac{M''}{M_\infty - M_0} = \frac{M''}{K_2 + \frac{4}{3}G_\infty} = \frac{2\alpha\mathfrak{V}}{\omega(\mathfrak{V}_\infty{}^2 - \mathfrak{V}_0{}^2)} .$$

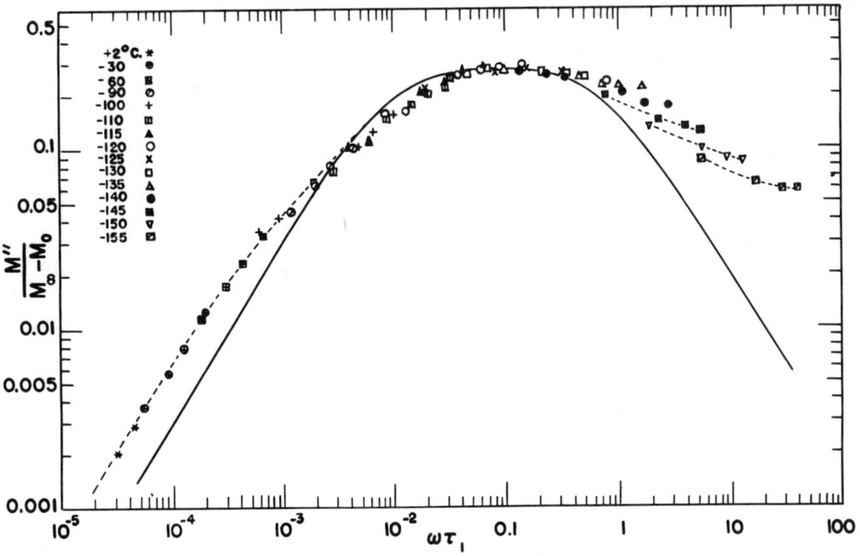

FIG. 107–3. Reduced plot of the imaginary part of the longitudinal modulus for *n*-propyl alcohol, plotted as a function of $\omega\tau_1'$. The dashed line is obtained using Eq. (107–6). The solid line is obtained assuming for τ_s the same distribution as for τ'.

The dashed line corresponds to Eq. (107–6), while the solid line again shows the effect of assuming that τ_s has the same distribution as τ'. It can be seen that the dashed lines give a good fit to both absorption and velocity data, except for absorption data at high frequencies. The value of G_∞ assumed here appears quite low in comparison with the results found for other associated liquids, although in polymeric liquids values of G_∞ as low as 10^8 dynes/cm^2 and even lower exist.

108. Transversal or Shear Waves in Liquids

(a) Classical Theory

It is often said that, in liquids, pure shear waves do not exist because there is no restoring force. That is not, however, correct.

In a shear wave, there is no density change

$$-\rho_0 \frac{\partial s}{\partial t} = \operatorname{div} \vec{w} = 0 \tag{108–1}$$

or, in two-dimensional motion

$$\frac{\partial w_1}{\partial x} + \frac{\partial w_2}{\partial y} = 0. \tag{108–2}$$

Taking the direction of propagation as the x-direction and the direction of motion as the y-direction, $w_1 = 0$, the equation of motion is

$$\rho_0 \frac{\partial w_2}{\partial t} = \frac{\partial}{\partial x} P_{yx} = \frac{\partial}{\partial x} \eta \frac{\partial w_2}{\partial x} = \eta \frac{\partial^2 w_2}{\partial x^2}. \tag{108–3}$$

Putting everything proportional to

$$\exp\left[i\omega t - i\omega x\left(\frac{1}{\mathfrak{V}_s} + \frac{\alpha}{i\omega}\right)\right]$$

one has

$$\rho_0 i\omega = -\eta\omega^2 \left[\frac{1}{\mathfrak{V}_s} + \frac{\alpha}{i\omega}\right]^2 \tag{108–4}$$

$$-i\frac{\rho_0}{\eta\omega} = \frac{1}{\mathfrak{V}_s{}^2} - \frac{\alpha^2}{\omega^2} + \frac{2\alpha}{i\mathfrak{V}_s\omega} \tag{108–4$'$}$$

or

$$\frac{\alpha}{\omega} = \frac{1}{\mathfrak{V}_s} \qquad \frac{\alpha\mathfrak{V}_s}{\omega} = \frac{\alpha\lambda}{2\pi} = 1$$

$$\frac{\rho_0}{\eta\omega} = \frac{2\alpha}{\omega\mathfrak{V}_s} = \frac{2}{\mathfrak{V}_s{}^2}$$

$$\mathfrak{V}_s = \sqrt{\frac{2\eta\omega}{\rho_0}} \qquad \alpha = \sqrt{\frac{\rho_0\omega}{2\eta}}$$

so that within a wave length the amplitude decreases by the factor $\exp(-2\pi) \sim 1/535$. The "radiation admittance" of the fluid is

$$\frac{1}{\rho_0}\left(\frac{1}{\mathfrak{V}_s} + \frac{\alpha}{i\omega}\right) = \frac{1}{\sqrt{2\eta\rho_0\omega}}(1 - i) \tag{108–5}$$

and the "radiation impedance" is

$$\tfrac{1}{2}\sqrt{2\eta\rho_0\omega}\,(1 + i) \tag{108–6}$$

i.e., the real part is equal to the imaginary part. These waves behave very much like electromagnetic waves penetrating a metal. Here, too, resistance, analogous to η, exists but no restoring force. In analogy

$$\frac{1}{\alpha} = \sqrt{\frac{2\eta}{\rho_0\omega}}$$

is the "skin depth". For water at 1 Mc, this is 5.6×10^{-5} cm.

(*b*) *Relaxation Theory*

If a liquid exhibits a shear modulus of rigidity, the differential equation governing the propagation of shear waves is obtained from Eq. (104–11) by setting equal to zero those terms contributing to a dilatation. Thus

$$\rho\frac{\partial w_i}{\partial t} = \rho\frac{\partial^2 X_i}{\partial t^2} = G\sum_{k=1}^{3}\frac{\partial^2 X_i}{\partial x_k}. \tag{108–7}$$

Taking the direction of propagation as the x-direction, and the direction of motion as the y-direction, the equation of motion becomes

$$\rho\frac{\partial^2 X_2}{\partial t} = G\frac{\partial^2 X_2}{\partial x^2} \tag{108–8}$$

where X_2 is the y-displacement of a volume element.

Assuming that X_2 is proportional to $\exp\{i\omega(t - x/\mathfrak{V}_s)\}$, one gets

$$\mathfrak{V}_s{}^2 = \frac{G}{\rho} \tag{108–9}$$

where $\mathfrak{V}_s$ is the velocity of the shear wave in an elastic medium.

If viscous losses are present, as is the case in liquids, then the shear modulus is complex and frequency dependent. An expression relating the shear modulus and the absorption and velocity of a shear wave can be obtained for the case of a steady-state sinusoidal wave. Assuming a sinusoidal shear wave one gets, from Eqs. (104–14) and (108–8)

$$-\rho\omega^2 X_2 = G\frac{\partial^2 X_2}{\partial x^2} \tag{108–10}$$

where G is the complex shear modulus.

Putting everything proportional to $\exp\,[i\omega t - (\alpha + i\omega/\mathfrak{V}_s)\,x]$ one has

$$\rho = G\left(\frac{1}{\mathfrak{V}_s} + \frac{\alpha}{i\omega}\right)^2. \tag{108–11}$$

Comparing Eq. (108–11) with Eq. (108–4), one sees that $\lim\limits_{\omega=0} G = i\omega\eta$.

Due to the high attenuation, α and $\mathfrak{V}_s$ cannot be directly measured in a liquid. However, the real and imaginary parts of the complex shear impedance can be calculated from measurement of the reflection coefficient of a shear wave when reflected from a solid-liquid boundary.[1]

The complex shear impedance, Z_s, of a liquid is given by, see Eq. (104–31)

$$Z_s = R_s + iX_s = \rho\left(\frac{1}{\mathfrak{V}_s} + \frac{\alpha}{i\omega}\right)^{-1} \tag{108–12}$$

where R_s is the real part and X_s the imaginary part. Combining Eqs. (108–11) and (108–12) one has, see Eq. (104–35)

$$Z_s^2 = \rho G = \rho[G' + iG'']. \tag{108–13}$$

By equating real and imaginary parts on both sides and solving, one finds

$$R_s^2 = \rho\frac{G'}{2}\{[1 + (G''/G')^2]^{1/2} + 1\} \tag{108–14}$$

$$X_s^2 = \rho\frac{G'}{2}\{[1 + (G''/G')^2]^{1/2} - 1\}. \tag{108–15}$$

Assuming single relaxation time theory, the measurable quantities, X_s and R_s, can be related to the parameters of the liquid by substituting

[1] W. P. Mason, W. O. Baker, H. J. McSkimin, and J. H. Heiss, *Phys. Rev.* **75**, 936 (1949).

the relaxation expression for G' and G'', as obtained from Eq. (104–9′), into Eqs. (108–14) and (108–15). Thus

$$\frac{R_s^2}{\rho} = \frac{G_\infty \omega^2 \tau_s^2}{2(1+\omega^2\tau_s^2)} \left\{ \left[1 + \frac{1}{\omega^2 \tau_s^2} \right]^{1/2} + 1 \right\} \tag{108–16}$$

$$\frac{X_s^2}{\rho} = \frac{G_\infty \omega^2 \tau_s^2}{2(1+\omega^2\tau_s^2)} \left\{ \left[1 + \frac{1}{\omega^2 \tau_s^2} \right]^{1/2} - 1 \right\}. \tag{108–17}$$

When $\omega\tau_s \ll 1$ Eqs. (108–16) and (108–17) become

$$R_s = \left(\frac{\rho G_\infty \omega \tau_s}{2} \right)^{1/2} = \left(\frac{\omega \eta \rho}{2} \right)^{1/2} \tag{108–18}$$

$$X_s = \left(\frac{\rho G_\infty \omega \tau_s}{2} \right)^{1/2} = \left(\frac{\omega \eta \rho}{2} \right)^{1/2}. \tag{108–19}$$

This result is identical with the prediction of classical theory, Eq. (108–6). However, at high frequencies or high viscosities (since τ_s is proportional to η) $\omega\tau_s \gg 1$. Therefore, Eqs. (108–16) and (108–17) become

$$R_s = (\rho G_\infty)^{1/2} \tag{108–20}$$

$$X_s = 0. \tag{108–21}$$

Relaxation theory predicts therefore that R_s approaches a limiting value as $\omega\eta$ becomes large. Classical theory predicts that R_s continues to increase indefinitely as the square root of $\omega\eta$. Also from relaxation theory, Eq. (108–20), we see that for $\omega\tau_s \gg 1$, $R_s^2/\rho = G_\infty$; thus, measurements of R_s in this frequency region allow a direct calculation of the limiting shear modulus of the liquid.

Furthermore, according to relaxation theory the imaginary part of the shear impedance approaches zero for large values of $\omega\eta$. The absorption of shear waves in the liquid will approach $\rho^{1/2}(G_\infty)^{-1/2}(2\tau_s)^{-1}$ under these conditions, see Eq. (104–34). The liquid behaves as a solid, exhibiting both compressional and shear moduli.

The most extensive measurements of ultrasonic shear relaxation have been made in the study of the mechanical properties of polymers. The work of Mason[1] and his co-workers at the Bell Telephone Laboratories has been outstanding in this respect. They have shown conclusively that in polymers shear relaxation effects occur and that at least two types of shear elasticities exist, each associated with its own set of relaxation times.

In ordinary liquids the data are much less extensive. Piccirelli[2] has studied ultrasonic shear relaxation in supercooled glycerol. In Fig. 108–1 the value of R_s^2/ρ (or $\rho\mathfrak{B}_s^2$) for glycerol is plotted as a function of temperature at various frequencies.[3] It can be seen that the values of R_s^2/ρ do not follow the behavior predicted by classical theory, Eq. (108–6). At low temperatures (high viscosities) the value of R_s^2/ρ becomes independent of frequency. This result is predicted by the relaxation theory.

If a relaxation theory is applicable it is possible to construct "reduced functions" or "reduced variables" from the values of R_s^2/ρ. By plotting reduced functions, data taken at different frequencies and temperatures can be reduced to one curve. In order for a function of the parameters of a liquid to be a reduced function it is necessary and sufficient for it to be a

---

[2] R. Piccirelli, Ph. D. Dissertation, Catholic University of America, Washington, D. C., 1956; R. Piccirelli and T. A. Litovitz, *J. Acoust. Soc. Am.* **29**, 1009 (1957).

[3] The value of R_s^2/ρ can be experimentally obtained by a method developed by Mason and his co-workers.[1] Radio-frequency ultrasonic pulses of shear waves are generated at one end of a fused quartz rod with plane parallel ends. Because of impedance mismatch at the rod ends there is set up in the rod a train of echoes which have an exponentially decaying envelope. By measuring the amplitude of these echoes the average value of the loss per echo is determined under two conditions: (1) when the end of the rod opposite the transducer is exposed to air (quartz-air interface); and (2) when this end of the rod has a liquid covering it (quartz-liquid interface). The difference in the value of the loss per echo, δDb, in these two measurements is related to the absolute magnitude of the reflection coefficient, r, by the following

$$r = \exp\left[-\frac{\delta Db}{20 \log_{10} e}\right].$$

The relation between r and the impedance of the quartz and liquid is given by

$$re^{i\theta} = \frac{Z_Q - Z_s}{Z_Q + Z_s}$$

where Z_Q is the shear impedance of quartz and ϑ is the phase angle of the reflection coefficient. For most liquids this expression can be rewritten

$$R_s^2 = \frac{Z_Q^2}{\rho}\left(\frac{1-r}{1+r}\right)$$

since ϑ is only a few degrees.

Piccirelli has shown this relation to hold for glycerol within 2%. By use of this relation, measurements of the absolute magnitude of the reflection coefficient give the real part of the shear impedance. Of course, if the transducer generates longitudinal waves the above method yields the longitudinal impedance of a liquid.

function of temperature only through the product $\omega\tau$, where τ is some relaxation time.

Such a reduced function is, for example

$$S = \frac{R_s^2}{\rho G_\infty}. \tag{108–22}$$

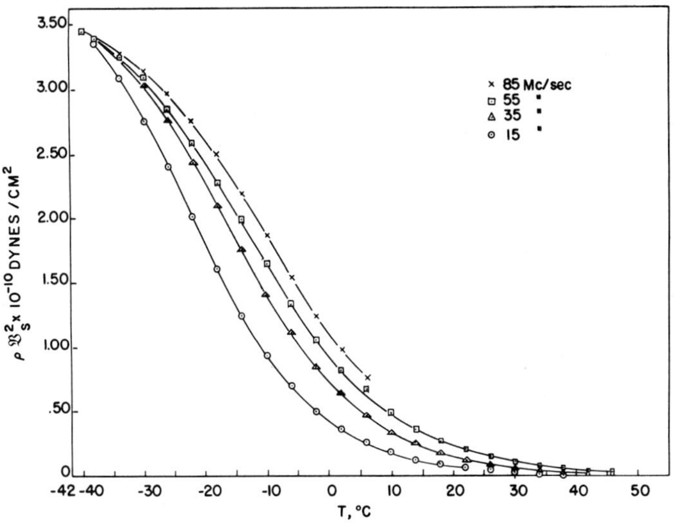

FIG. 108–1. Density times shear velocity squared, $\rho\mathfrak{V}_s^2$, plotted as a function of temperature for glycerol at various frequencies.

If single relaxation theory is applicable, one gets from Eq. (108–16)

$$S = \frac{\omega^2\tau^2}{2(1+\omega^2\tau^2)}\left[\left(1+\frac{1}{\omega^2\tau^2}\right)^{1/2}+1\right]. \tag{108–23}$$

If one plots S against $\omega\tau$ the family of curves in Fig. 108–1 is reduced to a single curve. In Fig. 108–2 S is plotted as a function of $\omega\eta/G_\infty$, which is chosen as the variable since $\tau_s = \eta/G_\infty$ according to single relaxation theory.[4] It is evident from Fig. 108–2 that a reduction is achieved, as follows from the general predictions of a single relaxation theory, since all the points

[4] The values of G_∞ are gotten as follows: At low temperatures where $\omega\tau_s \gg 1$, R_s^2/ρ is equal to G_∞. Values of G_∞ at higher temperatures are obtained by extrapolating the curve of G_∞ vs T.

for different frequencies and temperatures fall on a single curve. However, it can be seen by comparison with the superposed plot of Eq. (108–23) that a single relaxation theory is inadequate to give the exact shape of the curve.

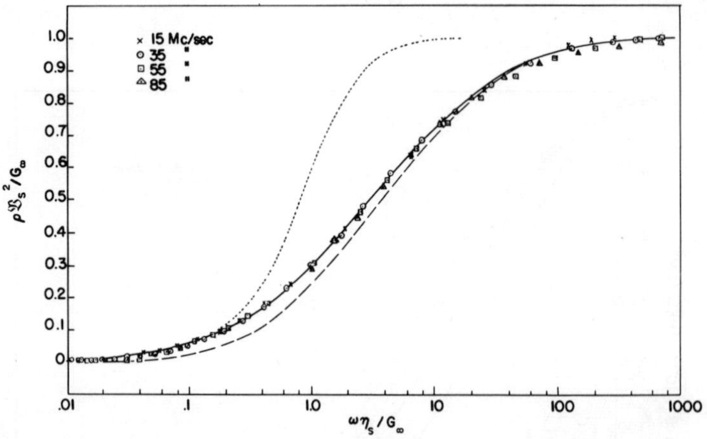

FIG. 108–2. Reduced plot of $\rho\mathfrak{B}_s^2/G_\infty$ (shear waves) plotted as a function of the temperature for glycerol at various frequencies. The dashed line is calculated from single relaxation theory. The solid line is the calculation of $\rho\mathfrak{B}_s^2/G_\infty$ using the Gaussian distribution function. The dotted line is a plot of G'/G_∞ calculated from the same Gaussian distribution function.

If one assumes a distribution of relaxation times, the expressions for the real and the imaginary part of the shear modulus are then given by Eqs. (105–7) and (105–8). Using these equations in combination with Eqs. (108–14) and (108–22), the expression for S becomes

$$S = \tfrac{1}{2}\int_0^\infty \frac{g(\tau)\omega^2\tau_s^2 d\tau_s}{1+\omega^2\tau_s^2}\left\{\left[\left(\frac{\displaystyle\int_0^\infty \frac{g(\tau)\omega\tau_s d\tau_s}{1+\omega^2\tau_s^2}}{\displaystyle\int_0^\infty \frac{g(\tau)\omega^2\tau_s^2 d\tau_s}{1+\omega^2\tau_s^2}}\right)^2 + 1\right]^{1/2} + 1\right\}. \tag{108–24}$$

Piccirelli has found that the data for S in glycerol can be fitted by assuming the following distribution function

$$g(\tau_s)d\tau_s = \frac{b}{\sqrt{\pi}} e^{-b^2z^2}\, dz \tag{108–25}$$

where

$$z = \ln \tau_s/\tau_s'.$$

This is a Gaussian distribution which has a maximum at τ_s equal to τ_s' and which is symmetric on a logarithmic plot. The parameter b determines the effective width and τ_s' determines the position of the maximum of the distribution.

This distribution was first used by Yager[5] in studying dielectric relaxation. In his paper the numerical evaluation of the integrals appearing in Eq. (108–24) can be found.

Equation (105–9) states that when a distribution of relaxation times exists η/G_∞ is identical with the average relaxation time. This is not equal to τ_s' in the distribution given above. Using the Gaussian distribution in combination with Eq. (105–9) one finds that

$$\frac{\eta}{G_\infty} = \frac{b\tau_s'}{\sqrt{\pi}} \int_{-\infty}^{\infty} \exp(-bz^2 + z)dz = \tau_s' \exp\left(\frac{1}{4b^2}\right) \tag{108–26}$$

showing that the average relaxation time η/G_∞ differs by a constant factor from τ_s', the most probable relaxation time.

One can show by inserting the distribution, Eq. (108–25), into Eq. (105–7) that for $\omega\tau_s' = 1$

$$G' = \tfrac{1}{2} G_\infty. \tag{108–27}$$

Thus τ_s' could be determined from the frequency at which the condition in Eq. (108–27) is fulfilled if G' as function of frequency were known. However, the directly measured quantity is R_s, and G' can be calculated from this only if G'' is also known, see Eq. (108–14). In the experiments on glycerol G'' was not measured and could be calculated only after the distribution of relaxation times had been obtained.

The distribution function contains only one independent parameter, namely, b, which determines the shape of the curve. For glycerol, the best theoretical representation of the shape of the experimental curve is obtained with $b = 0.42$. Equation (108–26) leads, with $b = 0.42$, to

$$\tau_s' = \frac{\eta}{4.14\, G_\infty}. \tag{108–28}$$

---

[5] W. A. Yager, *J. Appl. Physics* **7**, 434 (1936).

With this relationship Eq. (108–25) should have the form

$$g(\tau_s)d\tau_s = \frac{0.42}{\sqrt{\pi}} \frac{d\tau_s}{\tau_s} \exp - \left[\ln \frac{4.14\, G_\infty}{\eta} \tau_s\right]^2. \tag{108–29}$$

The curve of $\boldsymbol{S}$ against $\omega\eta/G_\infty$ so calculated is parallel to the experimental curve, but slightly shifted to the right. In Fig. 108–2 it can be seen that the experimental and theoretical curves nearly coincide if Eq. (108–28) is replaced empirically by

$$\tau_s' = \frac{\eta}{3.60\, G_\infty}. \tag{108–30}$$

There are two factors which could contribute to this discrepancy of about 12%. (1) The Gaussian distribution probably does not give the exact distribution of relaxation times in the liquid. This is borne out by the fact that at low values of $\omega\eta/G_\infty$, i.e., at low frequencies, the experimental points lie slightly below the theoretical curve. At low frequencies the larger values of τ_s are the most important. It appears possible, therefore, that the curve $g(\tau_s)$ against τ_s/τ_s' is not quite symmetrical. (2) It must be remembered that the uncertainty of G_∞ in this temperature range is of the order of 10%, and that of η is about $\pm$ 1%. If, for example, the experimental value of G_∞ is 12% high the discrepancy would be completely accounted for. Considering these possibilities the agreement of the distribution given by Eq. (108–29) with experiment is quite reasonable.

One can test this agreement in a slightly different manner. According to Piccirelli[2] one has in glycerol at $-18°$ C, $\tau_s' = 10.6 \times 10^{-8}$ sec,[6] $G_\infty = 3.08 \times 10^{10}$ dynes/cm^2, and $\eta = 11{,}300$ poise (determined in a viscosimeter). Using Eq. (108–28) one gets (from dynamic shear elasticity data) $\eta = 13{,}500$. Thus, the distribution function in combination with data at $-18°$ C gives a value of η about 20% high. This discrepancy, as discussed above, is just about the limit of the experimental accuracy.

In polymers[1] two moduli are found, a "rubberlike" modulus of about 10^6 to 10^7 dynes/cm^2 and an "ultrasonic" modulus of 10^{10} dynes/cm^2. The former has a much longer relaxation time than the latter, and therefore their contributions to the quasi-static viscosity are of the same order of magnitude. The fact that the distribution function, Eq. (108–29), gives

---

[6] Using the distribution function, G' is calculated from the R_s data as a function of frequency. It is found that at this temperature $G' = 0.5\, G_\infty$ at 15 Mc, and τ_s' follows from Eq. (108–27).

values of η somewhat too large (instead of too small a value) proves that it represents the principal part, if not all, of η, and that no rubberlike process with a long relaxation time is present but undetected in the large gap below 25 Mc.

Ultrasonic shear data are available for three other associated liquids.[7–9] In each of these a distribution of relaxation times was found necessary to fit the data. In two of these, butanediol-1,3 and 2-methyl-2,4, pentanediol, a Gaussian distribution function fits the data. In the third liquid, hexanetriol-1,2,6, it appears that two different shear relaxation mechanisms are present. These are associated with relaxation times that differ by a factor of about ten. This liquid is the only one to show two distinct relaxation mechanisms. Hexanetriol has the longest carbon chain of any of the liquids measured (6 carbons). The existence of two sets of relaxation times is quite usual for polymers. It is possible that the hexanetriol molecule is long enough to begin showing some polymeric behavior.

109. Compressional Relaxation in Associated Liquids. Comparison with Shear Relaxation

Measurements of only longitudinal velocity dispersion in liquids do not allow one to separate the effects due to shear and compressional relaxation. From Eq. (104–16) ($\rho\mathfrak{B}^2 = K' + \frac{4}{3}G'$), one sees that the longitudinal velocity is determined by both K' and G'. If data on the shear modulus are separately available, then by use of Eq. (104–16) data from longitudinal and shear waves can be combined to obtain the frequency and temperature dependence of the compressional modulus of a liquid.

From Eq. (104–7) one sees that according to single relaxation theory the real part of the compressional modulus is given by

$$K' = K_0 + \frac{(K_\infty - K_0)\omega^2\tau_v^2}{1 + \omega^2\tau_v^2} \tag{109–1}$$

where $K' - K_0$ is the relaxational part of the compressional modulus. The reduced relaxational part of the compressional modulus is

$$\boldsymbol{K} = \frac{K' - K_0}{K_\infty - K_0} = \frac{\omega^2\tau_v^2}{1 + \omega^2\tau_v^2}\,. \tag{109–2}$$

---

[7] F. E. Cotter, M. S. Dissertation, Catholic Univ., Washington, D. C. (1957).
[8] C. J. Marhoefer, Ph. D. Dissertation, Catholic Univ., Washington, D. C. (1957).
[9] R. Sciamanda, M. S. Dissertation, Catholic Univ. Washington, D. C. (1957).

This quantity has been calculated for glycerol from shear and longitudinal data by Piccirelli,[1] and the results appear in Fig. 109–1. At low temperature the values of $\rho\mathfrak{V}^2$ give K_∞. The values of K_∞ at the higher temperatures are obtained by extrapolating the curve of K_∞ vs temperature. Note that $\eta'/(K_\infty - K_0)$ is equal to τ_v on the basis of single relaxation theory—see Eq. (104–7‴); η' is evaluated here by using the fact that the low frequency absorption indicates that η' equals η. It is immediately seen in Fig. 109–1 that single relaxation theory is inadequate to describe the results. By comparison with Fig. 108–2 it can, however, be recognized that if a distribution of relaxation times is assumed, the distribution necessary to describe the compressional data is not the same as that for the shear data. The reduced shear modulus is logarithmically antisymmetric about its inflection point. The $\boldsymbol{K}$ data do not possess such a symmetry property.

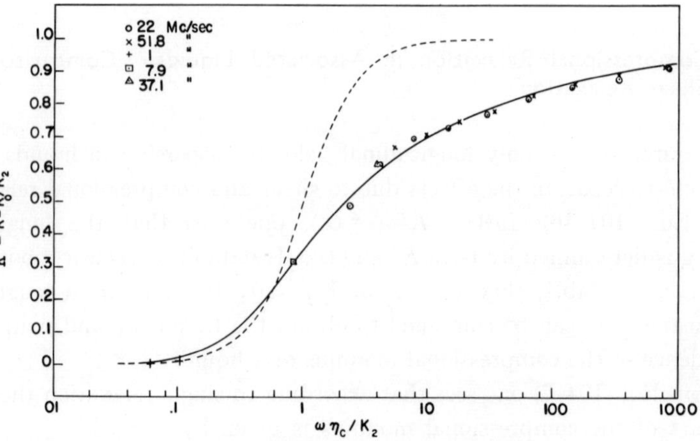

FIG. 109–1. Reduced plot of the real portion of the relaxational part of the compressional modulus. Dashed line is calculated using single relaxation theory.

Assuming a distribution of relaxation times one has, from Eq. (105–4)

$$\boldsymbol{K} = \int_0^\infty k(\tau)\,\frac{\omega^2\tau^2}{1+\omega^2\tau^2}\,d\tau. \tag{109–3}$$

---

[1] R. Piccirelli, Ph. D. Thesis, Catholic University of America, Washington, D. C., 1956; R. Piccirelli and T. A. Litovitz, *J. Acoust. Soc. Am.* **29**, 1009 (1957).

In order to fit the $\boldsymbol{K}$ data for glycerol, Piccirelli has made use of a distribution of relaxation times found by Davidson and Cole[2] in their studies on dielectric relaxation. This distribution is asymmetric on a logarithmic scale and is given by[3]

$$k(\tau)d\tau = \begin{cases} \dfrac{\sin \beta\pi}{\pi}\left(\dfrac{\tau_v/\tau_v'}{1-\tau_v/\tau_v'}\right)^{\beta} d\ln(\tau_v/\tau_v'), & 0 \leqslant \tau_v/\tau_v' < 1 \\ 0 & , \quad 1 < \tau_v/\tau' < \infty \end{cases} \tag{109–4}$$

where β and τ_v' are parameters which determine the width and the position of the distribution, respectively. Substituting this expression into Eq. (109–3) it is seen that

$$\boldsymbol{K} = \frac{K' - K_0}{K_\infty - K_0} = 1 - (\cos\varphi)^{\beta}\cos(\beta\varphi) \tag{109–5}$$

where φ is the principal value of the arctan $\omega\tau_v'$. After substitution of Eq. (109–4) into Eq. (105–6) it is concluded that the average compressional relaxation time is given by

$$\frac{\eta'}{K_\infty - K_0} = \beta\tau_v'. \tag{109–6}$$

Piccirelli finds good agreement between the *shape* of the experimental and theoretical curves of $\boldsymbol{K}$ vs $\eta'/(K_\infty - K_0)$ when $\beta = 0.32$ is taken. This value of β inserted into Eq. (109–6) gives $\tau_v' = \eta'/0.32\,(K_\infty - K_0)$. It was found empirically, however, that the position of the theoretical curve fits the data best if τ_v' is assumed to equal $\eta'/0.346\,(K_\infty - K_0)$. The solid line in Fig. 109–1 is this theoretical curve. This satisfactory fitting of the experimental results implies that $\eta'/(K_\infty - K_0) = 0.346\,\tau_v'$, while Eq. (109–6) indicates that for $\beta = 0.32$, $\eta'/(K_\infty - K_0) = 0.32\,\tau_v'$. This represents a good agreement between the calculated and experimentally determined average relaxation time if one notes that the uncertainty in $K_\infty - K_0$ is about $\pm$ 10% and the uncertainty in η' is about $\pm$ 6%.

As was the case for the shear relaxation this agreement implies that the total volume viscosity is governed by the distribution, Eq. (109–4). This

---

[2] D. W. Davidson and R. H. Cole, *J. Chem. Phys.* **19**, 1484 (1951).

[3] The quantity β used here, following Davidson and Cole, has nothing to do with the coefficient of thermal expansion, which is designated by this letter elsewhere in this book.

can be seen by calculating η' from the variation of K' vs frequency at constant temperature. At $-18°$ C Piccirelli gives the following numbers for glycerol. $K' = 7.47 \times 10^{10}$ dynes/cm^2 at 22 Mc, $K_0 = 5.12 \times 10^{10}$ dynes/cm^2, and $K_\infty - K_0 = 3.81 \times 10^{10}$ dynes/cm^2. A value of $\boldsymbol{K} = (K' - K_0)/(K_\infty - K_0) = 0.62$ results at this frequency. From Eq. (109–5) one finds that for $\boldsymbol{K} = 0.62$ and $\beta = 0.32$, $\omega\tau_v'$ must equal 14. Thus τ_v' at $-18°$ C in glycerol is equal to 1.01×10^{-7} sec.

Substituting these values in Eq. (109–6) yields[4] a value of 1.24×10^3 poise for η'. This is in good agreement with the value of 1.13×10^3 poise obtained by assuming that $\eta' = \eta$, as indicated by absorption measurements outside the dispersion region. If only part of η' had relaxed then, of course, Eq. (109–6) would have yielded a smaller value for the volume viscosity.

It is of interest to compare the shear and compressional relaxation times. The most meaningful comparison is between the average relaxation times for the two processes. For the data at $-18°$ C Piccirelli finds that $(\tau_s)_{\text{avg}} = \eta/G_\infty = 3.67 \times 10^{-8}$ sec and that $(\tau_v)_{\text{avg}} = \eta'/(K_\infty - K_0) = 2.97 \times 10^{-8}$ sec. This difference of about 20% is just within the sum of the experimental uncertainties. It appears that the average shear and compressional relaxation times in glycerol are very close in value.

The results in *n*-propyl alcohol (Sec. 107) suggest that this conclusion is probably not true for all the associated liquids.

The work of Cotter,[5] Meister,[6] Sciamanda,[7] and Marhoefer[8] indicates that the compressional relaxation in several other associated liquids behaves in a manner which is very similar to that in glycerol. In each of these liquids the assymetric Davidson-Cole distribution was found to fit the data.

For each liquid the average shear and compressional relaxation times have the same temperature dependence.

The magnitude of the average shear and compressional relaxation times are compared in Table 109–1. The parameters in the distribution function are also listed. It can be seen that $(\tau_v)_{\text{avg}}$ and $(\tau_s)_{\text{avg}}$ are reasonable close in value.

---

[4] This amounts to the calculation of G'' at low frequency.

[5] F. E. Cotter, M. S. Dissertation, Catholic University of America, Washington, D. C., 1957.

[6] R. Meister, Ph. D. Dissertation, Catholic University of America, Washington, D. C., 1957.

[7] R. Sciamanda, M. S. Dissertation, Catholic University of America, Washington, D. C., 1957.

[8] C. J. Marhoefer, Ph. D. Dissertation, Catholic University of America, Washington, D. C., 1957.

TABLE 109-1

COMPARISON OF SHEAR AND COMPRESSIONAL RELAXATION PARAMETERS IN SEVERAL ASSOCIATED LIQUIDS

	b	β	$(\tau_v)_{av}/(\tau_s)_{av}$	References
Butanediol 1,3	0.46	0.49	0.79	5
2-Methyl pentanediol-2,4	0.60	0.60	2.38	7
Glycerol	0.42	0.32	0.81	1
Hexanetriol-1,2,6	*	0.24	0.41	6,8
			(4.6)	

* In order to fit the hexanetriol shear data a Davidson-Cole distribution in addition to a single relaxation time was assumed. It appears that two shear relaxation mechanisms are present in hexanetriol for which the average times differ by a factor of about ten.

110. Velocity Dispersion in Associated Liquids

The measurements of sound velocity in diphenyl pentachloride[1] ($Cl_2C_6H_3C_6H_2Cl_3$), shown in Fig. 110-1, are typical of the dispersion in the associated liquids. Above 50° C no dispersion is detected in the frequency range between 7.5 and 50 Mc, because the relaxation time is short compared with $(2\pi \times 5 \times 10^7)^{-1} \sim 3 \times 10^{-9}$ sec. As the temperature is lowered, a dispersion region is found. The higher the frequency the higher the temperature (or lower the viscosity) at which dispersion occurs. Below 10° C there is again no dispersion in the range between 7.5 and 50 Mc, because at these temperatures the relaxation time is long compared with $(2\pi \times 7.5 \times 10^6)^{-1} \sim 2 \times 10^{-8}$ sec. Therefore, below 10° C a wave with a frequency above 7.5 Mc is propagated with $\mathfrak{V}_\infty$, the high frequency velocity of the liquid. In this temperature and frequency range the liquid is behaving with regard to the sonic wave as an amorphous solid and no structural rearrangements or flow can contribute to the compressibility. $\mathfrak{V}_\infty$ is determined now by both the compressional and shear modulus, assuming that the relaxation time for shear viscosity and compressional viscosity are about the same.

[1] T. A. Litovitz, T. Lyon, and L. Peselnick, *J. Acoust. Soc. Am.* **26**, 566 (1954).

It can be seen from Fig. 110–1 that the temperature dependence of $\mathfrak{B}_\infty$ is greater than that for $\mathfrak{B}_0$, the normal low frequency value of velocity.

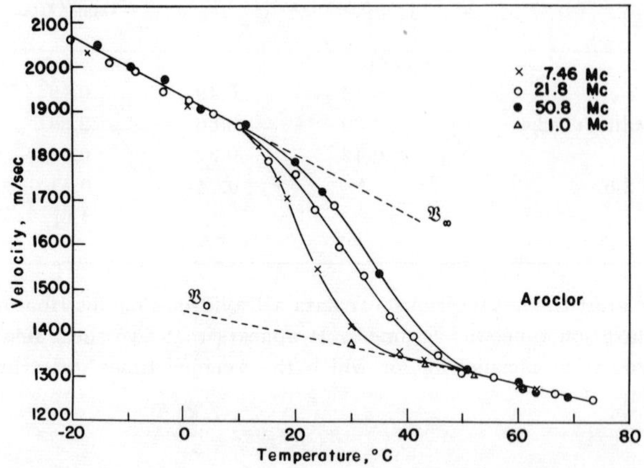

FIG. 110–1. Plot of ultrasonic velocity vs temperature in diphenyl pentachloride.

A comparison of the thermal coefficients of velocity and density in diphenyl pentachloride, with the units in $°C^{-1} \times 10^3$, gives the following results:

$$\frac{1}{\rho}\frac{\partial \rho}{\partial T} = 0.649$$

$$\frac{1}{\mathfrak{B}_0}\frac{\partial \mathfrak{B}_0}{\partial T} = 1.94$$

$$\frac{1}{\mathfrak{B}_\infty}\frac{\partial \mathfrak{B}_\infty}{\partial T} = 3.84$$

$$\frac{(1/\mathfrak{B}_0)\,(\partial \mathfrak{B}_0/\partial T)}{(1/\rho)\,(\partial \rho/\partial T)} = 2.99$$

$$\frac{(1/\mathfrak{B}_\infty)\,(\partial \mathfrak{B}_\infty/\partial T)}{(1/\rho)\,(\partial \rho/\partial T)} = 5.92.$$

As can be seen, the thermal coefficient of $\mathfrak{B}_\infty$ is about twice that found for $\mathfrak{B}_0$. The temperature dependence of $\mathfrak{B}_0$ is about three times that for density, as has been observed by Rao[2] to be true of most liquids. Comparison of $\mathfrak{V}_\infty$ and ρ shows this ratio of temperature coefficients to be about 6, indicating that Rao's rule does not apply to $\mathfrak{V}_\infty$.

Table 110–1 is a compilation of the results of dispersion measurements in a series of associated liquids. The values of $\mathfrak{V}_0$ and $\mathfrak{V}_\infty$ are obtained by extrapolating the data from upper and lower temperatures, respectively, as is done by the dotted line in Fig. 110–1. The magnitude of the dispersion $(\mathfrak{V}_\infty - \mathfrak{V}_0)/\mathfrak{V}_0$ varies between 15 and 60%, with most of the liquids exhibiting a value larger than 25%. Just as in diphenyl pentachloride, the thermal coefficient of $\mathfrak{V}_\infty$ is larger than that found for $\mathfrak{V}_0$ by a factor lying between 2 and 3.

From the velocity dispersion data it is possible to calculate a relaxation time τ_v'' which is roughly indicative of the center of the distribution of relaxation times.

Assuming $\omega\tau_v'' = 1$ at the half way point in the dispersion

$$\frac{\mathfrak{V}^2 - \mathfrak{V}_0^{\,2}}{\mathfrak{V}_\infty^{\,2} - \mathfrak{V}_0^{\,2}} = 0.5,$$

one finds τ_v'' if the ultrasonic frequency ω is known. The values of τ_v'' calculated in this manner are tabulated in Table 110–1. The results show that liquids with a viscosity of about 500 poise have a "central relaxation time," τ_v'', of about 10^{-8} sec.

This value of τ_v'' can be compared with that "effective relaxation time" predicted by Lucas (see Sec. 7), although it must be emphasized that in every liquid measured the character of the dispersion left no doubt that a relaxation theory is necessary and that the Lucas theory which predicts $\mathfrak{V}_\infty = \infty$ does not apply.

The relaxation time defined by Lucas, as modified in Sec. 7, is

$$\tau_L = \frac{\frac{4}{3}\eta + \eta'}{\rho\mathfrak{V}_0^{\,2}}. \tag{7–9'}$$

The values of τ_L calculated from Eq. (7–9′) are given in Table 110–1.

---

[2] M. R. Rao, *Indian J. Phys.* **14,** 109 (1941).

TABLE 110–1

COMPARISON OF VELOCITY DISPERSION DATA IN ASSOCIATED LIQUIDS

	T (°C)	η (poise)	$\frac{\alpha}{\alpha_{\text{class}}}$	$\mathfrak{V}_0$ (m/sec)	$\mathfrak{V}_\infty$ (m/sec)	$\frac{\mathfrak{V}_\infty - \mathfrak{V}_0}{\mathfrak{V}_0}$	$\frac{\frac{1}{\mathfrak{V}_\infty}\frac{\partial \mathfrak{V}_\infty}{\partial T}}{\frac{1}{\mathfrak{V}_0}\frac{\partial \mathfrak{V}_0}{\partial T}}$	τ_v'' ($\times 10^8$ sec)	τ_L ($\times 10^8$ sec)	References
Butanediol-1,3	−32.2	189	1.75	1695	2331	0.375	2.58	1.38	1.3	3
Propanediol-1,2	−37.8	905	2.08	1650	2360	0.43	3.39	1.41	6.1	4
Hexanetriol-1,2,6	−10.5	680	1.65	1820	2740	0.52	3.32	1.49	2.36	4
Glycerol	−14	616	1.78	1990	3150	0.59	2.64	1.10	2.2	5
n-Propanol	−130	450	1.77	1860	2160	0.15	—	1.59	2.5	6
2-Methyl pentanediol-2,4	−26	42.3	3.38	1460	1865	0.28	3.58	1.33	0.74	4
Diphenyl pentachloride	34.5	12	3.28	1310	1690	0.29	2.0	.32	0.14	1

* The values of $\alpha/\alpha_{\text{class}}$ listed are those measured in the nondispersion region. They are used in conjunction with Eq. (7–9′) to calculate τ_L.

[3] L. E. Cotter, M. S. Dissertation, Catholic University of America, Washington, D. C., 1957.
[4] R. Meister, Ph. D. Dissertation, Catholic University of America, Washington, D. C., 1957.
[5] R. Piccirelli, and T. A. Litovitz, *J. Acoust. Soc. Am.* **29**, 1009 (1957).
[6] T. Lyon and T. A. Litovitz, *J. Appl. Phys.* **27**, 179 (1956).

These values are larger than τ_v'' in most of the liquids but agree to within a factor of 5 with the values of τ_v'' listed.[7] It appears that even though the "exact" solution of the Stokes-Navier equation as evaluated by Lucas does not give good agreement with experiment, the "effective relaxation time" predicted by this nonrelaxational theory is useful in estimating the frequency region in which relaxation processes will occur in a viscous liquid.

111. Numerical Relationships Between the Moduli

The magnitudes of the compressional and shear moduli of several liquids are compared in Table 111–1 with a crystalline and an amorphous solid. The value of G_∞ for the organic liquids is less than one-tenth of the values found for typical solids. For the one polymer listed, polyisobutylene, the value of G_∞ is about one-hundredth the value of nickel. However the values of G_∞/K_∞ for the organic liquids are of the same order of magnitude as found in solids. This indicates that the same factors which cause a liquid to be more compressible than a solid affect the shear "elasticity" of the liquid.

---

[7] The fact that the "exact" theory is unnecessary in accounting for experimental results is often explained by noting that relaxation effects become important at lower frequencies or before the differences in the exact and "linearized" theory become important. It is therefore at first thought surprising that τ_L is larger than τ_v'' in most of the liquids listed in Table 110–1. This result is understood if one notes that in the exact or Lucas theory the peak in $\alpha\lambda_0$ occurs at $\omega\tau_L = \sqrt{3}$. However, relaxation theory predicts a peak in $\alpha\lambda_0$ (see Sec. 18) at $\omega\tau_v'' = (\mathfrak{B}_0/\mathfrak{B}_\infty)^{3/2}$. Thus, for example, for glycerol $(\mathfrak{B}_0/\mathfrak{B}_\infty)^{3/2} \cong \frac{1}{2}$. Therefore, even though $\tau_L = 1.6\,\tau_v''$, the peak in $\alpha\lambda_0$ occurs at about one-half the frequency predicted by the Lucas theory. Inserting Eq. (104–26) on the right side of Eq. (7–9′) one gets

$$\tau_L = \tau_v \frac{K_2 + \frac{4}{3} G_\infty \tau_s/\tau_v}{K_0}$$

$$= \tau_v \frac{\kappa'}{\kappa - \kappa'}\left(1 + \frac{4}{3}\frac{G_\infty}{K_2}\frac{\tau_s}{\tau_v}\right)$$

If one sets

$$\tfrac{4}{3} G_\infty = K_2; \qquad \tau_s = \tau_v; \qquad \kappa' = \tfrac{1}{3}\kappa$$

(Sects. 111, 109), the result is

$$\tau_L = \tau_v.$$

TABLE 111–1

COMPARISON OF SHEAR AND COMPRESSIONAL MODULI OF VARIOUS LIQUIDS AND SOLIDS AT 25° C; UNITS ARE DYNES/CM^2 $\times 10^{-10}$

Substance	G_∞	K_∞	G_∞/K_∞	References
Nickel	73.5	371	0.20	1
Fused quartz	31.2	37.3	0.84	2
Glycerol	2.27	7.38	0.31	3
Hexanetriol	2.02	5.67	0.35	4
Butanediol 1,3	0.74	3.30	0.22	5
Polyisobutylene	0.58	2.68	0.17	6
Arochlor	0.074	4.6	0.016	7

[1] C. D. Hodgman, ed., "Handbook of Chemistry and Physics," 38 Ed. Chemical Rubber Company, Cleveland, Ohio, 1956.

[2] H. J. McSkimin, *J. Appl. Phys.* **24**, 988 (1953).

[3] R. Piccirelli, and T. A. Litovitz, *J. Acoust. Soc. Am.* **29**, 1009 (1957).

[4] R. Meister and C. J. Marhoefer, Ph. D. Dissertations, Catholic University of America, Washington, D. C. 1957.

[5] L. E. Cotter, M. S. Dissertation, Catholic University of America, Washington, D. C., 1957.

[6] W. P. Mason, W. O. Baker, H. J. McSkimin, and J. H. Heiss, *Phys. Rev.* **75**, 936 (1949).

[7] R. Piccirelli, M. S. Dissertation, Catholic University of America, Washington, D. C., 1953.

From the data in Table 110–1 one can calculate $\mathfrak{V}_0{}^2$ and $\mathfrak{V}_\infty{}^2$, the high-frequency longitudinal modulus M_∞, the adiabatic compressional modulus K_0, and the sum $K_2 + \frac{4}{3} G_\infty$ for several liquids. These quantities are tabulated in Table 111–2. It can be seen that M_∞ is roughly proportional to K_0.

The value of $K_2 + \frac{4}{3} G_\infty = M_\infty - K_0$ lies between 25 and 60% of M_∞. The data of Table 111–2 indicate that for many liquids, K_2 is approximately equal to $\frac{4}{3} G_\infty$.

It can be seen from the last column in Table 111–2 that the fraction of the compressibility of a liquid which is due to structural rearrangements varies from about 20 to 60%.

Included in this table is a theoretical calculation of κ'/κ_0 for water. It can be seen that the relaxational part of the compressibility of water is only slightly higher for the other liquids.

It is of interest to compare these values of κ'/κ with those obtained by measuring the isothermal compressibility above and below the temperature of the glass transition (see Sec. 103).

TABLE 111–2

COMPARISON OF THE MAGNITUDE OF ELASTIC MODULI IN ASSOCIATED LIQUIDS; UNITS FOR MODULI AVE DYNES/CM^2 $\times$ 10^{-10}

Liquid	T (°C)	K_0	M_∞	$K_2+\frac{4}{3}G_\infty$	G_∞	κ'/κ_0
Butanediol-1,3	−32.2	2.92	6.17	3.25	1.23*	0.35
Propanediol-1,2	−37.8	3.14	6.16	3.02	1.13***	0.32***
Hexanetriol-1,2,6	−10.5	3.70	9.52	5.8	2.32†	0.43
Glycerol	−14	5.04	11.9	6.9	2.93‡	0.41
2-Methyl pentanediol-2,4	−26	2.35	3.85	1.5	0.61	0.19
n-Propyl alcohol	−130	3.2	4.3	1.1	≈0.01**	0.34
Diphenyl pentachloride	34.5	2.78	4.24	1.46	≈0.1‡	0.52
Water	20	—	—	—	—	0.61††

* See Ref. 5.

† See Ref. 8.

‡ See Ref. 7.

** See Ref. 9.

†† Calculated from Hall's theory for structural relaxation in water, where $\kappa_0 = 4.58 \times 10^{-11}$ dynes/cm^2; $\tilde{\kappa} = 1.8 \times 10^{-11}$ dynes/cm^2; and $\kappa' = \kappa_0 - \tilde{\kappa} = 2.78 \times 10^{-11}$ dynes/cm^2.

*** Calculated by assuming $K_2 = \frac{4}{3} G_\infty$ as in glycerol.

TABLE 111–3

COMPARISON OF GLASS AND LIQUID VALUES OF ISOTHERMAL COMPRESSIBILITY

Substance	T (°K)	κ_{glass} ($\times$ 10^{12} cm^2/dyne)	κ_{liq} ($\times$ 10^{12} cm^2/dyne)	κ'/κ_{liq}
Glucose	300	9.3	15.4	0.40
Selenium	300	24.4	30.2	0.19
Rubber	200−320	27	64	0.58
Polystyrene	350	23	98	0.76
Rosin	300	25	35	0.29

The results in Table 111–3 have been taken from Davies and Jones.[10]

---

[8] C. J. Marhoefer, Ph. D. Dissertation, Catholic University of America, Washington, D. C., 1957.

[9] T. Lyon and T. A. Litovitz, *J. Appl. Phys.* **27**, 179 (1956).

[10] R. O. Davies and G. O. Jones, *Proc. Roy. Soc.* **A217**, 26 (1953).

The κ' is obtained by assuming $\kappa' = \kappa_{\text{liq}} - \kappa_{\text{glass}}$; see Eq. (103–3). The results of the isothermal compressibility data in glass and liquid indicate that $\kappa'/\kappa_{\text{liq}}$ lies between 20 and 75%. This is in good agreement with the values found from ultrasonic dispersion. These results are in accord with the concept that high-frequency ultrasonic waves measure the "glasslike" properties of the liquid.

The data on the relaxational moduli of associated liquids are of interest in terms of the two-state theory. From Table 111–3 one sees that κ'/κ is roughly $\frac{1}{3}$ for liquids in which structural relaxation is occurring. On the basis of the two-state theory (see Sec. 100) this ratio can be written

$$\frac{\kappa'}{\kappa} = \frac{\rho\mathfrak{V}_0^2}{RT/V}\left(\frac{V_2 - V_1}{V}\right)^2 x_2(1 - x_2). \tag{111–1}$$

Using Eq. (111–1) and the data in Table 111–2, one can estimate the minimum value which $(V_2 - V_1)/V$ can have. Rewriting Eq. (111–1) one gets

$$\left(\frac{V_2 - V_1}{V}\right)^2 = \frac{\kappa'}{\kappa}\frac{RT}{V\rho\mathfrak{V}_0^2}\frac{1}{x_2(1 - x_2)}. \tag{111–2}$$

The maximum value of $x_2(1 - x_2)$ is 0.25. Using $\kappa'/\kappa \approx \frac{1}{3}$, $\rho\mathfrak{V}_0^2 \approx 3.3 \times 10^{10}$ dynes/cm^2, $RT/V \approx 2.1 \times 10^8$, and $x_2(1 - x_2) = 0.25$, one finds that the minimum value for $(V_2 - V_1)/V$ is about 0.09. A maximum value for $(V_2 - V_1)/V$ can be estimated by noting that the distance between molecules in a liquid is never much greater than the diameter of the molecules. Therefore the difference in volume between an open and a closed packing can never be much larger than 0.5 V; thus $0.09 \leqslant (V_2 - V_1)/V \leqslant 0.5$.

112. The Temperature Dependence of Elastic Moduli of Liquids

The shear data in organic liquids indicate that G_∞ decreases with increasing temperature. This is shown in Table 112–1, for glycerol.

The experimentally found magnitude and temperature dependence of the shear moduli of liquids can be compared with the predictions of the Eyring theory for shear viscosity as discussed in Sec. 90.

Eyring's formula[1] for shear viscosity as modified by Wirtz[2] is

$$\eta = 6\frac{RT}{V}\tau_j. \tag{90–46}$$

[1] H. Eyring, *J. Chem. Phys.* **4**, 283 (1936).
[2] K. Wirtz, *Z. Naturforsch.* **3a**, 672 (1948).

TABLE 112–1

TEMPERATURE DEPENDENCE OF THE SHEAR MODULUS AND OF THE RELAXATIONAL PART OF THE COMPRESSIONAL MODULUS OF GLYCEROL

(T°C)	η (poise)	G_∞ (dynes/cm$^2 \times 10^{-10}$)	$K_\infty - K_0$ (dynes/cm$^2 \times 10^{-10}$)
−42	1.09×10^5	3.52	4.36
−30	8.89×10^3	3.3	4.0
−10	6.16×10^2	2.9	3.6

By identifying τ_j with the average shear relaxation time, τ_s, one has

$$G_\infty = 6\frac{RT}{V}. \tag{112–1}$$

This obviously has the wrong temperature dependence, since it predicts that G_∞ increases with increasing temperature. Furthermore, using $V = 73.08$ cc/mole at $+ 25°$ C, this predicts that $G_\infty = 1.95 \times 10^9$ dynes/cm^2 for glycerol. This is an order of magnitude too small.[3]

In considering the shear data in liquids one finds that consistent results in reducing the data occur when it is assumed that

$$\frac{1}{G_\infty}\left(\frac{\partial G_\infty}{\partial T}\right) = \frac{1}{(K_\infty - K_0)}\left(\frac{\partial[K_\infty - K_0]}{\partial T}\right). \tag{112–2}$$

If this result and the experimental finding that $(\tau_s)_{\text{avg}}$ and $(\tau_v)_{\text{avg}}$ have the same temperature dependence are generally true for all associated liquids, one can explain why η'/η is independent of temperature for these liquids. Since the ratio, η'/η, equals $(K_\infty - K_0)\,(\tau_v)_{\text{avg}}/G_\infty(\tau_s)_{\text{avg}}$ the ratio $(K_\infty - K_0)/G_\infty$ must be independent of temperature if η'/η is. For $(K_\infty - K_0)/G_\infty$ to be constant, Eq (112–2) must hold.

The data in Table 112–2 indicate that the high-frequency compressional modulus, K_∞, is often more temperature dependent than the low-frequency compressional modulus, K_0. This is at first thought somewhat surprising, since the high-frequency behavior of a liquid is expected to resemble that of an amorphous solid, owing to absence of flow phenomena.

[3] Use of Eyring's original formula $\eta = (RT/V)(\tau_j)$ gives even poorer agreement with experimental values of G_∞.

TABLE 112–2

COMPARISON OF THE TEMPERATURE DEPENDENCE OF THE ELASTIC MODULI OF ASSOCIATED LIQUIDS AT 0° C

Units are $(°C)^{-1} \times 10^3$

	$-\frac{1}{G_\infty}\frac{\partial G_\infty}{\partial T}$*	$-\frac{1}{K_0}\frac{\partial K_0}{\partial T}$	$-\frac{1}{K_\infty}\frac{\partial K_\infty}{\partial T}$	$-\frac{1}{M_\infty}\frac{\partial M_\infty}{\partial T}$	$\frac{1}{G_\infty}\frac{\partial G_\infty}{\partial T}\Big/\left(\frac{1}{K_\infty}\frac{\partial K_\infty}{\partial T}\right)$	$\alpha/\alpha_{\text{class}}$	Reference
Glycerol	6.65	2.49	4.19	4.96	1.59	1.78	4
Hexanetriol-1,2,6	3.34	3.29	2.88	3.13	1.15	1.65	5
Butanediol-1,3	8.8	3.83	5.45	6.28	1.62	1.76	6
2-Methyl pentanediol-2,4	42.2	5.78	12.8	17.2	3.3	3.36	7

* In all the liquids listed $\frac{1}{G_\infty}\frac{\partial G_\infty}{\partial T}$ was found to be equal to $\frac{1}{K_2}\frac{\partial K_2}{\partial T}$.

[4] R. Piccirelli and T. A. Litovitz, *J. Acoust. Soc. Am.* **29**, 1009 (1957).

[5] R. Meister, Ph. D. Dissertation, Catholic University of America, Washington, D. C., 1957.

[6] F. E. Cotter, M. S. Dissertation, Catholic University of America, 1957.

[7] R. Sciamanda, M. S. Dissertation, Catholic University of America, Washington, D. C., 1958.

The temperature dependence of the elastic constants for solids is usually considerably less than for liquids. The thermal coefficients of the high-frequency moduli for the liquids tabulated are 100 times greater than that for the Young's modulus E for soft glass

$$\left(\frac{1}{E}\frac{\partial E}{\partial T} = -\ 0.067 \times 10^{-3}\,{}^{\circ}C^{-1}\right)$$

It is the glass which these supercooled liquids should most resemble. The high-frequency moduli are even ten times more temperature dependent than in a typical metal, aluminum.

$$\left(\frac{1}{G}\frac{\partial G}{\partial T} = -\ 0.72 \times 10^{-3}\right)$$

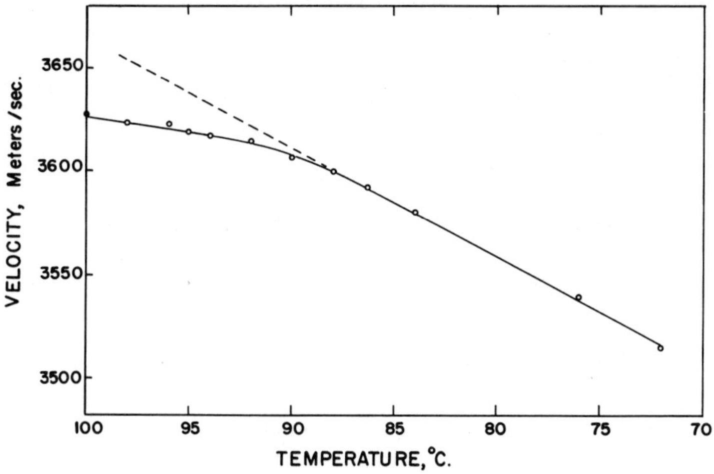

FIG. 112–1. Ultrasonic velocity in glycerol as a function of the temperature near the glass transition temperature. (The glass transition temperature for glycerol is about − 90° C.)

To understand this temperature dependence of K_∞ and G_∞ one must consider the factors determining the adiabatic modulus of crystals, as discussed by Zener.[8] In a crystal, the change of the moduli with temperature

---

[8] C. M. Zener, "Elasticity and Anelasticity of Metals." Univ. of Chicago Press, Chicago, 1948.

is a higher order effect, the lowest order being given by the second differential quotient of the elastic energy in respect to deformation.

At high frequencies, the liquid behaves, with regard to the sound wave, like a solid, and the moduli are again primarily being given ba $\partial^2U/\partial s^2$. However, if, above glass transition temperature, T is slowly changed, the order in the liquid changes, and U with it; i.e., above the glass transition, $(\partial U/\partial T)_{\text{liq}}$ is larger than it is in the solid, because at different temperatures we have different order. Therefore $\partial^2/\partial s^2(\partial U/\partial T) = \partial/\partial T(\partial^2 U/\partial s^2)$ is also larger.

If one measures the high-frequency, longitudinal velocity as a function of temperature, then it would be expected on the basis of the above explanation that the slope of M_∞ vs temperature should decrease considerably at the glass transition temperature. The experimental results for glycerol in Fig. 112–1 are in agreement with this prediction.

The above discussion explains why $1/M_\infty(\partial M_\infty/\partial T)$ is greater for liquids than for solids. The question of why $1/M_\infty(\partial M_\infty/\partial T)$ is greater than $1/M_0(\partial M_0/\partial T)$ still remains unanswered.

It follows from Table 112–2 that $[1/G_\infty\,(\partial G_\infty/\partial T)]\,[1/K_\infty\,(\partial K_\infty/\partial T)]^{-1}$ is often nearly equal to $\alpha/\alpha_{\text{class}}$. This is also unexplained.

113. The Origin of Volume Viscosity in Associated Liquids

The close similarity of the characteristics of the volume viscosity of water and the other associated liquids has suggested that the origin of this viscosity is similar in all the associated liquids, including water. However, this hypothesis has never been proven. Only in water has it been shown conclusively that a structural volume relaxation is the mechanism of the viscous loss. In this section the evidence concerning the nature of the volume viscosity found in the associated liquids will be considered.

If the loss in associated liquids has an origin similar to that in water then it is logical to apply a two-state theory to these liquids, since this approach was so successful for water. Sette[1] has reported a calculation of η' for ethyl alcohol which is based on the two-state model. The two states assumed here are (1) molecules bonded to one another in chains, and (2) molecules arranged in pairs with antiparallel dipole moments. The energy is lower in the first state and a compression increases the number of molecules in state (2). The difference in volume in the two states is evaluated

[1] D. Sette, *Phys. Rev.* **78**, 476 (1950).

by studying volumes of ethyl alcohol—carbon tetrachloride mixtures. The volume viscosity calculated on this basis is much too small to account for the compressional losses in ethyl alcohol.

The study of pressure dependence of sound absorption was shown in Sec. 102 to be useful in supporting the two-state theory for water. However, Carnevale and Litovitz[2] have found that the details of the pressure dependence of the compressional loss in methyl, ethyl, *n*-propyl, and *n*-butyl alcohols cannot be accounted for by the Hall two-state theory.

TABLE 113–1

ULTRASONIC PROPAGATION DATA AND COMPARISON OF EQUILIBRIUM CONSTANT* BETWEEN OPEN PHASE AND CLOSED PHASE METHYL ALCOHOL VS PRESSURE AT 30° C

p (kg/cm²)	α'/α_{class}	ρ (gm²/cc)	$\mathfrak{B}$ (meters/sec)	$(V_2 - V_1/V)^2 (1-x_2)x_2{}^2 \times 10^3$	$(1-x_2)x_2{}^2 \times 10^2$	x_2	K_{eq}†	K_{eq}‡
1	1.24	0.786	1086	3.5	3.53	0.21	0.266	0.266
500	1.12	0.82	1328	1.37	1.27	0.12	0.136	0.185
1000	0.95	0.847	1510	0.75	0.652	0.084	0.0915	0.127
1500	0.93	0.871	1651	0.50	0.41	0.065	0.0695	0.089
2000	0.83	0.889	1766	0.365	0.29	0.57	0.060	0.060

* Calculated from sound absorption, using Eq. (100–6); with values predicted by use of Eq. (102–3), assuming $V_2 - V_1 = 18.5$ cm³/mole.

† Experimental, from Eq. (100–6).

‡ Theoretical, from Eq. (102–3).

In Table 113–1 the data on absorption and velocity in methyl alcohol are tabulated as a function of pressure at 30° C. Assuming that methyl alcohol is a mixture of open and closed packing, these data can be compared with predictions of a two-state theory by use of Eq. (100–6), which allows one to calculate x_2, the mole fraction of alcohol molecules in the open state. To do this the difference in volume in the open and closed packing must be known or estimated. Then x_2 and K_{eq} can be calculated as a function of pressure from the acoustic data. This can be compared with the theoretical predictions of Eq. (102–3) concerning K_{eq}.

[2] E. H. Carnevale and T. A. Litovitz, *J. Acoust. Soc. Am.* **27**, 547 (1955).

The value of $V_2 - V_1$ for water was obtained from considerations of its structure as indicated by X-ray data. The structure of the alcohols is not as well known as that of water. For the purpose of comparing the experimental results with theory, a value of $V_2 - V_1$ is assumed which satisfies the data at both atmospheric pressure and at the highest pressure measured. On this basis a value of $V_2 - V_1$ equal to 18.5 cm³/mole is chosen. This gives a value for $(V_2 - V_1)/V$ of 0.45, compared to the value of 0.47 used for water.

From the results in Table 113–1 it can be seen that the values of K_{eq}, when adjusted to fit at 1 kg/cm² and 2000 kg/cm², do not agree in the mid-pressure range. The disagreement is as high as 40% at 1000 kg/cm².

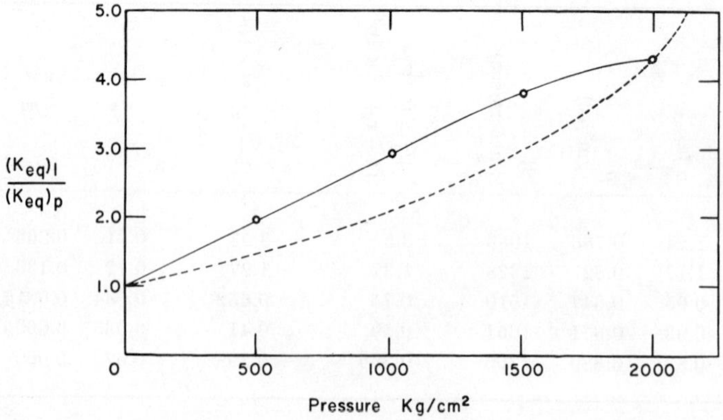

FIG. 113–1. Pressure dependence of the equilibrium constant between open and closed phase methyl alcohol calculated using Eq. (100–6). The dashed line is calculated using two-state theory.

In Fig. 113–1 the theoretical and experimental values of the ratio $(K_{eq})_1/(K_{eq})_p$ are plotted as a function of pressure. It can be seen that the values of this ratio obtained from acoustic data have a pressure dependence which *decreases* at high pressures, whereas the theoretical values are increasing exponentially with pressure. It appears from these results that the two-state model is not completely adequate to describe the experimental data in methyl alcohol. The other alcohols measured exhibit the same behavior as this. An explanation for the failure thus far of the two-state theories is the possibility that more than two states exist in the associated liquids other than water. It is implicit in the two-state theory that a single relaxation time exists, yet all measurements on associated liquids in the dispersion region indicate the presence of a distribution of relaxation times.

It is therefore reasonable to assume that the inability thus far to account for the compressional loss in the associated liquids represents a failure of the two-state concept—not a failure of the concept of structural relaxation.

Rather than thinking of two specific states the liquid may be considered from the viewpoint that was used to describe the glassy state (Sec. 103) and again in discussing the distribution of relaxation times (Sec. 100). At a given pressure and temperature the structure of the liquid has a specific "degree of order" or "degree of packing." A variation in volume or temperature causes a variation in this "degree of order."

There might be another possibility to account for the different behavior of most associated liquids from that of water. As discussed in Sec. 103 the existence of a "changing degree of order" in a liquid results in a structural contribution to the isothermal compressibility, κ'; to the specific heat, C'; and to the expansion coefficient, β'; of a liquid. As shown in Eqs. (103–1), (103–2), and (103–3) these quantities can be calculated if one has thermodynamic data in both the liquid and glassy state.

In water, the structural relaxation phenomena were explained by assuming that the shift in the structural composition during compression was determined exclusively by the difference in volume between the different structures, there being no (or not sufficient) accompanying temperature change.

In other liquids where $C_p - C_v$ is not zero and where, therefore, a temperature change does accompany an adiabatic compression, there are on principle two extreme possibilities, which might be nearly realized.

(a) The first is behavior like water, where the different structures have appreciably different volumes, but not different enthalpies, H', so that the shift between structures occurs in the same manner whether the pressure rise is adiabatic or isothermal. The corresponding acoustic loss is governed by the third term of Eq. (29–26). Such a liquid would, however, have an expansion coefficient of the order of magnitude of that in a solid (as water or glass has), since a temperature rise does not affect the order appreciably. $(C_p)_{\text{eff}}$ would be the same at low and high frequency, but $(C_p - C_v)_{\text{eff}}$ and, therefore, C_v would not.

(b) The different structures have essentially the same volume, but different energies, so that an isothermal pressure rise would not affect the structural order, but the temperature rise accompanying an adiabatic compression will shift the equilibrium. Therefore, there will be a contribution to the specific heat from the structural changes, but this part of the specific heat will adjust itself to temperature changes more slowly. The contribution of this effect to acoustic loss is given in the first term of Eq. (29–26). In a sense, such a liquid is a Kneser liquid, except that the part C' of the specific heat subject to relaxation is not internal vibrational specific heat, but structural. This liquid would have a glass type (solid type) compressibility and expansion coefficient; $C_p - C_v$ would not depend on frequency; see Eq. (4–9). However, $(C_p)_{\text{eff}}$ and $(C_v)_{\text{eff}}$ would be larger at low frequency than at high frequency.

There is also a mixed case, probably prevalent—all terms in Eq. (29–26)—if both effects, volume difference and energy difference, are simultaneously present. It is possible that the expansion coefficient is of the "liquid" type, since temperature changes at constant pressure shift the structural distribution because of the energy difference; and the isothermal compressibility is also of the "liquid" type, since isothermal pressure rise shifts the distribution because of the volume differences. Which effect is dominant in the acoustic absorption is a numerical question.

Using the data for κ in the liquid and glass state of glycerol, it can be shown that the main contribution to volume viscosity and associated velocity dispersion comes from the volume difference upon structural change, not from a structural specific heat.

In any of the above cases, κ' is equal to the difference between the corresponding low-frequency compressibility, κ_0, and the high-frequency (glass) compressibility, κ_∞. This gives, for adiabatic processes

$$\kappa_S' = \kappa_{0S} - \kappa_{\infty S} \qquad (113\text{–}1 = 103\text{–}3)$$

and for isothermal processes

$$\kappa_T' = \kappa_{0T} - \kappa_{\infty T}. \qquad (113\text{–}2)$$

If the relaxation loss is due to a structural specific heat—previous case (b)—κ_T' is zero

$$\kappa_{0T} = \kappa_{\infty T} \qquad (113\text{–}3)$$

and

$$\kappa_S' = \kappa_{0T}\left(\frac{1}{\gamma_0} - \frac{1}{\gamma_\infty}\right) = \frac{\kappa_{0T}}{\gamma_0}\left(1 - \frac{\gamma_0}{\gamma_\infty}\right) = \kappa_{0S}\left(1 - \frac{\gamma_0}{\gamma_\infty}\right). \qquad (113\text{–}4)$$

This is, of course, simply the formula for gases or Kneser liquids.

If, on the other hand, the relaxation loss is due mainly to the volume difference between different structures—previous case (a)

$$\kappa_S' = \kappa_T'. \qquad (113\text{–}5)$$

In the mixed case when effects of both volume and energy difference are simultaneously present the relationship among κ_S, κ_T, β, and C_p at either low or high frequencies obtained from thermodynamics is

$$\kappa_{0S} = \kappa_{0T} - TV\frac{\beta_0^{\,2}}{(C_p)_0} \tag{113–6}$$

$$\kappa_{\infty S} = \kappa_{\infty T} - TV\frac{\beta_\infty^{\,2}}{(C_p)_\infty} \tag{113–6'}$$

and κ_S' can be written[3]

$$\kappa_S' = [\kappa_{0T} - \kappa_{\infty T}] + TV\left[\frac{\beta_\infty^{\,2}}{(C_p)_\infty} - \frac{\beta_0^{\,2}}{(C_p)_0}\right]. \tag{113–7}$$

The first term on the right-hand side of Eq. (113–7) is the contribution to κ_S' due to the isothermal compressibility. The second term gives that part of κ_S' due to thermal effects. Using the concepts concerning the glassy state developed in Sec. 103 one can evaluate $\kappa_{\infty T}$, β_∞, and $(C_p)_\infty$ by identifying them with $(\kappa_T)_{\text{glass}}$, β_{glass}, and $(C_p)_{\text{glass}}$, respectively. The low-frequency values are simply the ordinary ones measured in the liquid state. Rewriting in terms of these quantities, one gets

$$\kappa_S' = [\kappa_{\text{liq}} - \kappa_{\text{glass}}]_T + TV\left[\frac{\beta^2{}_{\text{glass}}}{(C_p)_{\text{glass}}} - \frac{\beta^2{}_{\text{liq}}}{(C_p)_{\text{liq}}}\right]. \tag{113–8}$$

The value of κ_S' for glycerol at $-$ 93° C will now be considered. This is the glass transition temperature for glycerol. The data necessary to evaluate the second term in Eq. (113–8) are available. At this temperature $(c_p)_{\text{liq}} = 0.46$ cal/g, $(c_p)_{\text{glass}} = 0.25$ cal/g, $\beta_{\text{glass}} = 2.4 \times 10^{-4}$ °C^{-1}, and $\beta_{\text{liq}} = 4.8 \times 10^{-4}$ °C^{-1}.[4] The values of κ_S' and κ_{0S} can be obtained from

---

[3] In Sec. 102, $E' = 0$ instead of $H' = 0$ had been assumed for water; this gives $H' = pV'$; $C_v' = 0$. Then

$$\beta = \tilde{\beta} + x(1 - x)\,\frac{pV'}{RT^2}.$$

For an organic liquid, where $\beta \sim 10^{-3}$, the additional term is negligible for 1 atm pressure if $V' \sim 20$ cm³ and $T > 200$ °K. However, $C_p - C_v$ and therefore C_p now differs in the liquid and the glasslike state. Equation (113–7) takes the following form for moderate pressures if Eq. (4–9) is used:

$$\kappa_S' = \kappa_T' - TV\beta^2\left(\frac{1}{C_p} - \frac{1}{\tilde{C}_p}\right) = \kappa_T' - \frac{TV\beta^2}{C_v}\left(\frac{1}{\gamma_0} - \frac{1}{\gamma_\infty}\right)$$

$$= \kappa_T' - \frac{TV\beta^2}{C_v}\,\frac{\gamma_\infty - \gamma_0}{\gamma_0\gamma_\infty} = \kappa_T' - \left(\frac{TV\beta^2}{C_v}\right)^2 \frac{1}{\gamma_0\gamma_\infty}\left(\frac{1}{\kappa_\infty} - \frac{1}{\kappa_0}\right)_T$$

$$= \kappa_T'\left\{1 - \frac{1}{\gamma_0\gamma_\infty}\,\frac{TV\beta^2}{C_v\kappa_0}\,\frac{TV\beta^2}{C_v\kappa_\infty}\right\} = \kappa_T'\left\{1 - \frac{\gamma_0 - 1}{\gamma_0}\,\frac{\gamma_\infty - 1}{\gamma_\infty}\right\}.$$

ultrasonic velocity data[5] and are 7.7×10^{-12} cm²/dyne and 16.3×10^{-12} cm²/dyne, respectively.[6]

With the above data the second term in Eq. (113–8) is found to be equal to -0.8×10^{-12} cm²/dyne. It can be seen that the magnitude of this term is only about 10% of the observed value of κ_S'. Furthermore, it should be noted that this term is negative. It appears, therefore, that the relaxation of isothermal compressibility accounts for the greater part of κ_S'. The effects of a structural specific heat are present to a small extent but serve only to make κ_S' slightly *less* than κ_T'. It must be concluded that the volume viscosity found in glycerol cannot be adequately explained on the basis of a relaxing structural specific heat.[7]

---

[4] G. Tammann and W. Hesse, *Z. anorg. u. allgem. Chem.* **156**, 245 (1926).

[5] R. Piccirelli, Ph. D. Dissertation, Catholic University of America, Washington, D. C., 1956; R. Piccirelli, and T. A. Litovitz, *J. Acoust. Soc. Am.* **29**, 1009 (1957).

[6] The magnitude of the dispersion measured in a viscous liquid is related to both shear and compressional effects. Thus, from Eqs. (104–24) and (104–25), one has

$$\mathfrak{B}_0{}^2 = \frac{K_0}{\rho}$$

$$\mathfrak{B}_\infty{}^2 = \frac{K_\infty + 4/3\, G_\infty}{\rho}$$

If the shear modulus is known, then the value of K_∞ can be obtained from these equations. The value of κ_S' may be calculated from the following equation

$$\kappa_S' = \frac{1}{K_0} - \frac{1}{K_\infty}.$$

[7] It can be shown conclusively that κ_S' in glycerol is not due to a relaxing internal specific heat (e.g., internal vibrational degrees of freedom, as in nonassociated liquids). If one assumes that κ_S' is due to the same mechanism as it is in the Kneser (unassociated) liquids, then Eq. (113–4) can be applied. Rewriting this, one gets

$$\frac{\kappa_S'}{\kappa_{0S}} = 1 - \frac{\gamma_0}{\gamma_\infty} = (\gamma_0 - 1)\,\frac{(C_p)_0 - (C_p)_\infty}{(C_p)_\infty}$$

or

$$\frac{C'}{(C_p)_0} = \frac{(C_p)_0 - (C_p)_\infty}{(C_p)_0} = \left[1 - \frac{\gamma_0 - 1}{(\kappa_S'/\kappa_{0S}) + \gamma_0 - 1}\right]. \qquad (113\text{–}9)$$

For glycerol at $-93°$ C, $\gamma_0 = 1.09$ and $(\kappa'/\kappa_0)_S = 0.47$. Inserting these values in Eq. (113–9) one finds that C' would have to be equal to 0.84 $(C_p)_0$ to account for the measured dispersion. This, however, is impossible, since from the above data on the glassy state it can be seen that the structural specific heat of glycerol is equal to 0.54 $(C_p)_0$. Thus, C' can be at the utmost, only 0.46 $(C_p)_0$.

One must conclude that a relaxation of internal degrees of freedom cannot account for the volume viscosity found in glycerol.

Unfortunately, there are no measurements on the isothermal compressibility of glycerol in the liquid and glass state. However, data do exist on the isothermal compressibilities of other liquids in the liquid and glass state. The difference between the isothermal values of κ_{liq} and κ_{glass} are clearly due to a structural relaxation effect in the isothermal compressibility, and not to any structural specific heat. The values of $(\kappa'/\kappa_{\text{liq}})_T$ in Table 111–3 vary from about 0.2 to 0.75. The value of $(\kappa'/\kappa)_S$ for glycerol at $-93°$ C is 0.47. Comparison of the values of the isothermal ratio $(\kappa'/\kappa)_T$ with the adiabatic ratio $(\kappa'/\kappa)_S$ found in glycerol indicates the reasonableness of the assumption that the relaxation in glycerol is due mainly to a relaxing structural component of the isothermal compressibility.

The experiments of Davies and Jones[8] on glycerol near the glass temperature (see Sec. 103) allow one to measure the structural relaxation time, and thus to calculate the "structural" volume viscosity of a liquid by other than ultrasonic measurements.

It is of interest to compare these results in glycerol with the characteristics of the volume viscosity predicted at these low temperatures by ultrasonic absorption measurements.

The first point of similarity in the results of the two experiments is that the activation energies for structural rearrangement as measured by Davies and Jones are found to be the same as for shear flow within the experimental error. The second point of interest is that the data of Davies and Jones were found to depart from a simple exponential function of time. This is in agreement with the fact that a distribution of relaxation times exists for the ultrasonic relaxation effects in glycerol.

The value of τ_v found for glycerol by studying the kinetics of approach to equilibrium in the glassy state at 178 °K was 3.1×10^4 sec (see Sec. 103). The best value for K_2 at this temperature is obtained from ultrasonic relaxation data, and is 5.52×10^{10} dynes/cm². Using then the relation $\eta' = \tau_{Sp}\, \kappa'/\kappa_S{}^2$ yields a value of 0.85×10^{15} poise for the structural viscosity of glycerol at this temperature.

The ratio of η'/η as determined by measurements of ultrasonic absorption at room temperature ($\eta \approx 1$ poise) is found to be 1.0 and independent of temperature, Thus, the value of η' at 178 °K can be calculated if the shear viscosity is known. Davies and Jones, using data of Tammann and Hesse,[4] estimate that the shear viscosity of their glycerol (containing less than 0.5% water) is somewhere between 2.5×10^{15} and 6.0×10^{15} poise at 178 °K.

---

[8] R. O. Davies and G. O. Jones, *Proc. Roy. Soc.* **A217**, 26 (1953).

From ultrasonic absorption considerations the volume viscosity lies in the same range of values.

In view of the uncertainties involved because of the extended extrapolation of the shear viscosity to low temperatures and the existence of a distribution of relaxation times, agreement between the values of volume viscosity obtained from the different experiments is reasonable. These results are in accord with the concept that the volume viscosity in glycerol is a structural relaxation effect. It was previously shown that this volume viscosity could not be accounted for by assuming a relaxing structural specific heat. Therefore, it appears that in glycerol (and probably in all associated liquids) the volume viscosity is due mainly to a relaxing structural contribution to the isothermal compressibility. Thus, just as in water, the excess ultrasonic loss in these liquids is due mainly to the volume change, and not to the temperature change occurring in the sound wave.

114. The Relation of Ultrasonic and Dielectric Relaxation Times

The dielectric polarization of matter originates from the creation of new dipoles by the shifting of charges within the molecules, from the orientation of existing ones, or both. A liquid composed of molecules having a permanent dipole moment is said to be polar. In these liquids the molecules are not constrained in any particular orientation, and in the absence of a field their moments are directed at random. The application of an electric field tends to orient the direction of the molecules, according to the Maxwell-Boltzmann distribution law.

The orientation polarization process is time dependent. The time required for the orientation of a dipole depends upon the "frictional resistance" of the medium to changes in molecular orientation.

When an externally applied field is removed from a medium the polarization decreases exponentially to zero. This is known as dielectric relaxation. The relaxation time, τ_D, is the time for the polarization to decay to $(1/e)$th of its original value. For a gas, this time is of the order of 10^{-12} sec; for liquids of low viscosity, it is of the order of 10^{-10} sec; and in liquids of high viscosity, it can be longer than 10^{-6} sec.

When one applies an alternating electric field of very high frequency to a dielectric medium, the rotary motion of the molecules is not sufficiently rapid to attain equilibrium with the field. The polarization acquires a component out of phase with the electric field, which results in the dissipation of electrical energy. Under these conditions the dielectric constant of the medium is complex and frequency dependent.

The complex dielectric constant can be written[1]

$$\varepsilon = \varepsilon' - i\varepsilon'' \tag{114–1}$$

where

$$\varepsilon' = \frac{\varepsilon_0 - \varepsilon_\infty}{1 + \omega^2 \tau_D{}^2} + \varepsilon_\infty \tag{114–2}$$

and

$$\varepsilon'' = \frac{(\varepsilon_0 - \varepsilon_\infty)\omega\tau_D}{1 + \omega^2 \tau_D{}^2}. \tag{114–3}$$

where ε_0 is the low-frequency or static value of the dielectric constant and ε_∞ is the high-frequency or optical value, and is due to the displacement of charges within the molecule; $\varepsilon_0 - \varepsilon_\infty$ is the contribution to the dielectric constant from the orientation of permanent dipoles.

Debye,[1] using the idea of a sphere subject to rotational Brownian motion in a viscous, continuous medium, arrived at the relation

$$\tau_D = \frac{3\eta v}{kT} \tag{114–4}$$

where v is the volume of the molecule. Equation (114–4) predicts that τ_D is proportional to η, which is in agreement with experimental results.[2] However, for large molecules it has been shown that the magnitude of τ_D calculated from Eq. (114–4) is not always in agreement with experiment.[3]

Kauzmann[2] has given an extensive analysis of dielectric relaxation in terms of rate theory. The rate here involves the probability of a dipole passing over a potential barrier as it reorients itself.

Both the ultrasonic and dielectric relaxation times, τ_p and τ_D, have nearly the same temperature dependence as the shear viscosity. This does not, however, predict whether or not τ_p and τ_D will be equal. Litovitz and Sette[4] have compared the dielectric and ultrasonic relaxation in glycerol. The imaginary part of the complex compressibility may be written in the same form[5] as Eq. (114–3)

$$\kappa' = \frac{(\kappa_0 - \kappa_\infty)\omega\tau_p}{1 + \omega^2 \tau^2{}_p}. \tag{114–5}$$

---

[1] P. Debye, "Polar Molecules." Dover, New York, 1929.

[2] W. Kauzmann, *Revs. Modern. Phys.* **14**, 12 (1942).

[3] D. W. Davidson and R. H. Cole, *J. Chem. Phys.* **19**, 1484 (1951).

[4] T. A. Litovitz and D. Sette, *J. Chem. Phys.* **21**, 17 (1953).

[5] In a progressive electromagnetic wave ε' gives $\mathfrak{B}_0{}^2/\mathfrak{B}^2$ and ε'' gives $2\alpha\mathfrak{B}_0/\omega$.

In Fig. 114–1 the reduced quantities $\varepsilon''/(\varepsilon_0 - \varepsilon_\infty)$ and $\kappa'/(\kappa_0 - \kappa_\infty)$ are plotted vs shear viscosity at a fixed frequency of 30.0 Mc. It can be seen that both quantities have a peak at the same value of shear viscosity (i.e., T), indicating that $\tau_p = \tau_D$. It can be noted that both measured relaxation curves depart from the shape predicted by the single relaxation theory, as had been mentioned earlier for κ'. Thus, in both cases a distribution of relaxation times is necessary.

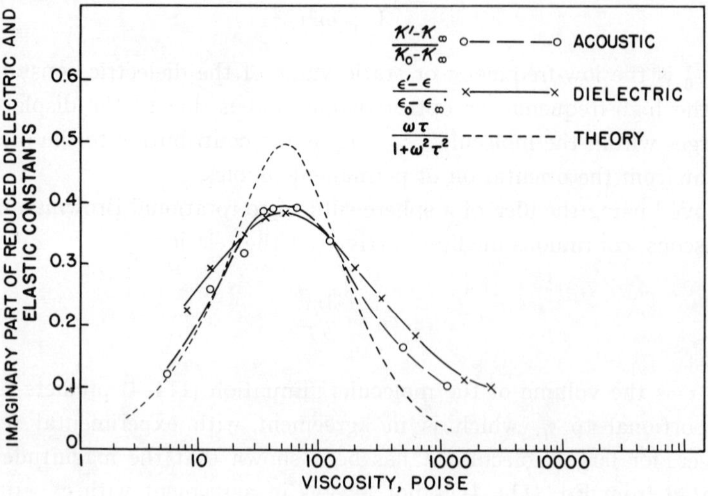

FIG. 114–1. Plot of the imaginary part of the reduced dielectric and elastic constants of glycerol. Measurements are made at a frequency of 30 Mc. The dashed line is calculated from single relaxation theory.

In no other liquid has it been found experimentally that $\tau_p = \tau_D$. Actual ultrasonic relaxation data are not available for most of the associated liquids for which dielectric measurements are at hand. However, it has been shown in Table 111–2 that $\kappa' \cong \frac{1}{3}\kappa_0$. This approximation appears to be good to within a factor of two. Using this, τ_p can be calculated from the excess ultrasonic absorption at low frequency by means of the following argument. Rewriting Eq. (104–26) one gets

$$\frac{\alpha'}{f^2} = 2\pi^2 \rho \mathfrak{B} \kappa' \tau_p \cong \frac{2\pi^2}{3} \rho \mathfrak{B} \kappa_0 \tau_p \cong 6.6 \frac{\tau_p}{\mathfrak{B}}. \tag{114–6}$$

It appears from Table 114–1 that when the ratio of the number of CH groups to OH groups is unity, the difference between τ_p and τ_D is smaller than it is in those molecules which have more CH than OH groups.

TABLE 114–1

COMPARISON OF ULTRASONIC AND DIELECTRIC RELAXATION TIMES IN LIQUIDS

Liquid	CH/OH	T (°C)	α'/f^2 (cm^{-1}sec^2 × 10^{17})	$\mathfrak{B}$ (cm/sec × 10^{-5})	τ_p (sec)	τ_D (sec)	τ_D/τ_p
$CH_2(OH)CH(OH)CH_2(OH)$ Glycerol	1	−5			8.1×10^{-9} [a]	8.1×10^{-9} [a]	1.0
HOH Water		20			2.1×10^{-12} [b]	10.1×10^{-12} [c]	4.8
$CH_2(OH)CH(OH)CH_3$ propanediol-1,2	1.5	−37.8			5.04×10^{-8} [d]	11.9×10^{-8} [d]	2.4
$CH_2(OH)CH(OH)C_2H_5$ butanediol-1,2	2.0	−12			4.06×10^{-9} [e]	2.76×10^{-8} [d]	6.8
$CH_3CH_2CH_2(OH)$ *n*-propyl alcohol	3	−130			2.7×10^{-8} [f]	1.75×10^{-7} [g]	6.5
		−130			3.1×10^{-6} [f]	4.4×10^{-5} [h]	14
$CH_3CH_2CH_2CH_2(OH)$ *n*-butyl alcohol	4	2	41.7 [j]	1.32	8.3×10^{-12} [i]	1.4×10^{-9} [g]	169

[a] T. A. Litovitz and D. Sette, *J. Chem. Phys.* **21**, 17 (1953).

[b] L. Hall, *Phys. Rev.* **73**, 775 (1948).

[c] J. A. Saxton and J. A. Lane, *Proc. Roy. Soc.* London **A213**, 400 (1952).

[d] P. E. Pilon, M. S. Dissertation, Catholic University of America, 1958.

[e] F. E. Cotter, M. S. Dissertation, Catholic University of America, 1958.

[f] T. Lyon and T. A. Litovitz, *J. Appl. Phys.* **27**, 174 (1956).

[g] R. H. Cole and D. W. Davidson, *J. Chem. Phys.* **20**, 1390 (1952).

[h] D. W. Davidson and R. H. Cole, *J. Chem. Phys.* **19**, 1484 (1951).

[i] τ_p was calculated using Eq. (114–6). Where τ_D was not available at the temperatures listed, these values were extrapolated on the assumption that τ_D varies as η.

J. R. Pellam and J. K. Galt, *J. Chem. Phys.* **14**, 608 (1946).

The data on n-propyl alcohol are of interest, since in both ultrasonic and dielectric studies more than one relaxation time was noted. Comparing the shorter times with each other and the longer times with each other gives about the same ratio of τ_D/τ_p.

In those liquids listed in Table 114–1, the OH group comprises the dipole. In glycerol the dipole is essentially the whole molecule; however, when considering the n-butyl alcohol, it can be seen that the dipole (OH group) is at one end and is a small part of the molecule. The dipole motion in this case can involve rotation about a C — C bond and need not involve reorientation of the whole molecule. It is at first thought surprising that the τ for rotation of part of a molecule should be larger than the τ for rotation of the whole molecule. A possible explanation has been offered by Litovitz.[6]

Hirai and Eyring[7] have suggested that in structural relaxation the process of rearrangement of molecules is a combined process which consists of the cooperative movement of many (around 6 to 12) molecules around a hole. For this cooperative motion, there is an entropy increase in the activated state due to the increased structural randomness possible inside the flowing molecules. It is this entropy which can explain the difference between τ_D and τ_p.

According to the Eyring rate process theory the relaxation time for either case is given by an expression of the form,

$$\tau^{-1} = \frac{kT}{h}\left[\exp\left(-\frac{F^* - F_1}{RT}\right) + \exp\left(-\frac{F^* - F_2}{RT}\right)\right]. \qquad (100\text{–}2)$$

Since $\partial\tau/\partial T$ is the same for both dielectric and viscous processes, H^* must be the same for both processes. The difference in the values of F^* must be due to the greater entropy in the activated state of the structural relaxation process. This effect makes $(F)^*_{\text{structural}}$ less than $(F)^*_{\text{dielectric}}$ and thus, τ_p less than τ_D.

In a liquid such as n-butyl alcohol rotation of the OH group about a C — C bond can occur without large rearrangements of the surrounding lattice structure. There is no need for local disruption of order and the entropy of the activated state for dielectric rotation can be much less than for volume relaxation. Thus in this liquid one would expect τ_p to be much

[6] T. A. Litovitz, in "Non-crystalline Solids" (W. D. Frechette, ed.) N. R. C. Monograph. Wiley, New York, to be published.

[7] N. Hirai and H. Eyring, *J. Applied Phys.* **29**, 810 (1958).

less than τ_D. In liquids like glycerol where the whole molecule is involved in dielectric rotation one would expect about the same structural randomness to occur in the activated states of both dielectric and structural relaxation processes and thus τ_D should be close in value to τ_p.

115. Ultrasonic Hysteresis at High Frequencies

It may be recalled that the distribution function used to fit the results in n-propyl alcohol did not give a good fit to the absorption data at high frequencies. This result is typical of the ultrasonic loss in viscous liquids at frequencies which are well above the main relaxation frequencies of the liquid. The absorption coefficient per wave length in this frequency region appears to have a component which is independent of frequency. This type of loss has been called a hysteresis effect. The term hysteresis is applied here because the loss per cycle in the stress—strain loop seems to be independent of frequency.

The mechanism behind this so-called hysteresis loss in highly viscous liquids is not clear at this time. The only liquids in which this loss has been studied in any detail are glycerol and diphenyl pentachloride.[1] The results in these liquids show that at frequencies well above the dispersion region the absorption coefficient per cm, α, can be represented by

$$\alpha = A_1 + A_2 f \tag{115–1}$$

where A_1 and A_2 are constants and f is the acoustic frequency. The constants A_1 and A_2 are dependent on the temperature. The results for diphenyl pentachloride are shown in Table 115–1. The value of $\ln A_1$ varies linearly with $1/T$. A_2 approaches this type of variation only at the lowest temperatures measured. The "apparent" activation energies for the two processes are between one-fifth and one-fourth the activation energy for the shear flow process in the same liquid.

The constant term in α is actually predicted by single relaxation theory. Rewriting Eqs. (104–22, 23) under the assumption that $\omega\tau_s \gg 1$, one finds that

$$A_1 = \alpha_\infty = \frac{\mathfrak{V}_\infty^2 - \mathfrak{V}_0^2}{2\mathfrak{V}_\infty^3} \frac{1}{\tau_s}. \tag{115–2}$$

---

[1] T. A. Litovitz and T. Lyon, *J. Acoust. Soc. Am.* **26**, 577–580 (1954).

The value of A_1 determined in this way is ten times smaller than the experimental result in the above liquids. However, this could possibly be accounted for if one recalls that a distribution of relaxation times exists. As a result of this the smaller values of τ in the denominator could lead to values of A_1 which are much larger than those predicted by use of an "average" τ, as was done above. The predominant importance at the high frequencies of the smaller τ values in the distribution could also lead to the "effective" activation energy found above, which is less than that for shear viscosity.

TABLE 115-1

ULTRASONIC ABSORPTION IN DIPHENYL PENTACHLORIDE AT VERY HIGH VISCOSITIES

Frequency (Mc)	Absorption coefficient at			
	2.5 °C	−2.5° C	−7.5° C	−12.5° C
7.8	1.68	0.90	0.47	0.24
21.3	3.20	1.76	0.94	0.49
38.0	5.00	2.87	1.61	0.89
53.0	6.70	3.87	2.17	1.20
Viscosity (poise)	8×10^4	5.0×10^5	3.5×10^6	2.6×10^7

It may at first seem reasonable to explain the hysteresis component of α by constructing some sort of distribution function which would give this linear frequency dependence. However, it is important in searching for the origin of this hysteresis to note how widespread it is. The hysteresis loss measured in highly viscous glycerol and diphenyl pentachloride appears to extend into the glassy state, as measurements in the "solid" glasses[2] indicate. It has been found in crystalline solids and polymers.[3]

The liquids above were measured in a frequency and viscosity region in which they behave as a solid in the sense that the normal liquid structural rearrangements do not occur during the period of the ultrasonic wave. It therefore seems quite reasonable to presume that the hysteresis loss in solids

---

[2] W. P. Mason and H. J. McSkimin, *J. Acoust. Soc. Am.* **19**, 464 (1947).

[3] W. P. Mason, W. O. Baker, H. J. McSkimin, and J. H. Heiss, *Phys. Rev.* **73**, 1074 (1948).

and in viscous liquids at high frequencies have a common origin. If this is so, it is very difficult to conceive of any viscous flow process related to that occurring at low frequencies and low viscosities which could extend into the solid state.

This, however, is what must be assumed if one proposes that a distribution of viscous relaxation times is responsible for this hysteresis loss. The hypothesis of a distribution of times is unlikely as an explanation.

Mason and co-authors[3] have suggested that this hysteresis loss is related to the hindered rotation of parts of the molecule. In their picture the acoustic wave exerts an "extreme biasing force" in the direction of twisting or rotation. This "biasing force" would effectively reduce the activation energy to zero. If one accepts this view, two difficulties are encountered. If a "biasing force" is necessary then the absorption coefficient should be amplitude dependent. There is no evidence for this.

Another difficulty arises in attempting to explain the apparently large temperature dependence of this hysteresis loss, if the biasing force does reduce the activation energy to zero.

116. Dissociation of Dimers: Acetic and Propionic Acids

As mentioned earlier, Bazulin[1] discovered a decrease in α/f^2 with increasing frequency in acetic acid. Lamb and Pinkerton[2] investigated this acid (CH_3COOH) very thoroughly with the pulse method over a range of temperatures, and could represent their results by an equation of the type

$$\alpha/f^2 = A/(1 + \omega^2\tau^2) + B.$$

The measurements lie very close to the theoretical curves. The constants so found are given, for selected temperatures, in Table 116–1. One can calculate τ from $\tau = 4.15 \times 10^{-11} \times T^{-1} \exp (8460/RT)$. Propionic acid was similarly investigated by Lamb and Huddart.[3] Their results are given in Table 116–2; τ can be represented by $\tau = 5.893 \times 10^{-11} \times T^{-1} \exp (7510/RT)$.

As mentioned earlier, this is also the first case in which dispersion was found in a liquid[1,4] The velocity increases over the dispersion region lie for acetic acid between 14 m/sec (17°) and 18 m/sec (60°) and agree with those

---

[1] P. Bazulin, *Compt. rend. acad. sci. U.R.S.S.* **3**, 285 (1936).

[2] J. Lamb and J. M. M. Pinkerton, *Proc. Roy. Soc.* **A199**, 114 (1949).

[3] J. Lamb and D. H. A. Huddart, *Trans. Faraday Soc.* **46**, 540 (1950).

[4] P. Biquard, *Ann. phys.* [11] **6**, 195 (1936), for deviations from α/f^2 = constant.

calculated from absorption. It is seen from the last column of Table 116–1, which shows $(\alpha\lambda)_{max}$, that the absorption is "weak" in the sense of Sec. 12

$$\frac{\alpha'\mathfrak{B}}{\omega} \leqq 10^{-3}$$

TABLE 116–1

ABSORPTION IN ACETIC ACID

T (°C)	$A \times 10^{17}$	$B \times 10^{17}$	f' (Mc)	τ (sec)	$(\alpha\lambda)_{max}$
17	178,000	160	0.488	32.5×10^{-8}	0.00501
25	132,000	140	0.725	21.9×10^{-8}	0.00537
30	107,000	132	0.915	17.4×10^{-8}	0.00545
45	58,800	112	1.87	8.14×10^{-8}	0.00587
60	33,800	95	3.77	4.04×10^{-8}	0.00641

TABLE 116–2

ABSORPTION IN PROPIONIC ACID

T (°C)	$A \times 10^{17}$	$B \times 10^{17}$	f' (Mc)	τ (sec)	$(\alpha\lambda)_{max}$
8	17,300	160	1.03	15.45×10^{-8}	0.0107
21	11,470	130	2.02	7.87×10^{-8}	0.0134
31	8550	120	3.23	4.93×10^{-8}	0.0154
41	6880	100	4.79	3.32×10^{-8}	0.0178
51	5210	90	7.26	2.19×10^{-8}	0.0201

Lamb and Pinkerton suggested in their first paper that the absorption just discussed is due to the slow adjustment of the chemical equilibrium between monomers and dimers. However, they tried to evaluate the equations with too many simplifications and got into numerical difficulties. The correct evaluation was completed by Freedman[5] in a very thorough and convincing manner. V' is equal to zero according to Pohl *et al.*,[6] so that only temperatures changes, not volume changes, affect the equilibrium. Freedman next evaluates C' from A and Eq. (14–1). The results are shown in Table 116–3.

[5] E. Freedman, *J. Chem. Phys.* **21**, 1784 (1953).

[6] H. A. Pohl, M. E. Hobbs, and P. M. Gross, *J. Chem. Phys.* **9**, 408 (1941).

TABLE 116–3
RELAXING SPECIFIC HEATS FOR ACETIC AND PROPIONIC ACIDS

Acetic acid, CH_3COOH		Propionic acid, $(CH_3)(CH_2)_2COOH$	
T (°C)	C'/R	T (°C)	C'/R
20	3.60	10.1	1.33
30	4.03	21.2	1.65
40	4.46	31.2	2.03
50	4.84	41.2	2.42
60	5.16	51.2	2.91

From C'/R at three temperatures and Eq. (28–6) the constants are evaluated. (Actually, under Freedman's assumption, there are only two constants, H' and S', assumed temperature independent.) Freedman finds $H' = -6.21$ kcal/mole for acetic acid and -9.33 for propionic acid. To compare this with other data he uses a formula of Moelwyn-Hughes[7] according to which

$$H'_{\text{liq}} : H'_{\text{vapor}} = \frac{\varepsilon + 2}{3\,\varepsilon}$$

where ε is the dielectric constant of the liquid. With $H' = -15.3$ kcal/mole for acetic acid and -15.2 for propionic acid, both in the vapor phase[6], and $\varepsilon = 7.1$ for the former and 3.2 for the latter, one calculates that $H'_{\text{liq}} = 6.5$ for the former and 8.2 for the latter, in pretty good agreement with experiment.

Then the following equilibrium constants are used[8]

$$K = 1.438 \times 10^{-3} \exp\left(\frac{6210}{RT}\right) \text{ for acetic acid} \tag{116–1}$$

$$K = 1.71 \times 10^{-4} \exp\left(\frac{9330}{RT}\right) \text{ for propionic acid.} \tag{116–2}$$

---

[7] E. A. Moelwyn-Hughes, "The Kinetics of Reactions in Solution," 2nd ed. Oxford Univ. Press, London and New York, 1947.

[8] This means a mole concentration for the monomer of 5.8% in acetic acid at 20° C and of 0.91% in propionic acid at 8° C.

TABLE 116–4

VALUES FOR $\tilde{k}$

Acetic acid			Propionic acid		
T (°K)	$10^{-5}\,\bar{k}$ sec^{-1}	$10^{-7}\,\tilde{k}$ sec^{-1}	T (°K)	$10^{-5}\,\bar{k}$ sec^{-1}	$10^{-7}\,\tilde{k}$ sec^{-1}
293	1.10	0.68	281.2	0.308	9.36
303	2.18	0.95	294.2	0.890	12.9
313	4.22	1.32	304.2	1.87	16.2
333	14.9	2.56	324.2	7.10	23.56

Using Eq. (28–7), Freedman finds the values for $\tilde{k}$ given in Table 116–4; $\tilde{k} = \bar{k}K$.

$$\bar{k} = 2.46 \times 10^{14} \exp\left(-\frac{12530}{RT}\right) \text{ for acetic acid} \qquad (116\text{–}3)$$

$$\bar{k} = 5.68 \times 10^{14} \exp\left(-\frac{13200}{RT}\right) \text{ for propionic acid.} \qquad (116\text{–}4)$$

It is seen that the true heats of activation for $\bar{k}$ are very different from the apparent ones used to represent τ.

It should be pointed out that B $(90 - 160 \times 10^{-17})$ is of the order of magnitude of the absorption which occurs in many liquids. With the preceding equations, Freedman then calculates backwards the values of $(\alpha\lambda)_{\max}$. In no case is there more than 2% deviation between calculated and observed values (it should be remembered that only the two constants in K are available for adjustment in each liquid). This seems very convincing for the dissociation mechanism.[9] The crucial experiment to decide whether the process producing absorption is a dissociation would be one of diluting the acid with an inert liquid. The dependence of C'/R and τ on x' (the total mole fraction of the acid, counted as monomer) is given by Eqs. (28–12′) and (28–13′). For these acids, one has $K \gg 1$, as Table 116–5 shows.

In general, the experimental data cannot be directly evaluated, since one has to know Δ and C_p for each mixture (to find C'/R) and $\bar{k}$ may depend on the composition (effect of foreign molecules, namely, of the solvent).

[9] Before the appearance of Freedman's paper, Lamb and Andreae[10] proposed that this absorption should be ascribed to the C-H bending vibration. See also J. E. Piercy and J. Lamb, *Trans. Faraday Soc.* **52**, 930 (1956).

TABLE 116–5*
DISSOCIATION CONSTANT K

Acetic acid		Propionic acid	
T (°K)	K	T (°K)	K
293	61.97	281.2	3040
303	43.58	294.2	1454
313	31.34	304.2	868
333	17.21	324.2	332

* Note the definition (28–9′) of K.

There is an exception to this when the solution is dilute, $x' < 1$, since one can then use Δ and C_p for the solvent, and $\bar{k}$ is independent of x', being determined by the interaction of a solute molecule and a solvent molecule. In this case Eqs. (28–12) and (28–13) can be used directly; $\bar{k}$ is, of course, different from the value in the pure acid.

The best method for testing the theory would be to measure α/ω^2 in dilute solutions as a function of the frequency for different concentrations. Then, according to Eq. (28–13″), the frequency of maximum absorption should be $\sim (x')^{-1/2}$, while the height of the maximum should be $\sim (x')^{1/2}$. However, this has not been done. Another possible method of testing would be to show that the low frequency value of α/ω^2 is independent of x'. Unfortunately, this is not possible if the solvent itself has appreciable absorption, because the solute acts as a foreign molecule, thereby decreasing the absorption of the solvent, as Maier and Mez[11] have pointed out.

117. Mixtures Containing Associated Liquids

The behavior of mixtures—either of a dipole liquid dissolved in a nonpolar liquid, or of mixtures between two dipole liquids—is rather varied.

In some cases, the absorption of a strongly absorbing liquid decreases rapidly with the addition of small amounts of another liquid, the slope decreasing when the amount of the added liquid is appreciable. This is the behavior of nonpolar liquids (see Sec. 99) and follows the theory and equation

[10] J. Lamb and J. H. Andreae, *Proc. Phys. Soc. London* **B64**, 1021 (1954).
[11] W. Maier and A. Mez, *Z. Naturforsch.* **7a**, 300 (1952).

of Bauer-Sette. Such is the case for water in glycerol[1] and nitrobenzene in benzene and chloroform.[2,3] In other cases the curve of α/f^2 against composition has a flat minimum, as in the mixture chloroform-carbon tetrachloride[2], or is a more or less straight line connecting the absorptions of the pure components (acetone-ethyl alcohol,[1] toluene-nitrobenzene,[2] chloroform-benzene,[2] and acetone-nitrobenzene[2]).

Finally, a number of cases exist in which the absorption has a maximum at certain compositions, e.g., acetone and water,[2,4] different alcohols and water,[2,5,6] ether-ethyl alcohol,[2,7 8] nitrobenzene-alcohol,[2,8,9] and nitrobenzene-*n*-hexane[8]. Solutions of phenol in various liquids also show such a maximum; they will be discussed in detail below.

The absorption coefficient decreases with increasing temperature. However, Storey[6] found that in water-ethyl alcohol mixtures, $\alpha/\alpha_{\text{class}}$ is not independent of the temperature, as it is in pure associated liquids. In mixtures of methyl alcohol or propyl alcohol with water and in mixtures of nitrobenzene with *n*-hexane Sette found a decrease of α/f^2 with increasing frequency in the range of 7 to 35 Mc. A similar result was found in water-triethylamine solutions, but according to Lamb, pure triethylamine probably also shows such an effect (see Sec. 98), while the other pure substances mentioned have α/f^2 constant in this frequency range.

The absorption maxima often occur at compositions at which other properties (viscosity of mixture, heat of mixing, freezing point) also show a maximum. Storey,[6] following a suggestion of Bauer[10] and Sette,[8] assumed that associated complexes are formed between the molecules of solvent and solute.[11] The composition at the maximum is the composition of the complex; e.g., in water-methyl alcohol, where the maximum occurs at the mole fraction

---

[1] F. H. Willis, *J. Acoust. Soc. Am.* **19**, 242 (1947).

[2] D. Sette, *J. Acoust. Soc. Am.* **23**, 359 (1951).

[3] For other examples, see Y. Wada and S. Shimbo, *J. Acoust. Soc. Am.* **24**, 199 (1952).

[4] G. W. Willard, *J. Acoust. Soc. Am.* **12**, 438 (1941).

[5] C. J. Burton, *J. Acoust. Soc. Am.* **20**, 186 (1948).

[6] L. R. O. Storey, *Proc. Phys. Soc. London* **B65**, 943 (1952).

[7] D. Sette, *Nuovo cimento Suppl.* **6**, 1 (1949).

[8] D. Sette, *Nuovo cimento* **1**, 800 (1955).

[9] D. Sette, *J. Chem. Phys.* **21**, 558 (1953).

[10] E. Bauer; see J. M. M. Pinkerton, *Colloq. Ultrasonore Trillingen, Koninkl. Vlaam. Acad. Wetenschap., Letter en Schone Kunsten Belgie, Brussels 1951*, p. 126.

[11] An attempt to explain the maxima by the effect of unmixing, analagous to the effect in gases (Sec. 41), was made by K. F. Herzfeld, *J. Chem. Phys.* **9**, 513 (1941), but gave results which were far too small.

of 0.25 of alcohol, the complex[8] is $(H_2O)_3CH_3OH$. The absorption is due to the low reaction rate of the decomposition of the complex, which rate is increased by the addition of either of the pure components.

Solutions of phenol (C_6H_5OH) in CCl_4, cyclohexane, and C_6H_5Cl were investigated by Maier and Mez[12,13] as a function of composition and temperature at 20 Mc, which they believe to be far below the relaxation region. Plotting α/f^2 for the CCl_4 solution at 20° and 30° C as a function of mole fraction x, they first find a decrease to a minimum (occurring at $x \sim 0.005$ to 0.012), then a rise to the maximum, after which α/f^2 decreases monotonously. Maier and Mez think[12] that this first drop is always present if there is a maximum, but has been overlooked because it lies at very small x-values. They interpret their results as a combination of the effect of foreign molecules (Sec. 99), which is alone effective in nonassociated liquids, and of the effect of association (complex formation), which is unimportant at high dilution, but is responsible for the maximum of absorption. Contrary to Storey's and Sette's assumption, the complexes are assumed to be phenol dimers. To isolate the two effects, they plot absorption at fixed concentration against temperature. In general, these curves first drop to a flat minimum and then rise again at high temperatures. The curves at higher temperatures but different composition are parallel to each other, just as in nonassociated liquids (end of Sec. 99). Therefore, the high temperature end—where dissociation is presumably complete—is taken to give the foreign molecule effect, which is then extrapolated to lower temperature and subtracted, to give the effect of slow chemical reaction (association) alone. This effect of chemical reaction is then calculated with Liebermann's theory.[14] (See Sec. 28.) One gets 6.7 at 20° C and 5 at 30° C for the equilibrium constant.

Maier and Rudolph[15] have measured α/f^2 for dilute solutions ($x \sim 0.01$ to 0.02) of benzoic acid (C_6H_5COOH) in CCl_4. They find an *increase* of α with increasing temperature. They interpret this as due to the temperature and concentration dependence of τ (Secs. 28 and 116); meaning here (with 20 Mc) that $\omega\tau \gg 1$, so that the increase of α with temperature is due to the decrease of τ with temperature. Unfortunately, they have not made measurements at higher frequencies to test their assumption, which requires α to be independent of ω. If one writes

---

[12] W. Maier and A. Mez, *Z. Naturforsch.* **7a**, 300 (1952).

[13] A. Mez and W. Maier, *Z. Naturforsch.* **10a**, 997 (1955).

[14] L. Liebermann, *Phys. Rev.* **76**, 1520 (1949).

[15] W. Maier and H. D. Rudolph, *Z. Naturforsch.* **10a**, 588 (1955).

$$\bar{k} = \bar{a} \exp\left(-\frac{\bar{E}}{RT}\right) \tag{117-1}$$

$$\tilde{k} = \tilde{a} \exp\left(-\frac{\tilde{E}}{RT}\right) \tag{117-1'}$$

and neglects the temperature variation of $\Delta/(C_v C_p T^2)$, one finds that the maximum of α/ω^2 as a function of the temperature lies at

$$\omega^2 = 8\bar{k}\tilde{k}\,\frac{\tilde{E}}{\bar{E}}\,x'. \tag{117-3}$$

From their data—taking account of the "foreign molecule effect" (Sec. 99)—Maier and Rudolph find

$$\bar{E} = 10.45 \text{ kcal}, \qquad \tilde{E} = 4.95 \text{ kcal}, \qquad H' = -5.5 \text{ kcal}.$$

Sette[8] has pointed out that in some cases of only partially miscible liquids, as in nitrobenzene—n-hexane and in water—triethylamine, the maximum of sound absorption lies at the composition at which the solubility as a function of temperature has a maximum. The absorption measurement is made only slightly above the temperature of this maximum (i.e., in a region in which the two liquids have just become completely miscible). One might expect[8] fluctuations to produce clusters of liquids of varying composition here. Such clusters can affect the absorption in the following ways:

(1) They may increase scattering[16] (see Sec. 32). This effect is too small to be noticed.

(2) They may increase viscosity.[16] This may contribute to increased absorption.

(3) There may be relaxation effects in the formation and dissolution of the clusters. This should be the main factor.

Sette gives estimates of cluster number and size.

118. Effect of Pressure on Ultrasonic Relaxation in Liquids

Absorption measurements in triethylamine and in acetic acid as a function of pressure at various frequencies were made by Litovitz and Carnevale.[1]

[16] R. Lucas, *J. phys. radium* **8**, 41 (1937).

[1] T. Litovitz and E. Carnevale, *J. Acoust. Soc. Am.* **30**, 134 (1958).

In these liquids the absorption coefficient could be expressed by the following

$$\frac{\alpha}{f^2} = \frac{A}{1 + (f/f'')^2} + B \tag{118–1}$$

where $f'' = 1/(2\pi\tau'')$.

TABLE 118–1

PRESSURE DEPENDENCE OF RELAXATION PARAMETERS OF TRIETHYLAMINE AT 0° C AND ACETIC ACID AT 50° C

Pressure (kg/cm^2)	A ($cm^{-1}\,sec^2 \times 10^{16}$)	B ($cm^{-1}\,sec^2 \times 10^{16}$)	f'' (Mc/sec)	$(\gamma - 1)\dfrac{C'}{C_p}$
		Triethylamine		
1	122	6.0	31.2	0.014
2000	50	3.3	32.8	0.010
3280	40.8	3.2	31.2	0.0089
		Acetic Acid		
1*	4840*	10.7*	2.4*	0.038*
1584	2000	5.5	2.4	0.025

* Values at atmospheric pressure taken from Lamb and Pinkerton.[2]

In Table 118–1 the relaxation parameters A, B, and f'' are tabulated as a function of pressure. In each of these liquids the loss has been attributed to some type of thermal relaxation mechanism, in which case A is given by

$$A = \frac{\pi}{\mathfrak{B}f''}(\gamma - 1)\frac{C'}{C_p}. \tag{118–2}$$

The quantity $(\gamma - 1)\,C'/C_p$ is tabulated in Table 118–1. Unfortunately, in neither liquid is the pressure dependence of γ or C_p known. Therefore, it is impossible to determine the pressure dependence of C'. It is of interest, however, that the rate of decrease of C'/C_p is about the same as was noted in CS_2 (Sec. 97).

In both acetic acid and triethylamine it is found that the relaxation frequency is independent of pressure to within the experimental error. In

[2] J. Lamb and J. M. M. Pinkerton, *Proc. Roy. Soc. London* **A199, 114** (1949).

Fig. 118–1 the pressure data on the relaxation frequencies in these two liquids and in carbon disulfide and glycerol[3] are presented.

It can be seen that the relaxation frequency of a liquid can decrease, increase, or remain constant with increasing pressure. The comparison emphasizes the fundamental differences which exist in the relaxation processes in these liquids.

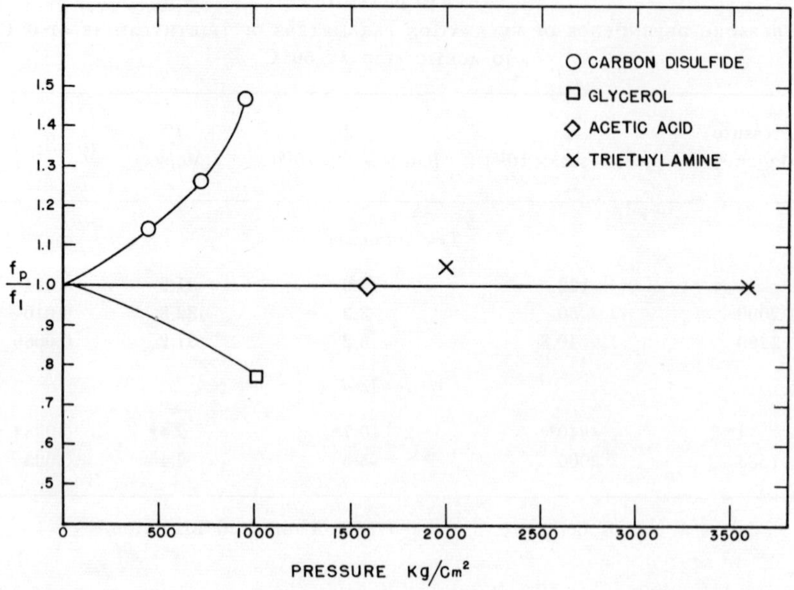

FIG. 118–1. Plot of the ratio of f_p, the relaxation frequency at any pressure, p, to f_1, the value of the relaxation frequency at atmospheric pressure, as a function of the hydrostatic pressure. Data from Refs. 1 and 3.

In glycerol the viscous relaxation effects are related to the motion of the molecule from one lattice site to another. (See Sec. 106.) As the pressure is raised and the density is increased, it becomes more difficult for a molecule to jump from one site to another in the lattice and the time between jumps increases. Thus, the relaxation frequency for intermolecular structural rearrangements which involve molecular motion should decrease with increasing pressure.

In CS_2 the relaxation effect is due to a perturbation of the equilibrium between vibrational and external degrees of freedom. (See Sec. 97.) The relaxation time is determined by two factors here: (1) the efficiency of a

[3] T. A. Litovitz, E. H. Carnevale, and P. Kendall, *J. Chem. Phys.* **26**, 465 (1957).

collision in exciting or de-exciting an internal degree of freedom, and (2) the number of collisions per second. The effect of increasing pressure is to increase the number of collisions per second without affecting the collision efficiency. It is for this reason that the relaxation frequency increases with increasing pressure in CS_2.

The pressure independence of the relaxation frequencies in triethylamine and acetic acid indicates that neither vibrational-translational relaxation nor structural relaxation of the liquid lattice is involved in these liquids. This conclusion is in agreement with the assumption made by Heasall and Lamb[4] that the loss in triethylamine is due to a rotational isomeric effect. This mechanism can cause ultrasonic relaxation, owing to the finite transition rates from one equilibrium configuration to another. It was assumed by Heasall and Lamb that the volume difference between the two states is negligible, and that the important contribution to the loss is related to the difference in enthalpy between the two isomeric forms.

The pressure independence of the relaxation frequency in triethylamine indicates that the transition rate from one rotational isomeric form to another is not limited in any way by the rate of transfer of the necessary energy from neighboring molecules. For example, the molecule does not need to await a collision to knock it from one isomeric form to another. The process is completely intramolecular, and the necessary energy for the transition seems to be obtained from coupling to other internal degrees of freedom.

It is interesting that comparison of the pressure dependence of relaxation frequencies in triethylamine and CS_2 leads to the same conclusion as comparison of the dependence of the relaxation frequencies upon impurities. Lamb[5] has found that mixing triethylamine with relatively large amounts of other liquids has no effect upon the relaxation frequency. Connolly and Litovitz[6] have found that addition of 0.2% by volume of pentane or *n*-butyl alcohol to CS_2 shifts the relaxation frequency by 31%.

Again it can be seen that in triethylamine the environment and the type of molecules with which it collides have no effect upon the transition rate, whereas in CS_2 they do have effects. Thus, even though in both CS_2 and triethylamine a thermal relaxation process is occurring, there are fundamental differences in the mechanism.

It was first suggested by Lamb and Pinkerton[2] that the loss in acetic acid was a thermal relaxation effect related to a perturbation of the monomer-

---

[4] E. L. Heasall and J. Lamb, *Proc. Roy. Soc. London* **A237,** 233 (1956).

[5] J. Lamb, Private communication, to be published.

[6] W. Connolly and T. A. Litovitz, to be published.

dimer equilibrium by the changes in temperature accompanying the sound wave (Sec. 116). Theoretical work by Freedman[7] appears to support this hypothesis. However, recent results of Piercy and Lamb[8] on the concentration dependence of the relaxation frequency in mixtures containing acetic acid are not in complete agreement with the monomer-dimer theory. Other than eliminating vibrational relaxation and a certain type of structural relaxation, the data on the pressure dependence of the relaxation frequency do not uniquely solve the problem of the origin of the loss in acetic acid. However, the results found here are in agreement with the monomer-dimer theory favored by Freedman.

It has been shown by Gross and co-workers[9] that the volume change in going from the monomer to the dimer form is zero. Under these conditions one would expect the activated state in this reaction to have zero volume change compared with either initial or final states. Therefore, the free energy in the activated state should be pressure independent, making the transition rate constant with pressure changes. This is, of course, in agreement with the experimental results found in acetic acid.

The results discussed above and presented in Fig. 118–1 demonstrate the role that the measurements of the pressure dependence of relaxation frequencies can play in determining the mechanism of the relaxation.

---

[7] E. Freedman, *J. Chem. Phys.* **21**, 1784 (1953).

[8] J. E. Piercy and J. Lamb, *Trans. Faraday Soc.* **52**, 930 (1956).

[9] H. A. Pohl, M. E. Hobbs, and P. M. Gross, *J. Chem. Phys.* **9**, 408 (1941).

AUTHOR INDEX

The numbers in parentheses are footnote numbers and are inserted to enable the reader to locate a cross reference when the author's name does not appear at the point of reference in the text.

C

D

E

F

G

SUBJECT INDEX

A

I

J

K

L

M

N

S

T

U

V

W